LOS	line of sight
LPF	low-pass filter
LSSB	lower single sideband
MAP	maximum a posteriori (criterion)
MPSK	*M*-ary phase shift keying
MQAM	*M*-ary quadrature amplitude modulation
MSK	minimum-shift keying
NBFM	narrowband frequency modulation
NCS	National Communications System of the federal government
NRZ	nonreturn-to-zero
OOK	on-off keying
OQPSK	offset quadrature phase shift keying
OSI	open system interconnection protocol model
PAM	pulse amplitude modulation
PCM	pulse code modulation
PD	phase detection
PDF	probability density function
PEP	peak envelope power
PLL	phase-locked loop
PM	phase modulation
PPM	pulse position modulation
PSD	power spectral density
PSK	phase shift keying
PTM	pulse time modulation
PWM	pulse width modulation
QAM	quadrature amplitude modulation
QPSK	quadrature phase shift
rms	root-mean-square
RT	remote telephone terminal
RZ	return-to-zero
SAW	surface acoustics wave
SDLC	synchronous data link control protocol
S/N	signal-to-noise ratio
SS	spread spectrum (system)
SSB	single sideband
TDM	time-division multiplexing
TDMA	time-division multiplex access
TELCO	telephone company
THD	total harmonic distortion
TTL	transistor transistor logic
TV	television
TVRO	TV receive only terminal
TWT	traveling-wave tube
UHF	ultra high frequency
USSB	upper single sideband
VCO	voltage-controlled oscillator
VF	voice frequency
VHF	very high frequency
VSB	vestigial sideband
WBFM	wideband frequency modulation

Modern Communication Systems
Principles and Applications

Modern Communication Systems

Principles and Applications

Leon W. Couch II

Professor of Electrical Engineering
University of Florida, Gainesville

PRENTICE HALL   Englewood Cliffs, New Jersey 07632

LIBRARY OF CONGRESS CATALOGING-IN-PUBLICATION DATA

Couch, Leon W.
  Modern communication systems : principles and applications / Leon
W. Couch, II.
      p.   cm.
  Includes bibliographical references and index.
  ISBN 0-02-325286-3
  1. Telecommunication systems.   2. Digital communications.
I. Title.
TK5101.A3C68   1994
621.382—dc20   93-47969
                                                            CIP

Editors: John Griffin and Linda Ratts
Production Supervisor: John Travis
Production Manager: Nick Sklitsis
Cover Designer: Robert Freese

 © 1995 by Prentice-Hall, Inc.
A Division of Simon & Schuster, Inc.
Englewood Cliffs, New Jersey 07632

PRINTED IN THE UNITED STATES OF AMERICA

10 9 8 7 6 5 4 3 2 1

Prentice-Hall International (UK) Limited, *London*
Prentice-Hall of Australia Pty. Limited, *Sydney*
Prentice-Hall Canada, Inc., *Toronto*
Prentice-Hall Hispanoamericana, S. A., *Mexico*
Prentice-Hall of India Private Limited, *New Delhi*
Prentice-Hall of Japan, Inc., *Tokyo*
Simon & Schuster Asia Pte. Ltd., *Singapore*
Editora Prentice-Hall do Brasil, Ltda., *Rio de Janiero*

To my wife,
Margaret Wheland Couch,
and to our children,
Leon III, Jonathan, and Rebecca

Preface

This book is designed for

- A one semester or a two-quarter introductory course
- Short courses
- Undergraduates in Electrical Engineering
- Undergraduates in Computer Engineering
- Undergraduates in Computer Information Science
- As a reference book for practicing engineers

It covers

- Principles of communication systems
- Digital and analog communications, with emphasis on digital
- Case studies of modern communication systems
- Standards used in communication systems
- Examples and homework problems solved via analytical methods
- Examples and homework problems solved via a personal computer

It is clear that a one-semester course can cover only a small number of topics in the communication area. More material is provided in this book than can be covered in a one semester course. This is done intentionally so that the instructor can emphasize topics that he/she believes to be of most interest. This book is written so that other topics can be left out or just summarized to provide a textbook that is tailored to the needs of the instructor and the class.

This book covers the basic principles of waveform representation and spectral analysis via Fourier theory and orthogonal function theory. The use of mathematics has been minimized as much as possible, even though mathematics is the basic tool that is used to solve communication problems. Elementary principles of probability and statistics are used and an appendix on probability and random variables is included. Results for the noise performance of communication systems is summarized but the details of noise performance calculations are left for a more advanced course where time permits the use of random processes. In summary, this book explains how communication systems work and summarizes their performance in the presence of noise. Effects of bandlimited and nonlinear channels are introduced. The emphasis is on design of communication systems.

This book includes mathematical tables, illustrative examples, homework problems with selected answers, computer-solution homework problems with solution templates available, and extensive references.

It is assumed that the reader has prerequisite courses in calculus, elementary circuits, and some signal analysis.

This book covers *practical aspects* of communication systems developed from sound *theoretical principles.*

The Theoretical Basis

- Representation of digital signals.
- Representation of analog signals.
- Magnitude and phase spectra.
- Fourier analysis.
- Orthogonal function theory.
- Power spectral density.
- Linear systems.
- Nonlinear systems.
- Simulation of communication systems.
- Intersymbol interference.
- Modulation theory.
- Random variables.
- Probability density.
- Block codes.
- Convolutional codes.

The Practical Applications

- PAM, PCM, DPCM, DM, PWM, and PPM baseband signaling.
- OOK, BPSK, QPSK, MPSK, MSK, and QAM bandpass digital signaling.
- AM, DSB-SC, SSB, VSB, PM, and FM bandpass analog signaling.
- Time-division multiplexing and the standards used.
- Digital line codes and spectra.
- Circuits used in communication systems.
- Bit synchronizers.
- Frame synchronizers.
- Carrier synchronizers.
- Frequency-division multiplexing and the standards used.
- Telecommunication systems.
- Telephone systems.
- ISDN.
- Satellite communication systems.

- Effective input-noise temperature and noise figure.
- Link budget analysis.
- S/N at the output of analog communication systems.
- Probability of bit error for digital communication systems.
- Fiber optic systems.
- Spread spectrum systems.
- Cellular radio telephone systems.
- Television systems.
- Technical standards for AM, FM, TV, HDTV, and CATV.
- Computer communication systems.
- Protocols for computer communications.
- Technical standards for computer communications.

Many of the equations and homework problems are marked with a personal computer symbol, ⬛, which indicates that there are a MathCAD[†] template solution and a MAT-LAB[‡] M file solution for this equation or problem on a floppy disk (available to the instructor free of charge from the publisher).

This book is an outgrowth of my teaching of graduate as well as undergraduate communication courses at the University of Florida and is tempered by my experiences as an amateur radio operator (K4GWQ). I believe that the reader does not fully understand the technical material unless he or she has the opportunity to work problems. Consequently, numerous problems have been included. Some of the problems are easy, so that the beginning student will not become frustrated, and some are difficult enough to challenge the more advanced students. All the problems are designed to provoke thought about, and understanding of, communication systems.

I appreciate the help of the many persons who contributed to this book. In particular I appreciate the very helpful comments that have been provided by the Macmillan reviewers, particularly Ted Rappaport, Virginia Polytechnic Institute; Steve Wilson, University of Virginia; Tadeusz Babij, Florida International University; and Kazimierz Siwiak, Motorola Corporation.

I also appreciate the help of my colleagues at the University of Florida, including Haniph Latchman and Scott Miller. Special thanks are extended to the many University of Florida students who have been most helpful in making suggestions. I am also grateful to the late Dr. T. S. George who taught me a great deal about communications while I was a graduate student under his direction. I am also very appreciative of the help of my wife, Dr. Margaret Couch, who typed the original and revised manuscripts and proofread the entire book.

Leon W. Couch II
Gainesville, Florida

[†]MathCAD is a trademark of MathSoft, Inc.
[‡]MATLAB is a trademark of The MatWorks, Inc.

Contents

List of Symbols   xxi

1 Introduction   1

    1-1   Historical Perspective   2
    1-2   What is a Communication System?   2
    1-3   Digital and Analog Sources and Systems   7
    1-4   Deterministic and Random Waveforms   8
    1-5   Use of a Personal Computer   9
    1-6   Frequency Allocations   10
    1-7   Propagation of Electromagnetic Waves   10
    1-8   Information Measure   16
          Example 1-1   Evaluation of Information and Entropy   17
    1-9   Channel Capacity and Other Fundamental Limits   18
    1-10   Coding   19
          Block Codes   21
          Convolutional Codes   22
          Code Interleaving   25
          Code Performance   25
          Trellis Coded Modulation   28
    1-11   Preview   29
    1-12   Appendix—Proof of Shannon's Limit   30
          Problems   31

2 Signals and Spectra   33

    2-1   Properties of Signals and Noise   33
          Physically Realizable Waveforms   33
          Time Average Operator   35

Dc Value   36

Power   36

Example 2-1   Evaluation of Power   37

Rms Value and Normalized Power   39

Energy Waveforms and Power Waveforms   40

Decibel   40

Phasors   42

2-2   Fourier Transform and Spectra   43

Definition   43

Example 2-2   Spectrum of an Exponential Pulse   45

Properties of Fourier Transform   46

Parseval's Theorem and Energy Spectral Density   47

Example 2-3   Spectrum of a Damped Sinusoid   50

Dirac Delta Function and Unit Step Function   50

Example 2-4   Spectrum of a Sinusoid   51

Rectangular and Triangular Pulses   53

Example 2-5   Spectrum of a Rectangular Pulse   54

Example 2-6   Spectrum of a Triangular Pulse   57

Convolution   58

Example 2-7   Convolution of a Rectangle with an Exponential   58

Example 2-8   Spectrum of a Triangular Pulse by Convolution   59

Example 2-9   Spectrum of a Switched Sinusoid   60

2-3   Power Spectral Density and Autocorrelation Function   62

Power Spectral Density   62

Autocorrelation Function   63

Example 2-10   PSD of a Sinusoid   63

2-4   Orthogonal Series Representation of Signals and Noise   65

Orthogonal Functions   65

Example 2-11   Orthogonal Complex Exponential Functions   65

Orthogonal Series   66

2-5   Fourier Series   68

Complex Fourier Series   68

Quadrature Fourier Series   69

Polar Fourier Series   70

Line Spectra for Periodic Waveforms   72

Example 2-12   Fourier Coefficients for a Square Wave   74

Power Spectral Density for Periodic Waveforms   76

Example 2-13   PSD for a Square Wave   77

Truncated Fourier Series   77

2-6   Summary   79

Problems   79

3   Linear Systems and Digital Signaling   90

3-1   Linear Time-Invariant Filters and Systems   90
3-2   Impulse Response   91
3-3   Transfer Function   92
   Example 3-1   RC Low-Pass Filter   93
3-4   Distortionless Transmission   95
   Example 3-2   Distortion Caused by a Filter   96
3-5   Bandlimited Signals and Noise   96
   Bandlimited Waveforms   98
   Sampling Theorem   99
   Impulse Sampling   101
   Dimensionality Theorem   104
3-6   Digital Signaling   105
   Vector Representation   106
   Example 3-3   Vector Representation of a Binary Signal   107
   Bandwidth Estimation   108
   Binary Signaling   109
   Example 3-4   Binary Signaling   109
   Multilevel Signaling   111
   Example 3-5   L = 4 Multilevel Signal   111
3-7   Discrete Fourier Transform   114
   Example 3-6   DFT or a Rectangular Pulse   118
   *Example 3-7   Use the DFT to Compute the Spectrum
   of a Sinusoid   120*
3-8   Bandwidths of Signals and Noise   120
   Example 3-8   Bandwidths for a BPSK Signal   124
3-9   Summary   128
   Problems   128

4   Baseband Pulse and Digital Signaling   134

4-1   Introduction   134
4-2   Pulse Amplitude Modulation   135
   Natural Sampling (Gating)   135
   Instantaneous Sampling (Flat-Top PAM)   139
4-3   Pulse Code Modulation   143
   Sampling, Quantizing, and Encoding   143
   Practical PCM Circuits   146
   Bandwidth of PCM   148
   Effects of Noise   149

Example 4-1   Design of a PCM System   151
Nonuniform Quantizing: μ-Law and A-Law Companding   153

4-4   Digital Signaling Formats   155

Binary Line Coding   155
Power Spectra of Line Codes   158
Differential Coding   164
Eye Patterns   166
*Regenerative Repeaters and Probability of Bit Error
  for Line Codes   167*
Bit Synchronization   170
Multilevel Signaling   173
Spectral Efficiency   176

4-5   Intersymbol Interference   177

Nyquist's First Method (Zero ISI)   179
Raised Cosine-Rolloff Filtering   180
Example 4-1   (continued)   182
Zero-Forcing Transversal Filter Equalizers   183
Nyquist's Second and Third Methods for Control of ISI   186

4-6   Differential Pulse Code Modulation   186

4-7   Delta Modulation   190

Granular Noise and Slope Overload Noise   191
Example 4-2   Design of a DM System   192
*Adaptive Delta Modulation and Continuously Variable Slope Delta
  Modulation   195*
Speech Coding   197

4-8   Time-Division Multiplexing   197

Frame Synchronization   199
Synchronous and Asynchronous Lines   201
Example 4-3   Design of a Time-Division Multiplexer   203
TDM Hierarchy   204
The T1 PCM System   207

4-9   Pulse Time Modulation: Pulse Width Modulation and Pulse Position
       Modulation   212

4-10   Summary   216

4-11   Appendix: PSD for Digital Signaling   217

Problems   218

5   Bandpass Signaling Principles and Circuits   230

5-1   Complex Envelope Representation of Bandpass Waveforms   230

Definitions: Baseband, Bandpass, and Modulation   230
Complex Envelope Representation   231

5-2   Representation of Modulated Signals   233
5-3   Spectrum of Bandpass Signals   236
5-4   Evaluation of Power   237
   Example 5-1 Amplitude-Modulated Signal 238
5-5   Bandpass Filtering and Linear Distortion   239
   Equivalent Low-pass Filter 239
   Linear Distortion 242
5-6   Bandpass Sampling Theorem   243
5-7   Received Signal Plus Noise   245
5-8   Classification of Filters and Amplifiers   246
   Filters 246
   Amplifiers 250
5-9   Nonlinear Distortion   251
5-10   Limiters   256
5-11   Mixers, Up Converters, and Down Converters   258
5-12   Frequency Multipliers   264
5-13   Detector Circuits   265
   Envelope Detector 265
   Product Detector 266
   Frequency Modulation Detector 268
5-14   Phase-Locked Loops   273
5-15   Transmitters and Receivers   281
   Generalized Transmitters 281
   Generalized Receiver: The Superheterodyne Receiver 283
   Example 5-2 AM Broadcast Superheterodyne Receiver 284
5-16   Summary   287
   Problems 287

6 AM and FM Systems   295

6-1   Amplitude Modulation   295
   Example 6-1 Power of an AM Signal 298
6-2   AM Broadcast Technical Standards   300
6-3   Double-Sideband Suppressed Carrier   302
6-4   Costas Loop and Squaring Loop   302
6-5   Assymetric Sideband Signals   304
   Single Sideband 304
   Amplitude-Companded Single Sideband 308
   Vestigial Sideband 309
6-6   Phase Modulation and Frequency Modulation   311
   Representation of PM and FM Signals 311

Spectra of Angle-Modulated Signals   316
Example 6-2   Spectrum of a PM or FM Signal With Sinusoidal Modulation   316
Narrowband Angle Modulation   323
Wideband Frequency Modulation   325
Example 6-3   Spectrum for WBFM with Triangular Modulation   327
Preemphasis and Deemphasis in Angle-Modulated Systems   328

6-7   Frequency-Division Multiplexing and FM Stereo   330
6-8   FM Broadcast Technical Standards   331
6-9   Noise Performance   334
Shannon's Ideal System   335
AM and FM Systems   335
Dolby and DBX Noise Reduction Systems   336

6-10   Summary   339
Problems   339

7   Bandpass Digital Signaling   349

7-1   Binary Signaling   349
On-Off Keying (OOK)   351
Binary-Phase Shift Keying (BPSK)   353
Differential Phase-Shift Keying (DPSK)   355
Frequency-Shift Keying   356
Example 7-1   Spectrum of the Bell-Type 103 PSK Modem   357

7-2   Multilevel Signaling   363
Quadrature Phase-Shift Keying (QPSK) and M-ary Phase-Shift Keying (MPSK)   364
Quadrature Amplitude Modulation (QAM)   366
Power Spectral Density for MPSK and QAM   368

7-3   Minimum-Shift Keying (MSK)   371
7-4   Comparison of Bandpass Digital Signaling Systems   374
Spectral Efficiency   375
Probability of Bit Error, P_e 376
Synchronization   378

7-5   Spread Spectrum Systems   380
Direct Sequence   381
Frequency Hopping   387

7-6   Summary   388
Problems   389

8   Case Studies of Communication Systems   395

8-1   Telecommunication Systems   395
    Time-Division Multiplexing   396
    Frequency-Division Multiplexing   396

8-2   Telephone Systems   398
    Historical Basis   398
    Modern Telephone Systems and Remove Terminals   399

8-3   Integrated Service Digital Network (ISDN)   405

8-4   Capacities of Public Switched Telephone Networks (PSTN)   409

8-5   Satellite Communication Systems   409
    Television Signal Transmission   414
    Data and Telephone Signal Multiple Access   415
    *Example 8-1   Fixed Assigned Multiple Access Mode Using an FDMA
        Format   417*
    Example 8-2   SPADE System   417

8-6   Link Budget Analysis   423
    Signal Power Received   423
    Thermal Noise Sources   425
    Characterization of Noise Sources   427
    Noise Characterization of Linear Devices   428
    Example 8-3 T_e and F for a Transmission Line   432
    Noise Characterization of Cascaded Linear Devices   433
    Link Budget Evaluation   435
    E_b/N_0 Link Budget for Digital Systems   437
    *Example 8-4   Link Budget Evaluation for a Television Receiver-Only
        Terminal for Satellite Signals   438*

8-7   Fiber Optic Systems   443
    Example 8-5   Link Budget for a Fiber Optic System   444

8-8   Cellular Telephone Systems   445

8-9   Television   452
    Black-and-white Television   452
    MTS Stereo Sound   459
    Color Television   459
    Standards for TV and CATV Systems   464
    HDTV   468

8-10   Summary   471
    Problems   472

APPENDIX A   Mathematical Techniques, Identities, and Tables   479

A-1   Trigonometry   479
  Definitions   479
  Trigonometric Identities   479
A-2   Differential Calculus   480
  Definition   480
  Differentiation Rules   480
  Derivative Table   480
A-3   Indeterminate Forms   481
A-4   Integral Calculus   481
  Definition   481
  Integration Techniques   482
A-5   Integral Tables   482
  Indefinite Integrals   482
  Definite Integrals   484
A-6   Series Expansions   485
  Finite Series   485
  Infinite Series   486
A-7   Hilbert Transform Pairs   486
A-8   The Dirac Delta Function   487
  Properties of Dirac Delta Function   488
A-9   Tabulation of $Sa(x) = (\sin x)/x$ 489
A-10   Tabulation of $Q(z)$ 490

APPENDIX B   Probability and Random Variables   492

B-1   Introduction   492
B-2   Sets   492
B-3   Probability and Relative Frequency   494
  Simple Probability   494
  Joint Probability   494
  Example B-1   Evaluation of Probabilities   495
  Conditional Probabilities   496
  Example B-1   (Continued)   496
B-4   Random Variables   496
  Example B-2   Random Variable   497
B-5   Cumulative Distribution Functions and Probability Density Functions   498
  Example B-2   (Continued)   498
  Properties of CDFs and PDFs   500

Discrete and Continuous Distributions 500
Example B-3 A Continuous Distribution 500

B-6   Ensemble Average and Moments   504
Ensemble Average 504
Example B-4 Evaluation of an Average 505
Moments 505

B-7   Examples of Important Distributions   507
Binomial Distribution 507
Poisson Distribution 510
Uniform Distribution 510
Gaussian Distribution 511
Sinusoidal Distribution 515

B-8   Functional Transformations of Random Variables   516
Example B-5 Sinusoidal Distribution 517
Example B-6 PDF for the Output of a Diode Characteristic 518

B-9   Multivariate Statistics   521
Multivariate CDFs and PDFs 521
Bivariate Statistics 523
Gaussian Bivariate Distribution 524
Multivariate Functional Transformation 524
Example B-7 PDF for the Sum of Two Random Variables 526
Central Limit Theorem 527
*Example B-8 PDF for the Sum of Three Independent Uniformly
   Distributed Random Variables 528*
Problems 529

APPENDIX C   Standards and Terminology for Computer
Communications   536

C-1   Codes   536
Morse Code 536
Punched Card 537
Baudot 538
EBCDIC 538
ASCII 540

C-2   DTE/DCE and Ethernet Interface Standards   540
Current Loop 541
RS-232C, RS-422A, RS-449, and RS-530 Interfaces 543
Centronics Parallel Interface 544
IEEE-488 Interface 545
Ethernet (IEEE 802.3) Interface 546

C-3   The ISO OSI Network Model   550

C-4   Data Link Control Protocols   551
      BISYNC   551
      SDLC   552
      HDLC   552
      CCITT X.25 Protocol   553
      Asynchronous Transfer Mode (ATM)   554
C-5   Telephone Line Standards   555
C-6   Modem Standards   556
C-7   Brief Computer Communications Glossary   561

APPENDIX **D**   Introduction to MathCAD   565

D-1   General Information   565
D-2   MathCAD Example   569

References   570

Answers to Selected Problems   578

Index   585

Front Endpapers
      Abbreviations

Back Endpapers
      Fourier Transform Theorems
      Fourier Transform Pairs
      Q(z) Function

List of Symbols

There are not enough symbols in the English and Greek alphabets to allow the use of each letter only once. Consequently, some symbols may be used to denote more than one entity, but their use should be clear from the context. Furthermore, the symbols are chosen to be generally the same as those used in the associated mathematical discipline. For example, in the context of complex variables, x denotes the real part of a complex number (i.e., $c = x + jy$), whereas in the context of statistics x might denote a random variable.

Symbols

a_n	a constant
a_n	quadrature Fourier series coefficient
A_c	level of modulated signal of carrier frequency f_c
A_e	effective area of an antenna
b_n	quadrature Fourier series coefficient
B	baseband bandwidth
B_p	bandpass filter bandwidth
B_T	transmission (bandpass) bandwidth
c	a complex number where $c = x + jy$
c	a constant
c_n	complex Fourier series coefficient
C	channel capacity
C	capacitance
$°C$	degrees Celsius
dB	decibel
D	dimensions/sec ($D = N/T_0$) or baud rate
D_f	frequency modulation gain constant
D_n	polar Fourier series coefficient
D_p	phase modulation gain constant

e	error
e	the natural number, 2.7183
E	modulation efficiency
E	energy
$\mathcal{E}(f)$	energy spectral density (ESD)
E_b/N_0	energy per bit/noise power spectral density ratio
f	frequency (Hz)
$f(x)$	probability density function (PDF)
f_c	carrier frequency
f_i	instantaneous frequency
f_0	a (frequency) constant; the fundamental frequency of a periodic waveform
f_s	sampling frequency
F	noise figure
$F(a)$	cumulative distribution function (CDF)
$g(t)$	complex envelope
$\tilde{g}(t)$	corrupted complex envelope
G	power gain
$G(f)$	power transfer function
h	Planck's constant, 6.2×10^{-34} joule-sec
$h(t)$	impulse response of a linear network
$h(x)$	mapping function of x into $h(x)$
H	entropy
$H(f)$	transfer function of a linear network
i	an integer
I_j	information in the jth message
j	the imaginary number $\sqrt{-1}$
j	an integer
k	Boltzmann's constant, 1.38×10^{-23} joule/K
k	an integer
$k(t)$	complex impulse response of a bandpass network
K	number of bits in a binary word that represents a digital message
K	degrees Kelvin (°C + 273)
l	an integer
ℓ	number of bits per dimension
L	inductance
L	number of levels permitted
m	an integer
m	mean value
$m(t)$	message (modulation) waveform
$\tilde{m}(t)$	corrupted (noisy received) message

M	an integer
M	number of messages permitted
n	an integer
n	number of bits in message
$n(t)$	noise waveform
N	an integer
N	number of dimensions used to represent a digital message
N	noise power
N_0	level of the power spectral density of white noise
$p(t)$	an absolutely time-limited pulse waveform
$p(t)$	instantaneous power
$p(m)$	probability density function of frequency modulation
P	average power
P_e	probability of bit error
$\mathcal{P}(f)$	power spectral density (PSD)
$Q(z)$	integral of Gaussian function
$r(t)$	received signal plus noise
R	data rate (bits/sec)
R	resistance
$R(t)$	real envelope
$R(\tau)$	autocorrelation function
$s(t)$	signal
$\tilde{s}(t)$	corrupted signal
S/N	signal power/noise power ratio
t	time
T	a time interval
T	absolute temperature (Kelvin)
T_b	bit period
T_e	effective input-noise temperature
T_0	duration of a transmitted symbol or message
T_0	period of a periodic waveform
T_0	standard room temperature (290 K)
T_s	sampling period
u_{11}	covariance
$v(t)$	a voltage waveform
$v(t)$	a bandpass waveform or a bandpass random process
$w(t)$	a waveform
$W(f)$	spectrum (Fourier transform) of $w(t)$

x	an input
x	a random variable
x	real part of a complex function or a complex constant
y	an output
y	an output random variable
y	imaginary part of a complex function or a complex constant
α	a constant
β	a constant
β_f	frequency modulation index
β_p	phase modulation index
δ	step size of delta modulation
δ_{ij}	Kronecker delta function
$\delta(t)$	impulse (Dirac delta function)
ΔF	peak frequency deviation (Hz)
$\Delta \theta$	peak-phase deviation
ϵ	a constant
ϵ	error
η	spectral efficiency [(bits/sec)/Hz]
$\theta(t)$	phase waveform
λ	dummy variable of integration
λ	wavelength
$\Lambda(r)$	likelihood ratio
π	3.14159
ρ	correlation coefficient
σ	standard deviation
τ	independent variable of autocorrelation function
τ	pulse width
$\varphi_j(t)$	orthogonal function
ϕ_n	polar Fourier series coefficient
ω_c	radian carrier frequency, $2\pi f_c$
$\equiv$	mathematical equivalence
$\triangleq$	mathematical definition of a symbol

Defined Functions

$J_n(\cdot)$	Bessel function of the first kind nth order
$\ln(\cdot)$	natural logarithm

$\log(\cdot)$	base 10 logarithm
$\log_2(\cdot)$	base 2 logarithm
$Q(z)$	integral of a Gaussian probability density function
$Sa(z)$	$(\sin z)/z$
$u(\cdot)$	unit step function
$\Lambda(\cdot)$	triangle function
$\Pi(\cdot)$	rectangle function

Operator Notation

$\text{Im}\{\cdot\}$	imaginary part of
$\text{Re}\{\cdot\}$	real part of
$\overline{[\cdot]}$	ensemble average
$\langle[\cdot]\rangle$	time average
$[\cdot] * [\cdot]$	convolution
$[\cdot]^*$	conjugate
$\underline{/[\cdot]}$	angle operator or angle itself, see (2-102)
$\lvert[\cdot]\rvert$	absolute value
$\hat{[\cdot]}$	Hilbert transform
$\mathcal{F}[\cdot]$	Fourier transform
$\mathcal{L}[\cdot]$	Laplace transform
$[\cdot] \cdot [\cdot]$	dot product

Introduction

The modern telecommunication age is here. We live in a world of cordless phones, electronic mail (e-mail), mobile cellular telephones, cable TV, satellite TV, inexpensive long-distance, national and international communications via fiber optic cables and satellites, personal computers (PC), data communication networks, and intelligent telecommunication systems. This is the information age—news, weather, sports, financial, shopping, business inventory, and other information sources are made available to us almost instantly via modern digital networks.

This book is designed to present the *big picture* of modern electronic communication systems. It is addressed to students and professionals in the electrical engineering (EE), computer engineering (CE), and computer information science (CIS) disciplines. The big picture includes an understanding of basic communication *principles* and *applications*. Basic principles include the development of fundamental communication theory in an easy-to-understand approach. Applications of principles include communication standards that have been adopted by industry and examples of design. Examples of design include new systems as well as modifications of existing systems to produce modern communications systems that are economical to build and operate. Digital communication systems are emphasized since they usually give superior performance and usually are more economical to implement and maintain. This book also incorporates the use of the personal computer (PC) to help evaluate and plot results.

Because of the explosion of the communications area in recent years, it is impossible to cover all theory and practice in one book. This book presents the essence of principles and practice that can be covered in a one-semester course, a two-quarter course, or an intensive short course. This book is also useful later as a reference for standards and design formulas when working in the industry.

In summary, this book is designed for:

- A one-semester course, a two-quarter course, or a short course.
- Students in electrical engineering, computer engineering, and computer information science.

- Professionals in electrical engineering, computer engineering, and computer information science.
- A reference for modern communication systems.

The book includes:

- Balanced theory and applications.
- Emphasis on digital communication systems.
- Standards for communication systems.
- Use of the personal computer (PC) to solve problems.
- Description of modern telecommunication systems.
- Math tables.

1-1 Historical Perspective

A time chart showing the historical development of communications is given in Table 1-1. The reader is encouraged to spend some time studying this table in order to obtain an appreciation for the chronology of communications. Note that although the telephone was developed late in the nineteenth century, the first transatlantic telephone cable was not completed until 1954. Previous to this date, transatlantic calls were handled via shortwave radio. Similarly, although the British began television broadcasting in 1936, transatlantic television relay was not possible until 1962 when the *Telstar I* satellite was placed into orbit. Digital transmission systems—embodied by telegraph systems—were developed in the 1850s before analog systems—the telephone—in the twentieth century.

This book provides technical details for most of the communication inventions listed in the table. For example, pulse code modulation—used for modern digital transmission of telephone voice signals—was invented by Alex Reeves in 1937 and is described in detail in Chapter 4. Superheterodyne receivers and FM systems are discussed in Chapters 5 and 6. Recent developments such as fiber optics, the cellular mobile telephone, satellite, and spread spectrum systems are described in Chapter 8. Computer communication system standards are tabulated in Appendix C.

More historical details about the engineers and their inventions that became the modern communication systems we enjoy today can be found in a book that was published in the centennial year for the Institute of Electrical and Electronic Engineers (IEEE) and its predecessors [Ryder and Fink, 1984].

1-2 What Is a Communication System?

The purpose of a communication system is to transmit message information of a source to a sink (user). The exact waveform present at the sink is *unknown* until after it is received—otherwise, no information would be transmitted and there would be no need for the communication system. More information is communicated to the sink when the user at the sink is ''surprised'' by the message that was transmitted. That is, the transmission of

TABLE 1-1 Important Dates in Communications

Year	Event
Before 3000 B.C.	Egyptians develop a picture language called *hieroglyphics*.
A.D. 800	Arabs adopt our present number system from India.
1827	Georg Simon Ohm formulates his law ($I = E/R$).
1834	Carl F. Gauss and Ernst H. Weber build the electromagnetic telegraph.
1838	William F. Cooke and Sir Charles Wheatstone build the telegraph.
1844	Samuel F. B. Morse demonstrates the Baltimore, MD, and Washington, DC, telegraph line.
1850	Gustav Robert Kirchhoff first publishes his circuit laws.
1858	The first transatlantic cable is laid, and fails after 26 days.
1864	James C. Maxwell predicts electromagnetic radiation.
1866	The second transatlantic cable is installed.
1871	The Society of Telegraph Engineers is organized in London.
1876	Alexander Graham Bell develops and patents the telephone.
1883	Thomas A. Edison discovers flow of electrons in a vacuum, called the ''Edison effect,'' the foundation of the electron tube.
1884	The American Institute of Electrical Engineers (AIEE) is formed.
1885	Edward Branly invents the ''coherer'' radio-wave detector.
1887	Heinrich Hertz verifies Maxwell's theory.
1889	The Institute of Electrical Engineers (IEE) forms from the Society of Telegraph Engineers in London.
1894	Oliver Lodge demonstrates wireless communication over a distance of 150 yards.
1897	Guglielmo Marconi patents a complete wireless telegraph system.
1900	Guglielmo Marconi transmits the first transatlantic wireless signal.
1904	John A. Fleming invents the vacuum-tube diode.
1905	Reginald Fessenden transmits speech and music by radio.
1906	Lee deForest invents the vacuum-tube triode amplifier.
1907	The Society of Wireless Telegraph Engineers is formed in the United States.
1908	A. A. Campbell-Swinton publishes basic ideas of television broadcasting.
1909	The Wireless Institute is established in the United States.
1912	The Institute of Radio Engineers (IRE) is formed in the United States from the Society of Wireless Telegraph Engineers and the Wireless Institute.
1915	Bell System completes a U.S. transcontinental telephone line.
1918	Edwin H. Armstrong invents the superheterodyne receiver circuit.
1920	KDKA, Pittsburgh, PA, begins the first scheduled radio broadcasts.
1920	J. R. Carson applies sampling to communications.
1926	J. L. Baird, England, and C. F. Jenkins, United States, demonstrate television.
1927	The Federal Radio Commission is created in the United States.

TABLE 1-1 Important Dates in Communications (*continued*)

Year	Event
1927	Harold Black develops the negative-feedback amplifier at Bell Laboratories.
1928	Philo T. Farnsworth demonstrates the first all-electronic television system.
1931	Teletypewriter service is initiated.
1933	Edwin H. Armstrong invents FM.
1934	The Federal Communication Commission (FCC) is created from the Federal Radio Commission in the United States.
1935	Robert A. Watson-Watt develops the first practical radar.
1936	The British Broadcasting Corporation (BBC) begins the first television broadcasts.
1937	Alex Reeves conceives pulse code modulation (PCM).
1939	The Klystron microwave tube is developed by R. H. Varian, S. F. Varian, W. C. Hahn, and G. F. Metcalf.
1941	John V. Atanasoff invents the computer at Iowa State College.
1941	The FCC authorizes television broadcasting in the United States.
1945	The ENIAC electronic digital computer is developed at the University of Pennsylvania by John W. Mauchly.
1947	Walter H. Brattain, John Bardeen, and William Shockley devise the transistor at Bell Laboratories.
1947	Steve O. Rice develops statistical representation for noise at Bell Laboratories.
1948	Claude E. Shannon publishes his work on information theory.
1950	Time-division multiplexing is applied to telephony.
1950s	Microwave telephone and communication links are developed.
1953	NTSC color television is introduced in the United States.
1953	The first transatlantic telephone cable (36 voice channels) is laid.
1954	J. P. Gordon, H. J. Zeiger, and C. H. Townes produce the first successful maser.
1957	First Earth satellite, *Sputnik I,* is launched by USSR.
1958	A. L. Schawlow and C. H. Townes publish the principles of the laser.
1960	Theodore H. Marman produces the first successful laser.
1961	Stereo FM broadcasts begin in the United States.
1962	The first active satellite, *Telstar I,* relays television signals between the United States and Europe.
1963	Bell System introduces the touch-tone phone.
1963	The Institute of Electrical and Electronic Engineers (IEEE) is formed by merger of IRE and AIEE.
1963–66	Error-correction codes and adaptive equalization for high-speed error-free digital communications are developed.
1964	The electronic telephone switching system (No. 1 ESS) is placed into service.

TABLE 1-1 Important Dates in Communications (*continued*)

Year	Event
1965	The first commercial communications satellite, *Early Bird,* is placed into service.
1966	K. C. Kao and G. A. Hockham publish the principles of fiber optic communications.
1968	Cable television systems are developed.
1971	Intel Corporation develops the first single-chip microprocessor, the 4004.
1972	Motorola demonstrates the cellular telephone to the FCC.
1976	Personal computers are developed.
1979	64-kbit random access memory ushers in the era of very-large-scale integrated (VLSI) circuits.
1980	Bell System FT3 fiber optic communication is developed.
1980	Compact disk is developed by Philips and Sony.
1981	IBM PC is introduced.
1982	AT&T agrees to divest its 22 Bell System telephone companies.
1984	Macintosh computer is introduced by Apple.
1985	FAX machines become popular.
1989	"Pocket" cellular telephone is introduced by Motorola.
1990–present	Era of digital signal processing with microprocessors, digital oscilloscopes, digitally tuned receivers, magaflop workstations, spread spectrum systems, integrated service digital networks (ISDNs), and high-definition television (HDTV).

information implies the communication of messages that are not known ahead of time (a priori). On the other hand, in energy or power systems it is known a priori what the received waveform will be, and it is the energy imparted by the received waveform that is the desired quantity.

Noise limits our ability to communicate. If there were no noise, we could communicate messages electronically to the outer limits of the universe using an infinitely small amount of power. This has been obvious on an intuitive basis since the early days of radio. However, the theory that describes noise and the effect of noise on the transmission of information was not developed until the 1940s by such persons as D. O. North [1943], S. O. Rice [1944], C. E. Shannon [1948], and N. Wiener [1949].

Communication systems may be described by the block diagram shown in Fig. 1-1. Regardless of the particular application, all communications systems involve three main subsystems: the *transmitter,* the *channel,* and the *receiver.* Throughout this book we use the symbols as indicated in this diagram so that the reader will not be confused about where the signals are located in the overall system. The message from the source is represented by the information input waveform $m(t)$. The message delivered to the sink is denoted by $\tilde{m}(t)$. The [˜] indicates that the message received may not be the same as that

FIGURE 1-1 Communication system.

transmitted. That is, the message at the sink, $\tilde{m}(t)$, may be corrupted if the noise in the channel is not sufficiently small or if there are other impairments in the system, such as undesired filtering or undesired nonlinearities. The message information may be in analog or digital form, depending on the particular system, and it may represent audio, video, or some other type of information. In multiplexed systems there may be multiple input and output message sources and sinks. The spectra (or frequencies) of $m(t)$ and $\tilde{m}(t)$ are concentrated about $f = 0$; consequently, they are said to be *baseband* signals.

The signal processing block at the transmitter conditions the source for more efficient transmission. For example, in a digital system the processor might consist of a minicomputer or microprocessor that provides redundancy reduction of the source. It may also provide channel encoding so that error detection and correction can be used at the signal processing unit at the receive site to reduce errors caused by noise in the channel. In an analog communication system the signal processor may be nothing more than an analog low-pass filter. In a hybrid system the signal processor might take samples of an analog input and digitize them to provide a pulse code modulation (PCM) "digital word" for transmission over the system. (We study PCM techniques in Chapter 4.) The signal at the output of the transmitter signal processor is also a baseband signal since it has frequencies concentrated near $f = 0$.

The transmitter carrier circuits convert the processed baseband signal into a frequency band that is appropriate for propagation over the transmission medium of the channel. For example, if the channel consists of a twisted-pair telephone line, the spectrum of $s(t)$ will be in the audio range, say 300 to 3700 Hz, but if the channel consists of a fiber optic link, the spectrum of $s(t)$ will be at light frequencies. If the channel propagates baseband signals, no carrier circuits are necessary and $s(t)$ can be just the output of the processing circuit at the transmitter. Carrier circuits are needed when the channel can only propagate frequencies located in a band around f_c where $f_c \gg 0$. (The c subscript denotes "carrier" frequency.) In this case $s(t)$ is said to be a *bandpass* signal since it is designed to have frequencies located in a band about f_c. For example, an amplitude modulated (AM) broadcasting station with an assigned frequency of 850 kHz has a carrier frequency of $f_c = 850$ kHz. The mapping of the baseband input information waveform $m(t)$ into the bandpass signal $s(t)$ is called *modulation*. [$m(t)$ is the audio signal in AM broadcasting.] In Chapter 5 it will be shown that any bandpass signal has the form

$$s(t) = R(t) \cos[\omega_c t + \theta(t)] \tag{1-1}$$

where $\omega_c = 2\pi f_c$. If $R(t) = 1$ and $\theta(t) = 0$, $s(t)$ would be a pure sinusoid of frequency $f = f_c$ with *zero* bandwidth. In the modulation process provided by the carrier circuits, the baseband input waveform $m(t)$ causes $R(t)$ and/or $\theta(t)$ to change as a function of $m(t)$. These fluctuations in $R(t)$ and $\theta(t)$ cause $s(t)$ to have a *finite* bandwidth that depends on the characteristics of $m(t)$ and on the mapping functions used to generate $R(t)$ and $\theta(t)$. In Chapter 6, 7, and 8 practical examples of both digital and analog bandpass signaling are presented.

Channels may be classified into two categories: hardwire and softwire. Some examples of *hardwire* channels are twisted-pair telephone lines, coaxial cables, waveguides, and fiber optic cables. Some typical *softwire* channels are air, vacuum, and seawater. It should be realized that the general principles of digital and analog modulation apply to all types of channels, although channel characteristics may impose constraints that favor a particular type of signaling. In general, the channel medium attenuates the signal so that the noise level of the channel and/or the noise introduced by an imperfect receiver cause the delivered information $\tilde{m}$ to be deteriorated from that of the source. The channel noise may arise from natural electrical disturbances (e.g., lightning) or from man-made sources such as high-voltage transmission lines, ignition systems of cars, or even switching circuits of a nearby digital computer. The channel may contain active amplifying devices, such as repeaters in telephone toll systems or satellite transponders in space communication systems. These devices, of course, are necessary to help keep the signal above the noise level. In addition, the channel may provide *multiple paths* between its input and output that have different time delays and attenuation characteristics. Even worse, these characteristics may vary with time. This variation produces signal fading at the channel output. You have probably observed this type of fading when listening to distant shortwave stations.

The receiver takes the corrupted signal at the channel output and converts it to a baseband signal that can be handled by the receiver baseband processor. The baseband processor "cleans up" this signal and delivers an estimate of the source information $\tilde{m}(t)$ to the communication system output.

The goal of the engineer is to design communication systems so that the information is transmitted to the sink with as little deterioration as possible while satisfying design constraints such as allowable transmitted energy, allowable signal bandwidth, and cost. In digital systems the measure of deterioration is usually taken to be the *probability of bit error* (P_e)—also called the *bit error rate* (BER)—of the delivered data $\tilde{m}$. In analog systems the performance measure is usually taken to be the *signal-to-noise ratio* (S/N) at the receiver output.

1-3 Digital and Analog Sources and Systems

DEFINITION: A *digital information source* produces a finite set of possible messages.

A typewriter is a good example of a digital source. There is a finite number of characters (messages) that can be emitted by this source.

> **DEFINITION:** An *analog information source* produces messages that are defined on a continuum.
>
> A microphone is a good example of an analog source. The output voltage describes the information in the sound, and it is distributed over a continuous range of values.
>
> **DEFINITION:** A *digital communication system* transfers information from a digital source to the sink.
>
> **DEFINITION:** An *analog communication system* transfers information from an analog source to the sink.

Strictly speaking, a *digital waveform* is defined as a function of time that can have only a discrete set of values. If the digital waveform is a binary waveform, only two values are allowed. An *analog waveform* is a function of time that has a continuous range of values.

An electronic *digital* communication system usually has voltages and currents that have digital waveforms; however, it *may* have analog waveforms. For example, the information from a binary source may be transmitted to the sink by using a sine wave of 1000 Hz to represent a binary 1 and a sine wave of 500 Hz to represent a binary 0. Here the digital source information is transmitted to the sink by use of analog waveforms, but this is still called a digital communication system. Furthermore, this analog waveform is called a *digital signal* because it describes a digital source. Similarly, an *analog signal* describes an analog source. From this point of view, we see that a *digital* communication engineer needs to know how to analyze analog circuits as well as digital circuits.

Digital communication has a number of advantages:

- Relatively inexpensive digital circuits can be used.
- Privacy is preserved by using data encryption.
- Greater dynamic range (the difference between largest and smallest value) is possible.
- Data from voice, video, and data sources can be merged and transmitted over a common digital transmission system.
- In long-distance systems, noise does not accumulate from repeater to repeater.
- Errors in detected data are small, even when there is a large amount of noise on the received signal.
- Errors can often be corrected by the use of coding.

Digital communication also has disadvantages:

- Generally, more bandwidth is required than that for analog systems.
- Synchronization is required.

The advantages of digital communication systems usually outweigh their disadvantages. Consequently, digital systems are becoming more and more popular.

1-4 Deterministic and Random Waveforms

In communication systems we are concerned with two broad classes of waveforms: deterministic and random (or stochastic).

DEFINITION: A *deterministic waveform* can be modeled as a completely specified function of time.

For example, if

$$w(t) = A \cos(\omega_0 t + \varphi_0) \tag{1-2}$$

describes a waveform where A, ω_0, and φ_0 are known constants, this waveform is said to be deterministic.

DEFINITION: A *random waveform* (or stochastic waveform) cannot be completely specified as a function of time and must be modeled probabilistically.

Here we are faced immediately with a dilemma when analyzing communication systems. We know that the waveforms that represent the source cannot be deterministic. For example, in a digital communication system we might send information corresponding to any one of the letters of the English alphabet. Each letter might be represented by a deterministic waveform, but when we examine the waveform that is emitted from the source we find that it is a random waveform because we do not know exactly which characters will be transmitted. Consequently, we really need to design the communication system using a random signal waveform, and, of course, any noise that is introduced would also be described by a random waveform. This technique requires the use of probability and statistical concepts that make the design and analysis procedure more complicated. Fortunately, if we represent the signal waveform by a "typical" deterministic waveform, we can obtain most, but not all, of the results we are seeking. In this book we are striving to obtain the practical results with a minimum of mathematical complexity. Consequently, most of the results will be obtained using the deterministic approach, although, when necessary, elementary probabilistic and stochastic concepts will be used.

1-5 Use of a Personal Computer

There are over 400 homework problems in this book and a large number of these are designed for computer solutions using a PC. These PC solution problems are marked with a PC symbol ( ). When one investigates possible ways of using the PC for solutions, one is faced with programming in Basic, Pascal, C, or FORTRAN, or one can use software packages that are designed to solve a particular class of problems. Obviously, it is better to use a good problem-specific package since it saves time and is less prone to mistakes in programming. For the PC, some of the popular EE packages are PSpice and Micro-CAP for circuit analysis, Touchstone for microwave circuits, and ACOLADE and TESS for communications. For workstations, some communication packages are BDSS, SYSTID, TOPSIM, CMSP, CHAMP, LINK, ICSSM, ICS, and MODEM. Most of the software that is designed for communication system work is not affordable by the average EE student. Consequently, the author has chosen to use either MathCAD or MATLAB, which are available in student versions at a reasonable price. Although MathCAD and MATLAB are not designed specifically for communications, they provide user-friendly solutions to those problems that can be formulated in a mathematical equation. Consequently, it is suggested that the homework problems designated with be worked out using either

MathCAD or MATLAB. See Appendix D for an introduction to MathCAD and a sample problem with the PC solution. (An IBM PC-compatible floppy disk with MathCAD solution templates and MATLAB M files is available to the instructor free of charge from the publisher.)

1-6 Frequency Allocations

In communication systems that use the atmosphere for the transmission channel, interference and propagation conditions are strongly dependent on the transmission frequency. Theoretically, any type of modulation (e.g., amplitude modulation, frequency modulation, single sideband, phase-shift keying, frequency-shift keying, etc.) could be used at any transmission frequency. However, to provide some semblance of order and for political reasons, government regulations specify the modulation type, bandwidth, and type of information that can be transmitted over designated frequency bands. On an international basis, frequency assignments and technical standards are set by two committees: the International Telegraph and Telephone Consultative Committee (CCITT) and the International Radio Consultative Committee (CCIR). These committees function under the auspices of International Telecommunications Union (ITU), which in turn is one of the organizations of the Economic and Social Council of the United Nations. An excellent overview of international, regional, and national standards organizations is the subject of a special issue of the *IEEE Communications Magazine* [Ryan, 1985]. In the United States the Federal Communication Commission (FCC) regulates radio, telephone, television, and satellite transmission systems. The international frequency assignments are divided into subbands by the FCC to accommodate 70 categories of services and 9 million transmitters. Table 1-2 gives a general listing of frequency bands, their common designations, typical propagation conditions, and typical services assigned to these bands.

1-7 Propagation of Electromagnetic Waves

The propagation characteristics of electromagnetic waves used in softwire channels are highly dependent on the frequency. This situation is shown in Table 1-2, where users are assigned frequencies that have the appropriate propagation characteristics for the coverage needed. The propagation characteristics are the result of changes in the radio-wave velocity as a function of altitude and boundary conditions. The wave velocity is dependent on changes in air temperature, air density, and levels of air ionization.

Ionization (i.e., free electrons) of the rarified air at high altitudes has a dominant effect on wave propagation in the medium-frequency (MF) and high-frequency (HF) bands. The ionization is caused by ultraviolet radiation from the sun, as well as cosmic rays. Consequently, the amount of ionization is a function of the time of day, season of the year, and the sun activity (sunspots). This results in several layers of varying ionization density located at various heights surrounding the Earth.

The dominant ionized regions are D, E, F_1, and F_2 layers. The D layer is located closest

TABLE 1-2 Frequency Bands

Frequency Band[a]	Designation	Propagation Characteristics	Typical Uses
3–30 kHz	Very low frequency (VLF)	Ground wave; low attenuation day and night; high atmospheric noise level	Long-range navigation; submarine communication
30–300 kHz	Low frequency (LF)	Similar to VLF, slightly less reliable; absorption in daytime	Long-range navigation and marine communication radio beacons
300–3000 kHz	Medium frequency (MF)	Ground wave and night sky wave; attenuation low at night and high in day; atmospheric noise	Maritime radio, direction finding, and emergency frequencies; AM broadcasting
3–30 MHz	High frequency (HF)	Ionospheric reflection varies with time of day, season, and frequency; low atmospheric noise at 30 MHz	Amateur radio; international broadcasting, military communication, long-distance aircraft and ship communication, telephone, telegraph, facsimile
30–300 MHz	Very high frequency (VHF)	Nearly line-of-sight (LOS) propagation, with scattering because of temperature inversions, cosmic noise	VHF television, FM two-way radio, AM aircraft communication, aircraft navigational aids
0.3–3 GHz	Ultra high frequency (UHF)	LOS propagation, cosmic noise	UHF television, navigational aids, radar, microwave links
	Letter designation		
1.0–2.0	L		
2.0–4.0	S		
3–30 GHz	Super high frequency (SHF)	LOS propagation; rainfall attenuation above 10 GHz, atmospheric attenuation because of oxygen and water vapor; high water vapor absorption at 22.2 GHz	Satellite communication, radar microwave links
	Letter designation		
2.0–4.0	S		
4.0–8.0	C		
8.0–12.0	X		
12.0–18.0	Ku		
18.0–27.0	K		
27.0–40.0	Ka		
26.5–40.0	R		

TABLE 1-2 Frequency Bands (*continued*)

Frequency Band[a]	Designation	Propagation Characteristics	Typical Uses
30–300 GHz	Extremely high frequency (EHF)	Same; high water vapor absorption at 183 GHz and oxygen absorption at 60 and 119 GHz	Radar, satellite, experimental
	Letter designation		
27.0–40.0	Ka		
26.5–40.0	R		
33.0–50.0	Q		
40.0–75.0	V		
75.0–110.0	W		
110–300	mm (millimeter)		
10^3–10^7 GHz	Infrared, visible light, and ultraviolet	LOS propagation	Optical communications

[a]kHz = 10^3 Hz; MHz = 10^6 Hz; GHz = 10^9 Hz.

to the Earth's surface at an altitude of about 45 or 55 miles. For $f > 300$ kHz, the D layer acts as a radio-frequency (RF) sponge to absorb (or attenuate) these radio waves. The attenuation is inversely proportional to frequency and becomes small for frequencies above 4 MHz. For $f < 300$ kHz, the D layer provides refraction (bending) of RF waves. The D layer is most pronounced during the daylight hours, with maximum ionization when the sun is overhead, and almost disappears at night. The E layer has a height of 65 to 75 miles, has maximum ionization around noon (local time), and practically disappears after sunset. It provides reflection of HF frequencies during the daylight hours. The F layer ranges in altitude between 90 and 250 miles. It ionizes rapidly at sunrise, reaches its peak ionization in early afternoon, and decays slowly after sunset. The F region splits into two layers, F_1 and F_2, during the day and combines into one layer at night. The F region is the most predominant medium in providing reflection of HF waves. As shown in Fig. 1-2, the electromagnetic spectrum may be divided into three broad bands that have one of three dominant propagation characteristics: ground wave, sky wave, and line of sight (LOS).

Ground-wave propagation is illustrated in Fig. 1-2a. It is the dominant mode of propagation for frequencies below 2 MHz. Here the electromagnetic wave tends to follow the contour of the Earth. That is, diffraction of the wave causes it to propagate along the surface of the Earth. This is the propagation mode used in AM broadcasting, where the local coverage follows the Earth's contour and the signal propagates over the visual horizon. The question is often asked: What is the lowest radio frequency that can be used? The answer is that the value of the lowest useful frequency depends on how long you want to make the antenna. For efficient radiation, the antenna needs to be longer than $\frac{1}{10}$ of a

(a) Ground–Wave Propagation (Below 2 MHz)

(b) Sky–Wave Propagation (2 to 30 MHz)

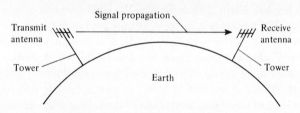

(c) Line–of–Sight (LOS) Propagation (Above 30 MHz)

FIGURE 1-2 Propagation of radio frequencies.

wavelength. For example, for signaling with a carrier frequency of $f_c = 10$ kHz, the wavelength is

$$\lambda = \frac{c}{f_c} \tag{1-3a}$$

or

$$\lambda = \frac{3 \times 10^8 \text{ m/sec}}{10^4} = 3 \times 10^4 \text{ m} \tag{1-3b}$$

where c is the speed of light. (The formula $\lambda = c/f_c$ is distance = velocity $\times$ time, where the time needed to traverse one wavelength is $t = 1/f_c$.) Thus an antenna needs to be at least 3000 m in length for efficient electromagnetic radiation at 10 kHz.

Sky-wave propagation is illustrated in Fig. 1-2b. It is the dominant mode of propagation in the 2- to 30-MHz frequency range. Here long-distance coverage is obtained by reflecting the wave at the ionosphere and at the Earth's boundaries. Actually, in the ionosphere the waves are refracted (i.e., bent) gradually in an inverted U shape since the index of refraction varies with altitude as the ionization density changes. The refraction index of the ionosphere is given by [Griffiths, 1987; Jordan and Balmain, 1968]

$$n = \sqrt{1 - \frac{81N}{f^2}} \tag{1-4}$$

where n is the refractive index, N is the free electron density (number of electrons per cubic meter), and f is the frequency of the wave (in hertz). Typical N values range between 10^{10} and 10^{12} depending on the time of day, season, and the number of sunspots. In an ionized region $n < 1$, since $N > 0$, and outside the ionized region $n \approx 1$ since $N \approx 0$. In the ionized region, since $n < 1$, the waves will be bent according to Snell's law:

$$n \sin \varphi_r = \sin \varphi_i \tag{1-5}$$

where φ_i is the angle of incidence (between the wave direction and vertical) measured just below the ionosphere and φ_r is the angle of refraction for the wave (from vertical) measured in the ionosphere. Furthermore, the refraction index will vary with altitude within the ionosphere since N varies. For frequencies selected from the 2- to 30-MHz band the refraction index will vary with altitude over the appropriate range so that the wave will be bent back to Earth. Consequently, the ionosphere acts as a reflector. The transmitting station will have coverage areas as indicated in Fig. 1-2b by heavy black lines along the Earth's surface. The coverage near the transmit antenna is due to the ground-wave mode, and the other coverage areas are due to sky wave. Notice that there are areas of no coverage along the Earth's surface between the transmit and receive antennas. The angle of reflection and the loss of signal at an ionospheric reflection point depend on the frequency, the time of day, the season of the year, and the sunspot activity of the sun [Jordan, 1985, Chap. 33].

During the daytime (at the ionospheric reflection points), the electron density will be high so that $n < 1$. Consequently, sky waves from distant stations on the other side of the world will be heard on the shortwave bands. However, the D layer is also present during the day. This absorbs frequencies below 4 MHz. This is the case for AM broadcast stations, where distant stations cannot be heard during the day, but at night the layer disappears and distant AM stations can be heard via sky-wave propagation.

Sky-wave propagation is caused primarily by reflection from the F layer (90 to 250 miles in altitude). Because of this layer, international broadcast stations in the HF band can be heard from the other side of the world at almost any time during the day or night.

Line-of-sight (LOS) propagation is illustrated in Fig. 1-2c. This is the dominant mode for frequencies above 30 MHz. Here the electromagnetic wave propagates in a straight line. In this case $f^2 \gg 81N$, so that $n \approx 1$ and there is very little refraction by the iono-

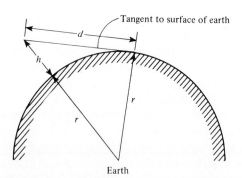

FIGURE 1-3 Calculation of distance to horizon.

sphere. In fact, the signal will propagate *through* the ionosphere. This property is used for satellite communications.

The LOS mode has the disadvantage that for communication between two terrestrial (Earth) stations, the signal path has to be above the horizon. Otherwise, the Earth will block the LOS path. Thus antennas need to be placed on tall towers so that the receiver antenna can "see" the transmitting antenna. A formula for the distance to the horizon, d, as a function of antenna height can be easily obtained by the use of Fig. 1-3. From this figure

$$d^2 + r^2 = (r + h)^2$$

or

$$d^2 = 2rh + h^2$$

where r is the radius of the Earth and h is the antenna height above the Earth's surface. In this application h^2 is negligible with respect to $2rh$. The radius of the Earth is 3960 statute miles. However, at LOS radio frequencies the effective Earth radius[†] is $\frac{4}{3}(3960)$ miles. Thus the distance to the radio horizon is

$$d = \sqrt{2h} \text{ miles} \tag{1-6}$$

where conversion factors have been used so that h is the antenna height measured in feet and d is in statute miles. For example, television stations have assigned frequencies above 30 MHz in the VHF or UHF range (see Table 1-2), and the fringe-area coverage of high-power stations is limited by the LOS radio horizon. For a television station with a 1000-ft tower, d is 44.7 miles. For a fringe-area viewer who has an antenna height of 30 ft, d is 7.75 miles. Thus for these transmitting and receiving heights, the television station would have fringe-area coverage out to a radius of 44.7 + 7.75 = 52.5 miles around the transmitting tower.

In addition to the LOS propagation mode, it is possible to have *ionospheric scatter propagation*. This mode occurs over the frequency range of 30 to 60 MHz, when the radio

---

[†] The refractive index of the atmosphere decreases slightly with height, which causes some bending of radio rays. This effect may be taken into account in LOS calculations by using an effective earth radius that is four-thirds of the actual radius.

frequency signal is scattered because of irregularities in the refractive index of the lower ionosphere (about 50 miles above the earth's surface). Because of this scattering, communications can be carried out over path lengths of 1000 miles even though this is beyond the LOS distance. Similarly, *tropospheric scattering* (within 10 miles above the Earth's surface) can propagate radio-frequency signals that are in the 40-MHz to 4-GHz range over paths of several hundred miles.

For more technical details about radio-wave propagation, the reader is referred to textbooks that include chapters on ground-wave and sky-wave propagation [Griffiths, 1987; Jordan and Balmain, 1968] and to a radio engineering handbook [Jordan, 1985]. A very readable description of this topic is also found in the ARRL handbook [ARRL, 1993], and a personal computer program, MINIMUF, is available that predicts sky-wave propagation conditions [Rose, 1982, 1984].

1-8 Information Measure

As we have seen, the purpose of communication systems is to transmit information from a source to a sink. However, what exactly is information, and how do we measure it? We know qualitatively that it is related to the surprise that is experienced when we receive the message. For example, the message "The ocean has been destroyed by a nuclear explosion" contains more information than the message "It is raining today."

> **DEFINITION:** The *information* sent from a digital source when the jth message is transmitted is given by

$$I_j = \log_2\left(\frac{1}{P_j}\right) \qquad \text{bits} \qquad (1\text{-}7a)$$

where P_j is the probability of transmitting the jth message.[†]

From this definition we see that messages that are less likely to occur (smaller value for P_j) provide more information (larger value of I_j). We also observe that this information measure depends only on the likelihood of sending the message and does not depend on possible interpretation of the content as to whether or not it makes sense.

The base of the logarithm determines the units used for the information measure. Thus for units of "bits," the base 2 logarithm is used. If the natural logarithm is used, the units are "nats"; and for base 10 logarithms, the unit is the "hartley," named after R. V. Hartley, who first suggested using the logarithm measure in 1928 [Hartley, 1948].

In this section the term *bit* denotes a unit of information as defined by (1-7a). In later sections, particularly in Chapter 3, *bit* is also used to denote a unit of binary data. Please do not confuse these two different meanings for the word *bit*. Some authors use *binit* to denote units of data and use *bit* exclusively to denote units of information. However, most engineers use the same word (*bit*) to denote both kinds of units, with the particular meaning understood from the context in which the word is used. This book follows that industry custom.

[†]The definition of probability is given in Appendix B.

For ease of evaluating I_j on a calculator, (1-7a) can be written in terms of the base 10 logarithm or the natural logarithm.

$$I_j = -\frac{1}{\log_{10} 2} \log_{10} P_j = -\frac{1}{\ln 2} \ln P_j \qquad (1\text{-}7b)$$

In general, the information content will vary from message to message since the P_j will not be equal. Consequently, we need an average information measure for the source, taking into account all the possible messages we can send.

DEFINITION: The *average information* measure of a digital source is

$$H = \sum_{j=1}^{m} P_j I_j = \sum_{j=1}^{m} P_j \log_2\left(\frac{1}{P_j}\right) \qquad \text{bits} \qquad (1\text{-}8)$$

where m is the number of possible different source messages and P_j is the probability of sending the jth message (m is finite since a digital source is assumed). The average information is called *entropy*.

Example 1-1   Evaluation of Information and Entropy

Find the information content of a message that consists of a digital word 12 digits long in which each digit may take on one of four possible levels. The probability of sending any of the four levels is assumed to be equal, and the level in any digit does not depend on the values taken on by previous digits.

In a string of 12 symbols (digits) where each symbol consists of one of four levels, there are $4 \cdot 4 \cdot \ldots \cdot 4 = 4^{12}$ different combinations (words) that can be obtained. Since each level is equally likely, all the different words are equally likely. Thus

$$P_j = \frac{1}{4^{12}} = \left(\frac{1}{4}\right)^{12}$$

or

$$I_j = \log_2\left(\frac{1}{(\frac{1}{4})^{12}}\right) = 12 \log_2(4) = 24 \text{ bits}$$

In this example we see that the information content in *any* of the possible messages equals that in any other possible message (24 bits). Thus the average information H is 24 bits.

Suppose that only two levels (binary) had been allowed for each digit and that all the words were equally likely. Then the information would be $I_j = 12$ bits for the binary words, and the average information would be $H = 12$ bits. Here, all the 12-bit words gave 12 bits of information since the words were equally likely. If they had not been equally likely, some of the 12-bit words would contain more than 12 bits of information and some would contain less, and the average information would have been less than 12 bits.

The rate of information is also important.

DEFINITION: The *source rate* is given by

$$R = \frac{H}{T} \quad \text{bits/sec} \tag{1-9}$$

where H is evaluated using (1-8) and T is the time required to send a message.

The definitions previously given apply to digital sources. The definitions for continuous sources are not presented here because the mathematics becomes more complicated and the physical meanings are more difficult to interpret. However, we do not need to be too concerned about the continuous case since, from a microscopic point of view, communication is inherently a discrete process, as pointed out by Shannon in 1948 and mentioned by Hartley in 1928. From a macroscopic point of view, analog sources can be approximated by digital sources with as much accuracy as we desire.

1-9 Channel Capacity and Other Fundamental Limits

A large number of criteria can be used to measure the effectiveness of a communication system to see if it is ideal or perfect. Some of these criteria are cost, channel bandwidth used, required transmitter power, signal-to-noise ratios at various points of the system, probability of bit error for digital systems, and time delay through the system.

In digital systems the optimum system might be defined as the system that minimizes the probability of bit error at the system output subject to constraints on transmitted energy and channel bandwidth. Thus bit error and signal bandwidth are of prime importance and are covered in subsequent chapters. This raises the question: Is it possible to invent a system with no bit error at the output even when we have noise introduced into the channel? This question was answered by Claude Shannon in 1948–1949 [Shannon, 1948, 1949]. The answer is yes, under certain assumptions. Shannon showed that (for the case of signal plus white Gaussian noise) a *channel capacity* C (bits/sec) could be calculated such that if the rate of information R (bits/sec) was less than C, the probability of error would approach zero. The equation for C is

$$C = B \log_2\left(1 + \frac{S}{N}\right) \tag{1-10}$$

where B is the channel bandwidth in hertz (Hz) and S/N is the signal-to-noise power ratio (watts/watt, not dB) at the input to the digital receiver. Shannon does not tell us how to build this system, but he proves that it is theoretically possible to have such a system. Thus Shannon gives us a theoretical performance bound that we can strive to achieve with practical communication systems. Systems that approach this bound usually incorporate error correction coding. The channel noise still causes errors at the input to the receiver decoder; however, enough redundancy has been added in the transmitted signal so that the decoder can detect and correct errors with its processing circuits.

Other fundamental limits for digital signaling were discovered by Nyquist in 1924 and Hartley in 1928. If a pulse represents one bit of data, Nyquist showed that noninterfering pulses could be sent over a channel no faster than $2B$ pulses/sec, where B is the channel bandwidth in hertz. This is now known as the dimensionality theorem and is discussed in Chapter 3. Hartley generalized Nyquist's result for the case of multilevel pulse signaling as discussed in Chapters 3, 4, and 8.

In analog systems the optimum system might be defined as the one that achieves the largest signal-to-noise ratio at the receiver output subject to design constraints such as channel bandwidth and transmitted power. Here the evaluation of the output signal-to-noise ratio is of prime importance. We might ask the question: Is it possible to design a system with infinite signal-to-noise ratio at the output when noise is introduced by the channel? The answer, of course, is no. The performance of practical analog systems with respect to that of Shannon's ideal system is illustrated in Chapter 6 (Fig. 6-18).

The following section describes the improvement that can be obtained in digital systems when practical coding is used and how these coded systems compare with Shannon's ideal system.

1-10 Coding

If the data at the output of a digital communication system have errors that are too frequent for the desired use, the errors can often be reduced by the use of either of two main techniques.

- Automatic repeat request (ARQ).
- Forward error correction (FEC).

In an ARQ system, when a receiver circuit detects errors in a block of data, it requests that the data block be retransmitted. In an FEC system, the transmitted data are encoded so that the receiver can correct as well as detect errors. These procedures are also classified as *channel coding* because they are used to correct errors caused by channel noise. This is different from *source coding*, described in Chapter 4, where the purpose of the coding is to extract the essential information from the source and encode it into digital form so that it can be saved or transmitted using digital techniques.

The choice between using the ARQ or the FEC technique depends on the particular application. ARQ is generally used in computer communication systems because it is relatively inexpensive to implement and there is usually a duplex (two-way) channel so that the receiving end can transmit back an acknowledgment (ACK) for correctly received data or a request for retransmission (NAC) when the data are received in error. (See Appendix C, Section C-4, for examples of ARQ signaling.) FEC techniques are used to correct errors on simplex (one-way) channels where returning of an ACK/NAC indicator (required for the ARQ technique) is not feasible. FEC is preferred on systems with large transmission delays because if the ARQ technique were used, the effective data rate would be small; the transmitter would have long idle periods while waiting for the ACK/NAC

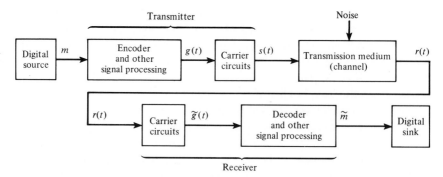

FIGURE 1-4 General digital communication system.

indicator, which is retarded by the long transmission delay. Since ARQ systems are covered in Appendix C, we concentrate on FEC techniques in the remainder of this section.

Communication systems with FEC are illustrated in Fig. 1-4, where encoding and decoding blocks have been designated. From a *theoretical viewpoint*, Shannon's channel capacity theorem states that a finite value for S/N limits only the *rate* of transmission. That is, the probability of error, $P(E)$, can approach zero provided that the information rate is less than the channel capacity. Of course, this theorem implies that coding is needed to make $P(E) \rightarrow 0$. The question is: *What $P(E)$ can be achieved when practical coding is used?*

The topic of coding is immense, and we will not even attempt to give an introduction to the numerous coding techniques that have been developed. However, we will summarize some of the basic concepts involved and cite results that indicate the practical improvement that can be achieved when coding is used. For further introduction to the topic of coding, an excellent textbook by Sweeney is recommended [Sweeney, 1991].

Coding provides improved performance because of the following phenomena:

- *Redundancy.* Redundant bits are added by the coder to accentuate the uniqueness of each (digital) message.
- *Noise averaging.* The code is designed so that the receiver can average out the noise over long time spans, T_0, where T_0 becomes very large.

The appropriate code is selected to provide the desired error performance within the allowed cost.

Codes may be classified into two broad categories:

- *Block codes.* A block code is a mapping of k input binary symbols into n output binary symbols. Consequently, the block coder is a *memoryless* device. Since $n > k$, the code can be selected to provide redundancy, such as *parity bits*, which are used by the decoder to provide some error detection and error correction. The codes are denoted by (n,k), where the code rate R is defined by $R = k/n$. Practical values of R range from $\frac{1}{4}$ to $\frac{7}{8}$, and k ranges from 3 to several hundred [Clark and Cain, 1981].
- *Tree codes.* A tree code is produced by a coder that has *memory*. *Convolutional codes* are a subset of tree codes. The convolutional coder accepts k binary symbols at its input

and produces n binary symbols at its output, where the n output symbols are affected by $v + k$ input symbols. Memory is incorporated since $v > 0$. The code rate is defined by $R = k/n$. Typical values for k and n range from 1 to 8, and the values for v range from 2 to 60. The range of R is between $\frac{1}{4}$ and $\frac{7}{8}$ [Clark and Cain, 1981]. A small value for code rate R indicates a high degree of redundancy, which should provide more effective error control at the expense of reducing the information throughput.

Block Codes

Before discussing block codes, several definitions are needed. The *Hamming weight* of a code word is the number of binary 1 bits. For example, the code word 110101 has a Hamming weight of 4. The *Hamming distance* between two code words, denoted by d, is the number of positions by which they differ. For example, the code words 110101 and 111001 have a distance of $d = 2$. A received code word can be checked for errors. Some of the errors can be detected and corrected if $d \geq s + t + 1$, where s is the number of errors that can be detected and t is the number of errors that can be corrected ($s \geq t$). Thus a pattern of t or fewer errors can be both detected and corrected if $d \geq 2t + 1$.

A general code word can be expressed in the form

$$i_1 i_2 i_3 \cdots i_k p_1 p_2 p_3 \cdots p_r$$

where k is the number of information bits, r is the number of parity check bits, and n is the total word length in the (n,k) block code, where $n = k + r$. This arrangement of the information bits at the beginning of the code word followed by the parity bits is most common. Such a block code is said to be *systematic*. Other arrangements with the parity bits interleaved between the information bits are possible and are usually considered to be equivalent codes.

Hamming has given a procedure for designing block codes that have single error-correction capability [Hamming, 1950]. A Hamming code is a block code having a Hamming distance of 3. Since $d \geq 2t + 1$, $t = 1$ and a single error can be detected and corrected. However, only certain (n,k) codes are allowable. These allowable Hamming codes are

$$(n,k) = (2^m - 1, 2^m - 1 - m) \tag{1-11}$$

where m is an integer and $m \geq 3$. Thus some of the allowable codes are (7,4), (15,11), (31,26), (63,57), and (127,120). The code rate R approaches 1 as m becomes large, which indicates that the information throughput efficiency becomes very good for large m.

In addition to Hamming codes, there are many other types of block codes. One popular class consists of the cyclic codes. *Cyclic codes* are block codes such that another code word can be obtained by taking any one code word, shifting the bits to the right, and placing the dropped-off bits on the left. These types of codes have the advantage of being easily encoded from the message source by the use of inexpensive linear shift registers with feedback. This structure also allows these codes to be easily decoded. Examples of cyclic and related codes are Bose–Chaudhuri–Hocquenhem (BCH), Reed–Solomon, Hamming, maximal-length, Reed–Müller, and Golay codes. Some properties of block codes are given in Table 1-3 [Bhargava, 1983].

TABLE 1-3 Properties of Block Codes

Property	Code[a]			
	BCH	Reed–Solomon	Hamming	Maximal-Length
Block length	$n = 2^m - 1$ $m = 3, 4, 5, \ldots$	$n = m(2^m - 1)$ bits	$n = 2^m - 1$	$n = 2^m - 1$
Number of parity bits		$r = m2t$ bits	$r = m$	
Minimum distance	$d \geq 2t + 1$	$d = m(2t + 1)$ bits	$d = 3$	$d = 2^m - 1$
Number of information bits	$k \geq n - mt$			$k = m$

[a]m is any positive integer unless otherwise indicated; n is the block length; k is the number of information bits.

Convolutional Codes

A convolutional encoder is illustrated in Fig. 1-5. Here k bits (one input frame) are shifted in each time and, concurrently, n bits (one output frame) are shifted out, where $n > k$. Thus every k-bit input frame produces an n-bit output frame. Redundancy is provided in the output, since $n > k$. Also, there is memory in the coder, since the output frame depends on the previous K input frames where $K > 1$. The *code rate* is $R = k/n$, which is $\frac{3}{4}$ in this illustration. The *constraint length, K,* is the number of input frames that are held in the kK-bit shift register.[†] Depending on the particular convolutional code that is to be generated, data from the kK stages of the shift register are added (modulo 2) and used to set the bits in the n-stage output register.

For example, consider the convolutional coder shown in Fig. 1-6. Here $k = 1$, $n = 2$, $K = 3$, and a commutator with two inputs performs the function of a two-stage output shift register. The convolutional code is generated by inputting a bit of data and then giving the commutator a complete revolution. This process is repeated for successive input bits to produce the convolutionally encoded output. In this example, each $k = 1$ input bit produces $n = 2$ output bits, so the code rate is $R = k/n = \frac{1}{2}$. The code tree of Fig. 1-7 gives the encoded sequences for the convolutional encoder example of Fig. 1-6. To use the code tree, one moves up if the input is a binary 0 or down if the input is a binary 1. The corresponding encoded bits are shown in parentheses. For example, if the input sequence $x_{11} = 1010$ is fed into the input (most recent input bit on the right), the corresponding encoded output sequence is $y_{11} = 11010001$, as shown by path A in Fig. 1-7.

A convolutionally encoded signal is decoded by "matching" the encoded received data to the corresponding bit pattern in the code tree. In sequential decoding (a suboptimal technique), the path is found like that of a car driver who occasionally makes a wrong turn

[†] Several different definitions for constraint length are used in the literature [Blahut, 1983; Clark and Cain, 1981; Proakis, 1983, 1989].

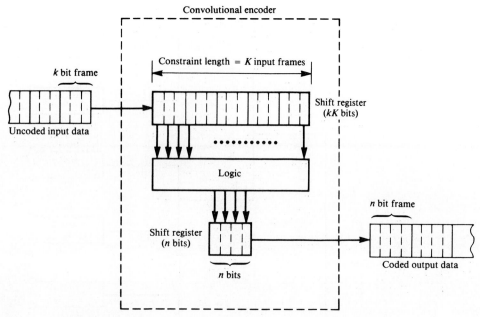

FIGURE 1-5 Convolutional encoding ($k = 3$, $n = 4$, $K = 5$, and $R = \frac{3}{4}$).

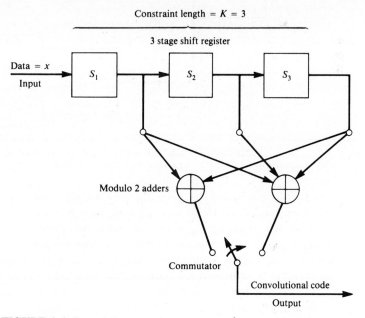

FIGURE 1-6 Convolutional encoder for a rate $\frac{1}{2}$, constraint length 3 code.

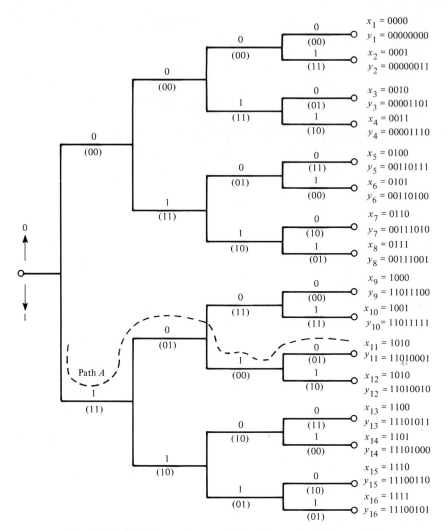

FIGURE 1-7 Code tree for convolutional encoder of Figure 1-6.

at a fork in a road but discovers the mistake, goes back, and tries another path. For example, if $y_{11} = 11010010$ was received, path A would be the closest match and the decoded data would be $x_{11} = 1010$. If noise was present in the channel, some of the received encoded bits might be in error, and then the paths would not match exactly. In this case, the match is found by choosing a path that will minimize the Hamming distance between the selected path sequence and the received encoded sequence.

An optimum decoding algorithm, called *Viterbi decoding*, uses a similar procedure. It examines the possible paths and selects the best ones based on some conditional probabilities [Forney, 1973]. The optimum Viterbi procedure uses so-called soft decisions. A *soft decision* algorithm first decides the result based on the test statistic[†] being above or below a decision threshold and then gives a "confidence" number that specifies how close the test statistic was to the threshold value. In *hard decisions* only the decision output is known, and it is not known if the decision was almost "too close to call" (because the test value was almost equal to the threshold value). The soft decision technique can translate into a 2-dB improvement (decrease) in the required receiver input E_b/N_0 [Clark and Cain, 1981]. E_b is the received signal energy over a one-bit time interval, and $N_0/2$ is the power spectral density (PSD) of the channel noise at the receiver input. Both E_b and N_0 will be defined in Chapter 4.

Code Interleaving

In the previous discussion it was assumed that if no coding was used, the channel noise would cause random bit errors at the receiver output that are more or less isolated, that is, not adjacent. When coding was added, the code redundancy allowed the receiver decoder to correct the errors so that the decoded output was almost error free. However, in some applications, large wide pulses of channel noise occur—such as in pulse jamming or in telephone channels with switching noise. If the usual coding techniques are used in these situations, bursts of errors will occur at the decoder output because the noise bursts are wider than the "redundancy time" of the code. This situation can be ameliorated by the use of code interleaving.

At the transmitting end the coded data are interleaved by shuffling (i.e., like shuffling a deck of cards) the coded bits over a time span of several block lengths (for block codes) or several constraint lengths (for convolutional codes). The required span length is several times the duration of the noise burst. At the receiver, before decoding, the data with error bursts are deinterleaved to produce coded data with isolated errors. The isolated errors are then corrected by passing the coded data through the decoder. This produces almost error-free output even when noise bursts occur at the receiver input. There are two classes of interleavers—block interleavers and convolutional interleavers [Sklar, 1988].

Code Performance

The improvement in the performance of a digital communication system that can be achieved by the use of coding is illustrated in Fig. 1-8. It is assumed that a digital signal plus channel noise is present at the receiver input. The performance of a system that uses binary-phase-shift-keyed (BPSK) signaling is shown both for the case when coding is used and for the case when there is no coding.[‡] For the coded case a (23,12) Golay code is used. P_e is the *probability of bit error*—also called the *bit error rate* (BER)—that is measured at the receiver output. E_b/N_0 is the energy-per-bit/noise-density ratio at the receiver input (as described in the preceding section). The *coding gain* is defined as the

---

[†] The test statistic is a value that is computed at the receiver based on the receiver input waveform during some specified time interval.

[‡] BPSK signaling is discussed in Chapter 7.

FIGURE 1-8 Performance of digital systems—with and without coding.

reduction in E_b/N_0 (in decibels) that is achieved when coding is used when compared to the E_b/N_0 required for the uncoded case at some specific level of P_e. For example, as can be seen in the figure, a coding gain of 1.33 dB is realized for a BER of 10^{-3}. The coding gain increases if the BER is smaller so that a coding gain of 2.15 dB is achieved when $P_e = 10^{-5}$. This improvement is significant in space communication applications where every decibel of improvement is valuable. It is also noted that there is a *coding threshold* in the sense that the coded system actually provides *poorer* performance than the uncoded system when E_b/N_0 is less than the threshold value. In this example the coding threshold is about 3.5 dB. A coding threshold is found in all coded systems.

For the case of optimum coding, Shannon's channel capacity theorem, (1-10), gives the minimum E_b/N_0 allowed for a noisy signal at the receiver input such that the data can be decoded with no error. This minimum value for E_b/N_0 is -1.59 dB and is called *Shannon's limit.*[†] That is, if optimum coding/decoding is used at the transmitter and receiver, error-free data will be recovered at the receiver output provided that the E_b/N_0 at the receiver input is larger than -1.59 dB. This "brick wall" limit is shown by the dashed line in Fig. 1-8, where P_e jumps from 0 ($10^{-\infty}$) to $\frac{1}{2}(0.5 \times 10^0)$ as E_b/N_0 becomes smaller

---

[†]For a proof of this statement, see the appendix for this chapter, Section 1-12.

than -1.59 dB, assuming that the ideal (unknown) code is used. Any practical system will perform worse than this ideal system described by Shannon's limit. Thus the goal of digital system designers is to find practical codes that approach the performance of Shannon's ideal (unknown) code.

When the performance of the optimum encoded signal is compared to that of BPSK without coding (10^{-5} BER), it is seen that the optimum (unknown) coded signal has a coding gain of $9.61 - (-1.59) = 11.2$ dB. Using Fig. 1-8, compare this to the coding gain of 2.15 dB that is achieved when a (23,12) Golay-encoded BPSK signal is used. Table 1-4 shows the coding gains that can be obtained for some other codes [Bhargava, 1983].

TABLE 1-4 Coding Gains with BPSK or QPSK

Coding Technique Used	Coding Gain (dB) at 10^{-5} BER	Coding Gain (dB) at 10^{-8} BER	Data Rate Capability
Ideal coding	11.2	13.6	
Concatenated[a] Reed–Solomon and convolution (Viterbi decoding)	6.5–7.5	8.5–9.5	Moderate
Convolutional with sequential decoding (soft decisions)	6.0–7.0	8.0–9.0	Moderate
Block codes (soft decisions)	5.0–6.0	6.5–7.5	Moderate
Concatenated[a] Reed–Solomon and short block	4.5–5.5	6.5–7.5	Very high
Convolutional with Viterbi decoding	4.0–5.5	5.0–6.5	High
Convolutional with sequential decoding (hard decisions)	4.0–5.0	6.0–7.0	High
Block codes (hard decisions)	3.0–4.0	4.5–5.5	High
Block codes with threshold decoding	2.0–4.0	3.5–5.5	High
Convolutional with threshold decoding	1.5–3.0	2.5–4.0	Very high

[a]Two different encoders are used in series at the transmitter (see Fig. 1-4), and the corresponding decoders are used at the receiver.
SOURCE: Bhargava [1983].

Trellis-Coded Modulation

All of the codes described above (excluding the ideal unknown code, predicted by Shannon) achieve their coding gains at the expense of *bandwidth expansion.* That is, when the redundant bits are added to provide the coding gain, the overall data rate and, consequently, the bandwidth are increased for the same information rate. Accordingly, we have to reduce the information rate when we attempt to implement these coding techniques on a bandlimited channel. Therefore, these techniques are not usually incorporated into modems that are designed for data communications over voice-frequency (VF) telephone channels that pass frequencies over a band in the 300- to 3000-Hz range. However, Gottfried Ungerboeck has invented a technique called *trellis-coded modulation* (TCM) that combines multilevel modulation and coding to achieve coding gain without bandwidth expansion [Biglieri, Divsalar, McLane, and Simon, 1991; Ungerboeck, 1982, 1987].[†] TCM has been adopted for use in the CCITT V.32 modem that allows an information data rate of 9600 b/s (bits per second) to be transmitted over conventional telephone lines—see Tables C-12 and C-14. As described earlier by (1-1), modulation is the process of mapping the baseband source information into amplitude and phase variations—$R(t)$ and $\theta(t)$, respectively—of a bandpass sinusoidal carrier signal, $s(t)$, which has a spectrum that is concentrated about the carrier frequency, f_c. The variations can be expressed mathematically as the complex envelope, $g(t)$, where

$$g(t) = R(t)e^{j\theta(t)}$$

(The complex envelope is indicated on the communication system block diagram in Fig. 1-4, and it will be described in detail in Chapter 5.) As seen in Fig. 1-9a, which describes conventional coded systems, the coding and modulation operations are carried out separately by first encoding the baseband data to produce a coded baseband waveform and then modulating this onto the carrier as amplitude and phase variations.

The combined modulation and coding operation of TCM is shown in Fig. 1-9b. Here, the serial data from the source, $m(t)$, are converted into parallel (m-bit) data, which are partitioned into k-bit and ($m - k$)-bit words where $k \le m$. The k-bit words (frames) are convolutionally encoded into ($n = k + 1$)-bit words so that the code rate is $R = k/(k + 1)$. The amplitude and phase are then set jointly on the basis of the coded n-bit word and the uncoded ($m - k$)-bit word. When a convolutional code of constraint length $K = 3$ is implemented, this TCM technique produces a coding gain of 3 dB relative to an uncoded signal that has the same bandwidth and information rate. Almost 6 dB of coding gain can be realized if coders of constraint length 9 are used. The larger constraint length codes are not too difficult to generate, but the corresponding decoder for a code of large constraint length is very complicated. However, very-high-speed integrated circuits (VHSIC) are making this feasible. As mentioned previously, the CCITT V.32 modem uses TCM. It has a coding gain of 4 dB and is described by Example 4 of Wei's paper [Wei, 1984; CCITT Study Group XVII, 1984].

[†] Spectral conservation provided by multilevel signaling is discussed in Chapters 3, 4, and 7.

(a) Conventional Coding Technique

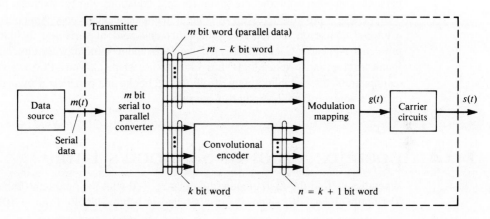

(b) Trellis-Coded Modulation Technique

FIGURE 1-9 Transmitters for conventional coding and for TCM.

For further study about coding, the reader is referred to several excellent books on the topic [Blahut, 1983; Clark and Cain, 1981; Gallagher, 1968; Lin and Costello, 1983; McEliece, 1977; Peterson and Weldon, 1972; Sweeney, 1991; Viterbi and Omura, 1979].

1-11 Preview

From the previous discussions, we see the need for some basic tools to understand and design communication systems. Some prime tools needed are: mathematical representations of signals and noise, time- and frequency-domain analysis using Fourier theory and orthogonal function theory, linear system analysis, and representations for bandlimited signals. Chapters 2 and 3 provides these tools. In Chapter 4 we describe baseband digital and pulse signals, digital-signal line codes, and intersymbol interference caused by filtering. In Chapter 5, bandpass signaling principles are introduced; and communication circuits such as limiters, down converters, and detectors are described. Amplitude modulation (AM) and frequency modulation (FM) bandpass signaling are covered in Chapter 6; and bandpass digital signaling, such as binary-phase-shift keying (BPSK) and quadrature AM (QAM), is covered in Chapter 7. Case studies of communications systems such as cellular telephone, satellite, TV, and modern telephone systems are given in Chapter 8 together with the standards adopted for these systems. The concept of noise figure is also introduced and case studies of link budget analysis are given.

Worked examples are scattered throughout this book to aid the reader. At the end of each chapter, ample exercise problems are given to help sharpen analytical skills and to provide insight in problem solving and communication system design. Answers for selected problems are provided at the end of the book. Numerous MathCAD and MATLAB personal-computer solutions are given for text equations and for exercise problems.

Appendix A provides a review of general mathematical concepts. Appendix B provides a tutorial course on the topic of probability and random variables, including exercise problems. Appendix C summarizes the standards and terminology used in computer communication systems. Appendix D shows how to use MathCAD on a PC to solve communications problems. A bibliography of referenced books and papers is provided to give the reader a source of in-depth study material.

1-12 Appendix: Proof of Shannon's Limit

We will now find the E_b/N_0 required so that $P_e \to 0$ with the optimum (unknown) code. The optimum encoded signal is not restricted in bandwidth, so, from (1-10),

$$C = \lim_{B \to \infty} \left\{ B \log_2\left(1 + \frac{S}{N}\right) \right\} = \lim_{B \to \infty} \left\{ B \log_2\left(1 + \frac{E_b/T_b}{N_0 B}\right) \right\}$$

$$= \lim_{x \to 0} \left\{ \frac{\log_2[1 + (E_b/N_0 T_b)x]}{x} \right\}$$

where T_b is the time that it takes to send one bit and N is the noise power that occurs within the bandwidth of the signal. The power spectral density (PSD) is $\mathcal{P}_n(f) = N_0/2$, and, as shown in Chapter 2, the noise power is

$$N = \int_{-B}^{B} \mathcal{P}_n(f)\, df = \int_{-B}^{B} \left(\frac{N_0}{2}\right) df = N_0 B \qquad (1\text{-}12)$$

where B is the signal bandwidth. L'Hospital's rule is used to evaluate this limit.

$$C = \lim_{x \to 0} \left\{ \frac{1}{1 + (E_b/N_0 T_b)x} \left(\frac{E_b}{N_0 T_b}\right) \log_2 e \right\} = \frac{E_b}{N_0 T_b \ln 2} \qquad (1\text{-}13)$$

If we signal at a rate approaching the channel capacity, $P_e \to 0$ and we have the maximum information rate allowed for $P_e \to 0$ (i.e., the optimum system). Thus $1/T_b = C$, or using (1-13),

$$\frac{1}{T_b} = \frac{E_b}{N_0 T_b \ln 2}$$

or

$$E_b/N_0 = \ln 2 = -1.59 \text{ dB} \qquad (1\text{-}14)$$

which is Shannon's limit as plotted in Fig. 1-8.

PROBLEMS

1-1   A high-power FM station of frequency 96.9 MHz has an antenna height of 1800 ft. If the signal is to be received 75 miles from the station, how high does a prospective listener need to mount his or her antenna in this fringe area?

1-2   Using geometry, prove that (1-6) is correct.

1-3   Referring to Sec. 1-7 concerning the propagation of electromagnetic waves, write a one-page discussion about radio-wave propagation for the 27-MHz citizen's-band (CB) radio service. Also, if you have experience as a CB operator, discuss how your prediction of CB signal propagation agrees with propagation conditions that you have observed.

1-4   A digital source emits -1.0- and 0.0-V levels with a probability of 0.2 each and $+3.0$- and $+4.0$-V levels with a probability of 0.3 each. Evaluate the average information of the source.

1-5   Prove that base 10 logarithms may be converted to base 2 logarithms by using the identity $\log_2(x) = [1/\log_{10}(2)] \log_{10}(x)$.

1-6   If all the messages emitted by a source are equally likely (i.e., $P_j = P$), show that (1-3) reduces to $H = \log_2(1/P)$.

1-7   For a binary source:
   (a) Show that the entropy, H, is a maximum when the probability of sending a binary 1 is equal to the probability of sending a binary 0.
   (b) Find the value of maximum entropy.

1-8   A single-digit, seven-segment liquid crystal display (LCD) emits a 0 with a probability of 0.25; a 1 and a 2 with a probability of 0.15 each; 3, 4, 5, 6, 7, and 8 with a probability of 0.07 each; and a 9 with a probability of 0.03. Find the average information for this source.

1-9   (a) A binary source sends a binary 1 with a probability of 0.3. Evaluate the average information for the source.
   (b) For a binary source find the probability for sending a binary 1 and a binary 0 such that the average source information will be maximized.

1-10   A numerical keypad has the digits 0, 1, 2, 3, 4, 5, 6, 7, 8, and 9. Assume that the probability of sending any one digit is the same as that for sending any of the other digits. Calculate how often the buttons must be pressed in order to send out information at the rate of 2 bits/sec.

1-11   Refer to Example 1-1 and assume that words, each 12 digits in length, are sent over a system and that each digit can take on one of two possible values. Half of the possible words have a probability of being transmitted that is $(\frac{1}{2})^{13}$ for each word. The other half have probabilities equal to $3(\frac{1}{2})^{13}$. Find the entropy for this source.

1-12   Evaluate the channel capacity for a teleprinter channel that has a 300-Hz bandwidth and a signal-to-noise ratio of 30 dB.

1-13 Assume that a computer terminal has 110 characters (on its keyboard) and that each character is sent using binary words.

(a) What are the number of bits needed to represent each character?

(b) How fast can the characters be sent (characters/sec) over a telephone line channel having a bandwidth of 3.2 kHz and a signal-to-noise ratio of 20 dB?

(c) What is the information content of each character if each is equally likely to be sent?

1-14 Using the definitions for terms associated with convolutional coding, draw a block diagram for a convolutional coder that has rate $R = \frac{2}{3}$ and constraint length $K = 3$.

1-15 For the convolutional encoder shown in Fig. P1-15, compute the output coded data when the input data is $\mathbf{x} = [10111]$. (The first input bit is the leftmost element of the $\mathbf{x}$ row vector.)

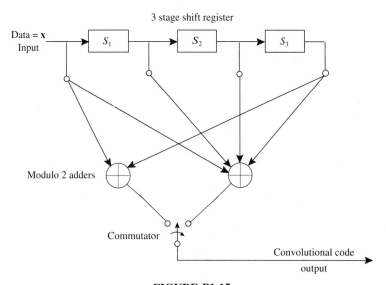

FIGURE P1-15

CHAPTER **2**

Signals and Spectra

2-1 Properties of Signals and Noise

In communication systems the received waveform is usually categorized into the desired part containing the information, and the extraneous or undesired part. The desired part is called the *signal* and the undesired part is called *noise*.

In this chapter we develop mathematical tools that are used to describe signals and noise waveforms. The waveforms are represented by direct mathematical expressions or by the use of orthogonal series representations such as the Fourier series. Properties for describing these waveforms, such as dc value, root mean square (rms) value, normalized power, magnitude spectrum, phase spectrum, and power spectral density, are also developed.

The waveform of interest may be the voltage variation as a function of time, $v(t)$, or the current variation as a function of time, $i(t)$. Often, the same mathematical techniques can be used when working with either type of waveform. Thus, for generality, waveforms will be denoted simply as $w(t)$ when the analysis applies to either case.

Physically Realizable Waveforms

Practical waveforms that are *physically realizable* (i.e., measurable in a laboratory) satisfy several conditions[†]:

1. The waveform has significant nonzero values over a composite time interval that is finite.
2. The spectrum of the waveform has significant values over a composite frequency interval that is finite.
3. The waveform is a continuous function of time.

[†]For an interesting discussion relative to the first and second conditions, see the paper by Slepian [1976].

4. The waveform has a finite peak value.
5. The waveform has only real values. That is, at any time, it cannot have a complex value $a + jb$ where b is nonzero.

   The first condition is necessary because systems (and their waveforms) appear to exist for a finite amount of time. Physical signals also produce only a finite amount of energy. The second condition is necessary since any transmission medium—such as wires, coaxial cable, waveguides, or fiber optic cable—has a restricted bandwidth. The third condition is a consequence of the second, as will become clear from spectral analysis as developed in Sec. 2-2. The fourth condition is necessary because physical devices are destroyed if voltage or current of infinite value is present within the device. The fifth condition follows from the fact that only real waveforms can be observed in the real world, although *properties* of waveforms, such as spectra, may be complex. Later, in Chapter 5, it will be shown that complex waveforms can be very useful in representing real bandpass signals mathematically.

   Mathematical models that violate some or all of the conditions listed above are often used, and for one main reason—to simplify the mathematical analysis. In fact, one often has to use a model that violates some of these conditions in order to calculate any type of answer. However, if one is careful with the mathematical model, the correct result can be obtained when the answer is properly interpreted. For example, consider the digital waveform shown in Fig. 2-1. The mathematical model waveform has discontinuities at the switching times. This situation violates the third condition—the physical waveform is

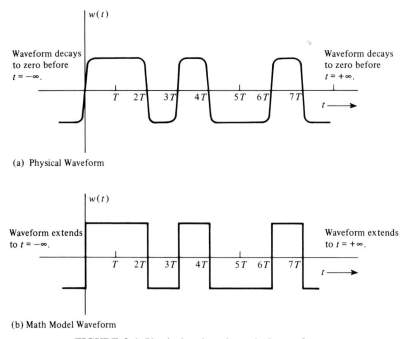

(a) Physical Waveform

(b) Math Model Waveform

FIGURE 2-1 Physical and mathematical waveforms.

continuous. The physical waveform is of finite duration (decays to zero before $t = \pm\infty$), but the duration of the mathematical waveform extends to infinity.

In other words, this mathematical model assumes that the physical waveform existed in its steady-state condition for all time. Spectral analysis of the model will approximate the correct results except for the extremely high-frequency components. The average power that is calculated from the model will give the correct value for the average power of the physical signal that is measured over a steady state time interval. The total energy of the mathematical model's signal will be infinity since it extends to infinite time, whereas that of the physical signal will be finite. Consequently, this model will not give the correct value for the total energy of the physical signal without using some additional information. However, the model can be used to evaluate the energy of the physical signal over some finite time interval in which the physical signal is in its steady-state condition. This model is said to be a *power signal* because it has the property of finite power (and infinite energy), whereas the physical waveform is said to be an *energy signal* because it has finite energy. (Mathematical definitions for power and energy signals will be given in a subsequent section.) All physical signals are energy signals, although we generally use power signal mathematical models to simplify the analysis.

As described previously, waveforms may often be classified as signals or noise, digital or analog, deterministic or nondeterministic, physically realizable or nonphysically realizable, and belonging to the power or energy type. Additional classifications such as periodic and nonperiodic are given in the next section.

Time Average Operator

Properties of signals and noise that are very useful to electrical engineers are dc (direct "current") value, average power, and rms (root mean square) value. Before these concepts are reviewed, the time average operator needs to be defined.

DEFINITION: The *time average operator*[†] is given by

$$\langle [\,\cdot\,] \rangle = \lim_{T \to \infty} \frac{1}{T} \int_{-T/2}^{T/2} [\cdot]\, dt \qquad (2\text{-}1)$$

(This can also be called the *time mean* value of $[\cdot]$.)

It is seen that this operator is a *linear* operator since, from (2-1), the average of the sum of two quantities is the same as the sum of their averages[‡]:

$$\langle a_1 w_1(t) + a_2 w_2(t) \rangle = a_1 \langle w_1(t) \rangle + a_2 \langle w_2(t) \rangle \qquad (2\text{-}2)$$

Equation (2-1) can be reduced to a simpler form if the operator is operating on a *periodic* waveform.

DEFINITION: A waveform $w(t)$ is *periodic* with period T_0 if

$$w(t) = w(t + T_0) \qquad \text{for all } t \qquad (2\text{-}3)$$

where T_0 is the smallest positive number that satisfies this relationship.[§]

[†] In Appendix B the ensemble average operator is defined.

[‡] See (3-1) for the definition of linearity.

[§] Nonperiodic waveforms are called *aperiodic* waveforms by some authors.

For example, as you know, a sinusoidal waveform of frequency $f_0 = 1/T_0$ hertz is periodic since it satisfies (2-3). From this definition it is clear that a periodic waveform will have significant values over an infinite time interval $(-\infty, \infty)$. Consequently, physical waveforms cannot be truly periodic, but they can have periodic values over a finite time interval. That is, (2-3) can be satisfied for t over some finite interval but not for all values of t.

Theorem

If the waveform involved is periodic, the time average operator can be reduced to

$$\langle [\cdot] \rangle = \frac{1}{T_0} \int_{-T_0/2+a}^{T_0/2+a} [\cdot]\, dt \tag{2-4}$$

where T_0 is the period of the waveform and a is an arbitrary real constant, which may be taken to be zero.

It is seen that (2-4) readily follows from (2-1) since, referring to (2-1), integrals over successive time intervals T_0 seconds wide have identical areas because the waveshape is periodic with period T_0. As these integrals are summed, the total area and T are proportionally larger, resulting in a value for the time average that is the same as just integrating over one period and dividing by the width of that interval, T_0.

In summary, it is seen that (2-1) may be used to evaluate the time average of any type of waveform, whether or not it is periodic. Equation (2-4) is valid only for periodic waveforms.

Dc Value

DEFINITION: The *dc* (*direct "current"*) value of a waveform $w(t)$ is given by its time average, $\langle w(t) \rangle$.

Thus

$$W_{dc} = \lim_{T \to \infty} \frac{1}{T} \int_{-T/2}^{T/2} w(t)\, dt \tag{2-5}$$

For any physical waveform, we are actually interested in evaluating the dc value only over a finite interval of interest, say from t_1 to t_2, so that the dc value is

$$\frac{1}{t_2 - t_1} \int_{t_1}^{t_2} w(t)\, dt$$

However, if we use a mathematical model with a steady-state waveform of infinite extent, we will obtain the correct result by using our definition (2-5), which involves the limit as $T \to \infty$. This will be demonstrated in Example 2-1.

Power

In communication systems, if the received (average) signal power is sufficiently large compared to the (average) noise power, information may be recovered. This concept was

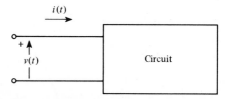

FIGURE 2-2 Polarity convention used for voltage and current.

demonstrated by the Shannon channel capacity formula (1-10), which indicates that information may be recovered even if the signal-to-noise power ratio is very small. Consequently, average power is an important concept that needs to be clearly understood. From physics it is known that power is defined as work per unit time, voltage is work per unit charge, and current is charge per unit time. Using these ideas we have the basis for the definition of power in terms of electrical quantities as given subsequently.

> **DEFINITION:** Let $v(t)$ denote the voltage across a set of circuit terminals, and let $i(t)$ denote the current into the terminal, as shown in Fig. 2-2. The *instantaneous power* (incremental work divided by incremental time) associated with the circuit is given by
>
> $$p(t) = v(t)i(t) \qquad (2\text{-}6)$$
>
> where the instantaneous power flows into the circuit when $p(t)$ is positive and flows out of the circuit when $p(t)$ is negative. The *average power* is given by
>
> $$P = \langle p(t) \rangle = \langle v(t)i(t) \rangle \qquad (2\text{-}7)$$

Example 2-1   Evaluation of Power

Let the circuit of Fig. 2-2 contain a 120-V 60-Hz fluorescent lamp wired in a high-power-factor configuration. Assume that the voltage and current are both sinusoids and in phase (unity power factor), as shown in Fig. 2-3.[†] The dc value of this (periodic) voltage waveform is

$$V_{dc} = \langle v(t) \rangle = \langle V \cos \omega_0 t \rangle$$
$$= \frac{1}{T_0} \int_{-T_0/2}^{T_0/2} V \cos \omega_0 t \, dt = 0 \qquad (2\text{-}8)$$

where $\omega_0 = 2\pi/T_0$ and $f_0 = 1/T_0 = 60$ Hz. Similarly, $I_{dc} = 0$. The instantaneous power is

$$p(t) = (V \cos \omega_0 t)(I \cos \omega_0 t) = \tfrac{1}{2}VI(1 + \cos 2\omega_0 t) \qquad (2\text{-}9)$$

[†]Two-lamp fluorescent circuits can be realized with a high-power-factor ballast that gives an overall power factor greater than 90% [Fink and Beaty, 1978].

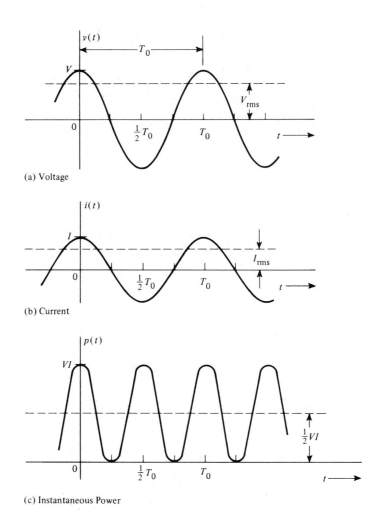

(a) Voltage

(b) Current

(c) Instantaneous Power

FIGURE 2-3 Steady state waveshapes for Example 2-1.

The average power is

$$P = \langle \tfrac{1}{2} VI(1 + \cos 2\omega_0 t) \rangle$$

$$= \frac{VI}{2T_o} \int_{-T_0/2}^{T_0/2} (1 + \cos 2\omega_0 t) \, dt$$

$$= \frac{VI}{2} \tag{2-10}$$

As can be seen from (2-9) and Fig. 2-3c, the power (i.e., light emitted) occurs in pulses at a rate of $2f_0 = 120$ pulses per second. (In fact, this lamp can be used as a stroboscope to "freeze" mechanically rotating objects.) The peak power is VI, and the average power is $\frac{1}{2}VI$, where V is the peak voltage and I is the peak current. Furthermore, for this case of sinusoidal voltage and sinusoidal current we see that the average power could be obtained by multiplying $V/\sqrt{2}$ with $I/\sqrt{2}$.

This subject brings up the concept of root mean square (rms) value.

RMS Value and Normalized Power

DEFINITION: The *root mean square (rms)* value of $w(t)$ is given by

$$W_{\mathrm{rms}} = \sqrt{\langle w^2(t) \rangle} \tag{2-11}$$

Theorem

If a load is resistive (i.e., unity power factor), the average power is given by

$$P = \frac{\langle v^2(t) \rangle}{R} = \langle i^2(t) \rangle R = \frac{V_{\mathrm{rms}}^2}{R}$$

$$= I_{\mathrm{rms}}^2 R = V_{\mathrm{rms}} I_{\mathrm{rms}} \tag{2-12}$$

where R is the value of the resistive load.

Equation (2-12) follows from (2-7) by the use of Ohm's law, which is $v(t) = i(t)R$, and (2-11).

Continuing Example 2-1, $V_{\mathrm{rms}} = 120$ V. It is seen from (2-11), when sinusoidal wave-shapes are used, that $V_{\mathrm{rms}} = V/\sqrt{2}$ and $I_{\mathrm{rms}} = I/\sqrt{2}$. Thus, using (2-12), we see that the average power is $\frac{1}{2}VI$, which is the same value that was obtained in the previous discussion.

The concept of *normalized* power is often used by communications engineers. In this concept R is assumed to be 1 Ω, although it may be another value in the actual circuit. Another way of expressing this concept is to say that the power is given on a per-ohm basis. In the signal-to-noise power ratio calculations R will automatically cancel out, so that normalized values of power may be used to obtain the correct ratio. If the actual value for the power is needed, say at the end of a long set of calculations, it can always be obtained by "denormalization" of the normalized value. From (2-12) it is also realized that the *square root of the normalized power is the rms value.*

DEFINITION: The *average normalized power* is given by

$$P = \langle w^2(t) \rangle = \lim_{T \to \infty} \frac{1}{T} \int_{-T/2}^{T/2} w^2(t) \, dt \tag{2-13}$$

where $w(t)$ represents a real voltage or current waveform.

Energy Waveforms and Power Waveforms[†]

DEFINITION: $w(t)$ is a *power waveform* if and only if the normalized average power, P, is finite and nonzero (i.e., $0 < P < \infty$).

DEFINITION: The *total normalized energy* is given by

$$E = \lim_{T \to \infty} \int_{-T/2}^{T/2} w^2(t)\ dt \qquad (2\text{-}14)$$

DEFINITION: $w(t)$ is an *energy waveform* if and only if the total normalized energy is finite and nonzero (i.e., $0 < E < \infty$).

From these definitions it is seen that if a waveform is classified as either one of these types, it cannot be of the other type. That is, if $w(t)$ has finite energy, the power averaged over infinite time is zero, and if the power (averaged over infinite time) is finite, the energy is infinite. On the other hand, mathematical functions can be found that have both infinite energy and infinite power and, consequently, cannot be classified into either of these two categories. One example is $w(t) = e^{-t}$. Physically realizable waveforms are of the energy type, but we will often model them by infinite-duration waveforms of the power type. Laboratory instruments that measure average quantities—such as dc value, rms value, and average power—average over a finite time interval. That is, T of (2-1) remains finite instead of approaching some large number. Thus nonzero average quantities for finite energy (physical) signals can be obtained. For example, when the dc value is measured with a conventional volt-ohm-milliamp meter containing a meter movement, the time-averaging interval is established by the mass of the meter movement that provides damping. Thus the average quantities calculated from a power-type mathematical model (averaged over infinite time) will give the results that are measured in the laboratory (averaged over finite time).

Decibel

The *decibel* is a base 10 logarithmic measure of power ratios. For example, the ratio of the power level at the output of a circuit compared to that at the input is often specified by the decibel gain instead of the actual ratio.

DEFINITION: The *decibel gain* of a circuit is given by[‡]

$$\text{dB} = 10 \log \left(\frac{\text{average power out}}{\text{average power in}} \right) = 10 \log \left(\frac{P_{\text{out}}}{P_{\text{in}}} \right) \qquad (2\text{-}15)$$

[†] This concept is also called *energy signals* and *power signals* by some authors, but it applies to noise as well as signal waveforms.

[‡] Logarithms to the base 10 will be denoted by $\log(\cdot)$, and logarithms to the base e will be denoted by $\ln(\cdot)$. Note that both dB and the ratio ($P_{\text{out}}/P_{\text{in}}$) are dimensionless quantities.

This definition gives a number that indicates the *relative* value of the *power out* with respect to the *power in* and does not indicate the actual magnitude of the power levels involved. If resistive loads are involved, (2-12) may be used to reduce (2-15) to

$$\text{dB} = 20 \log \left(\frac{V_{\text{rms out}}}{V_{\text{rms in}}} \right) + 10 \log \left(\frac{R_{\text{in}}}{R_{\text{load}}} \right) \qquad (2\text{-}16)$$

or

$$\text{dB} = 20 \log \left(\frac{I_{\text{rms out}}}{I_{\text{rms in}}} \right) + 10 \log \left(\frac{R_{\text{load}}}{R_{\text{in}}} \right) \qquad (2\text{-}17)$$

Note that the same value for decibels is obtained regardless of whether power, voltage, or current [(2-15), (2-16), or (2-17)] was used to obtain that value. That is, decibels are defined in terms of the logarithm of a power ratio but may be evaluated from voltage and/or current ratios.

If normalized powers are used,

$$\text{dB} = 20 \log \left(\frac{V_{\text{rms out}}}{V_{\text{rms in}}} \right) = 20 \log \left(\frac{I_{\text{rms out}}}{I_{\text{rms in}}} \right) \qquad (2\text{-}18)$$

This equation does not give the true value for decibels unless $R_{\text{in}} = R_{\text{load}}$; however, it is common engineering practice to use (2-18) even if $R_{\text{in}} \neq R_{\text{load}}$ and even if the number that is obtained is not strictly correct. Engineers understand that if the correct value is needed, it may be calculated from this pseudovalue if R_{in} and R_{load} are known.

If the dB value is known, the power ratio or the voltage ratio can be easily obtained by inversion of the appropriate equations just given. For example, if the power ratio is desired, (2-15) can be inverted to obtain

$$\frac{P_{\text{out}}}{P_{\text{in}}} = 10^{\text{dB}/10} \qquad (2\text{-}19)$$

The decibel measure can also be used to express a measure of the signal power to noise power ratio, as measured at some point in a circuit.

DEFINITION: The *decibel signal-to-noise ratio* is[†]

$$(\text{S/N})_{\text{dB}} = 10 \log \left(\frac{P_{\text{signal}}}{P_{\text{noise}}} \right) = 10 \log \left(\frac{\langle s^2(t) \rangle}{\langle n^2(t) \rangle} \right) \qquad (2\text{-}20)$$

Since the signal power is $\langle s^2(t) \rangle / R = V_{\text{rms signal}}^2 / R$ and the noise power is $\langle n^2(t) \rangle / R = V_{\text{rms noise}}^2 / R$, this definition is equivalent to

$$(\text{S/N})_{\text{dB}} = 20 \log \left(\frac{V_{\text{rms signal}}}{V_{\text{rms noise}}} \right) \qquad (2\text{-}21)$$

The decibel measure may also be used to indicate absolute levels of power with respect to some reference level.

[†]This definition involves the ratio of the *average signal* power to the *average noise* power. An alternative definition that is also useful for some applications involves the ratio of the *peak* signal power to the average noise power—see Sec. 4-3 and [Couch, 1993].

DEFINITION: The *decibel power level* with respect to 1 mW is given by

$$\text{dBm} = 10 \log\left(\frac{\text{actual power level (watts)}}{10^{-3}}\right)$$

$$= 30 + 10 \log[\text{actual power level (watts)}] \qquad (2\text{-}22)$$

where the "m" in the dBm denotes a milliwatt reference.

Laboratory radio frequency (RF) signal generators are usually calibrated in terms of dBm.

Other decibel measures of absolute power levels are also used. When a 1-watt reference level is used, the decibel level is denoted dBW; when a 1-kilowatt reference level is used, the decibel level is denoted dBk. For example, a power of 5 W could be specified as $+36.99$ dBm, 6.99 dBW, or -23.0 dBk. The telephone industry uses a decibel measure with a "reference noise" level of 1 picowatt (10^{-12} W) [Jordan, 1985]. This decibel measure is denoted dBrn. A level of 0 dBrn corresponds to -90 dBm. The cable television (CATV) industry uses a 1-millivolt rms level across a 75-Ω load as a reference. This decibel measure is denoted dBmV, and it is defined as follows:

$$\text{dBmV} = 20 \log\left(\frac{V_{\text{rms}}}{10^{-3}}\right) \qquad (2\text{-}23)$$

0 dBmV corresponds to -48.75 dBm.

It should be emphasized that the general expression for evaluating power is given by (2-7). That is, (2-7) can be used to evaluate average power for any type of waveshape and load condition, whereas (2-12) is useful only for resistive loads. In other books, especially in the power area, equations are given that are valid only for sinusoidal waveshapes.

Phasors

Sinusoidal test signals occur so often in electrical engineering problems that a shorthand notation called *phasor notation* is often used.

DEFINITION: A complex number c is said to be a *phasor* if it is used to represent a *sinusoidal* waveform. That is,

$$w(t) = |c| \cos[\omega_0 t + \underline{/c}] = \text{Re}\{ce^{j\omega_0 t}\} \qquad (2\text{-}24)$$

where the phasor $c = |c|e^{j\underline{/c}}$ and Re$\{\cdot\}$ denotes the real part of the complex quantity $\{\cdot\}$.

We will refer to $ce^{j\omega_0 t}$ as the *rotating* phasor, as distinguished from the phasor c. When c is given to represent waveform, it is *understood* that the actual waveform that appears in the circuit is a sinusoid as specified by (2-24). Since the phasor is a complex number, it can be written in either Cartesian form or polar form:

$$c \overset{\triangle}{=} x + jy = |c|e^{j\phi} \qquad (2\text{-}25)$$

where x and y are real numbers along the Cartesian coordinates and $|c|$ and $\underline{/c} = \phi = \tan^{-1}(y/x)$ are the length and angle (real numbers) in the polar coordinate system. Shorthand notation for the polar form on the right-hand side of (2-25) is $|c| \underline{/\phi}$.

For example, $25 \sin(2\pi 500t + 45°)$ could be denoted by the phasor $25\underline{/-45°}$ since

$$25 \sin(\omega_0 t + 45°) = 25 \cos(\omega_0 t - 45°) = \text{Re}\{(25e^{-j\pi/4})e^{j\omega_0 t}\}$$

where $\omega_0 = 2\pi f_0$ and $f_0 = 500$ Hz. Similarly, $10 \cos(\omega_0 t + 35°)$ could be denoted by $10\underline{/35°}$.

Some other authors may use a slightly different definition for the phasor. For example, $w(t)$ may be expressed in terms of the imaginary part of a complex quantity instead of the real part as defined in (2-24). In addition, the phasor may denote the rms value of $w(t)$ instead of the peak value [Kaufman and Seidman, 1979]. In this case, $10 \sin(\omega_0 t + 45°)$ should be denoted by the phasor $7.07\underline{/45°}$. However, throughout this book, the definition as given by (2-24) will be used, and it is obvious that phasors can represent only *sinusoidal* waveshapes.

2-2 Fourier Transform and Spectra

Definition

In electrical engineering problems the signal, the noise, or the combined signal plus noise usually consists of a voltage or current waveform that is a function of time. Let $w(t)$ denote the waveform of interest (either voltage or current). If desired, we could look at the waveform on an oscilloscope. The value of the voltage (or current) fluctuates as a function of time; consequently, certain frequencies or a frequency range is one of the main properties of interest to the electrical engineer. Theoretically, in order to evaluate the frequencies that are present, one needs to view the waveform over all time (i.e., $-\infty < t < \infty$) to be sure that the measurement is accurate and to guarantee that none of the frequency components is neglected. The relative level of one frequency as compared to another is given by the *voltage* (or *current*) *spectrum*. This is obtained by taking the *Fourier* transform of the voltage (or current) waveform.

DEFINITION: The *Fourier transform* (FT) of a waveform $w(t)$ is

$$W(f) = \mathcal{F}[w(t)] = \int_{-\infty}^{\infty} [w(t)]e^{-j2\pi ft}\, dt \qquad (2\text{-}26)$$

where $\mathcal{F}[\,\cdot\,]$ denotes the Fourier transform of $[\cdot]$ and f is the frequency parameter with units of Hz (i.e., 1/sec).[†] This *defines* the term *frequency;* frequency is the parameter f in the Fourier transform.

This is also called a *two-sided spectrum* of $w(t)$ since both positive and negative frequency components are obtained from (2-26).

In general, since $e^{-j2\pi ft}$ is complex, $W(f)$ is a complex function of frequency. $W(f)$ may be decomposed into two real functions $X(f)$ and $Y(f)$ such that

$$W(f) = X(f) + jY(f) \qquad (2\text{-}27)$$

[†] Some authors define the FT in terms of the frequency parameter ω (radians per second), where $\omega = 2\pi f$. That definition is identical to (2-26) when ω is replaced by $2\pi f$. I prefer (2-26) since spectrum analyzers are usually calibrated in units of hertz, not radians per second.

This is identical to writing a complex number in terms of pairs of real numbers that can be plotted in a two-dimensional Cartesian coordinate system. For this reason, (2-27) is sometimes called the *quadrature* form or *Cartesian* form. Similarly, (2-26) can be written equivalently in terms of a polar coordinate system where the pair of real functions denotes the magnitude and phase. That is,

$$W(f) = |W(f)|e^{j\theta(f)} \tag{2-28}$$

where

$$|W(f)| = \sqrt{X^2(f) + Y^2(f)} \quad \text{and} \quad \theta(f) = \tan^{-1}\left(\frac{Y(f)}{X(f)}\right) \tag{2-29}$$

This is called the *magnitude-phase* form or *polar* form. To determine if certain frequency components are present, one would examine the magnitude spectrum $|W(f)|$, and sometimes engineers loosely call this just the *spectrum.*

It should be clear that the spectrum of a voltage (or current) waveform is obtained by a mathematical calculation and that it does not appear physically in an actual circuit. f is just a parameter (called *frequency*) that determines which point of the spectral function is to be evaluated. For example, the frequency $f = 10$ Hz is present in the waveform $w(t)$ if and only if $|W(10)| \neq 0$. From (2-26) it is realized that an exact spectral value can be obtained only if the waveform is observed over the infinite time interval $(-\infty, \infty)$. However, a special instrument called a *spectrum analyzer* may be used to obtain an approximation (i.e., finite time integral) for the magnitude spectrum $|W(f)|$.

If one happens to have the mathematical function for the spectrum $W(f)$, the time waveform may be calculated by using the inverse Fourier transform

$$w(t) = \int_{-\infty}^{\infty} W(f)e^{j2\pi ft}\, df \tag{2-30}$$

The functions $w(t)$ and $W(f)$ are said to constitute a *Fourier transform pair* where $w(t)$ is the time domain description and $W(f)$ is the frequency domain description. In this book, the time domain function is usually denoted by a lowercase letter and the frequency domain function by an uppercase letter. Shorthand notation for the pairing between the two domains will be denoted by a double arrow: $w(t) \leftrightarrow W(f)$. If the signal or noise description is known in one domain, the corresponding description in the other domain is known theoretically by using (2-26) or (2-30), as appropriate.

The waveform $w(t)$ is Fourier transformable (i.e., sufficient conditions) if it satisfies the *Dirichlet conditions*:

- Over any time interval of finite width, the function $w(t)$ is single valued with a finite number of maxima and minima and the number of discontinuities (if any) is finite.
- $w(t)$ is absolutely integrable. That is,

$$\int_{-\infty}^{\infty} |w(t)|\, dt < \infty \tag{2-31}$$

Although these conditions are sufficient, they are not necessary. In fact, some of the examples given subsequently do not satisfy the Dirichlet conditions and yet the Fourier transform can be found. The second Dirichlet condition is obtained by taking the absolute value of (2-26).

$$|W(f)| = \left| \int w(t)e^{-j2\pi ft} \, dt \right| \le \int_{-\infty}^{\infty} |w(t)e^{-j2\pi ft}| \, dt = \int_{-\infty}^{\infty} |w(t)| \, dt$$

Thus $|W(f)|$ is finite. Consequently, the Fourier transform exists if

$$\int_{-\infty}^{\infty} |w(t)| \, dt < \infty$$

Furthermore, a weaker sufficient condition for the existence of the Fourier transform is

$$E = \int_{-\infty}^{\infty} |w(t)|^2 \, dt < \infty \tag{2-32}$$

where E is the normalized energy [Goldberg, 1961]. This is the finite energy condition that is satisfied by all physically realizable waveforms. Thus all physical waveforms encountered in engineering practice are Fourier transformable.

It should also be noted that mathematicians sometimes use other definitions, rather than (2-26), for the Fourier transform. However, in these cases, the corresponding inverse transforms, equivalent to (2-30), would also be different, so that when the transform and its inverse are used together, the original $w(t)$ would be recovered. This is a consequence of the Fourier integral theorem, which is

$$w(t) = \int_{-\infty}^{\infty} \int_{-\infty}^{\infty} w(\lambda)e^{j2\pi f(t-\lambda)} \, d\lambda \, df \tag{2-33}$$

Equation (2-33) may be decomposed into (2-26) and (2-30), as well as other definitions for Fourier transform pairs. The Fourier integral theorem is strictly true only for well-behaved functions (i.e., physical waveforms). For example, if $w(t)$ is an ideal square wave, then at a discontinuous point of $w(\lambda)$, denoted by λ_0, $w(t)$ will have a value that is the average of the two values that are obtained for $w(\lambda)$ on each side of the discontinuous point λ_0.

Example 2-2   Spectrum of an Exponential Pulse

Let $w(t)$ be a decaying exponential pulse that is switched on at $t = 0$.

$$w(t) = \begin{cases} e^{-t}, & t > 0 \\ 0, & t < 0 \end{cases}$$

The spectrum of this pulse is given by the Fourier transform

$$W(f) = \int_0^{\infty} e^{-t}e^{-j2\pi ft} \, dt$$

or

$$W(f) = \frac{1}{1 + j2\pi f}$$

In other words, this Fourier transform pair is

$$\begin{Bmatrix} e^{-t}, & t > 0 \\ 0, & t < 0 \end{Bmatrix} \leftrightarrow \frac{1}{1 + j2\pi f} \qquad (2\text{-}34)$$

The spectrum can also be expressed in terms of the quadrature functions by rationalizing the denominator of (2-34); thus

$$X(f) = \frac{1}{1 + (2\pi f)^2} \qquad \text{and} \qquad Y(f) = \frac{-2\pi f}{1 + (2\pi f)^2}$$

The magnitude-phase form is

$$|W(f)| = \sqrt{\frac{1}{1 + (2\pi f)^2}} \qquad \text{and} \qquad \theta(f) = -\tan^{-1}(2\pi f)$$

More examples will be given after some helpful theorems are developed.

Properties of Fourier Transforms

Many useful and interesting theorems follow from the definition of the spectrum as given by (2-26). One of particular interest is the consequence of working with real-time waveforms. In any physical circuit that can be built, the voltage (or current) waveforms are real functions (as opposed to complex functions) of time.

Theorem: Spectral symmetry of real signals.

If $w(t)$ is real, then

$$W(-f) = W^*(f) \qquad (2\text{-}35)$$

The asterisk superscript denotes the conjugate operation.

PROOF.   From (2-26)

$$W(-f) = \int_{-\infty}^{\infty} w(t)e^{j2\pi ft}\, dt \qquad (2\text{-}36)$$

and taking the conjugate of (2-26) yields

$$W^*(f) = \int_{-\infty}^{\infty} w^*(t)e^{j2\pi ft}\, dt \qquad (2\text{-}37)$$

But since $w(t)$ is real, $w^*(t) = w(t)$ and (2-35) follows since the right sides of (2-36) and (2-37) are equal. It can also be shown that if real $w(t)$ happens to be an even function of t, $W(f)$ is *real*. Similarly, if real $w(t)$ is an odd function of t, $W(f)$ is *imaginary*.   ∎

Another useful corollary of (2-35) is that for $w(t)$ real, the magnitude spectrum is even about the origin (i.e., $f = 0$):

$$|W(-f)| = |W(f)| \qquad (2\text{-}38)$$

and the phase spectrum is odd about the origin:

$$\theta(-f) = -\theta(f) \qquad (2\text{-}39)$$

This can easily be demonstrated by writing the spectrum in polar form:

$$W(f) = |W(f)|e^{j\theta(f)}$$

Then

$$W(-f) = |W(-f)|e^{j\theta(-f)}$$

and

$$W^*(f) = |W(f)|e^{-j\theta(f)}$$

Using (2-35), we see that (2-38) and (2-39) are true.

In summary, from the discussion above, some properties of the Fourier transform are:

- f, called frequency and having units of hertz, is just a parameter of the FT that specifies what frequency we are interested in looking for in the waveform $w(t)$.
- The FT looks for the frequency f in the $w(t)$ over *all* time, that is, over $-\infty < t < \infty$.
- $W(f)$ can be complex even though $w(t)$ is real.
- If $w(t)$ is real, then $W(-f) = W^*(f)$.

Parseval's Theorem and Energy Spectral Density

Parseval's Theorem

$$\int_{-\infty}^{\infty} w_1(t)w_2^*(t)\, dt = \int_{-\infty}^{\infty} W_1(f)W_2^*(f)\, df \qquad (2\text{-}40)$$

If $w_1(t) = w_2(t) = w(t)$, this reduces to[†]

$$E = \int_{-\infty}^{\infty} |w(t)|^2\, dt = \int_{-\infty}^{\infty} |W(f)|^2\, df \qquad (2\text{-}41)$$

PROOF. Work with the left side of (2-40), using (2-30) to replace $w_1(t)$.

$$\int_{-\infty}^{\infty} w_1(t)w_2^*(t)\, dt = \int_{-\infty}^{\infty} \left[\int_{-\infty}^{\infty} W_1(f)e^{j2\pi ft}\, df \right] w_2^*(t)\, dt$$

$$= \int_{-\infty}^{\infty} \int_{-\infty}^{\infty} W_1(f)w_2^*(t)e^{j2\pi ft}\, df\, dt$$

Interchanging the order of integration on f and t[‡]

$$\int_{-\infty}^{\infty} w_1(t)w_2^*(t)\, dt = \int_{-\infty}^{\infty} W_1(f) \left[\int_{-\infty}^{\infty} w_2(t)e^{-j2\pi ft}\, dt \right]^*\, df$$

Using (2-26) produces the result of (2-40).

■

[†] This is also known as *Rayleigh's energy theorem*.
[‡] Fubini's theorem states that the order of integration may be exchanged if all of the integrals are absolute convergent. That is, these integrals are finite valued when the integrands are replaced by their absolute values. We assume that this condition is satisfied.

Parseval's theorem gives an alternative method for evaluating the energy by using the frequency domain description instead of the time domain definition. This leads to the concept of the energy spectral density function.

DEFINITION: The *energy spectral density (ESD)* is defined for energy waveforms by

$$\mathcal{E}(f) = |W(f)|^2 \tag{2-42}$$

where $w(t) \leftrightarrow W(f)$. $\mathcal{E}(f)$ has units of joules per hertz.

By using Parseval's theorem, we see that the total normalized energy is given by the area under the ESD function:

$$E = \int_{-\infty}^{\infty} \mathcal{E}(f) \, df \tag{2-43}$$

For power waveforms, a similar function called the *power spectral density (PSD)* can be defined. This is developed in Sec. 2-3. Later we will find that the PSD function is a very useful tool for solving communication problems.

There are many other Fourier transform theorems in addition to Parseval's theorem. Some of them are summarized in Table 2-1. These theorems can be proved by substituting the corresponding time function into the definition for the Fourier transform and reducing the result to that given in the rightmost column of the table. For example, the scale change theorem is proved by substituting $w(at)$ into (2-26). We get

$$\mathcal{F}[w(at)] = \int_{-\infty}^{\infty} w(at)e^{-j2\pi ft} \, dt$$

Letting $t_1 = at$ and assuming that $a > 0$, we get

$$\mathcal{F}[w(at)] = \int_{-\infty}^{\infty} \frac{1}{a} w(t_1)e^{-j2\pi(f/a)t_1} \, dt_1 = \frac{1}{a} W\left(\frac{f}{a}\right)$$

For $a < 0$ this becomes

$$\mathcal{F}[w(at)] = \int_{-\infty}^{\infty} \frac{-1}{a} w(t_1)e^{-j2\pi(f/a)t_1} \, dt_1 = \frac{1}{|a|} W\left(\frac{f}{a}\right)$$

Thus, for either $a > 0$ or $a < 0$, we get

$$w(at) \leftrightarrow \frac{1}{|a|} W\left(\frac{f}{a}\right)$$

The other theorems in Table 2-1 are proved in a similar straightforward manner, except for the integral theorem. The integral theorem is more difficult to derive since the transform result involves a Dirac delta function, $\delta(f)$. This theorem may be proved by the use of the convolution theorem, as illustrated by Prob. 2-36. The bandpass signal theorem will be discussed in more detail in Chapter 5. It is the basis for the digital and analog modulation techniques covered in Chapters 6 and 7. In Sec. 3-7 the relationship between the Fourier transform and the discrete Fourier transform (DFT) will be studied.

As we will see in the following examples, these theorems can greatly simplify the calculations required to solve Fourier transform problems. Consequently, the reader should study Table 2-1 and be prepared to use it when needed. After the Fourier transform

TABLE 2-1 Some Fourier Transform Theorems[a]

Operation	Function	Fourier Transform
Linearity	$a_1 w_1(t) + a_2 w_2(t)$	$a_1 W_1(f) + a_2 W_2(f)$
Time delay	$w(t - T_d)$	$W(f)e^{-j\omega T_d}$
Scale change	$w(at)$	$\dfrac{1}{|a|} W\left(\dfrac{f}{a}\right)$
Conjugation	$w^*(t)$	$W^*(-f)$
Duality	$W(t)$	$w(-f)$
Real signal frequency translation [$w(t)$ is real]	$w(t)\cos(\omega_c t + \theta)$	$\frac{1}{2}[e^{j\theta}\,W(f - f_c) + e^{-j\theta}\,W(f + f_c)]$
Complex signal frequency translation	$w(t)e^{j\omega_c t}$	$W(f - f_c)$
Bandpass signal	$\text{Re}\{g(t)e^{j\omega_c t}\}$	$\frac{1}{2}[G(f - f_c) + G^*(-f - f_c)]$
Differentiation	$\dfrac{d^n w(t)}{dt^n}$	$(j2\pi f)^n W(f)$
Integration	$\displaystyle\int_{-\infty}^{t} w(\lambda)\,d\lambda$	$(j2\pi f)^{-1} W(f) + \frac{1}{2}W(0)\,\delta(f)$
Convolution	$w_1(t) * w_2(t)$ $= \displaystyle\int_{-\infty}^{\infty} w_1(\lambda)\,w_2(t - \lambda)\,d\lambda$	$W_1(f)W_2(f)$
Multiplication[b]	$w_1(t)w_2(t)$	$W_1(f) * W_2(f) = \displaystyle\int_{-\infty}^{\infty} W_1(\lambda)\,W_2(f - \lambda)\,d\lambda$
Multiplication by t^n	$t^n w(t)$	$(-j2\pi)^{-n}\dfrac{d^n W(f)}{df^n}$

[a] $\omega_c = 2\pi f_c$.
[b] $*$ denotes convolution as described in detail by (2-62).

is evaluated, one should check to see that the easy-to-verify properties of Fourier transforms are satisfied; otherwise, there is a mistake. For example, if $w(t)$ is real:

- $W(-f) = W^*(f)$, or $|W(f)|$ is even and $\theta(f)$ is odd.
- $W(f)$ is real when $w(t)$ is even.
- $W(f)$ is imaginary when $w(t)$ is odd.

Example 2-3   Spectrum of a Damped Sinusoid

Let the damped sinusoid be given by

$$w(t) = \begin{cases} e^{-t/T} \sin \omega_0 t, & t > 0, T > 0 \\ 0, & t < 0 \end{cases}$$

The spectrum of this waveform is obtained by evaluating the Fourier transform. This is easily accomplished by using the result of the previous example plus some of the Fourier theorems. From (2-34), and using the scale change theorem, where $a = 1/T$,

$$\begin{cases} e^{-t/T}, & t > 0 \\ 0, & t < 0 \end{cases} \leftrightarrow \frac{T}{1 + j(2\pi f T)}$$

Using the real signal frequency translation theorem with $\theta = -\pi/2$, we get

$$W(f) = \frac{1}{2} \left\{ e^{-j\pi/2} \frac{T}{1 + j2\pi T(f - f_0)} + e^{j\pi/2} \frac{T}{1 + j2\pi T(f + f_0)} \right\}$$

$$= \frac{T}{2j} \left\{ \frac{1}{1 + j2\pi T(f - f_0)} - \frac{1}{1 + j2\pi T(f + f_0)} \right\} \tag{2-44}$$

where $e^{\pm j\pi/2} = \cos(\pi/2) \pm j \sin(\pi/2) = \pm j$. This spectrum is complex (i.e., neither real nor imaginary) since $w(t)$ does not have even or odd symmetry about $t = 0$.

As expected, (2-44) shows that the peak of the magnitude spectrum for the damped sinusoid occurs at $f = \pm f_0$. Compare this to the peak of the magnitude spectrum for the exponential decay (Example 2-2) that occurs at $f = 0$. That is, the $\sin \omega_0 t$ factor caused the spectral peak to move from $f = 0$ to $f = \pm f_0$.

Dirac Delta Function and Unit Step Function

Another type of function that often occurs in communication problems is the Dirac delta function.

DEFINITION: The *Dirac delta function* $\delta(x)$ is defined by

$$\int_{-\infty}^{\infty} w(x)\, \delta(x)\, dx = w(0) \tag{2-45}$$

where $w(x)$ is any function that is continuous at $x = 0$.

In this definition the variable x could be time or frequency depending on the application. An alternative definition for $\delta(x)$ is

$$\int_{-\infty}^{\infty} \delta(x)\, dx = 1 \tag{2-46a}$$

and

$$\delta(x) = \begin{cases} \infty, & x = 0 \\ 0 & x \neq 0 \end{cases} \tag{2-46b}$$

where both (2-46a) and (2-46b) need to be satisfied. It is obvious that the Dirac delta function is not a true function, so it is said to be a *singular function*. However, $\delta(x)$ can be defined as a function in a more general sense and treated as such in a branch of mathematics called *generalized functions* and the *theory of distributions*.

From (2-45), the *sifting property* of the δ function is

$$\int_{-\infty}^{\infty} w(x)\, \delta(x - x_0)\, dx = w(x_0) \tag{2-47}$$

That is, the δ function sifts out the value $w(x_0)$ from the integral.

In some problems it is also useful to use the equivalent integral for the δ function, which is

$$\delta(x) = \int_{-\infty}^{\infty} e^{\pm j2\pi xy}\, dy \tag{2-48}$$

where either the $+$ or the $-$ sign may be used as needed. This assumes that $\delta(x)$ is an even function: $\delta(-x) = \delta(x)$. Equation (2-48) may be verified by taking the Fourier transform of a delta function

$$\int_{-\infty}^{\infty} \delta(t) e^{-j2\pi ft}\, dt = e^0 = 1$$

and then taking the inverse Fourier transform of both sides of this equation; (2-48) follows. For additional properties of the delta function, see Appendix A.

Another function that is closely related to the Dirac delta function is the unit step function.

DEFINITION: The *unit step function* $u(t)$ is

$$u(t) = \begin{cases} 1, & t > 0 \\ 0, & t < 0 \end{cases} \tag{2-49}$$

Since $\delta(\lambda)$ is zero except at $\lambda = 0$, the Dirac delta function is related to the unit step function by

$$\int_{-\infty}^{t} \delta(\lambda)\, d\lambda = u(t) \tag{2-50}$$

and consequently,

$$\frac{du(t)}{dt} = \delta(t) \tag{2-51}$$

Example 2-4   Spectrum of a Sinusoid

Find the spectrum of a sinusoidal voltage waveform that has a frequency f_0 and a peak value of A volts.

$$v(t) = A \sin \omega_0 t \quad \text{where } \omega_0 = 2\pi f_0$$

From (2-26), the spectrum is

$$V(f) = \int_{-\infty}^{\infty} A\left(\frac{e^{j\omega_0 t} - e^{-j\omega_0 t}}{2j}\right) e^{-j\omega t} \, dt$$

$$= \frac{A}{2j} \int_{-\infty}^{\infty} e^{-j2\pi(f-f_0)t} \, dt - \frac{A}{2j} \int_{-\infty}^{\infty} e^{-j2\pi(f+f_0)t} \, dt$$

By (2-48), these integrals are equivalent to Dirac delta functions. That is,

$$V(f) = j\frac{A}{2} \left[\delta(f+f_0) - \delta(f-f_0)\right]$$

Note that this spectrum is imaginary, as expected, since $v(t)$ is real and odd. In addition, a meaningful expression was obtained for the Fourier transform, although $v(t)$ was of the infinite energy type and not absolutely integrable. That is, this $v(t)$ does not satisfy the sufficient (but not necessary) Dirichlet conditions as given by (2-31) and (2-32).

The magnitude spectrum is

$$|V(f)| = \frac{A}{2}\,\delta(f-f_0) + \frac{A}{2}\,\delta(f+f_0)$$

where A is a positive number. Since only two frequencies ($f = \pm f_0$) are present, $\theta(f)$ is strictly defined only at these two frequencies. That is, $\theta(f_0) = \tan^{-1}(-1/0) = -90°$ and $\theta(-f_0) = \tan^{-1}(1/0) = +90°$. However, because $|V(f)| = 0$ for all frequencies except $f = \pm f_0$ and $V(f) = |V(f)|e^{j\theta(f)}$, $\theta(f)$ can be taken to be any convenient set of values for $f \neq \pm f_0$. Thus the phase spectrum is taken to be

$$\theta(f) = \begin{cases} -\pi/2, & f > 0 \\ +\pi/2, & f < 0 \end{cases} \text{ radians} = \begin{cases} -90°, & f > 0 \\ 90°, & f < 0 \end{cases}$$

Plots of these spectra are shown in Fig. 2-4. It is seen that the magnitude spectrum is even and the phase spectrum is odd, as expected from (2-38) and (2-39).

Now let us generalize the sinusoidal waveform to one with an arbitrary phase angle θ_0. Then

$$w(t) = A\,\sin(\omega_0 t + \theta_0) = A\,\sin[\omega_0(t + \theta_0/\omega_0)]$$

and, by using the time delay theorem, the spectrum becomes

$$W(f) = j\frac{A}{2}\,e^{j\theta_0(f/f_0)}[\delta(f+f_0) - \delta(f-f_0)]$$

The resulting magnitude spectrum is the same as that obtained before for the $\theta_0 = 0$ case. The new phase spectrum is the sum of the old phase spectrum plus the linear function $(\theta_0/f_0)f$. However, since the overall spectrum is zero except at $f = \pm f_0$, the value for the phase spectrum can be arbitrarily assigned at all frequencies except $f = \pm f_0$. At $f = f_0$ the phase is $(\theta_0 - \pi/2)$ radians, and at $f = -f_0$ the phase is $-(\theta_0 - \pi/2)$ radians.

(a) Magnitude Spectrum   (b) Phase Spectrum ($\theta_0 = 0$)

FIGURE 2-4 Spectrum of a sine wave.

From a *mathematical* viewpoint, Fig. 2-4 demonstrates that two frequencies are present in the sine wave, one at $f = +f_0$ and another at $f = -f_0$. This can also be seen from the time waveform; that is,

$$v(t) = A \sin \omega_0 t = \frac{A}{j2} e^{j\omega_0 t} - \frac{A}{j2} e^{-j\omega_0 t}$$

which implies that the sine wave consists of two rotating phasors, one rotating with a frequency $f = +f_0$ and another rotating with $f = -f_0$. From the *engineering* point of view it is said that one frequency is present, namely, $f = f_0$, since for any physical (i.e., real) waveform, (2-35) shows that for any positive frequency present, there is also a mathematical negative frequency present. The phasor associated with $v(t)$ is $c = 0 - jA = A\underline{/-90°}$. Another interesting observation is that the magnitude spectrum consists of *lines* (i.e., Dirac delta functions). Later, it will be shown that the lines are a consequence of $v(t)$ being a periodic function. If the sinusoid is switched on and off (i.e. not periodic), the spectrum is continuous as demonstrated by Example 2-9. A damped sinusoid also has a continuous spectrum, as demonstrated by Example 2-3.

Rectangular and Triangular Pulses

Some additional waveshapes frequently occur in communications problems, so some special symbols will be defined to shorten the notation.

DEFINITION: Let $\Pi(\cdot)$ denote a single *rectangular pulse*

$$\Pi\left(\frac{t}{T}\right) \triangleq \begin{cases} 1, & |t| \le \dfrac{T}{2} \\[2mm] 0, & |t| > \dfrac{T}{2} \end{cases} \tag{2-52}$$

DEFINITION: Let Sa($\cdot$) denote the function[†]

$$\text{Sa}(x) = \frac{\sin x}{x} \tag{2-53}$$

DEFINITION: Let $\Lambda(\cdot)$ denote the triangular function

$$\Lambda\left(\frac{t}{T}\right) \triangleq \begin{cases} 1 - \dfrac{|t|}{T}, & |t| \le T \\[2mm] 0, & |t| > T \end{cases} \tag{2-54}$$

These waveshapes are shown in Fig. 2-5. A tabulation of Sa(x) is given in Sec. A-9 (Appendix A).

Example 2-5   Spectrum of a Rectangular Pulse

The spectrum is obtained by taking the Fourier transform of $w(t) = \Pi(t/T)$.

$$W(f) = \int_{-T/2}^{T/2} 1 e^{-j\omega t}\, dt = \frac{e^{-j\omega T/2} - e^{j\omega T/2}}{-j\omega}$$

$$= T\,\frac{\sin(\omega T/2)}{\omega T/2} = T\,\text{Sa}(\pi T f)$$

Thus,

$$\Pi\left(\frac{t}{T}\right) \leftrightarrow T\,\text{Sa}(\pi T f) \tag{2-55}$$

This Fourier transform pair is shown in Fig. 2-6a. Note the inverse relationship between the pulse width T and the spectral zero crossing $1/T$. Also, by use of the duality theorem, the spectrum of a $(\sin x)/x$ pulse is a rectangle. That is, realizing that $\Pi(x)$ is an even function, and applying the duality theorem to (2-55), we get

$$T\,\text{Sa}(\pi T t) \leftrightarrow \Pi\left(-\frac{f}{T}\right) = \Pi\left(\frac{f}{T}\right)$$

Replacing the parameter T by $2W$, we obtain the following Fourier transform pair:

$$2W\,\text{Sa}(2\pi W t) \leftrightarrow \Pi\left(\frac{f}{2W}\right) \tag{2-56}$$

where W is the absolute bandwidth in hertz. This Fourier transform pair is also shown in Fig. 2-6b.

[†]This is related to the sinc function by Sa(x) = sinc(x/π) since sinc(λ) $\triangleq$ (sin $\pi\lambda$)/$\pi\lambda$. The notation Sa(x) and sinc(x) represent the same concept but can be confused because of scaling. In this book $(\sin x)/x$ will often be used because it avoids confusion and does not take much more text space.

(a) Rectangular Pulse

(b) Sa(x) Function

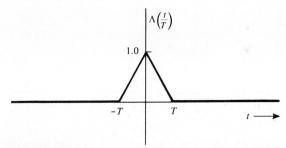

(c) Triangular Function

FIGURE 2-5 Waveshapes and corresponding symbolic notation.

The spectra shown in Fig. 2-6 are real since the time-domain pulses are real and even. If the pulses are offset in time to destroy the even symmetry, the spectra will be complex. For example, let

$$v(t) = \begin{Bmatrix} 1, & 0 < t < T \\ 0, & t \text{ elsewhere} \end{Bmatrix} = \Pi\left(\frac{t - T/2}{T}\right)$$

Then, using the time delay theorem and (2-55), we get the spectrum

$$V(f) = Te^{-j\pi fT} \, \text{Sa}(\pi Tf) \qquad (2\text{-}57)$$

Time Domain

Frequency Domain

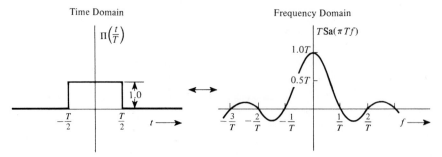

(a) Rectangular Pulse and Its Spectrum

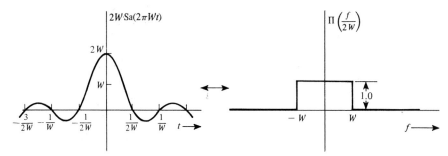

(b) Sa(x) Pulse and Its Spectrum

(c) Triangular Pulse and Its Spectrum

FIGURE 2-6 Spectra of rectangular, (sin x)/x, and triangular pulses.

In terms of quadrature notation, (2-57) becomes

$$V(f) = \underbrace{[T\,\mathrm{Sa}(\pi fT)\,\cos(\pi fT)]}_{X(f)} + \underbrace{j[-T\,\mathrm{Sa}(\pi fT)\,\sin(\pi fT)]}_{Y(f)} \qquad (2\text{-}58)$$

Examining (2-57), the magnitude spectrum is

$$|V(f)| = T\left|\frac{\sin \pi fT}{\pi fT}\right| \qquad (2\text{-}59)$$

and the phase spectrum is

$$\theta(f) = \underline{/e^{-j\pi fT}} + \underline{/Sa(\pi fT)} = -\pi fT + \begin{cases} 0, \text{ if } \dfrac{n}{T} < f < \dfrac{n+1}{T}, \ n \text{ odd} \\[2mm] \pi, \text{ if } \dfrac{n}{T} < f < \dfrac{n+1}{T}, \ n \text{ even} \end{cases} \tag{2-60}$$

Example 2-6 Spectrum of a Triangular Pulse

The spectrum may be evaluated directly by taking the Fourier transform of $\Lambda(t/T)$ where the triangle is described by piecewise linear lines as shown in Fig. 2-6c. Another approach is to use the integral theorem. We will take the latter approach to demonstrate this technique. Let

$$w(t) = \Lambda(t/T)$$

Then

$$\frac{dw(t)}{dt} = \frac{1}{T} u(t+T) - \frac{2}{T} u(t) + \frac{1}{T} u(t-T)$$

and

$$\frac{d^2 w(t)}{dt^2} = \frac{1}{T} \delta(t+T) - \frac{2}{T} \delta(t) + \frac{1}{T} \delta(t-T)$$

Consequently, we have the Fourier transform pair

$$\frac{d^2 w(t)}{dt^2} \leftrightarrow \frac{1}{T} e^{j\omega T} - \frac{2}{T} + \frac{1}{T} e^{-j\omega T}$$

or

$$\frac{d^2 w(t)}{dt^2} \leftrightarrow \frac{1}{T} (e^{j\omega T/2} - e^{-j\omega T/2})^2 = \frac{-4}{T} (\sin \pi fT)^2$$

Applying the integral theorem twice, we get

$$w(t) \leftrightarrow \frac{-4}{T} \frac{(\sin \pi fT)^2}{(j2\pi f)^2}$$

Thus

$$w(t) = \Lambda\left(\frac{t}{T}\right) \leftrightarrow T \, Sa^2(\pi fT) \tag{2-61}$$

This is illustrated in Fig. 2-6c.

Convolution

The convolution operation, first described in Table 2-1, is very useful. In Chapter 3 we will show that the convolution operation can be used to describe the waveform at the output of a linear system.

> **DEFINITION:** The *convolution* of a waveform $w_1(t)$ with a waveform $w_2(t)$ to produce a third waveform $w_3(t)$ is
>
> $$w_3(t) = w_1(t) * w_2(t) \triangleq \int_{-\infty}^{\infty} w_1(\lambda) w_2(t - \lambda) \, d\lambda \qquad (2\text{-}62a)$$
>
> where $w_1(t) * w_2(t)$ is shorthand notation that delineates this integral operation and $*$ is read "convolved with."

When this integral is examined, we realize that t is a parameter and λ is the variable of integration.

If discontinuous waveshapes are to be convolved, it is usually easier to evaluate the equivalent integral

$$w_3(t) = \int_{-\infty}^{\infty} w_1(\lambda) w_2(-(\lambda - t)) \, d\lambda \qquad (2\text{-}62b)$$

Thus the integrand for (2-26b) is obtained by:

1. Time reversal of w_2 to obtain $w_2(-\lambda)$.
2. Time shifting of w_2 to obtain $w_2(-(\lambda - t))$.
3. Multiplying this result by w_1 to form the integrand $w_1(\lambda) w_2(-(\lambda - t))$.

These three operations are illustrated in the following examples.

Example 2-7 Convolution of a Rectangle with an Exponential

Let

$$w_1(t) = \Pi\left(\frac{t - \frac{1}{2}T}{T}\right) \quad \text{and} \quad w_2(t) = e^{-t/T} \, u(t)$$

as shown in Fig. 2-7. Implementing step 3 above with the help of the figure, the convolution of $w_1(t)$ with $w_2(t)$ is 0 if $t < 0$ because the product $w_1(\lambda) w_2(-(\lambda - t))$ is zero for all values of λ. If $0 < t < T$, (2-62b) becomes

$$w_3(t) = \int_0^t 1 \cdot e^{+(\lambda - t)/T} \, d\lambda = T(1 - e^{-t/T})$$

If $t > T$, then (2-62b) becomes

$$w_3(t) = \int_0^T 1 \cdot e^{+(\lambda - t)/T} \, d\lambda = T(e - 1)e^{-t/T}$$

Thus

$$w_3(t) = \begin{cases} 0, & t < 0 \\ T(1 - e^{-t/T}), & 0 < t < T \\ T(e - 1)e^{-t/T}, & t > T \end{cases}$$

This result is plotted in Fig. 2-7.

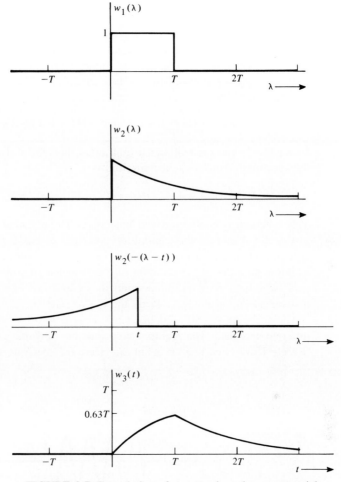

FIGURE 2-7 Convolution of a rectangle and an exponential.

Example 2-8 Spectrum of a Triangular Pulse by Convolution

In Example 2-6 the spectrum of a triangular pulse was evaluated by using the integral theorem. The same result can be obtained by using the convolution theorem of Table 2-1. If the rectangular pulse of Fig. 2-6a is convolved with itself and then scaled (i.e., multiplied) by the constant $1/T$, the resulting time waveform is the triangular pulse of Fig. 2-6c. Applying the convolution theorem, we obtain the spectrum for the triangular pulse by multiplying the spectrum of the rectangular pulse (of Fig. 2-6a) with itself and scaling with a constant $1/T$. As expected, the result is the spectrum shown in Fig. 2-6c.

Example 2-9   Spectrum of a Switched Sinusoid

In Example 2-4 a continuous sinusoid was found to have a line spectrum with the lines located at $f = \pm f_0$. In this example we will see how the spectrum changes when the sinusoid is switched on and off. The switched sinusoid can be represented by

$$w(t) = \Pi\left(\frac{t}{T}\right) A \sin \omega_0 t = \Pi\left(\frac{t}{T}\right) A \cos\left(\omega_0 t - \frac{\pi}{2}\right)$$

Using (2-55) and the real signal translation theorem of Table 2-1, we see that the spectrum of this switched sinusoid is

$$W(f) = j \frac{A}{2} T[\text{Sa}(\pi T(f + f_0)) - \text{Sa}(\pi T(f - f_0))] \qquad (2\text{-}63)$$

This spectrum is continuous and imaginary. The magnitude spectrum is shown in Fig. 2-8. Compare this continuous spectrum of Fig. 2-8 with the discrete spectrum obtained for the continuous sine wave, as shown in Fig. 2-4a. In addition, note that if the duration of the switched sinusoid is allowed to become very large (i.e., $T \rightarrow \infty$), the continuous spectrum of Fig. 2-8 becomes the discrete spectrum of Fig. 2-4a by the use of (A-103) in Appendix A.

The spectrum for the switched sinusoid may also be evaluated using a different approach. The multiplication theorem of Table 2-1 may be used where $w_1(t) = \Pi(t/T)$ and $w_2(t) = A \sin \omega_0 t$. Here the spectrum of the switched

(a) Time Domain

(b) Frequency Domain (Magnitude Spectrum)

FIGURE 2-8 Waveform and spectrum of a switched sinusoid.

sinusoid is obtained by working a convolution problem in the frequency domain:

$$W(f) = W_1(f) * W_2(f) = \int_{-\infty}^{\infty} W_1(\lambda) W_2(f - \lambda) \, d\lambda$$

This convolution integral is easy to evaluate since the spectrum of $w_2(t)$ consists of two delta functions. The details of this approach are left as a homework exercise for the reader.

A summary of Fourier transform pairs is given in Table 2-2. Numerical techniques using the discrete Fourier transform are discussed in Sec. 3-7.

TABLE 2-2 Some Fourier Transform Pairs

Function	Time Waveform $w(t)$	Spectrum $W(f)$
Rectangular	$\Pi\left(\dfrac{t}{T}\right)$	$T[\mathrm{Sa}(\pi f T)]$
Triangular	$\Lambda\left(\dfrac{t}{T}\right)$	$T[\mathrm{Sa}(\pi f T)]^2$
Unit step	$u(t) \triangleq \begin{cases} +1, & t > 0 \\ 0, & t < 0 \end{cases}$	$\frac{1}{2}\,\delta(f) + \dfrac{1}{j2\pi f}$
Signum	$\mathrm{sgn}(t) \triangleq \begin{cases} +1, & t > 0 \\ -1, & t < 0 \end{cases}$	$\dfrac{1}{j\pi f}$
Constant	1	$\delta(f)$
Impulse at $t = t_0$	$\delta(t - t_0)$	$e^{-j2\pi f t_0}$
Sinc	$\mathrm{Sa}(2\pi W t)$	$\dfrac{1}{2W}\,\Pi\left(\dfrac{f}{2W}\right)$
Phasor	$e^{j(\omega_0 t + \phi)}$	$e^{j\phi}\,\delta(f - f_0)$
Sinusoid	$\cos(\omega_c t + \phi)$	$\frac{1}{2}e^{j\phi}\,\delta(f - f_c) + \frac{1}{2}e^{-j\phi}\,\delta(f + f_c)$
Gaussian	$e^{-\pi(t/t_0)^2}$	$t_0 e^{-\pi(f t_0)^2}$
Exponential, one-sided	$\begin{cases} e^{-t/T}, & t > 0 \\ 0, & t < 0 \end{cases}$	$\dfrac{T}{1 + j2\pi f T}$
Exponential, two-sided	$e^{-|t|/T}$	$\dfrac{2T}{1 + (2\pi f T)^2}$
Impulse train	$\displaystyle\sum_{k=-\infty}^{k=\infty} \delta(t - kT)$	$\displaystyle f_0 \sum_{n=-\infty}^{n=\infty} \delta(f - n f_0),$ where $f_0 = 1/T$

2-3 Power Spectral Density and Autocorrelation Function

Power Spectral Density

The normalized power of a waveform will now be related to its frequency domain description by the use of a function called the *power spectral density (PSD)*. The PSD is very useful in describing how the power content of signals and noise is affected by filters and other devices in communication systems. In (2-42) the energy spectral density (ESD) was defined in terms of the magnitude squared version of the Fourier transform of the waveform. The PSD will be defined in a similar way. The PSD is more useful than the ESD since power-type models are generally used in solving communication problems.

First, define the truncated version of the waveform by

$$w_T(t) = \begin{cases} w(t), & -T/2 < t < T/2 \\ 0, & t \text{ elsewhere} \end{cases} = w(t)\Pi\left(\frac{t}{T}\right) \tag{2-64}$$

Using (2-13), we obtain the average normalized power

$$P = \lim_{T \to \infty} \frac{1}{T} \int_{-T/2}^{T/2} w^2(t)\, dt = \lim_{T \to \infty} \frac{1}{T} \int_{-\infty}^{\infty} w_T^2(t)\, dt$$

By the use of Parseval's theorem, (2-41), this becomes

$$P = \lim_{T \to \infty} \frac{1}{T} \int_{-\infty}^{\infty} |W_T(f)|^2\, df = \int_{-\infty}^{\infty} \left(\lim_{T \to \infty} \frac{|W_T(f)|^2}{T} \right) df \tag{2-65}$$

where $W_T(f) = \mathcal{F}[w_T(t)]$. The integrand of the right-hand integral has units of watts/hertz (or, equivalently, volts^2/hertz or amperes^2/hertz, as appropriate) and can be defined as the PSD.

DEFINITION: The *power spectral density (PSD)* for a deterministic power waveform is[†]

$$\mathcal{P}_w(f) \triangleq \lim_{T \to \infty} \left(\frac{|W_T(f)|^2}{T} \right) \tag{2-66}$$

where $w_T(t) \leftrightarrow W_T(f)$ and $\mathcal{P}_w(f)$ has units of watts per hertz.

Note that the PSD is always a real nonnegative function of frequency. In addition, the PSD is not sensitive to the phase spectrum of $w(t)$ since that is lost because of the absolute value operation used in (2-66). From (2-65), the normalized average power is[†]

$$P = \langle w^2(t) \rangle = \int_{-\infty}^{\infty} \mathcal{P}_w(f)\, df \tag{2-67}$$

That is, the area under the PSD function is the normalized average power.

[†] Equations (2-66) and (2-67) give normalized (with respect to 1 Ω) PSD and average power, respectively. For unnormalized (i.e., actual) values, $\mathcal{P}_w(f)$ is replaced by the appropriate expression as follows. If $w(t)$ is a voltage waveform that appears across a resistive load of R ohms, the unnormalized PSD is $\mathcal{P}_w(f)/R$ watts/Hz, where $\mathcal{P}_w(f)$ has units of volts^2/Hz. Similarly, if $w(t)$ is a current waveform passing through a resistive load of R ohms, the unnormalized PSD is $\mathcal{P}_w(f)R$ watts/Hz, where $\mathcal{P}_w(f)$ has units of amperes^2/Hz.

Autocorrelation Function

A related function called the *autocorrelation, $R(\tau)$,* can also be defined.

DEFINITION: The *autocorrelation* of a real (physical) waveform is[†]

$$R_w(\tau) \overset{\triangle}{=} \langle w(t)w(t+\tau)\rangle = \lim_{T\to\infty} \frac{1}{T}\int_{-T/2}^{T/2} w(t)w(t+\tau)\,dt \qquad (2\text{-}68)$$

Furthermore, it can be shown that the PSD and the autocorrelation function are Fourier transform pairs.

$$R_w(\tau) \leftrightarrow \mathcal{P}_w(f) \qquad (2\text{-}69)$$

where $\mathcal{P}_w(f) = \mathcal{F}[R_w(\tau)]$. This is called the *Wiener–Khintchine theorem.* This theorem, along with properties for $R(\tau)$ and $\mathcal{P}(f)$, are developed in detail in Chapter 6 of *Digital and Analog Communications Systems* [Couch, 1993] using the more general theory of random processes that is applicable to nondeterministic waveforms.

In summary, the PSD can be evaluated by either of two methods:

1. Direct evaluation using the definition, (2-66).
2. Indirect evaluation by first evaluating the autocorrelation function and then taking the Fourier transform, $\mathcal{P}_w(f) = \mathcal{F}[R_w(\tau)]$.

Furthermore, the total average normalized power for the waveform $w(t)$ can be evaluated using any of the *four* techniques:

$$P = \langle w^2(t)\rangle = W_{\text{rms}}^2 = \int_{-\infty}^{\infty} \mathcal{P}_w(f)\,df = R_w(0) \qquad (2\text{-}70)$$

Example 2-10   PSD of a Sinusoid

Let

$$w(t) = A\,\sin\,\omega_0 t$$

The PSD will be evaluated using the indirect method. The autocorrelation is

$$R_w(\tau) = \langle w(t)w(t+\tau)\rangle$$

$$= \lim_{T\to\infty} \frac{1}{T}\int_{-T/2}^{T/2} A^2\,\sin\,\omega_0 t\,\sin\,\omega_0(t+\tau)\,dt$$

Using a trigonometric identity, (A-12), we obtain

$$R_w(\tau) = \frac{A^2}{2}\cos\,\omega_0\tau \lim_{T\to\infty}\frac{1}{T}\int_{-T/2}^{T/2} dt - \frac{A^2}{2}\lim_{T\to\infty}\frac{1}{T}\int_{-T/2}^{T/2}\cos(2\omega_0 t + \omega_0\tau)\,dt$$

which reduces to

$$R_w(\tau) = \frac{A^2}{2}\cos\,\omega_0\tau \qquad (2\text{-}71\text{a})$$

[†]The autocorrelation of a complex waveform is $R_w(\tau) \overset{\triangle}{=} \langle w^*(t)w(t+\tau)\rangle$.

The PSD is then

$$\mathcal{P}_w(f) = \mathcal{F}\left[\frac{A^2}{2}\cos \omega_0\tau\right] = \frac{A^2}{4}\left[\delta(f - f_0) + \delta(f + f_0)\right] \qquad (2\text{-}71b)$$

as shown in Fig. 2-9. It may be compared to the "voltage" spectrum for a sinusoid that was obtained in Example 2-4 and shown in Fig. 2-4.

The average normalized power may be obtained by using (2-67):

$$P = \int_{-\infty}^{\infty} \frac{A^2}{4}\left[\delta(f - f_0) + \delta(f + f_0)\right] df = \frac{A^2}{2}$$

This value, $A^2/2$, checks with the known result for the normalized power of a sinusoid:

$$P = \langle w^2(t)\rangle = W_{rms}^2 = (A/\sqrt{2})^2 = A^2/2$$

It is also realized that $A \sin \omega_0 t$ and $A \cos \omega_0 t$ have exactly the same PSD (and autocorrelation function) since the phase has no effect on the PSD. This can be verified by evaluating the PSD for $A \cos \omega_0 t$, using the same procedure that was used above to evaluate the PSD for $A \sin \omega_0 t$.

Thus far, properties of signals and noise such as spectrum, average power, and rms value have been studied, but how do we represent the signal or noise waveform itself? The direct approach, of course, is to write a closed-form mathematical equation for the waveform itself. Other equivalent ways of modeling the waveform are often found to be very useful. One, which the reader has already studied in calculus, is to represent the waveform by the use of a Taylor series (i.e., power series) expansion about a point a:

$$w(t) = \sum_{n=0}^{\infty} \frac{w^{(n)}(a)}{n!} (t - a)^n \qquad (2\text{-}72)$$

where

$$w^{(n)}(a) = \frac{d^n w(t)}{dt^n}\bigg|_{t=a}$$

In this case, if the derivatives at $t = a$, $\{w^{(n)}(a)\}$, are known, this algorithm can be used to reconstruct the waveform. Another type of series representation that is especially useful in communication problems is the orthogonal series expansion, which is discussed in the next section.

FIGURE 2-9 Power spectrum of a sinusoid.

2-4 Orthogonal Series Representation of Signals and Noise

An orthogonal series representation of signals and noise is a general representation that has many significant applications in communication problems such as Fourier series, sampling function series, and representation of digital signals. These specific cases are so important that they will be studied in some detail in separate sections that follow.

Orthogonal Functions

Before the orthogonal series is studied, a definition for orthogonal functions is needed.

> **DEFINITION:** Functions $\varphi_n(t)$ and $\varphi_m(t)$ are said to be *orthogonal* with respect to each other over the interval $a < t < b$ if they satisfy the condition

$$\int_a^b \varphi_n(t)\varphi_m^*(t)\,dt = 0 \qquad where\ n \neq m \tag{2-73}$$

Furthermore, if the functions in the set $\{\varphi_n(t)\}$ are orthogonal, they also satisfy the relation

$$\int_b^a \varphi_n(t)\varphi_m^*(t)\,dt = \left\{ \begin{array}{ll} 0, & n \neq m \\ K_n, & n = m \end{array} \right\} = K_n\delta_{nm} \tag{2-74}$$

where

$$\delta_{nm} \triangleq \left\{ \begin{array}{ll} 0, & n \neq m \\ 1, & n = m \end{array} \right\} \tag{2-75}$$

δ_{nm} is called the *Kronecker delta function*. If the constants K_n are all equal to 1, the $\varphi_n(t)$ are said to be *orthonormal functions*.[†]

In other words, (2-73) is used to test pairs of functions to see if they are orthogonal. They are orthogonal over the interval (a,b) if the integral of their product is zero. The zero result implies that these functions are ''independent'' or in ''disagreement.'' If the result is not zero, they are not orthogonal, and consequently, the two functions have some ''dependence'' or ''alikeness'' to each other.

Example 2-11 Orthogonal Complex Exponential Functions

Show that the set of complex exponential functions $\{e^{jn\omega_0 t}\}$ are orthogonal over the interval $a < t < b$, where $b = a + T_0$, $T_0 = 1/f_0$, $\omega_0 = 2\pi f_0$, and n is an integer.

Solution: Substitute $\varphi_n(t) = e^{jn\omega_0 t}$ and $\varphi_m(t) = e^{jm\omega_0 t}$ into (2-73). We get

$$\int_a^b \varphi_n(t)\varphi_m^*(t)\,dt = \int_a^{a+T_0} e^{jn\omega_0 t}e^{-jm\omega_0 t}\,dt = \int_a^{a+T_0} e^{j(n-m)\omega_0 t}$$

$$= \int_a^{a+T_0} e^{j(n-m)\omega_0 t}\,dt \tag{2-76}$$

[†]To normalize a set of functions, take each old $\varphi_n(t)$ and divide it by $\sqrt{K_n}$ to form the normalized $\varphi_n(t)$.

For $m \neq n$ this becomes

$$\int_a^{a+T_0} e^{j(n-m)\omega_0 t} \, dt = \frac{e^{j(n-m)\omega_0 a}[e^{j(n-m)2\pi} - 1]}{j(n-m)\omega_0} = 0$$

since $e^{j(n-m)2\pi} = \cos[2\pi(n-m)] + j \sin[2\pi(n-m)] = 1$. Thus (2-73) is satisfied and, consequently, the complex exponential functions are orthogonal to each other over the interval $a < t < a + T_0$, where a is any real constant.

Also, for the case $n = m$, (2-76) becomes

$$\int_a^{a+T_0} \varphi_n(t)\varphi_n^*(t) \, dt = \int_a^{a+T_0} 1 \, dt = T_0$$

Using this in (2-74), we find that $K_n = T_0$ for all (integer) values of n. Since $K_n \neq 1$, these $\varphi_n(t)$ are not orthonormal (but they are orthogonal). An orthonormal set of exponential functions is obtained by scaling the old set where the functions in the new set are $\varphi_n(t) = (1/\sqrt{T_0}) \, e^{jn\omega_0 t}$.

Orthogonal Series

Assume that $w(t)$ represents some practical waveform (signal, noise, or signal–noise combination) that we wish to represent over the interval $a < t < b$. Then we can obtain an equivalent orthogonal series representation by using the following theorem.

Theorem

$w(t)$ can be represented over the interval (a,b) by the series

$$w(t) = \sum_n a_n \varphi_n(t) \tag{2-77}$$

where the orthogonal coefficients are given by

$$a_n = \frac{1}{K_n} \int_a^b w(t)\varphi_n^*(t) \, dt \tag{2-78}$$

and the range of n is over the integer values that correspond to the subscripts that were used to denote the orthogonal functions in the complete orthogonal set.

In order for (2-77) to be a valid representation for any physical signal (i.e., one with finite energy), the orthogonal set has to be complete. This implies that the set $\{\varphi_n(t)\}$ can be used to represent any function with an arbitrarily small error [Wylie, 1960]. In practice, it is usually difficult to prove that a given set of functions is complete. It can be shown that the complex exponential set and the harmonic sinusoidal sets that are used for the Fourier series in Sec. 2-5 are complete [Courant and Hilbert, 1953]. Many other useful sets are also complete such as Bessel functions, Legendre polynomials, and the $(\sin x)/x$-type sets [described by (3-32)].

PROOF OF THEOREM.   Assume that the set $\{\varphi_n(t)\}$ is sufficient to represent the waveform. Then in order for (2-77) to be correct, we only need to show that we can evaluate the a_n value by using (2-77). Using

$$w(t) = \sum_n a_n \varphi_n(t)$$

we operate on both sides of this equation with the integral operator

$$\int_a^b [\cdot]\ \varphi_m^*(t)\ dt \tag{2-79}$$

$$\int_a^b [w(t)]\ \varphi_m^*(t)\ dt = \int_a^b \left[\sum_n a_n \varphi_n(t) \right] \varphi_m^*(t)\ dt$$

$$= \sum_n a_n \int_a^b \varphi_n(t)\ \varphi_m^*(t)\ dt = \sum_n a_n K_n\ \delta_{nm}$$

$$= a_m K_m \tag{2-80}$$

Thus (2-78) follows.   ∎

It is also possible to use (2-77) to generate $w(t)$ from the $\varphi_n(t)$ functions and the coefficients a_n. In this case $w(t)$ is approximated by using a reasonable number of the $\varphi_n(t)$ functions. As shown in Fig. 2-10, for the case of real values for a_n and real functions for $\varphi_n(t)$, $w(t)$ can be synthesized by adding up weighted versions of $\varphi_n(t)$ where the weighting factors are given by $\{a_n\}$. The summing and gain weighting operation may be conveniently realized by using an operational amplifier with multiple inputs.

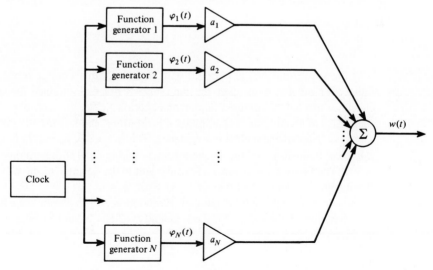

FIGURE 2-10 Waveform synthesis using orthogonal functions.

2-5 Fourier Series

The Fourier series is a particular type of orthogonal series representation that is very useful in solving engineering problems, especially communication problems. The orthogonal functions that are used are either sinusoids, or, equivalently, complex exponential functions.[†]

Complex Fourier Series

The complex Fourier series uses the orthogonal exponential functions.

$$\varphi_n(t) = e^{jn\omega_0 t} \tag{2-81}$$

where n ranges over all possible integer values, negative, positive, and zero; $\omega_0 = 2\pi/T_0$, where $T_0 = (b - a)$ is the length of the interval over which the series, (2-77), is valid; and, from Example 2 $K_n = T_0$. Using (2-77), the Fourier series theorem follows.

Theorem

Any physical waveform (i.e., finite energy) may be represented over the interval $a < t < a + T_0$ by the complex exponential Fourier series

$$w(t) = \sum_{n=-\infty}^{n=\infty} c_n e^{jn\omega_0 t} \tag{2-82}$$

where the complex (phasor) Fourier coefficients c_n are given by

$$c_n = \frac{1}{T_0} \int_a^{a+T_0} w(t) e^{-jn\omega_0 t} \, dt \tag{2-83}$$

and $\omega_0 = 2\pi f_0 = 2\pi/T_0$.

If the waveform $w(t)$ is periodic with period T_0, this Fourier series representation is valid *over all time* (i.e., over the interval $-\infty < t < +\infty$) since the $\varphi_n(t)$ are periodic functions that have a common fundamental period T_0. For this case of periodic waveforms, the choice of a value for the parameter a is arbitrary, and it is usually taken to be $a = 0$ or $a = -T_0/2$ for mathematical convenience. The frequency $f_0 = 1/T_0$ is said to be the *fundamental* frequency, and the frequency nf_0 is said to be the nth harmonic frequency, when $n > 1$. The Fourier coefficient c_0 is equivalent to the dc value of the waveform $w(t)$, since the integral is identical to that of (2-4) when $n = 0$.

c_n is, in general, a complex number. Furthermore, it is a phasor since it is the coefficient of a function of the type $e^{j\omega t}$. Consequently, (2-82) is said to be a complex or phasor Fourier series.

[†] Mathematicians generally call any orthogonal series a Fourier series.

Some properties of the complex Fourier series are as follows.

1. If $w(t)$ is real,

$$c_n = c^*_{-n} \tag{2-84}$$

2. If $w(t)$ is real and even [i.e., $w(t) = w(-t)$],

$$\mathrm{Im}[c_n] = 0 \tag{2-85}$$

3. If $w(t)$ is real and odd [i.e., $w(t) = -w(-t)$],

$$\mathrm{Re}\,[c_n] = 0$$

4. Parseval's theorem is

$$\frac{1}{T_0} \int_a^{a+T_0} |w(t)|^2 \, dt = \sum_{n=-\infty}^{n=\infty} |c_n|^2 \tag{2-86}$$

See (2-121) for the proof.

5. The complex Fourier series coefficients of a real waveform are related to the quadrature Fourier series coefficients by

$$c_n = \begin{cases} \frac{1}{2}a_n - j\frac{1}{2}b_n, & n > 0 \\ a_0, & n = 0 \\ \frac{1}{2}a_{-n} + j\frac{1}{2}b_{-n}, & n < 0 \end{cases} \tag{2-87}$$

See (2-90) through (2-92).

6. The complex Fourier series coefficients of a real waveform are related to the polar Fourier series coefficients by

$$c_n = \begin{cases} \frac{1}{2}D_n \; \underline{/\varphi_n}, & n > 0 \\ D_0, & n = 0 \\ \frac{1}{2}D_{-n} \underline{/-\varphi_{-n}}, & n < 0 \end{cases} \tag{2-88}$$

See (2-100) and (2-101).

Note that these properties for the complex Fourier series coefficients are similar to those of the Fourier transform as given in Sec. 2-2.

Quadrature Fourier Series

The *quadrature* form of the Fourier series representing any physical waveform $w(t)$ over the interval $a < t < a + T_0$ is

$$w(t) = \sum_{n=0}^{n=\infty} a_n \cos n\omega_0 t + \sum_{n=1}^{n=\infty} b_n \sin n\omega_0 t \tag{2-89}$$

where the orthogonal functions are $\cos n\omega_0 t$ and $\sin n\omega_0 t$. Using (2-78), we find that these Fourier coefficients are given by

$$a_n = \begin{cases} \dfrac{1}{T_0} \displaystyle\int_a^{a+T_0} w(t) \, dt, & n = 0 \\ \dfrac{2}{T_0} \displaystyle\int_a^{a+T_0} w(t) \cos n\omega_0 t \, dt, & n \geq 1 \end{cases} \tag{2-90}$$

and

$$b_n = \frac{2}{T_0} \int_a^{a+T_0} w(t) \sin n\omega_0 t \, dt, \qquad n > 0 \tag{2-91}$$

Once again, since these sinusoidal orthogonal functions are periodic, this series is periodic with the fundamental period T_0, and if $w(t)$ is periodic with period T_0, the series will represent $w(t)$ over the whole real line (i.e., $-\infty < t < \infty$).

The complex Fourier series, (2-82), and the quadrature Fourier series, (2-89), are equivalent representations. This can be demonstrated by expressing the complex number c_n in terms of its conjugate parts, x_n and y_n. That is, using (2-83) yields

$$c_n = x_n + jy_n$$
$$= \left[\frac{1}{T_0} \int_a^{a+T_0} w(t) \cos n\omega_0 t \, dt \right] + j \left[\frac{-1}{T_0} \int_a^{a+T_0} w(t) \sin n\omega_0 t \, dt \right] \tag{2-92}$$

for all integer values of n. Thus

$$x_n = \frac{1}{T_0} \int_a^{a+T_0} w(t) \cos n\omega_0 t \, dt \tag{2-93}$$

and

$$y_n = \frac{-1}{T_0} \int_a^{a+T_0} w(t) \sin n\omega_0 t \, dt \tag{2-94}$$

Using (2-90) and (2-91), we obtain the identities

$$a_n = \begin{cases} c_0, & n = 0 \\ 2x_n, & n \geq 1 \end{cases} = \begin{cases} c_0, & n = 0 \\ 2 \ \mathrm{Re}\{c_n\}, & n \geq 1 \end{cases} \tag{2-95}$$

and

$$b_n = -2y_n = -2 \ \mathrm{Im}\{c_n\}, \qquad n \geq 1 \tag{2-96}$$

where $\mathrm{Re}\{\cdot\}$ denotes the real part of $\{\cdot\}$ and $\mathrm{Im}\{\cdot\}$ denotes the imaginary part of $\{\cdot\}$.

Polar Fourier Series

The quadrature Fourier series, (2-89), may be rearranged and written in a polar (amplitude-phase) form. The *polar* form is

$$w(t) = D_0 + \sum_{n=1}^{n=\infty} D_n \cos(n\omega_0 t + \phi_n) \tag{2-97}$$

where $w(t)$ is real and

$$a_n = \begin{cases} D_0, & n = 0 \\ D_n \cos \phi_n, & n \geq 1 \end{cases} \tag{2-98}$$

$$b_n = -D_n \sin \phi_n, \qquad n \geq 1 \tag{2-99}$$

The latter two equations may be inverted, and we obtain

$$D_n = \begin{cases} a_0, & n = 0 \\ \sqrt{a_n^2 + b_n^2}, & n \geq 1 \end{cases} = \begin{cases} c_0, & n = 0 \\ 2|c_n|, & n \geq 1 \end{cases} \qquad (2\text{-}100)$$

and

$$\phi_n = -\tan^{-1}\left(\frac{b_n}{a_n}\right) = \underline{/c_n}, \qquad n \geq 1 \qquad (2\text{-}101)$$

where the angle operator is defined by

$$\underline{/[\cdot]} = \tan^{-1}\left(\frac{\text{Im}[\cdot]}{\text{Re}[\cdot]}\right) \qquad (2\text{-}102)$$

It should be clear from the context whether $\underline{/\quad}$ denotes the angle operator or the angle itself. For example, $\underline{/90°}$ denotes an angle of 90°, but $\underline{/1 + j2}$ denotes the angle operator and is equal to 63.4° when evaluated.

The equivalence between the Fourier series coefficients is demonstrated geometrically in Fig. 2-11. It is seen that, in general, when a physical (real) waveform $w(t)$ is represented by a Fourier series, c_n is a complex number with a real part x_n and an imaginary part y_n (which are both real numbers) and, consequently, a_n, b_n, D_n, and ϕ_n are real numbers. Furthermore, D_n is a nonnegative number for $n \geq 1$.

As we have seen, the complex, quadrature, and polar forms of the Fourier series are all equivalent, but the question is: *Which is the best form to use?* The answer is that it depends on the particular problem being solved! If the problem is being solved analytically, the complex coefficients are *usually* easier to evaluate. On the other hand, if measurements of a waveform are being made in a laboratory, the polar form is usually more convenient since measuring instruments, such as voltmeters, scopes, vector voltmeters, and wave analyzers, usually give magnitude and phase readings. Using the laboratory results, engi-

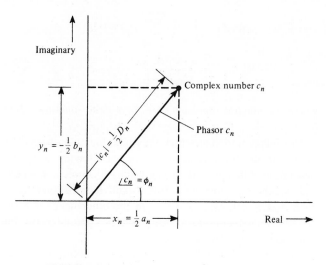

FIGURE 2-11 Fourier series coefficients, $n \geq 1$.

neers often draw *one-sided* spectral plots where lines are drawn corresponding to each D_n value at $f = nf_0$, where $n \geq 0$ (i.e., positive frequencies only). Of course, this one-sided spectral plot may be converted to the two-sided spectrum given by the c_n plot by using (2-100). It is understood that the actual spectrum is defined to be the Fourier transform of $w(t)$ and consists of two two-sided plots, one plot for $|c_n|$ and the other for $\underline{/c_n}$. This is demonstrated by Fig. 2-4 where (2-103), from the following theorem, may be used.

Line Spectra for Periodic Waveforms

For *periodic* waveforms, the Fourier series representations are valid over all time (i.e., $-\infty < t < \infty$). Consequently, the (two-sided) spectrum, which depends on the waveshape from $t = -\infty$ to $t = \infty$, may be evaluated in terms of Fourier coefficients.

Theorem

If a waveform is periodic with period T_0, the spectrum of the waveform $w(t)$ is

$$W(f) = \sum_{n=-\infty}^{n=\infty} c_n \, \delta(f - nf_0) \tag{2-103}$$

where $f_0 = 1/T_0$ and c_n are the phasor Fourier coefficients of the waveform as given by (2-83).

PROOF

$$w(t) = \sum_{n=-\infty}^{n=\infty} c_n e^{jn\omega_0 t}$$

Taking the Fourier transform of both sides, we obtain

$$W(f) = \int_{-\infty}^{\infty} \left(\sum_{n=-\infty}^{n=\infty} c_n e^{jn\omega_0 t} \right) e^{-j\omega t} \, dt$$

$$= \sum_{n=-\infty}^{n=\infty} c_n \int_{-\infty}^{\infty} e^{-j2\pi(f-nf_0)t} \, dt = \sum_{n=-\infty}^{n=\infty} c_n \, \delta(f - nf_0) \tag{2-104}$$

where the integral representation for a delta function, (2-48), was used. ∎

This theorem indicates that a periodic function *always* has a line (delta function) spectrum with the lines being at $f = nf_0$ and having weights given by the c_n values. An illustration of this property was given by Example 2-4, where $c_1 = -jA/2$ and $c_{-1} = jA/2$ and the other c_n's were zero. It is also obvious that there is no dc component since there is no line at $f = 0$ (i.e., $c_0 = 0$). On the other hand, if a function does not contain any periodic component, the spectrum will be continuous (no lines) except for a line at $f = 0$ when the function has a dc component.

It is also possible to evaluate the Fourier coefficients by sampling the Fourier transform of a pulse corresponding to $w(t)$ over a period. This is shown by the following theorem.

Theorem

If $w(t)$ is a periodic function with period T_0 and is represented by

$$w(t) = \sum_{n=-\infty}^{n=\infty} h(t - nT_0) = \sum_{n=-\infty}^{n=\infty} c_n e^{jn\omega_0 t} \qquad (2\text{-}105)$$

where

$$h(t) = \begin{cases} w(t), & |t| < \dfrac{T_0}{2} \\ 0, & t \quad \text{elsewhere} \end{cases} \qquad (2\text{-}106)$$

then the Fourier coefficients are given by

$$c_n = f_0 H(nf_0) \qquad (2\text{-}107)$$

where $H(f) = \mathscr{F}[h(t)]$ and $f_0 = 1/T_0$.

PROOF

$$w(t) = \sum_{n=-\infty}^{\infty} h(t - nT_0) = \sum_{n=-\infty}^{\infty} h(t) * \delta(t - nT_0) \qquad (2\text{-}108)$$

where $*$ denotes the convolution operation. Thus

$$w(t) = h(t) * \sum_{n=-\infty}^{\infty} \delta(t - nT_0) \qquad (2\text{-}109)$$

But the impulse train may itself be represented by its Fourier series[†]

$$\sum_{n=-\infty}^{\infty} \delta(t - nT_0) = \sum_{n=-\infty}^{\infty} c_n e^{jn\omega_0 t} \qquad (2\text{-}110)$$

where all the Fourier coefficients are just $c_n = f_0$. Substituting (2-110) into (2-109), we obtain

$$w(t) = h(t) * \sum_{n=-\infty}^{\infty} f_0 e^{jn\omega_0 t} \qquad (2\text{-}111)$$

Taking the Fourier transform of both sides of (2-111), we have

$$W(f) = H(f) \sum_{n=-\infty}^{\infty} f_0 \, \delta(f - nf_0)$$

$$= \sum_{n=-\infty}^{\infty} [f_0 H(nf_0)] \, \delta(f - nf_0) \qquad (2\text{-}112)$$

Comparing (2-112) with (2-103), we see that (2-107) follows. ∎

[†]This is called the *Poisson sum formula.*

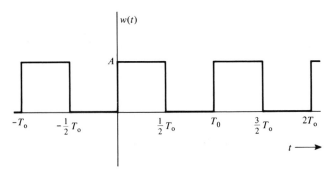

FIGURE 2-12 Periodic square wave used in Example 2-12.

This theorem is useful for evaluating the Fourier coefficients c_n when the Fourier transform of the fundamental pulse shape $h(t)$ for the periodic waveform is known or can easily be obtained (such as from a Fourier transform table, e.g., Table 2-2).

Example 2-12   Fourier Coefficients for a Square Wave

Find the Fourier coefficients for the periodic square wave shown in Fig. 2-12. The complex Fourier coefficients, using (2-83), are

$$c_n = \frac{1}{T_0} \int_0^{T_0/2} A e^{-jn\omega_0 t} \, dt = j \frac{A}{2\pi n} (e^{-jn\pi} - 1) \tag{2-113}$$

which reduce, using l'Hospital's rule for evaluating the indeterminant form for $n = 0$, to

$$c_n = \begin{cases} \dfrac{A}{2}, & n = 0 \\[2mm] -j \dfrac{A}{n\pi}, & n = \text{odd} \\[2mm] 0, & n \quad \text{otherwise} \end{cases} \tag{2-114}$$

This result may be verified by using (2-107) and the result of Example 2-5, where $T_0 = 2T$. That is,

$$c_n = \frac{A}{T_0} V(nf_0) = \frac{A}{2} e^{-jn\pi/2} \frac{\sin(n\pi/2)}{n\pi/2} \tag{2-115}$$

which is identical to (2-119). It is realized that the dc value of the waveform is $c_0 = A/2$, which checks with the result by using (2-4). The spectrum of the square wave is easily obtained by using (2-103).

The other types of Fourier coefficients may also be obtained. Using (2-95) and (2-96), we obtain the quadrature Fourier coefficients

$$a_n = \begin{cases} \dfrac{A}{2}, & n = 0 \\ 0, & n > 0 \end{cases} \tag{2-116}$$

$$b_n = \begin{cases} \dfrac{2A}{\pi n}, & n = \text{odd} \\ 0, & n = \text{even} \end{cases} \tag{2-117}$$

Here all the $a_n = 0$, except for $n = 0$, because, if the dc value were suppressed, the waveform would be an odd function about the origin. Using (2-100) and (2-101), we find that the polar Fourier coefficients are

$$D_n = \begin{cases} \dfrac{A}{2}, & n = 0 \\ \dfrac{2A}{n\pi}, & n = 1, 3, 5, \dots \\ 0, & n \quad \text{otherwise} \end{cases} \tag{2-118}$$

and

$$\phi_n = -90° \quad \text{for } n \geq 1 \tag{2-119}$$

In communication problems the normalized average power is often needed, and, for the case of periodic waveforms, it can be evaluated using Fourier series coefficients.

Theorem

For a periodic waveform $w(t)$, the normalized power is given by

$$P_w = \langle w^2(t) \rangle = \sum_{n=-\infty}^{n=\infty} |c_n|^2 \tag{2-120}$$

where $\{c_n\}$ are the complex Fourier coefficients for the waveform.

PROOF. For periodic $w(t)$, the Fourier series representation is valid over all time and may be substituted into (2-12) to evaluate the normalized (i.e., $R = 1$) power.

$$P_w = \left\langle \left(\sum_n c_n e^{jn\omega_0 t} \right)^2 \right\rangle = \left\langle \sum_n \sum_m c_n c_m^* e^{jn\omega_0 t} e^{-jm\omega_0 t} \right\rangle$$

$$= \sum_n \sum_m c_n c_m^* \langle e^{j(n-m)\omega_0 t} \rangle = \sum_n \sum_m c_n c_m^* \delta_{nm} = \sum_n c_n c_n^*$$

or

$$P_w = \sum_n |c_n|^2 \qquad (2\text{-}121)$$

∎

Equation (2-120) is a statement for a special case of Parseval's theorem as applied to power signals.

If a large number of the Fourier coefficients are nonzero, then calculating the average power by summing the magnitude squared values of the Fourier coefficients is tedious. Then it is usually easier to evaluate the normalized average power directly by use of the time average, $\langle w^2(t) \rangle$.

Power Spectral Density for Periodic Waveforms

Theorem

For a periodic waveform, the power spectral density (PSD) is given by

$$\mathcal{P}(f) = \sum_{n=-\infty}^{n=\infty} |c_n|^2 \, \delta(f - nf_0) \qquad (2\text{-}122)$$

where $T_0 = 1/f_o$ is the period of the waveform and the $\{c_n\}$ are the corresponding Fourier coefficients for the waveform.

PROOF. Let $w(t) = \sum_{-\infty}^{\infty} c_n e^{jn\omega_0 t}$. Then the autocorrelation function of $w(t)$ is

$$R(\tau) = \langle w^*(t)w(t + \tau) \rangle$$

$$= \left\langle \sum_{n=-\infty}^{\infty} c_n^* e^{-jn\omega_0 t} \sum_{m=-\infty}^{\infty} c_m e^{jm\omega_0(t+\tau)} \right\rangle$$

or

$$R(\tau) = \sum_{n=-\infty}^{\infty} \sum_{m=-\infty}^{\infty} c_n^* c_m e^{jm\omega_0 \tau} \langle e^{j\omega_0(m-n)t} \rangle \qquad (2\text{-}123)$$

But $\langle e^{j\omega_0(n-m)t} \rangle = \delta_{nm}$, so (2-123) reduces to

$$R(\tau) = \sum_{n=-\infty}^{\infty} |c_n|^2 e^{jn\omega_0 \tau} \qquad (2\text{-}124)$$

The PSD is then

$$\mathcal{P}(f) = \mathcal{F}[R(\tau)] = \mathcal{F}\left[\sum_{-\infty}^{\infty} |c_n|^2 e^{jn\omega_0 \tau} \right]$$

$$= \sum_{-\infty}^{\infty} |c_n|^2 \, \mathcal{F}[e^{jn\omega_0 \tau}] = \sum_{-\infty}^{\infty} |c_n|^2 \, \delta(f - nf_0) \qquad (2\text{-}125)$$

∎

Equation (2-122) not only gives a way to evaluate the PSD for periodic waveforms but also can be used to evaluate the bandwidths of the waveforms. For example, the frequency interval could be found where 90% of the waveform power was concentrated.

Example 2-13 PSD for a Square Wave

The PSD for the periodic square wave shown in Fig. 2-12 will be found. Since the waveform is periodic, (2-12) can be used to evaluate the PSD. Consequently, this problem becomes one of evaluating the Fourier series (FS) coefficients. Furthermore, the FS coefficients for a square wave are given by (2-115). Thus

$$\mathcal{P}(f) = \sum_{-\infty}^{\infty} \left(\frac{A}{2}\right)^2 \left(\frac{\sin(n\pi/2)}{n\pi/2}\right)^2 \delta(f - nf_0) \qquad (2\text{-}126)$$

This PSD is shown by the solid lines in Fig. 2-13, where the delta functions (which have infinite amplitudes) are represented by vertical lines that have length equal to the weight (i.e., area) of the corresponding delta function.

Truncated Fourier Series

In practice, the FS is often truncated to a finite number of terms. For example, five or ten harmonics might be used to approximate the FS series for a square wave. Thus an impor-

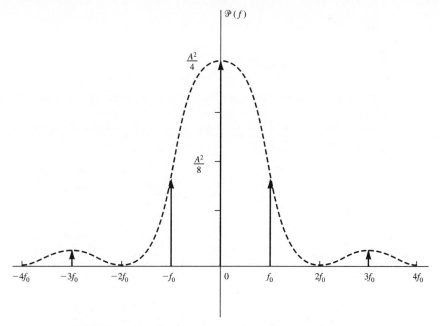

FIGURE 2-13 PSD for a square wave used in Example 2-13.

tant question arises: For the finite series, are the optimum values for the series coefficients the same as those for the corresponding terms in the infinite series, or should the coefficients for the finite series be adjusted to some new values to give the best finite-series approximation? The answer: *The optimum values for the coefficients of the truncated FS are the same as those for the corresponding terms in the nontruncated FS.* This is proven as follows, provided that the term "optimum" means that the coefficients for the truncated FS are chosen to minimize the mean square error (MSE).

Let $w(t)$ denote the real waveform and let $\tilde{w}(t)$ denote the truncated series approximation of $w(t)$. That is,

$$\tilde{w}(t) = \sum_{m=-M}^{M} d_m e^{jm\omega_0 t} \qquad (2\text{-}127)$$

The MSE between $w(t)$ and $\tilde{w}(t)$ is

$$\text{MSE} = \langle [w(t) - \tilde{w}(t)]^2 \rangle \qquad (2\text{-}128)$$

or

$$\text{MSE} = \left\langle \left[w(t) - \sum_{m=-M}^{M} d_m e^{jn\omega_0 t} \right]^2 \right\rangle$$

Now find the optimum d_m values such that the MSE is minimized. This is equivalent to finding the d_n values that make $\partial \text{MSE}/\partial d_n = 0$ for all $-M \le n \le M$. Thus

$$\frac{\partial \text{MSE}}{\partial d_n} = \left\langle 2 \left[w(t) - \sum_{m=-M}^{M} d_m e^{jm\omega_0 t} \right] (-e^{jn\omega_0 t}) \right\rangle = 0$$

or

$$\langle w(t) e^{jn\omega_0 t} \rangle = \left\langle \sum_{m=-M}^{M} d_m e^{j(m+n)\omega_0 t} \right\rangle \qquad (2\text{-}129)$$

Using (2-4), where (for convenience) a is replaced by $a + (T_0/2)$, (2-129) becomes

$$\frac{1}{T_0} \int_a^{a+T_0} w(t) e^{jn\omega_0 t}\, dt = \sum_{m=-M}^{M} d_m \frac{1}{T_0} \int_a^{a+T_0} e^{j(n+m)\omega_0 t}\, dt$$

$$= \sum_{m=-M}^{M} d m \begin{cases} 0, & m \ne -n \\ 1, & m = -n \end{cases} = d_{-n}$$

or

$$d_{-n} = \frac{1}{T_0} \int_a^{a+T_0} w(t) e^{jn\omega_0 t}\, dt$$

Substituting n for $-n$, we obtain

$$d_n = \frac{1}{T_0} \int_a^{a+T_0} w(t) e^{-jn\omega_0 t}\, dt \qquad (2\text{-}130)$$

for the optimum values of the coefficients for the truncated FS. Comparing this with (2-83), which gives the c_n coefficients for the infinite FS, we see that $c_n = d_n$. This shows that the optimum values for the truncated FS coefficient d_n values are identical to the coefficient c_n values for the infinite FS.

2-6 Summary

Signals and noise in communication systems are contained in voltage and/or current waveforms. Consequently, waveform characteristics are of fundamental concern. In this chapter the important waveform characteristics, such as dc value, rms value, dB value, and average power, were defined and computed.

The critical concept of the frequencies that are embodied in a waveform was introduced by use of the Fourier transform. Examples illustrating spectral calculations were worked out. The autocorrelation and power spectral density (PSD) were defined and studied.

Waveforms may be represented by orthogonal series expansions. One example is the Fourier series, which is especially useful for representing periodic signals. In Chapter 3 the sampling-function orthogonal series will be found to be useful for representing bandlimited signals.

PROBLEMS

2-1   For a sinusoidal waveform with a peak value of A and a frequency of f_0, use the time average operator to show that the rms value for this waveform is $A/\sqrt{2}$.

2-2   A function generator produces a periodic voltage waveform as shown in Fig. P2-2.
(a) Find the value for the dc voltage.
(b) Find the value for the rms voltage.
(c) If this voltage waveform is applied across a 1000-Ω load, what is the power dissipated in the load?

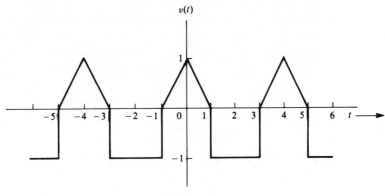

FIGURE P2-2

2-3   The voltage across a load is given by $v(t) = A_0 \cos \omega_0 t$, and the current through the load is a square wave,

$$i(t) = I_0 \sum_{n=-\infty}^{\infty} \left[\Pi\left(\frac{t - nT_0}{T_0/2}\right) - \Pi\left(\frac{t - nT_0 - (T_0/2)}{T_0/2}\right) \right]$$

where $\omega_0 = 2\pi/T_0$, $T_0 = 1$ sec, $A_0 = 10$ V, and $I_0 = 5$ mA.
(a) Find the expression for the instantaneous power and sketch this result as a function of time.
(b) Find the value of the average power.

2-4   The voltage across a 50-Ω resistive load is the positive portion of a cosine wave. That is,

$$v(t) = \begin{cases} 10 \cos \omega_0 t, & |t - nT_0| < T_0/4 \\ 0, & t \text{ elsewhere} \end{cases}$$

where n is any integer.
(a) Sketch the voltage and current waveforms.
(b) Evaluate the dc values for the voltage and current.
(c) Find the rms values for the voltage and current.
(d) Find the total average power dissipated in the load.

2-5   For Prob. 2-4, find the energy dissipated in the load during a 1-hr interval if $T_0 = 1$ sec.

2-6   Determine whether each of the following signals is an energy signal or a power signal and evaluate the normalized energy or power, as appropriate.
(a) $w(t) = \Pi(t/T_0)$.
(b) $w(t) = \Pi(t/T_0) \cos \omega_0 t$.
(c) $w(t) = \cos^2 \omega_0 t$.

2-7   An average reading power meter is connected to the output circuit of a transmitter. The transmitter output is fed into a 75-Ω resistive load and the wattmeter reads 67 W.
(a) What is the power in dBm units?
(b) What is the power in dBk units?
(c) What is the value in dBmV units?

2-8   Assume that a waveform with a known rms value, V_{rms}, is applied across a 50-Ω load. Derive a formula that can be used to compute the dBm value from V_{rms}.

2-9   An amplifier is connected to a 50-Ω load and driven by a sinusoidal current source, as shown in Fig. P2-9. The output resistance of the amplifier is 10 Ω and the input resistance is 2 kΩ. Evaluate the true decibel gain of this circuit.

FIGURE P2-9

2-10 The voltage (rms) across the 300-Ω antenna input terminals of an FM receiver is 3.5 μV.

(a) Find the input power (watts).

(b) Evaluate the input power as measured in decibels below 1 mW (dBm).

(c) What would be the input voltage (in microvolts) for the same input power if the input resistance were 75 Ω instead of 300 Ω?

2-11 What is the value for the phasor that corresponds to the voltage waveform $v(t) = 12 \sin(\omega_0 t - 25°)$, where $\omega_0 = 2000\pi$?

2-12 A signal is $w(t) = 3 \sin(100\pi t - 30°) + 4 \cos(100\pi t)$. Find the corresponding phasor.

2-13 Evaluate the Fourier transform of

$$w(t) = \begin{cases} e^{-\alpha t}, & t \geq 1 \\ 0, & t < 1 \end{cases}$$

2-14 Find the spectrum for the waveform $w(t) = e^{-\pi(t/T)^2}$. What can we say about the width of $w(t)$ and $W(f)$ as T increases? [*Hint:* Use (A-75).]

2-15 Using the convolution property, find the spectrum for

$$w(t) = \sin 2\pi f_1 t \cos 2\pi f_2 t$$

2-16 Find the spectrum (Fourier transform) of the triangle waveform

$$s(t) = \begin{cases} At, & 0 < t < T_0 \\ 0, & t \text{ elsewhere} \end{cases}$$

in terms of A and T_0.

2-17 Find the spectrum for the waveform shown in Fig. P2-17.

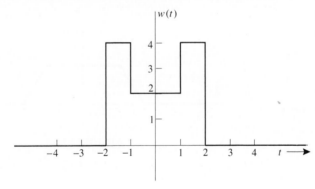

FIGURE P2-17

2-18 If $w(t)$ has the Fourier transform

$$W(f) = \frac{j2\pi f}{1 + j2\pi f}$$

find $X(f)$ for the following waveforms.

(a) $x(t) = w(2t + 2)$.

(b) $x(t) = e^{-jt}w(t - 1)$.

(c) $x(t) = 2\dfrac{dw(t)}{dt}$.

(d) $x(t) = w(1 - t)$.

2-19 Using (2-30), find $w(t)$ for $W(f) = A\Pi(f/2B)$ and verify your answer using the duality property.

2-20 Find the quadrature spectral functions $X(f)$ and $Y(f)$ for the damped sinusoidal waveform

$$w(t) = u(t)e^{-at} \sin \omega_0 t$$

where $u(t)$ is a unit step function, $a > 0$, and $W(f) = X(f) + jY(f)$.

2-21 Derive the spectrum of $w(t) = e^{-|t|/T}$.

2-22 Find the Fourier transforms for the following waveforms. Plot the waveforms and their magnitude spectra. [*Hint:* Use (3-68).]

(a) $\Pi\left(\dfrac{t - 3}{4}\right)$.

(b) 2.

(c) $\Lambda\left(\dfrac{t - 5}{5}\right)$.

2-23 Find the approximate Fourier transform for the following waveform using (3-68).

$$x(t) = \begin{cases} \sin(2\pi t/512) + \sin(70\pi t/512), & 5 < t < 75 \\ 0, & t \text{ elsewhere} \end{cases}$$

2-24 Evaluate the spectrum for the trapezoidal pulse shown in Fig. P2-24.

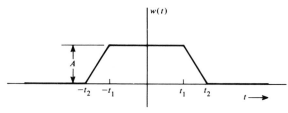

FIGURE P2-24

2-25 Show that

$$\mathcal{F}^{-1}\{\mathcal{F}[w(t)]\} = w(t)$$

[*Hint:* Use (2-33).]

2-26 Using the definition of the inverse Fourier transform, show that the value of $w(t)$ at $t = 0$ is equal to the area under $W(f)$. That is, show that

$$w(0) = \int_{-\infty}^{\infty} W(f)\, df$$

2-27 Prove that:
(a) If $w(t)$ is real and an even function of t, $W(f)$ is real.
(b) If $w(t)$ is real and an odd function of t, $W(f)$ is imaginary.

2-28 Suppose that the spectrum of a waveform as a function of frequency in hertz is

$$W(f) = \frac{1}{2}\delta(f - 4) + \frac{1}{2}\delta(f + 4) + \frac{j\pi f}{2 + j2\pi f}e^{j\pi f}$$

Find the corresponding spectrum as a function of radian frequency, $W(\omega)$.

2-29 The unit impulse can also be defined as follows:

$$\delta(t) = \lim_{a \to \infty}\left[Ka\left(\frac{\sin at}{at}\right)\right]$$

Find the value of K needed, and show that this definition is consistent with those given in the text. Give another example of an ordinary function such that in the limit of some parameter, the function becomes a Dirac delta function.

2-30 Use $v(t) = ae^{-at}$, $a > 0$, to approximate $\delta(t)$ as $a \to \infty$.
(a) Plot $v(t)$ for $a = 0.1$, 1, and 10.
(b) Plot $V(f)$ for $a = 0.1$, 1, and 10.

2-31 Show that

$$\text{sgn}(t) \leftrightarrow \frac{1}{j\pi f}$$

[Hint: Use (2-30) and $\int_0^\infty (\sin x)/x \, dx = \pi/2$ from Appendix A.]

2-32 Show that

$$u(t) \leftrightarrow \tfrac{1}{2}\delta(f) + \frac{1}{j2\pi f}$$

[Hint: Use the linearity (superposition) theorem and the result of Prob. 2-31.]

2-33 Show that the sifting property of δ functions, (2-47), may be generalized to evaluate integrals that involve derivatives of the delta function. That is, show that

$$\int_{-\infty}^{\infty} w(x)\,\delta^{(n)}(x - x_0)\,dx = (-1)^n w(n)(x_0)$$

where the superscript (n) denotes the nth derivative. (Hint: Use integration by parts.)

2-34 Let $x(t) = \Pi\left(\dfrac{t - 0.05}{0.1}\right)$. Plot the spectrum of $x(t)$ using MathCAD or MATLAB with the help of (2-59) and (2-60). Check your results by using the FFT and (3-68).

2-35 If $w(t) = w_1(t)w_2(t)$, show that

$$W(f) = \int_{-\infty}^{\infty} W_1(\lambda)W_2(f - \lambda)\,d\lambda$$

where $W(f) = \mathcal{F}[w(t)]$.

2-36 Show that:

(a) $\int_{-\infty}^{t} w(\lambda)\, d\lambda = w(t) * u(t)$.

(b) $\int_{-\infty}^{t} w(\lambda)\, d\lambda \leftrightarrow (j2\pi f)^{-1} W(f) + \frac{1}{2} W(0)\, \delta(f)$.

(c) $w(t) * \delta(t - a) = w(t - a)$.

2-37 Show that

$$\frac{dw(t)}{dt} \leftrightarrow (j2\pi f) W(f)$$

[*Hint:* Use (2-26) and integrate by parts. Assume that $w(t)$ is absolutely integrable.]

2-38 As discussed in Example 2-8, show that

$$\frac{1}{T} \Pi\left(\frac{t}{T}\right) * \Pi\left(\frac{t}{T}\right) = \Lambda\left(\frac{t}{T}\right)$$

2-39 Given the waveform $w(t) = A\Pi(t/T) \sin \omega_0 t$. Find the spectrum of $w(t)$ by using the multiplication theorem as discussed in Example 2-9.

2-40 Evaluate the following integrals.

(a) $\displaystyle\int_{-\infty}^{\infty} \frac{\sin 4\lambda}{4\lambda}\, \delta(t - \lambda)\, d\lambda$.

(b) $\displaystyle\int_{-\infty}^{\infty} (\lambda^3 - 1)\, \delta(2 - \lambda)\, d\lambda$.

2-41 Prove that

$$M(f) * \delta(f - f_0) = M(f - f_0)$$

2-42 Evaluate $y(t) = w_1(t) * w_2(t)$, where

$$w_1(t) = \begin{cases} 1, & |t| < T_0 \\ 0, & t \text{ elsewhere} \end{cases}$$

$$w_2(t) = \begin{cases} [1 - 2|t|], & |t| < \frac{1}{2}T_0 \\ 0, & t \text{ elsewhere} \end{cases}$$

2-43 Given $w(t) = 5 + 12 \cos \omega_0 t$ where $f_0 = 10$ Hz:

(a) Find $R_w(\tau)$.

(b) $\mathcal{P}_w(f)$.

2-44 Given the waveform

$$w(t) = A_1 \cos(\omega_1 t + \theta_1) + A_2 \cos(\omega_2 t + \theta_2)$$

where $A_1, A_2, \omega_1, \omega_2, \theta_1,$ and θ_2 are constants.

(a) Find the autocorrelation for $w(t)$ as a function of the constants.

(b) Find the PSD function for $w(t)$.

(c) Sketch the PSD for the case of $\omega_1 \neq \omega_2$.

(d) Sketch the PSD for the case of $\omega_1 = \omega_2$ and $\theta_1 = \theta_2 + 90°$.

(e) Sketch the PSD for the case of $\omega_1 = \omega_2$ and $\theta_1 = \theta_2$.

2-45 Given the periodic voltage waveform shown in Fig. P2-45:
   (a) Find the dc value for this waveform.
   (b) Find the rms value for this waveform.
   (c) Find the complex exponential Fourier series.
   (d) Find the voltage spectrum for this waveform.

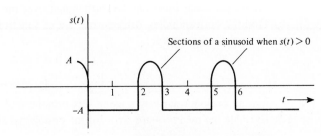

FIGURE P2-45

2-46 (a) Find a mathematical representation for a periodic triangular waveform that has a peak value of A volts, an average value of $\frac{1}{4}A$ volts, a period of T seconds, and a zero crossing at $t = 0$ with a positive slope. Assume that the slope of the sides of the triangle are equal with opposite signs.
   (b) Find the spectrum for this triangular waveform.
   (c) Find the rms value for this triangular waveform.
   (d) Find the bandwidth required to pass 95% of the power. (*Hint:* Use the Fourier series.)

2-47 Determine if $s_1(t)$ and $s_2(t)$ are orthogonal over the interval $(-\frac{5}{2}T_2 < t < \frac{5}{2}T_2)$, where $s_1(t) = A_1 \cos(\omega_1 t + \varphi_1)$, $s_2(t) = A_2 \cos(\omega_2 t + \varphi_2)$, and $\omega_2 = 2\pi/T_2$ for the following cases.
   (a) $\omega_1 = \omega_2$ and $\varphi_1 = \varphi_2$.
   (b) $\omega_1 = \omega_2$ and $\varphi_1 = \varphi_2 + \pi/2$.
   (c) $\omega_1 = \omega_2$ and $\varphi_1 = \varphi_2 + \pi$.
   (d) $\omega_1 = 2\omega_2$ and $\varphi_1 = \varphi_2$.
   (e) $\omega_1 = \frac{4}{5}\omega_2$ and $\varphi_1 = \varphi_2$.
   (f) $\omega_1 = \pi\omega_2$ and $\varphi_1 = \varphi_2$.

2-48 Let $s(t) = A_1 \cos(\omega_1 t + \varphi_1) + A_2 \cos(\omega_2 t + \varphi_2)$. Determine the rms value of $s(t)$ in terms of A_1 and A_2 for the following cases.
   (a) $\omega_1 = \omega_2$ and $\varphi_1 = \varphi_2$.
   (b) $\omega_1 = \omega_2$ and $\varphi_1 = \varphi_2 + \pi/2$.
   (c) $\omega_1 = \omega_2$ and $\varphi_1 = \varphi_2 + \pi$.
   (d) $\omega_1 = 2\omega_2$ and φ_1 and φ_2.
   (e) $\omega_1 = 2\omega_2$ and $\varphi_1 = \varphi_2 + \pi$.

2-49 Show that

$$\sum_{k=-\infty}^{\infty} \delta(t - kT_0) \leftrightarrow f_0 \sum_{n=-\infty}^{\infty} \delta(f - nf_0)$$

where $f_0 = 1/T_0$. [*Hint:* Expand $\sum_{k=-\infty}^{\infty} \delta(t - kT_0)$ into a Fourier series and then take the Fourier transform.]

2-50 Three functions are shown in Fig. P2-50.
   (a) Show that these functions are orthogonal over the interval $(-4,4)$.
   (b) Find the corresponding orthonormal set of functions.
   (c) Expand the waveform

$$w(t) = \begin{cases} 1, & 0 \le t \le 4 \\ 0, & t \text{ elsewhere} \end{cases}$$

   into an orthonormal series using this orthonormal set.
   (d) Evaluate the mean square error for the orthogonal series obtained in part (c) by evaluating

$$\epsilon = \int_{-4}^{4} \left[w(t) - \sum_{j=1}^{3} a_j \varphi_j(t) \right]^2 dt$$

   (e) Repeat parts (c) and (d) for the waveform

$$w(t) = \begin{cases} \cos(\tfrac{1}{4}\pi t), & -4 \le t \le 4 \\ 0, & t \text{ elsewhere} \end{cases}$$

   Are the three orthonormal functions a complete orthonormal set?

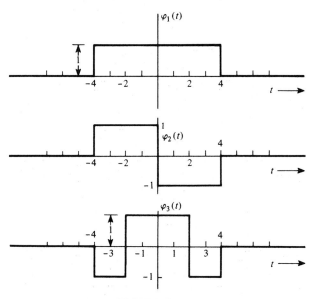

FIGURE P2-50

2-51 Show that the quadrature Fourier series basis functions, $\cos n\omega_0 t$ and $\sin n\omega_0 t$ as given in (2-89), are orthogonal over the interval $a < t < a + T_0$ where $\omega_0 = 2\pi/T_0$.

2-52 Find expressions for the complex Fourier series coefficients that represent the waveform shown in Fig. P2-52.

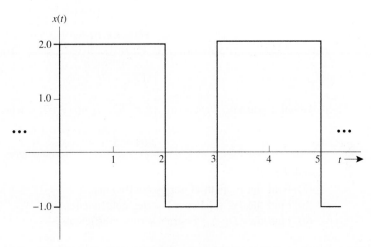

FIGURE P2-52

2-53 Find the complex Fourier series for the periodic waveform given in Figure P2-2.

2-54 Find the complex Fourier series coefficients for the periodic rectangular waveform shown in Fig. P2-54 as a function of A, T, b, and τ_0. [*Hint:* The answer can be reduced to a $(\sin x)/x$ form multiplied by a phase-shift factor, $e^{j\theta_n(\tau_0)}$.]

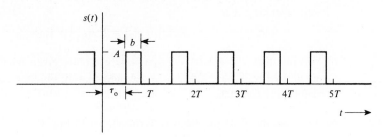

FIGURE P2-54

2-55 For the waveform shown in Fig. P2-55, find:
(a) The complex Fourier series.
(b) The quadrature Fourier series.

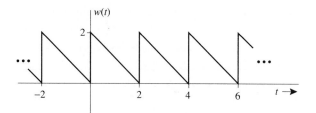

FIGURE P2-55

2-56 Given a periodic waveform $s(t) = \sum_{n=-\infty}^{\infty} p(t - nT_0)$, where

$$p(t) = \begin{cases} At, & 0 < t < T \\ 0, & t \text{ elsewhere} \end{cases}$$

and $T \le T_0$.
   (a) Find the c_n Fourier series coefficients.
   (b) Find the $\{x_n, y_n\}$ Fourier series coefficients.
   (c) Find the $\{D_n, \phi_n\}$ Fourier series coefficients.

2-57 Prove that the polar form of the Fourier series, (2-97), can be obtained by rearranging the terms in the complex Fourier series, (2-82).

2-58 Prove that (2-87) is correct.

2-59 Verify the relationships between the Fourier coefficients c_n, a_n, b_n, D_n, and ϕ_n as given by (2-95), (2-96), (2-98), (2-99), (2-100), and (2-101).

2-60 Let two complex numbers c_1 and c_2 be represented by $c_1 = x_1 + jy_1$ and $c_2 = x_2 + jy_2$, where x_1, x_2, y_1, and y_2 are real numbers. Show that Re$\{\cdot\}$ is a linear operator by demonstrating that

$$\text{Re}\{c_1 + c_2\} = \text{Re}\{c_1\} + \text{Re}\{c_2\}$$

2-61 Assume that $y(t) = s_1(t) + 2s_2(t)$, where $s_1(t)$ is given by Fig. P2-45 and $s_2(t)$ is given by Fig. P2-54. $T = 3$, $b = 1.5$, and $\tau_0 = 0$. Find the complex Fourier coefficients $\{c_n\}$ for $y(t)$.

2-62 Evaluate the PSD for the waveform shown in Fig. P2-2.

2-63 Assume that $v(t)$ is a triangular waveform, as shown in Fig. P2-63.
   (a) Find the complex Fourier series for $v(t)$.
   (b) Calculate the normalized average power.
   (c) Calculate and plot the voltage spectrum.
   (d) Calculate and plot the PSD.

FIGURE P2-63

2-64 Calculate and plot the PSD for the half-wave rectified sinusoid described by P2-4.

2-65 Let a complex number c be represented by $c = x + jy$ where x and y are real numbers. Show that:

(a) $\mathrm{Re}\{c\} = \frac{1}{2}c + \frac{1}{2}c^*$.

(b) $\mathrm{Im}\{c\} = \dfrac{1}{2j}\,c - \dfrac{1}{2j}\,c^*$.

where c^* is the complex conjugate of c. Note that when $c = e^{jz}$, (a) gives the definition of cos z and (b) gives the definition of sin z.

2-66 The basic definitions for sine and cosine waves are

$$\sin z_1 \;\overset{\triangle}{=}\; \frac{e^{jz_1} - e^{-jz_1}}{2j} \quad \text{and} \quad \cos z_2 \;\overset{\triangle}{=}\; \frac{e^{jz_2} + e^{-jz_2}}{2}$$

Show that:

(a) $\cos z_1 \cos z_2 = \frac{1}{2}\cos(z_1 - z_2) + \frac{1}{2}\cos(z_1 + z_2)$.

(b) $\sin z_1 \sin z_2 = \frac{1}{2}\cos(z_1 - z_2) - \frac{1}{2}\cos(z_1 + z_2)$.

(c) $\sin z_1 \cos z_2 = \frac{1}{2}\sin(z_1 - z_2) + \frac{1}{2}\sin(z_1 + z_2)$.

2-67 Let two complex numbers c_1 and c_2 be represented by $c_1 = x_1 + jy_1$ and $c_2 = x_2 + jy_2$, where x_1, x_2, y_1, and y_2 are real numbers. Show that

$$\mathrm{Re}\{c_1\}\,\mathrm{Re}\{c_2\} = \tfrac{1}{2}\mathrm{Re}\{c_1 c_2^*\} + \tfrac{1}{2}\mathrm{Re}\{c_1 c_2\}$$

Note that this is a generalization of the cos z_1 cos z_2 identity of Prob. 2-66, where for the cos z_1 cos z_2 identity, $c_1 = e^{jz_1}$ and $c_2 = e^{jz_2}$.

3

Linear Systems and Digital Signaling

In this chapter we describe (1) the effects of linear filters on signals and noise, (2) how bandlimited signals can be described and reproduced by using their sample values, (3) the representation of digital signals, (4) the use of the discrete Fourier transform (DFT), and (5) bandwidth measures for signals and noise. All of these topics are important for analysis and design of communication systems.

3-1 Linear Time-Invariant Filters and Systems

An electronic filter or system is *linear* when *superposition* holds. That is,

$$y(t) = \mathscr{L}[a_1 x_1(t) + a_2 x_2(t)] = a_1 \mathscr{L}[x_1(t)] + a_2 \mathscr{L}[x_2(t)] \tag{3-1}$$

where $y(t)$ is the output and $x(t)$ is the input as shown in Fig. 3-1. $\mathscr{L}[\cdot]$ denotes the linear (differential equation) system operator acting on $[\cdot]$. The system is said to be time invariant if, for any delayed input $x(t - t_0)$, the output is just delayed by the same amount $y(t - t_0)$. That is, the *shape* of the response is the same no matter when the input is applied to the system.

A detailed discussion of the theory and practice of linear systems is beyond the scope of this book. That would require a book in itself [Irwin, 1984, 1987, or 1993]. However, some basic ideas that are especially relevant to communication problems are reviewed here.

FIGURE 3-1 Linear system.

3-2 Impulse Response

The linear time-invariant filter or system is described by a linear ordinary differential equation with constant coefficients and may be characterized by its impulse response, $h(t)$. The *impulse response* is the solution to the differential equation when the forcing function is a Dirac delta function. That is, $y(t) = h(t)$ when $x(t) = \delta(t)$. In physical networks the impulse response has to be *causal*. That is, $h(t) = 0$ for $t < 0$.[†]

This impulse response for the system may be used to obtain the system output when the input is *not* an impulse. In this case, a general waveform at the input may be approximated by[‡]

$$x(t) = \sum_{n=0}^{\infty} x(n \, \Delta t)[\delta(t - n \, \Delta t)] \, \Delta t \tag{3-2}$$

which indicates that samples of the input are taken at Δt-second intervals. Then using the time-invariant and superposition properties, the output is approximately

$$y(t) = \sum_{n=0}^{\infty} x(n \, \Delta t)[h(t - n \, \Delta t)] \, \Delta t \tag{3-3}$$

This expression becomes the exact result as Δt becomes zero. Letting $n \, \Delta t = \lambda$, we obtain

$$y(t) = \int_{-\infty}^{\infty} x(\lambda)h(t - \lambda) \, d\lambda \equiv x(t) * h(t) \tag{3-4}$$

An integral of this type is called the *convolution* operation, as first described by (2-62) in Sec. 2-2. That is, the output waveform for a time-invariant network can be obtained by

---

[†]The Paley–Wiener criterion gives the frequency domain equivalence for the causality condition of the time domain. It is that $H(f)$ must satisfy the condition

$$\int_{-\infty}^{\infty} \frac{|\ln |H(f)| \,|}{1 + f^2} \, df < \infty$$

[‡]Δt corresponds to dx of (2-47).

convolving the input waveform with the impulse response for the system. Consequently, the impulse response can be used to characterize the response of the system in the time domain (see Fig. 3-1).

3-3　Transfer Function

The spectrum of the output signal is obtained by taking the Fourier transform of both sides of (3-4). Using the convolution theorem of Table 2-1, we get

$$Y(f) = X(f)H(f) \tag{3-5}$$

or

$$H(f) = \frac{Y(f)}{X(f)} \tag{3-6}$$

where $H(f) = \mathcal{F}[h(t)]$ is said to be the *transfer function* or *frequency response* of the network. That is, the impulse response and frequency response are a Fourier transform pair:

$$h(t) \leftrightarrow H(f)$$

Of course, the transfer function $H(f)$ is, in general, a complex quantity and can be written in polar form

$$H(f) = |H(f)|e^{j\underline{/H(f)}} \tag{3-7}$$

where $|H(f)|$ is the *amplitude* (or *magnitude*) response and

$$\theta(f) = \underline{/H(f)} = \tan^{-1}\left[\frac{\text{Im}\{H(f)\}}{\text{Re}\{H(f)\}}\right] \tag{3-8}$$

is the phase response of the network. Furthermore, since $h(t)$ is a real function of time (for real networks), it follows from (2-38) and (2-39) that $|H(f)|$ is an even function of frequency and $\underline{/H(f)}$ is an odd function of frequency.

The transfer function of a linear time-invariant network can be measured by using a sinusoidal testing signal (that is swept over the frequency of interest) since the spectrum of a sinusoid is a line at the frequency under test. For example, if

$$x(t) = A \cos \omega_0 t$$

then the output of the network will be

$$y(t) = A|H(f_0)| \cos\left[\omega_0 t + \underline{/H(f_0)}\right] \tag{3-9}$$

where the amplitude and phase may be evaluated on an oscilloscope or by the use of a vector voltmeter.

If the input to the network is a periodic signal with a spectrum given by

$$X(f) = \sum_{n=-\infty}^{n=\infty} c_n \, \delta(f - nf_0) \tag{3-10}$$

where, using (2-103), $\{c_n\}$ are the complex Fourier coefficients of the input signal, the spectrum of the periodic output signal, using (3-5), is

$$Y(f) = \sum_{n=-\infty}^{n=\infty} c_n H(nf_0)\, \delta(f - nf_0) \tag{3-11}$$

We can also obtain the relationship between the power spectral density (PSD) at the input, $\mathcal{P}_x(f)$, and the output, $\mathcal{P}_y(f)$ of a linear time-invariant network. From (2-66) we know that

$$\mathcal{P}_y(f) = \lim_{T \to \infty} \frac{1}{T} |Y_T(f)|^2 \tag{3-12}$$

Using (3-5) in a formal sense, we obtain

$$\mathcal{P}_y(f) = |H(f)|^2 \lim_{T \to \infty} \frac{1}{T} |X_T(f)|^2$$

or

$$\mathcal{P}_y(f) = |H(f)|^2 \mathcal{P}_x(f) \tag{3-13}$$

Consequently, the *power transfer function* of the network is

$$G_h(f) = \frac{\mathcal{P}_y(f)}{\mathcal{P}_x(f)} = |H(f)|^2 \tag{3-14}$$

Example 3-1 *RC* Low-Pass Filter

An *RC* low-pass filter is shown in Fig. 3-2, where $x(t)$ and $y(t)$ denote the input and output voltage waveforms, respectively. Using Kirchhoff's law for the sum of voltages around a loop, we get

$$x(t) = Ri(t) + y(t)$$

where $i(t) = C\, dy(t)/dt$ or

$$RC \frac{dy}{dt} + y(t) = x(t) \tag{3-15}$$

Using Table 2-1, we find that the Fourier transform of this differential equation is

$$RC(j2\pi f)Y(f) + Y(f) = X(f)$$

Thus the transfer function for this network is

$$H(f) = \frac{Y(f)}{X(f)} = \frac{1}{1 + j(2\pi RC)f} \tag{3-16}$$

(a) RC Low–Pass Filter

(b) Impulse Response

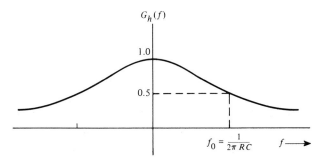

(c) Power Transfer Function

FIGURE 3-2 Characteristics of an *RC* low-pass filter.

Using the Fourier transform Table 2-2, we obtain the impulse response

$$h(t) = \begin{cases} \dfrac{1}{\tau_0}\, e^{-t/\tau_0}, & t \geq 0 \\ 0, & t < 0 \end{cases} \tag{3-17}$$

where $\tau_0 = RC$ is called the *time constant*. When we combine (3-14) and (3-16), the power transfer function is

$$G_h(f) = |H(f)|^2 = \frac{1}{1 + (f/f_0)^2} \tag{3-18}$$

where $f_0 = 1/(2\pi RC)$.

The impulse response and the power transfer function are shown in Fig. 3-2. Note that the value of the power gain at $f = f_0$ (called the *corner frequency*) is $G_h(f_0) = \frac{1}{2}$. That is, the frequency component in the output waveform at $f = f_0$ is attenuated by 3 dB as compared to that at $f = 0$. Consequently, $f = f_0$ is said to be the 3-dB bandwidth of this filter. The topic of bandwidth is discussed in more detail in Sec. 3-7.

3-4 Distortionless Transmission

In communication systems a *distortionless channel* is often desired. This implies that the channel output is just proportional to a delayed version of the input

$$y(t) = Ax(t - T_d) \tag{3-19}$$

where A is the gain (which may be less than 1) and T_d is the delay.

The corresponding requirement in the frequency-domain specification is obtained by taking the Fourier transform of both sides of (3-19).

$$Y(f) = AX(f)e^{-j2\pi f T_d}$$

Thus, for distortionless transmission, we require that the transfer function of the channel be given by

$$H(f) = \frac{Y(f)}{X(f)} = Ae^{-j2\pi f T_d} \tag{3-20}$$

This implies that for no distortion at the output of a linear time-invariant system, two requirements must be satisfied:

1. The amplitude response is flat. That is,

$$|H(f)| = \text{constant} = A \tag{3-21a}$$

2. The phase response is a *linear* function of frequency. That is,

$$\theta(f) = \underline{/H(f)} = -2\pi f T_d \tag{3-21b}$$

When the first condition is satisfied, it is said that there is no *amplitude distortion*. When the second condition is satisfied, there is no *phase distortion*. For distortionless transmission both conditions must be satisfied.

The second requirement is often specified in an equivalent way using the time delay. Define the *time delay* of the system by

$$T_d(f) = -\frac{1}{2\pi f}\,\theta(f) = -\frac{1}{2\pi f}\,\underline{/H(f)} \tag{3-22}$$

By (3-20), it is required that

$$T_d(f) = \text{constant} \tag{3-23}$$

for distortionless transmission. If $T_d(f)$ is not a constant as a function of frequency, there is phase distortion because the phase response, $\theta(f)$, is not a linear function of frequency.

Example 3-2   Distortion Caused by a Filter

Let us examine the distortion effect caused by the RC low-pass filter studied in Example 3-1. From (3-16) the amplitude response is

$$|H(f)| = \frac{1}{\sqrt{1 + (f/f_0)^2}} \tag{3-24}$$

and the phase response is

$$\theta(f) = \underline{/H(f)} = -\tan^{-1}(f/f_0) \tag{3-25}$$

The corresponding time delay function is

$$T_d(f) = \frac{1}{2\pi f} \tan^{-1}(f/f_0) \tag{3-26}$$

These results are plotted in Fig. 3-3, as indicated by the solid lines. Obviously, this filter will produce some distortion since (3-21a) and (3-21b) are not satisfied. The dashed lines give the equivalent results for the distortionless filter. Several observations can be made. First, if the signals involved have spectral components at frequencies below $0.5f_0$, the filter will provide almost distortionless transmission since the error in the magnitude response (with respect to the distortionless case) is less than 0.5 dB and the error in the phase is less than 2.1° (8%). For $f < f_0$, the magnitude error is less than 3 dB and the phase error is less than 12.3° (27%). In engineering practice, this type of error is often considered to be tolerable. Waveforms with spectral components below $0.50f_0$ would be delayed by $1/(2\pi f_0)$ seconds. That is, if the cutoff frequency of the filter was $f_0 = 1$ kHz, the delay would be 0.2 msec. For wideband signals the higher-frequency components would be delayed less than the lower-frequency components.

The distortion effects discussed previously were based on the assumption that the system was linear and time invariant. A linear time-invariant system will produce amplitude distortion if the amplitude response is not flat and it will produce phase (i.e., time delay) distortion if the phase response is not a linear function of frequency. Moreover, if the system is nonlinear and/or time varying, other types of distortion will be produced. As a result, there are new frequency components at the output that are not present at the input. In some communication applications, these new frequencies are actually a desired result. The reader is referred to Sec. 5-3 for a study of these effects.

3-5 Bandlimited Signals and Noise

Often, we deal with signal and noise waveforms that may be considered to be *bandlimited,* which implies that their spectra are nonzero only within a certain frequency band. In this

(a) Magnitude Response

(b) Phase Response

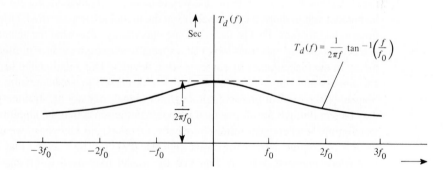

(c) Time Delay

FIGURE 3-3 Distortion caused by an *RC* low-pass filter.

case we can apply some very powerful theorems, namely, the sampling theorem to process the waveform. As we will show, these ideas are *especially applicable to digital communication* problems.

First, we examine some properties of bandlimited signals. Then the sampling and dimensionality theorems are developed.

Bandlimited Waveforms

DEFINITION: A waveform $w(t)$ is said to be (absolutely) *bandlimited* to B hertz if

$$W(f) = \mathscr{F}[w(t)] = 0 \qquad \text{for } |f| \geq B \qquad (3\text{-}27)$$

DEFINITION: A waveform $w(t)$ is (absolutely) *time limited* if

$$w(t) = 0 \qquad \text{for } |t| > T \qquad (3\text{-}28)$$

Theorem

An absolutely bandlimited waveform cannot be absolutely time limited, and vice versa.

The result of this theorem is illustrated by examining the spectrum for the rectangular pulse waveform of Example 2-5. This time-limited waveform is shown to have a spectrum that is not bandlimited. A relatively simple proof of this theorem can be obtained by contradiction [Wozencraft and Jacobs, 1965].

This theorem raises an engineering paradox. If we observe that a waveform is bandlimited, for example, by viewing its spectrum on a spectrum analyzer, the waveform cannot be time limited. However, we believe that this physical waveform *is* time limited because the device that generates the waveform was built at some finite past time and the device will decay at some future time (thus producing a time-limited waveform). This paradox is resolved by realizing that we are modeling a physical process with a mathematical model and perhaps the assumptions in the model are not satisfied, although we believe them to be satisfied. That is, there is some uncertainty as to what the actual time waveform and corresponding spectrum look like, especially at extreme values of time and frequency, owing to the inaccuracies of our measuring devices. This relationship between the physical process and our mathematical model is discussed in an interesting paper by David Slepian [1976]. In our problem, although the signal may not be absolutely bandlimited, it may be bandlimited for all practical purposes in the sense that the amplitude spectrum has a negligible level above a certain frequency. Of course, as engineers, we use mathematical models to help us predict the correct results. It should be realized that as measurement techniques improve, we may find that the model may need to be changed in order to predict what we perceive to be the correct answer. In short, common sense has to be used in formulating the mathematical model and interpreting the correct result.

Another interesting theorem states that if $w(t)$ is absolutely *bandlimited,* it is an *analytic* function. An analytic function is a function that possesses finite valued derivatives when they are evaluated for any finite value of t. This makes common sense. That is, a bandlimited function will not have frequency components above B hertz; consequently, the values of the function cannot fluctuate too rapidly as a function of time. This theorem may be proved by using a Taylor series expansion [Wozencraft and Jacobs, 1965].

Sampling Theorem

As indicated earlier, the sampling theorem is certainly one of the most useful theorems since it applies to digital communication systems, which are proliferating constantly. The sampling theorem is another application of an orthogonal series expansion.

Sampling Theorem

Any physical waveform may be represented over the interval $-\infty < t < \infty$ by

$$w(t) = \sum_{n=-\infty}^{n=\infty} a_n \frac{\sin\{\pi f_s[t - (n/f_s)]\}}{\pi f_s[t - (n/f_s)]} \tag{3-29}$$

where

$$a_n = f_s \int_{-\infty}^{\infty} w(t) \frac{\sin\{\pi f_s[t - (n/f_s)]\}}{\pi f_s[t - (n/f_s)]} \, dt \tag{3-30}$$

and f_s is a parameter that is assigned some convenient value greater than zero. Furthermore, if $w(t)$ is bandlimited to B hertz and $f_s \geq 2B$, then (3-29) becomes the sampling function representation, where

$$a_n = w(n/f_s) \tag{3-31}$$

That is, for $f_s \geq 2B$, the orthogonal series coefficients are simply the values of the waveform that are obtained when the waveform is sampled every $1/f_s$ seconds.

The series given by (3-29) and (3-31) is sometimes called the *cardinal series*. It has been known by mathematicians since at least 1915 [Whittaker, 1915] and to engineers since the pioneering work of Shannon, who connected this series with information theory [Shannon, 1949]. An excellent tutorial paper on this topic has been published in the *Proceedings of the IEEE* [Jerri, 1977].

PROOF.   We need to show that

$$\varphi_n(t) = \frac{\sin\{\pi f_s[t - (n/f_s)]\}}{\pi f_s[t - (n/f_s)]} \tag{3-32}$$

form a set of the orthogonal functions. From (2-74) we need to demonstrate that (3-32) satisfies

$$\int_{-\infty}^{\infty} \varphi_n(t)\varphi_m^*(t) \, dt = K_n \delta_{nm} \tag{3-33}$$

Using Parseval's theorem, (2-40), we see that the left side becomes

$$\int_{-\infty}^{\infty} \varphi_n(t)\varphi_m^*(t) \, dt = \int_{-\infty}^{\infty} \Phi_n(f)\Phi_m^*(f) \, df \tag{3-34}$$

where

$$\Phi_n(f) = \mathcal{F}[\varphi_n(t)] = \frac{1}{f_s} \, \Pi\left(\frac{f}{f_s}\right) e^{-j2\pi(nf/f_s)} \tag{3-35}$$

We have

$$\int_{-\infty}^{\infty} \varphi_n(t)\varphi_m^*(t) \, dt = \frac{1}{(f_s)^2} \int_{-\infty}^{\infty} \left[\Pi\left(\frac{f}{f_s}\right)\right]^2 e^{-j2\pi(n-m)f/f_s} \, df$$

$$= \frac{1}{(f_s)^2} \int_{-f_s/2}^{f_s/2} e^{-j2\pi(n-m)(f/f_s)} \, df = \frac{1}{f_s} \, \delta_{nm} \tag{3-36}$$

Thus $\varphi_n(t)$ as given by (3-32) are orthogonal functions with $K_n = 1/f_s$. Using (2-78), we see that (3-30) follows. Furthermore, we will show that (3-31) follows for the case of $w(t)$ being absolutely bandlimited to B hertz with $f_s \geq 2B$. Using (2-78) and Parseval's theorem, (2-40), we get

$$a_n = f_s \int_{-\infty}^{\infty} w(t)\varphi_n^*(t) \, dt$$

$$= f_s \int_{-\infty}^{\infty} W(f) \, \Phi_n^*(f) \, df \tag{3-37}$$

Substituting (3-35) yields

$$a_n = \int_{-f_s/2}^{f_s/2} W(f)e^{j2\pi f(n/f_s)} \, df \tag{3-38}$$

But since $W(f)$ is zero for $|f| > B$, where $B \leq f_s/2$, the limits on the integral may be extended to $(-\infty,\infty)$ without changing the value of the integral. This integral with infinite limits is just the inverse Fourier transform of $W(f)$ evaluated at $t = n/f_s$. Thus $a_n = w(n/f_s)$, which is (3-31). ∎

From (3-38) it is obvious that the minimum sampling rate allowed to reconstruct a bandlimited waveform without error is given by

$$(f_s)_{\min} = 2B \tag{3-39}$$

This is called the *Nyquist frequency*.

Since this sampling theorem is a special case of an orthogonal series expansion, orthogonal series properties hold such as describing the waveform by the use of an N-dimensional vector and the corresponding relationship for the energy of the waveform over a T_0-second interval in terms of the square of the elements for that vector.

For example, let us now examine the problem of reproducing a bandlimited waveform by using N sample values. Suppose that we are interested in reproducing the waveform over a T_0-second interval as shown in Fig. 3-4a. Then we can truncate the sampling function series of (3-29) so that we include only N of the $\varphi_n(t)$ functions that have their peaks within the T_0 interval of interest. That is, the waveform can be approximately reconstructed using N samples:

$$w(t) \approx \sum_{n=n_1}^{n=n_1+N} a_n\varphi_n(t) \tag{3-40}$$

(a) Waveform and Sample Values

(b) Waveform Reconstructed from Sample Values

FIGURE 3-4 Sampling theorem.

where the $\{\varphi_n(t)\}$ are described by (3-32). Figure 3-4b shows the reconstructed waveform (solid line) which is obtained by the weighted sum of time-delayed $(\sin x)/x$ waveforms (dashed lines), where the weights are the sample values, $a_n = w(n/f_s)$, denoted by the dots. The waveform is bandlimited to B hertz with the sampling frequency $f_s \geq 2B$. The sample values may be saved, for example, in the memory of a digital computer, so that the waveform may be reconstructed at a later time or the values may be transmitted over a communication system for waveform reconstruction at the receiving end. In either case, the waveform may be reconstructed from the sample values by the use of the equation above. That is, each sample value is multiplied by the appropriate $(\sin x)/x$ function, and these weighted $(\sin x)/x$ functions are summed to give the original waveform. This procedure is illustrated in Fig. 3-4b. The minimum number of sample values that are needed for waveform reconstruction is

$$N = \frac{T_0}{1/f_s} = f_s T_0 \geq 2BT_0 \tag{3-41}$$

and there are N orthogonal functions in the reconstruction algorithm.

Impulse Sampling

If one wants to reconstruct a waveform on a real-time basis, an alternative approach, called *impulse sampling*, is often used. The waveform is sampled with a unit-weight impulse train. This is accomplished by multiplying the waveform with a unit-weight impulse train. The resulting sampled waveform is

$$w_s(t) = w(t) \sum_{n=-\infty}^{\infty} \delta(t - nT_s)$$

$$= \sum_{n=-\infty}^{\infty} w(nT_s) \, \delta(t - nT_s) \tag{3-42}$$

where $T_s = 1/f_s$. This situation is illustrated in Fig. 3-5.[†] In the figure the weight (area) of each impulse, $w(nT_s)$, is indicated by the height. The spectrum for the impulse sampled waveform, $w_s(t)$, can be evaluated by substituting the Fourier series of the (periodic) impulse train into (3-42).

$$w_s(t) = w(t) \sum_{n=-\infty}^{\infty} \frac{1}{T_s} e^{jn\omega_s t} \tag{3-43}$$

Taking the Fourier transform of both sides of this equation, we get

$$W_s(f) = \frac{1}{T_s} W(f) * \mathscr{F}\left[\sum_{n=-\infty}^{\infty} e^{jn\omega_s t} \right] = \frac{1}{T_s} W(f) * \sum_{n=-\infty}^{\infty} \mathscr{F}[e^{jn\omega_s t}]$$

$$= \frac{1}{T_s} W(f) * \sum_{n=-\infty}^{\infty} \delta(f - nf_s) \tag{3-44}$$

[†]For illustrative purposes, assume that $W(f)$ is real.

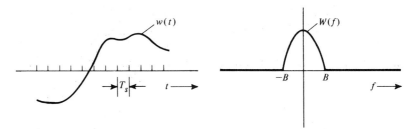

(a) Waveform and Its Spectrum

(b) Impulse Sampled Waveform and Its Spectrum ($f_s > 2B$)

FIGURE 3-5 Impulse sampling.

or

$$W_s(f) = \frac{1}{T_s} \sum_{n=-\infty}^{\infty} W(f - nf_s) \qquad (3\text{-}45)$$

The spectrum of the impulse sampled waveform consists of the spectrum of the unsampled waveform that is replicated every f_s hertz.[†] This is shown in Fig. 3-5b. Note that this technique of impulse sampling may be used to translate the spectrum of a signal to another frequency band that is centered on some harmonic of the sampling frequency. A more general circuit that can translate the spectrum to any desired frequency band is called a mixer. Mixers are discussed in Sec. 5-3.

If $f_s \geq 2B$, as illustrated in Fig. 3-5, the replicated spectra do not overlap and the original spectrum can be regenerated by chopping $W_s(f)$ off above $f_s/2$. Thus $w(t)$ can be reproduced from $w_s(t)$ by simply passing $w_s(t)$ through an ideal low-pass filter that has a cutoff frequency of $f_c = f_s/2$ where $f_s \geq 2B$.

If $f_s < 2B$ (i.e., the waveform is undersampled), the spectrum of $w_s(t)$ will consist of overlapped, replicated spectra of $w(t)$, as illustrated in Fig. 3-6.[‡] The spectral overlap or

[†] In Chapter 4 this result is generalized to that of instantaneous sampling with a pulse train consisting of pulses with finite width and arbitrary shape (instead of impulses). The resulting spectrum is given by (4-10).

[‡] For illustrative purposes, assume that $W(f)$ is real.

(a) Spectrum of Unsampled Waveform

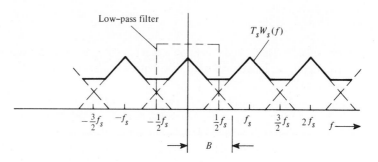

(b) Spectrum of Impulse Sampled Waveforn $(f_s < 2B)$

FIGURE 3-6 Undersampling and aliasing.

tail inversion is called *aliasing* or *spectral folding*.[†] In this case, the low-pass filtered version of $w_s(t)$ will not be exactly $w(t)$. The recovered $w(t)$ will be distorted because of the aliasing. The alias distortion can be eliminated by *prefiltering* the original $w(t)$ before sampling so that the prefiltered $w(t)$ has no spectral components above $|f| = f_s/2$. The prefiltering still produces distortion on the recovered waveform because the prefilter chops off the spectrum of the original $w(t)$ above $f = f_s/2$. However, from Fig. 3-6, it can be shown that if a prefilter is used, the recovered waveform obtained from the low-pass version of the sample signal will have one-half of the error energy compared to the error energy that would be obtained without using the presampling filter.

A physical waveform, $w(t)$, has finite energy. From (2-42) and (2-43) it follows that the magnitude spectrum of the waveform, $|W(f)|$, has to be negligible for $|f| > B$ where B is an appropriately chosen positive number. Consequently, from a practical standpoint, the physical waveform is essentially bandlimited to B Hz where B is chosen to be large enough so that the error energy is below some specified amount.

Dimensionality Theorem

The sampling theorem may be restated in a more general way called the *dimensionality theorem*.

Theorem

A real waveform may be completely specified by

$$N = 2BT_0 \tag{3-46}$$

independent pieces of information that will describe the waveform over a T_0 interval. N is said to be the number of dimensions required to specify the waveform, and B is the absolute bandwidth of the waveform.

The N sample values do not necessarily have to be periodic samples; they just have to be independent quantities. This can be demonstrated for the case of nonperiodic sampling by use of the complex Fourier series. We will represent the real $w(t)$ over a T_0-second interval by the Fourier series

$$w(t) = \sum_n c_n e^{jn\omega_0 t}$$

where $\omega_0 = 2\pi/T_0$, and it is known that $c_n^* = c_{-n}$ for any real signal. If $w(t)$ is bandlimited to B hertz, the range of n needed to represent $w(t)$ is $-B \le nf_0 \le B$, and since $f_0 = 1/T_0$, we have[‡]

$$w(t) = \sum_{n=-BT_0}^{n=BT_0} c_n e^{jn\omega_0 t}$$

[†] $f_s/2$ is the folding frequency where f_s is the sampling frequency. For no aliasing, $f_s > 2B$ is required, where $2B$ is the Nyquist frequency.

[‡] Actually, for $-B \le nf_0 \le B$ to hold with equality, we need an integer multiple of f_0 equal to B (which may be any real positive number). Thus, in general, T_0 needs to be large.

The c_0 term is the dc level for $w(t)$, and a dc level does not impart any information (see Chapter 1). Since $c_n = |c_n| e^{j\angle c_n}$ and $c_{-n} = c_n^*$, there are $N = 2BT_0$ independent (real) values required. Note that the c_n's in this example are not time samples of $w(t)$, and each c_n depends on the waveshape of $w(t)$ over the whole T_0 interval, as seen from (2-83).

The dimensionality theorem, (3-46), says simply that the information that can be conveyed by a bandlimited waveform or a bandlimited communication system is proportional to the product of the bandwidth of that system and the time allowed for transmission of the information. The *dimensionality theorem has profound implications in the design and performance of all types of communication systems*. For example, in radar systems it is well known that the time–bandwidth product of the received signal needs to be large for superior performance.

There are *two distinct ways in which the dimensionality theorem can be applied. First,* if any bandlimited waveform is given and we want to store some numbers in a table (or a computer memory bank) that could be used to reconstruct the waveform over a T_0-second interval, *at least N* numbers must be stored and, furthermore, the average sampling rate must be at least the Nyquist rate. That is,[†]

$$f_s \geq 2B \qquad (3\text{-}47)$$

Thus, in this first type of application, the dimensionality theorem is used to calculate the number of storage locations (amount of memory) required to represent a waveform.

The *second* type of application is the inverse type of problem. Here the dimensionality theorem is used to give a lower bound for the bandwidth of waveforms for digital signals. This is discussed in some detail in the next section for the cases of binary digital signals and multilevel digital signals.

3-6 Digital Signaling

The voltage (or current) waveforms for digital signals can be expressed as an orthogonal series with a finite number of terms, N. That is, the waveform can be written as

$$w(t) = \sum_{k=1}^{N} w_k \varphi_k(t), \qquad 0 < t < T_0 \qquad (3\text{-}48)$$

where w_k represents the digital data and $\varphi_k(t)$, $k = 1, 2, \ldots, N$, are N orthogonal functions that help give the waveform its waveshape. (This will be illustrated by examples that follow in the sections on binary waveforms and multilevel waveforms.) As described previously, *N is the number of dimensions* required to describe the waveform. The term *dimension* arises from the geometric interpretation as described in the next section, "Vector Representation." The waveform $w(t)$ as given by (3-48) can be used to represent any message of the M-message digital source, where each message is assigned a unique set of digital data $\{w_k\}$, $k = 1, 2, \ldots, N$, to represent that message. For example, for a binary

---

[†] If the spectrum of the waveform being sampled has a line at $f = \pm B$, there is some ambiguity as to whether or not the line is included within bandwidth B. The line is included by letting $f_s > 2B$ (i.e., dropping the equality sign).

source consisting of an ASCII computer keyboard, the letter X is assigned the code word 0001101. (See App. C, Table C-5.) Thus, in this case, $w_1 = 0$, $w_2 = 0$, $w_3 = 0$, $w_4 = 1$, $w_5 = 1$, $w_6 = 0$, $w_7 = 1$, *and N = 7*. If this message (i.e., the letter X) is sent out over a time interval of T_0 seconds, the voltage (or current waveform) representing this message, as described by (3-48), would have a time span of T_0 seconds and the data rate could be computed using the following definitions:

DEFINITION: The *baud (symbol rate) is*[†]

$$D = N/T_0 \qquad \text{symbols/sec} \tag{3-49}$$

where N is the number of dimensions used in T_0 seconds.

DEFINITION: The *bit rate* is

$$R = n/T_0 \qquad \text{bits/sec} \tag{3-50}$$

where n is the number of data bits sent in T_0 seconds. For the case when the w_k's have binary values, $n = N$, and $w(t)$ is said to be a *binary signal*. When the w_k's are assigned more than two possible values (i.e., not binary) $w(t)$ is said to be a *multilevel signal*. These two types of signaling are discussed in separate sections below.

A critical question is: If the waveform of (3-48) is transmitted over a channel and appears at the input to the receiver, how can a receiver be built to detect the data? Since $w(t)$ is an orthogonal series, the formal way to detect the data is for the receiver to evaluate the orthogonal series coefficient. That is, using (2-8), we have

$$w_k = \frac{1}{K_k} \int_0^{T_0} w(t)\varphi_k^*(t) \, dt, \qquad k = 1, 2, \ldots, N \tag{3-51}$$

where $w(t)$ is the waveform at the receiver input and $\varphi_k(t)$ is the known orthogonal function that was used to generate the received waveform. It can also be shown that (3-51) is the optimum way to detect data when the received signal is corrupted by white additive noise; this procedure is called *matched filter* detection using correlation processing [Couch, 1993, Chap. 6]. Detection of data is illustrated in Examples 3-4 and 3-5.

Vector Representation

The orthogonal function space representation of (3-48) corresponds to the orthogonal vector space represented by

$$\mathbf{w} = \sum_{j=1}^{N} w_j \boldsymbol{\varphi}_j \tag{3-52a}$$

where the boldface type denotes a vector representing the waveform of (3-48), and $\{\boldsymbol{\varphi}_j\}$ is an orthogonal vector set. $\mathbf{w}$ is an N-dimensional vector in Euclidean vector space, and $\{\boldsymbol{\varphi}_j\}$

[†]In the technical literature, the term *baud rate* instead of baud is sometimes used even though baud rate is a misnomer, since the term *baud*, by definition, is the symbol rate (symbols/sec).

is a set of N directional vectors that become a unit vector set if the K_j's (2-74) are all unity. A shorthand notation for the vector $\mathbf{w}$ of (3-52a) is given by a row vector:

$$\mathbf{w} = (w_1, w_2, w_3, \ldots, w_N) \tag{3-52b}$$

Example 3-3   Vector Representation of a Binary Signal

Examine the representation for the waveform of a 3-bit (binary) signal shown in Fig. 3-7a. This signal could be represented directly by

$$s(t) = \sum_{j=1}^{N=3} d_j p[t - (j - \tfrac{1}{2})T] = \sum_{j=1}^{N=3} d_j p_j(t) \tag{3-53}$$

where $p(t)$ is shown in Fig. 3-7b and $p_j(t) \triangleq p[t - (j - \tfrac{1}{2})T]$.

The $\{p_j(t)\}$ is a set of orthogonal functions that are not normalized.

$$\mathbf{d} = (d_1, d_2, d_3) = (1, 0, 1) \tag{3-54}$$

is the binary word with 1 representing a binary 1 and 0 representing a binary 0. $p(t)$ is the pulse shape for each bit.

Using the orthogonal function approach, we can represent the waveform by

$$s(t) = \sum_{j=1}^{N=3} s_j \varphi_j(t) \tag{3-55}$$

Let $\{\varphi_j(t)\}$ be the corresponding set of ortho*normal* functions. Then, using (2-74), we obtain

$$\varphi_j(t) = \frac{p_j(t)}{\sqrt{K_j}} = \frac{p_j(t)}{\sqrt{\int_0^{T_o} p_j^2(t)\, dt}} = \frac{p_j(t)}{\sqrt{25T}} \tag{3-56}$$

or

$$\varphi_j(t) = \begin{cases} \dfrac{1}{\sqrt{T}}, & (j-1)T < t < jT \\[2mm] 0, & t \quad \text{otherwise} \end{cases} \tag{3-57}$$

where $j = 1, 2,$ or 3. Using (2-78) where $a = 0$ and $b = 3T$, we find that the orthonormal series coefficients for the digital signal shown in Fig. 3-7a are

$$\mathbf{s} = (s_1, s_2, s_3) = (5\sqrt{T}, 0, 5\sqrt{T}) \tag{3-58}$$

The vector representation for $s(t)$ is shown in Fig. 3-7d. Note that for this $N = 3$-dimensional case with binary signaling, only $2^3 = 8$ different messages could be represented. Each message would correspond to a vector that terminates on a vertex of a cube.

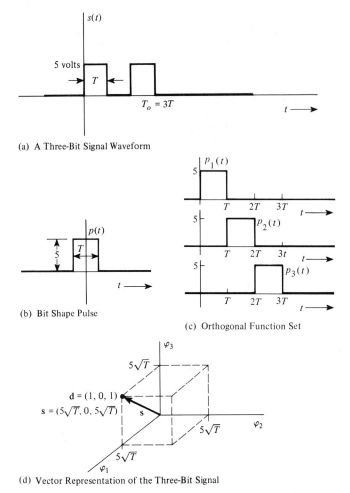

(a) A Three-Bit Signal Waveform

(b) Bit Shape Pulse

(c) Orthogonal Function Set

(d) Vector Representation of the Three-Bit Signal

FIGURE 3-7 Representation for a 3-bit binary digital signal.

Bandwidth Estimation

The lower bound for the bandwidth of the waveform representing the digital signal, (3-48), can be obtained from the dimensionality theorem. Thus, using (3-46) and (3-49), the bandwidth of the waveform $w(t)$ is

$$B \geq \frac{N}{2T_0} = \frac{1}{2}D \qquad hertz \qquad (3\text{-}59)$$

If the $\varphi_k(t)$ are of the $(\sin x)/x$ type, the lower-bound absolute bandwidth of $N/(2T_0) = D/2$ will be achieved; otherwise (i.e., for other pulse shapes), the bandwidth will be larger than this lower bound. Equation (3-59) is very useful for predicting the bandwidth of digital signals, especially when the exact bandwidth of the digital signal is difficult (or impossible) to calculate. This is illustrated in Examples 3-4 and 3-5.

Binary Signaling

A waveform representing a binary signal can be described by the N-dimensional orthogonal series of (3-48) where the orthogonal series coefficients, w_k, take on binary values. More details about binary signaling, including their waveforms, data rate, and waveform bandwidth, are illustrated by the following example.

Example 3-4   Binary Signaling

Let us examine some properties of *binary signaling* from a digital source that can produce $M = 256$ distinctly different messages. Each message could be represented by $n = 8$-bit binary words since $M = 2^n = 2^8 = 256$. Assume that it takes $T_0 = 8$ msec to transmit one message and that a particular message corresponding to the code word 01001110 is to be transmitted. Then $w_1 = 0$, $w_2 = 1$, $w_3 = 0$, $w_4 = 0$, $w_5 = 1$, $w_6 = 1$, $w_7 = 1$, *and* $w_8 = 0$.

CASE 1. RECTANGULAR PULSE ORTHOGONAL FUNCTIONS
Assume that the orthogonal functions $\varphi_k(t)$ are given by unity-amplitude rectangular pulses that are $T_b = T_0/n = 8/8 = 1$ msec wide, where T_b is the time that it takes to send one bit of data. Then, with the use of (3-48) and MathCAD, the resulting waveform transmitted is given by Fig. 3-8a.

The data can be detected at the receiver by evaluation the orthogonal-series coefficients as given by (3-51). For the case of rectangular pulses, this is equivalent to sampling the waveform anywhere within each bit interval.[†] Referring to Fig. 3-8a, it is seen that sampling within each $T_b = 1$-msec interval results in detecting the correct 8-bit data word 01001110.

The bit rate and the baud (symbol rate) of the binary signal are $R = n/T_0$ $= 1$ kbit/sec and $D = N/T_0 = 1$ kbaud since $N = n = 8$ and $T_0 = 8$ msec. That is, the bit rate and the baud rate are equal for binary signaling.

What is the bandwidth for the waveform in Fig. 3-8a? Using (3-59), the lower bound for the bandwidth is $\frac{1}{2}D = 500$ Hz. In Chapter 4 it will be shown that the actual null bandwidth of this binary signal with a rectangular pulse shape is $B = 1/T_s = D = 1000$ Hz. This is larger than the lower bound for the bandwidth, so the question arises: What is the waveshape that gives the lower-bound bandwidth of 500 Hz? The answer, of course, is the $(\sin x)/x$-pulse as described in Case 2.

CASE 2. (SIN X/X) PULSE ORTHOGONAL FUNCTIONS
From an intuitive point of view, we know that the sharp corners of the rectangular pulse need to be rounded to reduce the bandwidth of the waveform. Furthermore, recalling our study with the sampling theorem, (3-29), it is realized that the $(\sin x)/x$ type of pulse shape has the minimum bandwidth.

[†] Sampling detection is optimum only if the received waveform is noise free. See the discussion following (3-51).

t := 0,0.05 ..8   k := 0 ..7   Tb := 1.0   Ts := Tb

$$w := \begin{bmatrix} 0 \\ 1 \\ 0 \\ 0 \\ 1 \\ 1 \\ 1 \\ 0 \end{bmatrix}$$

x := -5·Ts,(-5·Ts + 0.05) ..5·Ts

$$p1(x) := if\left[|x| < \frac{Ts}{2}, 1, 0\right]$$

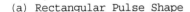

w1(t) := $\sum_k$ w$_k$·p1(t - (k·Ts + 0.5·Ts))

$$p2(x) := if\left[x \neq 0, \frac{\sin\left[\pi·\dfrac{x}{Ts}\right]}{\pi·\dfrac{x}{Ts}}, 1\right]$$

w2(t) := $\sum_k$ w$_k$·p2(t - (k·Ts + 0.5·Ts))

(a) Rectangular Pulse Shape

(b) Sin(x)/x Pulse Shape

FIGURE 3-8 Binary signaling.

Consequently, choose the $\varphi_k(t)$ to be

$$\varphi_k(t) = \frac{\sin\left\{\dfrac{\pi}{T_s}(t - kT_s)\right\}}{\dfrac{\pi}{T_s}(t - kT_s)} \tag{3-60}$$

where $T_s = T_b$ for the case of binary signaling. The resulting waveform that is transmitted is shown in Fig. 3-8b.

Once again, the data can be detected at the receiver by evaluating the orthogonal-series coefficients. Since $(\sin x)/x$ orthogonal functions are used, (3-31) shows that the data can be recovered simply by sampling[†] the received waveform at the midpoint of each symbol interval. Referring to Fig. 3-8b, and sampling at the midpoint of each $T_s = 1$-msec interval, the correct 8-bit word 01001110 is detected.

For Case 2, the bit rate and the baud rate are still $R = 1$ kbit/sec and $D = 1$ kbaud. The absolute bandwidth of (3-60) can be evaluated with the help of Fig. 2-6b, where $2W = 1/T_s$. That is, $B = 1/(2T_s) = 500$Hz. Thus the lower-bound bandwidth (as predicted by the dimensionality theorem) is achieved.

Note that when the rectangular pulse shape is used, as shown in Fig. 3-8a, the digital source information is transmitted via a binary *digital waveform*. That is, the digital signal is a digital waveform. However, when the $(\sin x)/x$ pulse shape is used, as shown in Fig. 3-8b, the digital source information is transmitted via an *analog* waveform (i.e., an infinite number of voltage values ranging between -0.4 and 1.2 V are used). In this case the digital signal is an *analog waveform*.

Multilevel Signaling

In the binary signaling example that was just completed, the lower-bound bandwidth of $B = N/(2T_0)$ was achieved. That is, for Case 2, $N = 8$ pulses were required and gave a bandwidth of 500 Hz for a message duration of $T_0 = 8$ msec. However, this bandwidth could be made smaller if N could be reduced. N (and, consequently, the bandwidth) can be reduced by letting the w_k's of (3-48) take on $L > 2$ possible values (instead of the two possible values that were used for binary signaling). When the w_k's have $L > 2$ possible values, the resulting waveform obtained from (3-48) is called a *multilevel signal*.

Example 3-5 $L = 4$ Multilevel Signal

Here the $M = 256$-message source of Example 3-4 will be encoded into a $L = 4$ multilevel signal and the message will be sent, once again, in $T_0 = 8$ msec.

[†] Sampling detection is optimum only if the received waveform is noise free. See the discussion following (3-51).

FIGURE 3-9 Binary-to-multilevel signal conversion.

Multilevel data can be obtained by encoding the ℓ-bit binary data of the message source into L-level data by using a *digital-to-analog converter* (DAC),[†] as shown in Fig. 3-9. For example, one possible encoding scheme for an $\ell = 2$-bit DAC is shown in Table 3-1. $\ell = 2$ bits are read in at a time to produce an output that is one of $L = 4$ possible levels where $L = 2^{\ell}$. Thus for the binary code word 01001110, the sequence of four-level outputs would be -3, -1, $+3$, $+1$. Consequently, the w_k's of (3-48) would be $w_1 = -3$, $w_2 = -1$, $w_3 = +3$, and $w_4 = +1$, where $N = 4$ dimensions are used. The corresponding $L = 4$ multilevel waveform is shown in Fig. 3-10. Figure 3-10a gives the multilevel waveform when rectangular pulses are used for $\varphi_k(t)$ and Fig. 3-10b gives the multilevel waveform when $(\sin x)/x$ pulses are used. For either case, the receiver could recover the four-level data corresponding to the w_k values by sampling the received waveform at the middle of the $T_s = 2$-msec symbol intervals.[‡]

For these $L = 4$ multilevel signals, the equivalent bit interval is $T_b = 1$ msec since each symbol carries $\ell = 2$ bits of data (i.e., one of $L = 4$ levels as shown in Table 3-1). The bit rate is $R = n/T_0 = \ell/T_s = 1$ kbit/sec (same as for Example 3-4) and the baud rate is $D = N/T_0 = 1/T_s = 0.5$ kbaud (different from Example 3-4). The bit rate and the baud rate are related by

$$R = \ell D \tag{3-61}$$

[†] The term *analog* in *digital-to-analog converter* is a misnomer since the output is an L-level digital signal. However, these devices are called digital-to-analog converters in data manuals.

[‡] Sampling detection is optimum only if the received waveform is noise free. See the discussion following (3-51).

TABLE 3-1 Two-bit Digital-to-Analog Converter

Binary Input ($\ell = 2$ bits)	Output Level (volts)
11	+3
10	+1
00	−1
01	−3

$t := 0, 0.05 \;..8 \qquad k := 0 \;..3 \qquad Tb := 1.0 \qquad Ts := 2 \cdot Tb$

$$w := \begin{bmatrix} -3 \\ -1 \\ 3 \\ 1 \end{bmatrix}$$

$x := -5 \cdot Ts, (-5 \cdot Ts + 0.05) \;..5 \cdot Ts$

$$p1(x) := if\left[|x| < \frac{Ts}{2}, 1, 0\right]$$

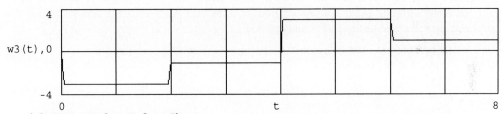

$$w3(t) := \sum_{k} w_k \cdot p1(t - (k \cdot Ts + 0.5 \cdot Ts))$$

$$p2(x) := if\left[x \neq 0, \frac{\sin\left[\pi \cdot \dfrac{x}{Ts}\right]}{\pi \cdot \dfrac{x}{Ts}}, 1\right]$$

$$w4(t) := \sum_{k} w_k \cdot p2(t - (k \cdot Ts + 0.5 \cdot Ts))$$

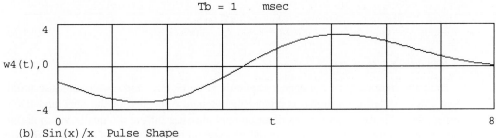

(a) Rectangular Pulse Shape

(b) Sin(x)/x Pulse Shape

FIGURE 3-10 $L = 4$ multilevel signaling.

where $\ell = \log_2(L)$ is the number of bits read in by the DAC on each clock cycle.

The null bandwidth of the rectangular-pulse multilevel waveform (Fig. 3-10a) is $B = 1/T_s = D = 500$ Hz. Using (3-59), the absolute bandwidth of the $(\sin x)/x$-pulse multilevel waveform (Fig. 3-10b) is $B = N/(2T_0) = 1/(2T_s) = D/2 = 250$ Hz. Thus each of these $L = 4$ multilevel waveforms has one-half the bandwidth of the corresponding binary signal (with the same pulse shape). In general, an L-level multilevel signal would have $1/\ell$ the bandwidth of the corresponding binary signal where $\ell = \log_2(L)$. This bandwidth reduction is achieved because the symbol duration of the multilevel signal is ℓ times that of the binary signal. The bit rate, R, of the binary signal is ℓ times the symbol rate of the multilevel signal.

3-7 Discrete Fourier Transform

With the convenience of personal computers and the availability of digital signal processing integrated circuits, the spectrum of a waveform can be easily approximated by using the discrete Fourier transform (DFT). Here we show briefly how the DFT can be used to compute samples of the continuous Fourier transform (CFT), (2-26), and values for the complex Fourier series coefficients (2-83).

DEFINITION: The *discrete Fourier transform* (DFT) is defined by

$$X(n) = \sum_{k=0}^{k=N-1} x(k)e^{-j(2\pi/N)nk} \tag{3-62a}$$

where $n = 0, 1, 2, \ldots, N - 1$, and the *inverse discrete Fourier transform (IDFT)* is defined by

$$x(k) = \frac{1}{N} \sum_{n=0}^{n=N-1} X(n)e^{j(2\pi/N)nk} \tag{3-62b}$$

where $k = 0, 1, 2, \ldots, N - 1$.

Time and frequency do not appear explicitly since (3-62a) and (3-62b) are just definitions implemented on a digital computer to compute N values for the DFT and IDFT, respectively. Please be aware that other authors may use different (equally valid) definitions. For example, a $1/\sqrt{N}$ factor could be used on the right side of (3-62a) if the $1/N$ factor of (3-62b) is replaced by $1/\sqrt{N}$. This produces a different scale factor when the DFT is related to the CFT. Also, the signs of the exponents in (3-62a) and (3-62b) could be exchanged. This would reverse the spectral samples along the frequency axis. In fact, these changes in the definitions are used in the MathCAD fast Fourier transform (FFT) algorithm.[†] Thus the MathCAD FFT algorithms icfft and cfft are related to the definitions of (3-62) by

$$\mathbf{X} = \sqrt{N} \text{ icfft } (\mathbf{x}) \tag{3-63a}$$

and

$$\mathbf{x} = (1/\sqrt{N}) \text{ cfft } (\mathbf{X}) \tag{3-63b}$$

where $\mathbf{x}$ is an N-element array corresponding to samples of the waveform and $\mathbf{X}$ is the N-element DFT array. N is chosen to be a power of 2 (i.e., $N = 2^m$, where m is a positive integer). If other FFT software is used, the user should be aware of the specific definitions that are implemented so that the results can be interpreted properly.

The relationship between the DFT, as defined by (3-62), and the CFT will now be examined. It involves three concepts: windowing, sampling, and periodic sample generation. These are illustrated in Fig. 3-11, where the left side is time domain and the right side is the corresponding frequency domain. Suppose that the CFT of a waveform $w(t)$ is to be evaluated by use of the DFT. The time waveform is first windowed (truncated) over the interval $(0,T)$ so that only a finite number of samples, N, are needed. The windowed waveform, denoted by a w subscript, is

$$w_w(t) = \begin{cases} w(t), & 0 \le t \le T \\ 0, & t \text{ elsewhere} \end{cases} = w(t) \prod\left(\frac{t - (T/2)}{T}\right) \tag{3-64}$$

The Fourier transform of the windowed waveform is

$$W_w(f) = \int_{-\infty}^{\infty} w_w(t)e^{-j2\pi ft}\, dt = \int_{0}^{T} w(t)e^{-j2\pi ft}\, dt \tag{3-65}$$

Now approximate the CFT by using a finite series to represent the integral where $t = k\,\Delta t$, $f = n/T$, $dt = \Delta t$, and $\Delta t = T/N$. Then

$$W_w(f)\big|_{f=n/T} \approx \sum_{k=0}^{N-1} w(k\,\Delta t)e^{-j(2\pi/N)nk}\,\Delta t \tag{3-66}$$

Comparing this with (3-62a), the relation between the CFT and DFT is obtained:

$$W_w(f)\big|_{f=n/T} \approx \Delta t\, X(n) \tag{3-67}$$

where $f = n/T$ and $\Delta t = T/N$. The sample values used in the DFT computation are $x(k) = w(k\,\Delta t)$, as shown in the left part of Fig. 3-11c. Also, since $e^{-j(2\pi/N)nk}$ of (3-66) is periodic in n—that is, the same values will be repeated for $n = N, N + 1, \ldots$ as were obtained for $n = 0, 1, \ldots$ —then $X(n)$ is periodic (although only the first N values are returned by DFT computer programs since the others are just repetitions). Another way of seeing that the DFT (and the IDFT) are periodic is to recognize that since samples are used, the discrete transform is an example of impulse sampling, and consequently, the spectrum must be periodic about the sampling frequency, $f_s = 1/\Delta t = N/T$ (as illustrated in Fig. 3-5 and again here in Fig. 3-11c and d). Furthermore, if the spectrum is desired for negative

---

[†] FFT algorithms are described in many books and papers [Bergland, 1969; Glisson, 1986; Harris, 1982; Ziemer, Tranter, and Fannin, 1989].

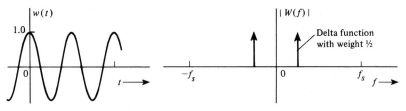

(a) Waveform and Its Spectrum

(b) Windowed Waveform and Its Spectrum

(c) Sampled Windowed Waveform and Its Spectrum ($f_s = 1/\Delta t$)

(d) Periodic Sampled Windowed Waveform and Its Spectrum ($f_0 = 1/T$)

FIGURE 3-11 Comparison of CFT and DFT spectra.

frequencies—the computer returns $X(n)$ for the positive n values of $0, 1, \ldots, N - 1$—(3-67) must be modified to give spectral values over the entire fundamental range of $-f_s/2 < f < f_s/2$. Thus for positive frequencies we use

$$W_w(f)\big|_{f=n/T} \approx \Delta t \, X(n), \qquad 0 \le n < \frac{N}{2} \qquad (3\text{-}68a)$$

and for negative frequencies we use

$$W_w(f)\big|_{f=(n-N)/T} \approx \Delta t \, X(n), \qquad \frac{N}{2} < n < N \qquad (3\text{-}68b)$$

In summary, four fundamental considerations need to be kept in mind when evaluating the CFT by use of the DFT:

1. Waveform windowing over $(0,T)$ is required so that a *finite* number of samples can be realized.
2. N sample values are used where the samples are taken at the times $t = k \, \Delta t$ ($k = 0, 1, \ldots, N - 1$ and $\Delta t = T/N$).
3. The DFT gives the spectra of N frequencies ($f = n/T$, $n = 0, 1, \ldots, N - 1$) over the frequency interval $(0, f_s)$, where $f_s = 1/\Delta t = N/T$.
4. The DFT and IDFT are periodic with periods f_s and T, respectively.

Figure 3-11 illustrates that if one is not careful, the DFT may give significant errors when used to approximate the CFT. The errors are due to a number of factors that may be categorized into three basic effects: *leakage, aliasing,* and the *picket-fence effect.*

The first effect is caused by windowing in the time domain. In the frequency domain this corresponds to convolving the spectrum of the unwindowed waveform with the spectrum (Fourier transform) of the window function. This spreads the spectrum of the frequency components of $w(t)$, as illustrated in Fig. 3-11b, and causes each frequency component to "leak" into adjacent frequencies. The leakage may produce errors when the DFT is compared with the CFT. This effect can be reduced by increasing the window width T or, equivalently, by increasing the number of points, N, that are used in the DFT. Window shapes other than the rectangle can also be used to reduce the sidelobes in the spectrum of the window function [Harris, 1978; Ziemer, Tranter, and Fannin, 1989]. Large periodic components in $w(t)$ cause more leakage, and if these components are known to be present, they might be eliminated before evaluating the DFT to reduce leakage.

From our previous study of sampling, it is known that the spectrum of a sampled waveform consists of replicating the spectrum of the unsampled waveform about harmonics of the sampling frequency. If $f_s < 2B$, where B is the highest significant frequency component in the unsampled waveform, aliasing errors will occur. The aliasing error can be decreased by using a higher sampling frequency or a presampling low-pass filter. Note that the highest frequency component that can be evaluated with an N-point DFT is $f = f_s/2 = N/(2T)$.

The third type of error, the picket-fence effect, occurs because the N-point DFT cannot resolve the spectral components any closer than the spacing $\Delta f = 1/T = f_s/N$. If the sampling rate is fixed, Δf can be decreased by increasing the number of points in the DFT. If the data length is limited to T_0 seconds, where $T_0 \leq T$, T may be extended by adding additional zero-value sampling points. This is called *zero-padding* and will reduce Δf to produce better spectral resolution.

The computer cannot compute values that are infinite; therefore, the DFT will approximate Dirac delta functions by finite-amplitude pulses. However, the weights of the delta functions can be computed accurately by using the DFT to evaluate the Fourier series coefficients. This is demonstrated in Example 3-7.

Example 3-6   DFT for a Rectangular Pulse

Figure 3-12 demonstrates the calculation of the spectrum for a rectangular pulse using the MathCAD DFT algorithm. Note that (3-63a) and (3-67) are used to relate the MathCAD DFT results to the spectrum (i.e., the CFT). Also, the parameters M, tend, and T are selected so that the computed magnitude and phase spectral results compare favorably (i.e., little error) with the true spectrum for a rectangular pulse as given by (2-59) and (2-60) of Example 2-5. (T in Example 2-5 is equivalent to tend in Fig. 3-12). The MathCad template shown in Fig. 3-12 may be found on the computer disk for this book (as described in Chapter 1). The reader should try other values of M, tend, and T to see how leakage, aliasing, and picket-fence errors become large if the parameters are not carefully selected. Also, note that significant errors occur if tend = T. Why?

In a similar way the DFT may be also used to evaluate Fourier series coefficients. Using (2-83) yields

$$c_n = \frac{1}{T} \int_0^T w(t) e^{-j2\pi n f_0 t}\, dt \tag{3-69}$$

Approximate this integral by using a finite series where $t = k\,\Delta t$, $f_0 = 1/T$, $dt = \Delta t$, and $\Delta t = T/N$. Then

$$c_n \approx \frac{1}{T} \sum_{k=0}^{N-1} w(k\,\Delta t) e^{-j(2\pi/N)nk}\, \Delta t \tag{3-70}$$

Using (3-62a), the Fourier series coefficient is related to the DFT by

$$c_n \approx \frac{1}{N} X(n) \tag{3-71}$$

The DFT returns $X(n)$ values for $n = 0, 1, \ldots, N-1$. Consequently, (3-71) must be modified to give c_n values for negative n. For positive n we use

$$c_n = \frac{1}{N} X(n), \qquad 0 \le n < \frac{N}{2} \tag{3-72a}$$

and for negative n we use

$$c_n = \frac{1}{N} X(N + n), \qquad -\frac{N}{2} < n \le 0 \tag{3-72b}$$

Calculate DFT for a truncated step.

$M := 7$ $N := 2^M$ $N = 128$ $k := 0 ..N - 1$

Let xend be end of step.

$tend := 1$ $T := 10$

$dt := \dfrac{T}{N}$ $t_k := k \cdot dt$

WAVEFORM

$w_k := 1.0 - \Phi(k \cdot dt - tend)$

$w_0 = 1$ $dt = 0.078$

$f4 := \dfrac{4}{tend}$

$n := 0 ..N - 1$

$W_n := dt \cdot \left[\sqrt{N}\right] \cdot icfft(w)$

$f_n := \dfrac{n}{T}$ $fs := \dfrac{1}{dt}$

$W_0 = 1.016$ $fs = 12.8$

$f_1 = 0.1$ $f4 = 4$

MAGNITUDE SPECTRUM out to 4th null

PHASE SPECTRUM

$$\left[\dfrac{180}{\pi}\right] \cdot \arg\left[W_n + 0.001\right]$$

MAGNITUDE SPECTRUM over whole DFT frequency range

FIGURE 3-12 Spectrum for a rectangular pulse using the MathCAD DFT.

Example 3-7   Use the DFT to Compute the Spectrum of a Sinusoid

Let

$$w(t) = 3\sin(\omega_0 t + 20°) \tag{3-73}$$

where $\omega_0 = 2\pi f_0$ and $f_0 = 10$ Hz. Since $w(t)$ is periodic, (2-103) is used to obtain the spectrum

$$W(f) = \sum_n c_n \delta(f - nf_0) \tag{3-74}$$

where $\{c_n\}$ are the complex Fourier series coefficients for $w(t)$. Furthermore, since $\sin(x) = (e^{jx} - e^{-jx})/(2j)$,

$$3\sin(\omega_0 t + 20°) = \left(\frac{3}{2j}e^{j20}\right)e^{j\omega_0 t} + \left(\frac{-3}{2j}e^{-j20}\right)e^{-j\omega_0 t}$$

Consequently, the FS coefficients are known to be

$$c_1 = \left(\frac{3}{2j}e^{j20}\right) = 1.5\underline{/-70°} \tag{3-75a}$$

$$c_{-1} = \left(\frac{-3}{2j}e^{-j20}\right) = 1.5\underline{/+70°} \tag{3-75b}$$

and the other c_n values are zero. Now, see if this known correct answer can be computed by using the DFT. Referring to Fig. 3-13, MathCAD computes the FFT and plots the spectrum. The computed result checks with the known (correct) analytical result.

Note that the error bar plot option of MathCAD is used so that the δ functions of (3-74) can be represented. That is, δ functions cannot be plotted because $\delta(0) = \infty$. Consequently, the weights of the δ functions are plotted instead to indicate the magnitude spectra. Also at frequencies where $|W(f)| = 0$, *any* value may be used for $\theta(f)$ since $W(f) = |W(f)|\underline{/\theta(f)} = 0$. Thus if the 0.001 constant is deleted in the MathCAD equation for $\theta(f)$, different values will be obtained in the phase plot except at the frequencies $f = \pm f_0 = \pm 10$ Hz, where $|W(f)| \neq 0$ and $\theta(\pm f_0) = \mp 70°$.

These results can also be compared with those of Example 2-4, where the spectrum for a sinusoid was obtained by direct evaluation of the Fourier transform integral.

3-8 Bandwidth of Signals and Noise

Spectral width of signals and/or noise in communication systems is a very important concept, for two main reasons. First, more and more users are being assigned to increasingly crowded radio-frequency (RF) bands, so that the spectral width required for each

Calculate the spectrum for a
sinusoid using the DFT

$fo := 10$ $\omega o := 2 \cdot \pi \cdot fo$

$M := 4$

$N := 2^M$

$M := 4$ $N = 16$ $k := 0 \ .. \ N - 1$ $T := \dfrac{1}{fo}$

$dt := \dfrac{T}{N}$ $t_k := k \cdot dt$

WAVEFORM

$w_k := 3 \cdot \sin\left[\omega o \cdot t_k + \left[\dfrac{\pi}{180} \cdot 20\right]\right]$

$w_0 = 1.026$ $dt = 0.006$

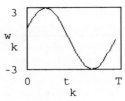

Compute the FFT data points.

$n := 0 \ .. \ N - 1$

$W := \sqrt{N} \cdot icfft(w)$

FFT Data Points

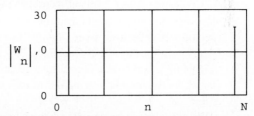

$n := \dfrac{-N}{2}, \dfrac{-N}{2} + 1 \ .. \dfrac{N}{2}$

SINCE THE WAVEFORM IS PERIODIC, USE COMPLEX FOURIER SERIES TO GET SPECTRUM.
==> Compute the FS coefficients from the FFT data using (3-72).
    Then, use (2-103) to get the spectrum.

$c(n) := if\left[n \geq 0, \dfrac{1}{N} \cdot W_n, \dfrac{1}{N} \cdot W_{N+n}\right]$ $f(n) := \dfrac{n}{T}$ $fs := \dfrac{1}{dt}$

$\theta(n) := \left[\dfrac{180}{\pi}\right] \cdot arg(c(n) + 0.001)$

MAGNITUDE SPECTRUM, $|W(f)|$ PHASE SPECTRUM, $\theta(f)$

FIGURE 3-13 Spectrum for a sinusoid using the MathCAD DFT.

one needs to be considered carefully. Second, the spectral width of signals/noise is important from the equipment design viewpoint since the circuits need to have enough bandwidth to accommodate the signal but reject the noise. The question is: What is *bandwidth?* As we will see, there are numerous definitions for bandwidth, just as there are numerous measures for length (centimeters, meters, feet, inches, etc.).

As long as we use the same definition when working with several signals and noise, we can compare their spectral widths by using the particular bandwidth definition that was selected. If we change definitions, "conversion factors" will be needed to compare the spectral widths that were obtained by using different definitions. Unfortunately, the conversion factors usually depend on the type of spectral *shape* involved [e.g., (sin *x*)/*x* type of spectrum or rectangular spectrum].

In engineering definitions, the bandwidth is taken to be the width of a *positive* frequency band. (We are describing the bandwidth of real signals or the bandwidth of a physical filter that has a real impulse response; consequently, the magnitude spectra of these waveforms are even about the origin $f = 0$.) In other words, the bandwidth would be $f_2 - f_1$, where $f_2 > f_1 \geq 0$ and f_2 and f_1 are determined by the particular definition that is used. For baseband waveforms or networks, f_1 is usually taken to be zero since the spectrum extends down to dc ($f = 0$). For bandpass signals, $f_1 > 0$ and the band $f_1 < f < f_2$ encompasses the carrier frequency f_c of the signal. It is recalled that as we increase the "signaling speed" of a signal (i.e., decrease T) the spectrum gets wider (see Fig. 2-6). Consequently, for engineering definitions of bandwidth, we require the bandwidth to vary as $1/T$.

We will give six engineering definitions and one legal definition of bandwidth that are often used. It is realized that there are also other definitions that might be useful, depending on the situation.

1. *Absolute bandwidth* is $f_2 - f_1$, where the spectrum is zero outside the interval $f_1 < f < f_2$ along the positive frequency axis.
2. *3-dB bandwidth* (or half-power bandwidth) is $f_2 - f_1$, where for frequencies inside the band $f_1 < f < f_2$, the magnitude spectra, say $|H(f)|$, fall no lower than $1/\sqrt{2}$ times the maximum value of $|H(f)|$, where the maximum value falls at a frequency inside the band.
3. *Equivalent noise bandwidth* is the width of a fictitious rectangular spectrum (height specified below) such that the power in that rectangular band is equal to the power associated with the actual spectrum over positive frequencies. For example, from (3-13), the PSD is proportional to the magnitude squared of the spectrum. Let f_0 be the frequency where the magnitude spectrum has a maximum; then the power in the equivalent rectangular band is proportional to

$$\text{equivalent power} = B_{\text{eq}}|H(f_0)|^2 \tag{3-76}$$

where B_{eq} is the equivalent bandwidth that is to be determined. The actual power for positive frequencies is proportional to

$$\text{actual power} = \int_0^\infty |H(f)|^2 \, df \tag{3-77}$$

Setting (3-76) equal to (3-77), we have the formula that gives the *equivalent noise bandwidth*,

$$B_{eq} = \frac{1}{|H(f_0)|^2} \int_0^\infty |H(f)|^2 \, df \qquad (3\text{-}78)$$

4. *Null-to-null bandwidth* (or zero-crossing bandwidth) is $f_2 - f_1$, where f_2 is the first null in the envelope of the magnitude spectrum above f_0 and, for bandpass filters, f_1 is the first null in the envelope below f_0, where f_0 is the frequency where the magnitude spectrum is a maximum.[†] For baseband filters f_1 is usually zero.

5. *Bounded spectrum bandwidth* is $f_2 - f_1$ such that outside the band $f_1 < f < f_2$, the PSD, which is proportional to $|H(f)|^2$, must be down by at least a certain amount, say 50 dB, below the maximum value of the power spectral density.

6. *Power bandwidth* is $f_2 - f_1$, where $f_1 < f < f_2$ defines the frequency band in which 99% of the total power resides. This is similar to the FCC definition of *occupied bandwidth*, which states that the power above the upper band edge f_2 is $\frac{1}{2}$% and the power below the lower band edge is $\frac{1}{2}$%, leaving 99% of the total power within the occupied band (FCC Rules and Regulations, Sec. 2.202).

7. *FCC bandwidth* is an authorized bandwidth parameter assigned by the FCC to specify the spectrum allowed in communication systems. When the FCC bandwidth parameter is substituted into the FCC formula, the minimum attenuation is given for the power level allowed in a 4-kHz band at the band edge with respect to the total average signal power. Quoting Sec. 21.106 of the FCC Rules and Regulations: "For operating frequencies below 15 GHz, in any 4 kHz band, the center frequency of which is removed from the assigned frequency by more than 50 percent up to and including 250 percent of the authorized bandwidth, as specified by the following equation, but in no event less than 50 dB:

$$A = 35 + 0.8(P - 50) + 10 \log_{10}(B) \qquad (3\text{-}79)$$

(attenuation greater than 80 dB is not required)

where A = attenuation (in decibels) below the mean output power
                level,
        P = percent removed from the carrier frequency,
        B = authorized bandwidth in megahertz."

The FCC definition (as well as many other legal rules and regulations) is somewhat obscure, but it will be interpreted in Example 3-8. It actually defines a spectral mask. That is, the spectrum of the signal must be less than or equal to the values given by this spectral mask at all frequencies. This spectral mask is illustrated by the FCC envelope curve in Fig. 3-15. The FCC bandwidth parameter B for the spectral mask is assigned different values in different frequency bands: for example, $B = 30$ MHz in the 6-GHz band and 40 MHz in the 11-GHz band. It will be discussed later in the example associated with Fig. 3-15. The FCC bandwidth parameter is not consistent with the other definitions that are listed in the sense that it is not proportional to $1/T$, the "signaling speed" of the corresponding signal

[†] In cases where there is no definite null in the magnitude spectrum, this definition is not applicable.

[Amoroso, 1980]. In this sense the FCC bandwidth parameter B is a *legal* definition instead of an engineering definition.

Example 3-8   Bandwidths for a BPSK Signal

A binary-phase-shift-keyed (BPSK) signal will be used to illustrate how the bandwidth is evaluated for the different definitions just given.

The BPSK signal is described by

$$s(t) = m(t) \cos \omega_c t \qquad (3\text{-}80)$$

where $\omega_c = 2\pi f_c$, f_c being the carrier frequency (hertz), and $m(t)$ is a serial binary (± 1 values) modulating waveform originating from a digital information source such as a digital computer and is illustrated in Fig. 3-14a. Let us evaluate the spectrum of $s(t)$ for the worst case (widest bandwidth).

The worst-case (widest-bandwidth) spectrum occurs when the digital modulating waveform has transitions that occur most often. In this case $m(t)$ would be a square wave, as shown in Fig. 3-14a. Here a binary 1 is represented by a $+1$-V level and a binary 0 by a -1-V level, and the signaling rate is $R =$

(a) Digital Modulating Waveform

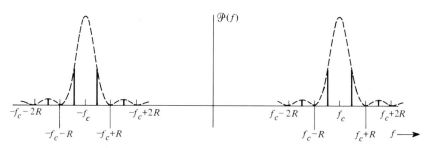

(b) Resulting BPSK spectrum

FIGURE 3-14 Spectrum of a BPSK signal.

$1/T_b$ bits/sec. The power spectrum of the square-wave modulation can be evaluated using Fourier series analysis. Using (2-122) and (2-115),

$$\mathcal{P}_m(f) = \sum_{\substack{n=-\infty}}^{\infty} |c_n|^2 \, \delta(f - nf_0) = \sum_{\substack{n=-\infty \\ n \neq 0}}^{\infty} \left[\frac{\sin(n\pi/2)}{n\pi/2} \right]^2 \delta\left(f - n\frac{R}{2}\right) \quad (3\text{-}81)$$

where $f_0 = 1/(2T_b) = R/2$. The PSD of $s(t)$ can be expressed in terms of the PSD for $m(t)$ by evaluating the autocorrelation of $s(t)$.

$$R_s(\tau) = \langle s(t)s(t + \tau) \rangle$$
$$= \langle m(t)m(t + \tau) \cos \omega_c t \cos \omega_c(t + \tau) \rangle$$
$$= \tfrac{1}{2}\langle m(t)m(t + \tau) \rangle \cos \omega_c\tau + \tfrac{1}{2}\langle m(t)m(t + \tau) \cos(2\omega_c t + \omega_c\tau) \rangle$$

or

$$R_s(\tau) = \tfrac{1}{2}R_m(\tau) \cos \omega_c\tau + \tfrac{1}{2} \lim_{T \to \infty} \frac{1}{T} \int_{-T/2}^{T/2} m(t)m(t + \tau) \cos(2\omega_c t + \omega_c\tau) \, dt$$
$$(3\text{-}82)$$

The integral is negligible since $m(t)m(t + \tau)$ is constant over small time intervals, but $\cos(2\omega_c t + \omega_c\tau)$ has many cycles of oscillation because $f_c \gg R$.[†] Any small area that is accumulated by the integral becomes negligible when divided by T, $T \to \infty$. Thus

$$R_s(\tau) = \tfrac{1}{2}R_m(\tau) \cos \omega_c\tau \quad (3\text{-}83)$$

The PSD is obtained by taking the Fourier transform of both sides of (3-83). Using the real-signal frequency transform theorem (Table 2-1), we get

$$\mathcal{P}_s(f) = \tfrac{1}{4}[\mathcal{P}_m(f - f_c) + \mathcal{P}_m(f + f_c)] \quad (3\text{-}84)$$

Substituting (3-81) into (3-84), we obtain the PSD for the BPSK signal:

$$\mathcal{P}_s(f) = \tfrac{1}{4} \sum_{\substack{n=-\infty \\ n \neq 0}}^{\infty} \left[\frac{\sin(n\pi/2)}{n\pi/2} \right]^2$$
$$\times \{\delta[f - f_c - n(R/2)] + \delta[f + f_c - n(R/2)]\} \quad (3\text{-}85)$$

This spectrum is shown in Fig. 3-14b.

The spectral shape that results from using this worst-case deterministic modulation is essentially the same as that obtained when random data are used; however, for the random case, the spectrum is continuous. The result for the random data case, as worked out in Chapters 4 and 7 where $\mathcal{P}_m(f)$ is given by (4-37), is

$$\mathcal{P}(f) = \tfrac{1}{4}T_b \left[\frac{\sin \pi T_b(f - f_c)}{\pi T_b(f - f_c)} \right]^2 + \tfrac{1}{4}T_b \left[\frac{\sin \pi T_b(f + f_c)}{\pi T_b(f + f_c)} \right]^2 \quad (3\text{-}86)$$

[†] This is a consequence of the Riemann–Lebesque lemma from integral calculus [Olmsted, 1961].

when the data rate is $R = 1/T_b$ bits/sec. This is shown by the dashed curve in Fig. 3-14b. This demonstrates that we can often use (deterministic) square-wave test signals to help us analyze a digital communication system instead of using a more complicated random data model.

The bandwidth for the BPSK signal will now be evaluated for each of the bandwidth definitions given previously. To accomplish this, the shape of the PSD for the positive frequencies is needed. From (3-86) it is

$$\mathcal{P}(f) = \left[\frac{\sin \pi T_b(f - f_c)}{\pi T_b(f - f_c)} \right]^2 \tag{3-87}$$

Substituting this equation into the definitions, we obtain the resulting BPSK bandwidths as shown in Table 3-2, except for the FCC bandwidth.

The relationship between the spectrum and the FCC bandwidth parameter is a little more tricky to evaluate. We need to evaluate the decibel attenuation

$$A(f) = -10 \log_{10} \left[\frac{P_{4\text{kHz}}(f)}{P_{\text{total}}} \right] \tag{3-88}$$

where $P_{4\text{kHz}}(f)$ is the power in a 4-kHz band centered at frequency f and P_{total} is the total signal power. The power in a 4-kHz band (assuming that the PSD is approximately constant across the 4-kHz bandwidth) is

$$P_{4\text{kHz}}(f) = 4000 \, \mathcal{P}(f) \tag{3-89}$$

and, using the definition of equivalent bandwidth, we find that the total power is

$$P_{\text{total}} = B_{\text{eq}}\mathcal{P}(f_c) \tag{3-90}$$

where the spectrum has a maximum value at $f = f_c$. Using these two equations, (3-88) becomes

$$A(f) = -10 \log_{10} \left[\frac{4000 \, \mathcal{P}(f)}{B_{\text{eq}}\mathcal{P}(f_c)} \right] \tag{3-91}$$

TABLE 3-2 Bandwidths for BPSK Signaling Where the Bit Rate Is $R = 1/T_b$ Bits/Sec

Definition Used	Bandwidth	Bandwidth (kHz) for $R = 9600$ bits/sec
1. Absolute bandwidth	∞	∞
2. 3-dB bandwidth	$0.88R$	8.45
3. Equivalent noise bandwidth	$1.00R$	9.60
4. Null-to-null bandwidth	$2.00R$	19.20
5. Bounded spectrum bandwidth (50 dB)	$201.04R$	1930.0
6. Power bandwidth	$20.56R$	197.4

where $A(f)$ is the decibel attenuation of power measured in a 4-kHz band at frequency f compared to the total average power level of the signal. For the case of BPSK signaling, using (3-87), we find that the decibel attenuation is

$$A(f) = -10 \log_{10} \left\{ \frac{4000}{R} \left[\frac{\sin \pi T_b(f - f_c)}{\pi T_b(f - f_c)} \right]^2 \right\} \tag{3-92}$$

where $R = 1/T_b$ is the data rate. If we attempt to find the value of R such that $A(f)$ will fall below the specified FCC spectral envelope shown in Fig. 3-15 ($B = 30$ MHz), we will find that R is so small that there will be numerous zeros in the $(\sin x)/x$ function of (3-92) within the desired frequency range, -50 MHz $< (f - f_c) < 50$ MHz. This is difficult to plot, so we plot the envelope of $A(f)$ instead, by replacing $\sin \pi T(f - f_c)$ with its maximum value (unity). The resulting BPSK envelope curve for the decibel attenuation is shown in Fig. 3-15, where $R = 0.0171$ Mbits/sec.

It is obvious that the data rate allowed for a BPSK signal to meet the FCC $B = 30$ MHz specification is ridiculously low. This is because the FCC bandwidth parameter specifies an almost absolutely bandlimited spectrum. In order to signal with a reasonable data rate, the pulse shape used in the

FIGURE 3-15 FCC-allowed envelope for $B = 30$ MHz.

transmitted signal must be modified from a rectangular shape (that gives the BPSK signal) to a rounded pulse such that the bandwidth of the transmitted signal will be almost absolutely bandlimited. Recalling our study of the sampling theorem, we realize that $(\sin x)/x$ pulse shapes are prime candidates since they have an absolutely bandlimited spectrum. However, the $(\sin x)/x$ pulses are not absolutely time-limited, so that this exact pulse shape cannot be used. Frank Amoroso and others have studied this problem, and a quasi-bandlimited version of the $(\sin x)/x$ pulse shape has been proposed [Amoroso, 1980]. The decibel attenuation curve for this type of signaling, shown in Fig. 3-15, is seen to fit very nicely under the allowed FCC spectral envelope curve for the case of $R = 25$ Mbits/sec. This allowable data rate of 25 Mbits/sec is a fantastic improvement over the $R = 0.0171$ Mbits/sec that was allowed for BPSK. It is also interesting to note that analog pulse shapes $[(\sin x)/x$ type] are required instead of a digital (rectangular) pulse shape. *This is another way of saying that it is vital for digital communication engineers to be able to analyze and design analog systems as well as digital systems.*

3-9 Summary

Linear systems were reviewed, and the condition for distortionless transmission was found.

The properties of bandlimited signals and noise were developed. This resulted in the sampling theorem and the dimensionality theorem.

Representation of binary and multilevel digital signals was described in some detail. Examples of digital signaling with rectangular and $(\sin x)/x$ pulse shapes were presented.

The discrete Fourier transform (DFT) and its inverse were studied. Examples of spectral computation and Fourier series coefficient computation using the DFT were shown.

The concept of bandwidth was discussed, and seven popular definitions were given. An example of a BPSK signal was used to illustrate how different measures of bandwidth resulted from the same signal. It was demonstrated that rounded pulse shapes are often required to meet FCC regulatory constraints.

PROBLEMS

3-1 Prove that the Fourier transform is a linear operator. That is, show that

$$\mathcal{F}[ax(t) + by(t)] = a\mathcal{F}[x(t)] + b\mathcal{F}[y(t)]$$

3-2 Plot the amplitude and phase response for the transfer function

$$H(f) = \frac{j10f}{5 + jf}$$

3-3   Given the filter shown in Fig. P3-3.
      (a) Find the transfer function for this filter.
      (b) Plot the magnitude and phase response.
      (c) Find the power transfer function for this filter.
      (d) Plot the power transfer function.

FIGURE P3-3

3-4   The periodic signal as shown in Fig. P2-52 is passed through a linear filter having
      the impulse response $h(t) = e^{-\alpha t}u(t)$, where $t > 0$ and $\alpha > 0$.
      (a) Find expressions for the complex Fourier series coefficients associated with the
          output waveform $y(t) = x(t) * h(t)$.
      (b) Find an expression for the normalized power of the output, $y(t)$.

3-5   A signal with a PSD of

$$\mathcal{P}_x(f) = \frac{2}{(1/4\pi)^2 + f^2}$$

      is applied to the network shown in Fig. P3-5.
      (a) Find the PSD for $y(t)$.
      (b) Find the average normalized power for $y(t)$.

FIGURE P3-5

3-6   A signal $x(t)$ has a PSD

$$\mathcal{P}_x(f) = \frac{K}{[1 + (2\pi f/B)^2]^2}$$

      where $K > 0$ and $B > 0$.
      (a) Find the 3-dB bandwidth in terms of B.
      (b) Find the equivalent noise bandwidth in terms of B.

3-7   The signal $x(t) = e^{-400\pi t}u(t)$ is applied to a brick-wall low-pass filter, $H(f)$, where

$$H(f) = \begin{cases} 1, & |f| \leq B \\ 0, & |f| > B \end{cases}$$

Find the value of B such that the filter passes one-half the energy of $x(t)$.

3-8   The signal $x(t) = 0.5 + 1.5 \cos[(\frac{2}{3})\pi t] + 0.5 \sin[(\frac{2}{3})\pi t)]$ volts is passed through an RC low-pass filter (see Fig. 3-2a) where $R = 1\ \Omega$ and $C = 1$ F.
(a) What is the input PSD, $\mathcal{P}_x(f)$?
(b) What is the output PSD, $\mathcal{P}_y(f)$?
(c) What is the average normalized output power, P_y?

3-9   The input to the RC low-pass filter shown in Fig. 3-2 is

$$x(t) = 0.5 + 1.5 \cos \omega_x t + 0.5 \sin \omega_x t$$

Assume that the cutoff frequency is $f_0 = 1.5 f_x$.
(a) Find the input PSD, $\mathcal{P}_x(f)$.
(b) Find the output PSD, $\mathcal{P}_y(f)$.
(c) Find the normalized average power of the output, $y(t)$.

3-10 Using MathCAD or MATLAB, plot the frequency magnitude response and phase response for the low-pass filter shown in Fig. P3-10, where $R_1 = 7.5\ \text{k}\Omega$, $R_2 = 15\ \text{k}\Omega$, and $C = 0.1\ \mu\text{F}$.

FIGURE P3-10

3-11 A comb filter is shown in Fig. P3-11. Let $T_d = 0.1$.
(a) Plot the magnitude of the transfer function for this filter.
(b) If the input is $x(t) = \Pi(t/T)$, where $T = 1.0$, plot the spectrum of the output $|Y(f)|$.

FIGURE P3-11

3-12 A signal $x(t) = \Pi(t - 0.5)$ passes through a filter that has the transfer function $H(f) = \Pi(f/B)$. Plot the output waveform when:
(a) $B = 0.6$ Hz.
(b) $B = 1$ Hz.
(c) $B = 50$ Hz.

3-13 Examine the distortion effect of an RC low-pass filter. Assume that a unity-amplitude square wave with a 50% duty cycle is present at the filter input and that the filter has a cutoff frequency of 1500 Hz. Using a computer or a programmable calculator, find the output waveshape if the square wave has a frequency of:
(a) 300 Hz.
(b) 500 Hz.
(c) 1000 Hz.

Sketch each of these results.

3-14 Given that the PSD of a signal is flat [i.e., $\mathcal{P}_s(f) = 1$], design an RC low-pass filter that will attenuate this signal by 20 dB at 15 kHz. That is, find the value for the RC of Fig. 3-2 such that the design specifications are satisfied.

3-15 The bandwidth of $g(t) = e^{-0.1t}$ is approximately 0.5 Hz; thus it can be sampled with a sampling frequency of $f_s = 1$ Hz without significant aliasing. Take samples a_n over the time interval (0,14). Use the sampling theorem, (3-29), to reconstruct the signal. Plot and compare the reconstructed signal with the original signal. Do they match? What happens when the sampling frequency is reduced?

3-16 A waveform, $20 + 20 \sin(500t + 30°)$, is to be sampled periodically and reproduced from these sample values.
(a) Find the maximum allowable time interval between sample values.
(b) How many sample values need to be stored in order to reproduce 1 sec of this waveform?

3-17 Determine the minimum (Nyquist) sampling frequency for the signal

$$s(t) = g_1^2(t) + g_2^2(t)$$

where $g_1(t)$ has a bandwidth of B_1 hertz and $g_2(t)$ has a bandwidth of $3B_1$ hertz where $B_1 > 0$. [Hint: Assume that $g_1(t)$ and $g_2(t)$ are sinusoidal signals.]

3-18 A baseband digital communication system sends one of 16 possible levels over the channel every 0.8 msec.
(a) What is the word length (number of bits) corresponding to each level?
(b) What is the data rate of the system?

3-19 A digital information source sends one of 256 possible messages over a channel every 2 msec. The probability of sending any one of the messages is 1/256. Assume that the source output is a four-level serial-data waveform such that each message is represented by N symbols (i.e., an N-dimensional orthogonal series).
(a) Calculate the information rate of the source.
(b) What is the value of N required?
(c) What is the baud (rate) of the output waveform?

(d) What is the minimum required channel bandwidth (Hz)?

(e) If a rectangular pulse shape is used for the output symbols, what is the null bandwidth (Hz) of the output waveform?

3-20 A baseband digital communication system is to operate at a data rate of 9600 bits/ sec.

(a) If 4-bit words are encoded into each level for transmission over the system, what is the minimum required bandwidth of the channel?

(b) Repeat part (a) for the case of 8-bit words.

3-21 Using a computer program, calculate the DFT of a rectangular pulse, $\Pi(t)$. Take five samples of the pulse and pad it with 59 zeros so that a 64-point FFT algorithm can be used. Sketch the resulting magnitude spectrum. Compare this result with the actual spectrum for the pulse. Try other combinations of number of pulse samples and zero-pads to see how the resulting FFT changes.

3-22 Using the DFT, compute and plot the spectrum of $\Lambda(t)$. Check your results with those given in Fig. 2-6c.

3-23 Using the DFT, compute and plot $|W(f)|$ for the pulse shown in Fig. P2-24, where $A = 1$, $t_1 = 1$ sec, and $t_2 = 2$ sec.

3-24 Given the waveform

$$w(t) = 4 \sin(2\pi f_1 t + 30°) + 2 \cos(2\pi f_2 t - 10°)$$

where $f_1 = 10$ Hz and $f_2 = 25$ Hz:

(a) Using the DFT, compute and plot $|W(f)|$ and $\theta(f)$.

(b) Let $\mathcal{P}_w(f)$ denote the PSD of $w(t)$. Using the DFT, compute and plot $\mathcal{P}_w(f)$.

(c) Check your computed results obtained in parts (a) and (b) with known correct results that you have evaluated by using analytical methods.

3-25 Using the DFT, compute and plot $|S(f)|$ for the periodic signal shown in Fig. P2-45 where $A = 5$.

3-26 Given the low-pass filter shown in Fig. 3-2:

(a) Find the equivalent bandwidth in terms of R and C.

(b) Find the first zero-crossing (null) bandwidth of the filter.

(c) Find the absolute bandwidth of the filter.

3-27 Assume that the PSD of a signal is given by

$$\mathcal{P}_s(f) = \left[\frac{\sin(\pi f/B_n)}{\pi f/B_n} \right]^2$$

where B_n is the null bandwidth. Find the expression for the equivalent bandwidth in terms of the null bandwidth.

3-28 Table 3-2 gives the bandwidths of a BPSK signal using six different definitions. Using the six definitions and (3-87), show that the results given in the table are correct.

3-29 Given a triangular pulse signal

$$s(t) = \Lambda(t/T_0)$$

(a) Find the absolute bandwidth of this signal.
(b) Find the 3-dB bandwidth in terms of T_0.
(c) Find the equivalent bandwidth in terms of T_0.
(d) Find the zero-crossing bandwidth in terms of T_0.

Baseband Pulse and Digital Signaling

4-1 Introduction

In this chapter we show how to encode analog waveforms (from analog sources) into baseband pulse signals and how to approximate analog signals with digital signals. As we will see, the digital approximation to the analog signal can be made very precise if we wish. In addition, we will learn how to process the digital baseband signals so that their bandwidth is minimized.

Digital signaling is popular and becoming even more popular because of the low cost of digital circuits and the flexibility of the digital approach. This flexibility arises, for example, because the digital data from digital sources may be merged with digitized data derived from analog sources to provide a general-purpose communication system.

The signals involved in the analog-to-digital conversion problem are *baseband* signals. We also realize that *bandpass* digital communication signals are produced by using baseband digital signals to modulate a carrier, as described in Chapter 1. For example, if a digital (baseband) signal phase modulates a carrier, the resulting digital bandpass signal is said to be a *phase-shift-keyed* (PSK) signal. Bandpass digital communication systems such as PSK are discussed in more detail in Chapter 7.

The three main goals of this chapter are:

1. To study how analog waveforms can be converted to digital waveforms that are acceptable for transmission over a digital communication system. The most popular technique is called *pulse code modulation* (PCM).
2. To examine how filtering of pulse signals affects our ability to recover the digital information at the receiver. This filtering can produce what is called *intersymbol interference* (ISI) in the recovered data signal.
3. To study how we can *multiplex* (combine) data from several digital bit streams into one

high-speed digital stream for transmission over a digital system. One such technique, called *time-division multiplexing* (TDM), will be studied in this chapter. Another technique, called *frequency-division multiplexing* (FDM), is described in Chapter 6.

4-2 Pulse Amplitude Modulation

Pulse amplitude modulation (PAM) is an engineering term that is used to describe the conversion of the analog signal to a pulse-type signal where the amplitude of the pulse denotes the analog information. As we will see in Sec. 4-3, this PAM signal can be converted into a PCM digital signal (baseband), which in turn is modulated onto a carrier in bandpass digital communication systems. Consequently, the analog-to-PAM conversion process is the first step in converting an analog waveform to a PCM (digital) signal. (In some applications the PAM signal is used directly, and conversion to PCM is not required.)

The purpose of PAM signaling is to provide *another* waveform that looks like pulses, yet contains the information that was present in the analog waveform. The pulse rate, f_s, for PAM is the same as that required by the sampling theorem, namely, $f_s \geq 2B$, where B is the highest frequency in the analog waveform and $2B$ is called the *Nyquist rate*.

There are two classes of PAM signals: PAM that uses *natural sampling* (gating) and PAM that uses *instantaneous sampling* to produce a flat-top pulse. These signals are illustrated in Figs. 4-1 and 4-5, respectively. The flat-top type is more useful for conversion to PCM; however, the naturally sampled type is easier to generate and is used in other applications.

Natural Sampling (Gating)

DEFINITION: If $w(t)$ is an analog waveform bandlimited to B hertz, the *PAM* signal that uses *natural sampling* (gating) is

$$w_s(t) = w(t)s(t) \tag{4-1}$$

where

$$s(t) = \sum_{k=-\infty}^{\infty} \Pi\left(\frac{t - kT_s}{\tau}\right) \tag{4-2}$$

is a rectangular wave switching waveform and $f_s = 1/T_s \geq 2B$.

Theorem

The spectrum for a naturally sampled *PAM* signal is

$$W_s(f) = \mathcal{F}[w_s(t)] = d \sum_{n=-\infty}^{\infty} \frac{\sin \pi n d}{\pi n d} W(f - nf_s) \tag{4-3}$$

where $f_s = 1/T_s$, $\omega_s = 2\pi f_s$, the duty cycle of $s(t)$ is $d = \tau/T_s$, and $W(f) = \mathcal{F}[w(t)]$ is the spectrum of the original unsampled waveform.

(a) Baseband Analog Waveform

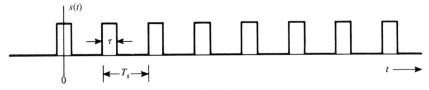

(b) Switching Waveform with Duty Cycle $d = \tau/T_s = 1/3$

(c) Resulting PAM Signal (natural sampling, $d = \tau/T_s = 1/3$)

FIGURE 4-1 PAM signal with natural sampling.

PROOF. Taking the Fourier transform of (4-1), we get

$$W_s(f) = W(f) * S(f) \tag{4-4}$$

Since $s(t)$ is periodic, it may be represented by the Fourier series

$$s(t) = \sum_{n=-\infty}^{\infty} c_n e^{jn\omega_s t} \tag{4-5a}$$

where

$$c_n = d\,\frac{\sin n\pi d}{n\pi d} \tag{4-5b}$$

Thus

$$S(f) = \mathscr{F}[s(t)] = \sum_{n=-\infty}^{\infty} c_n \delta(f - nf_s) \tag{4-6}$$

and (4-4) becomes

$$W_s(f) = W(f) * \left(\sum_{n=-\infty}^{\infty} c_n \delta(f - nf_s) \right) = \sum_{n=-\infty}^{\infty} c_n W(f) * \delta(f - nf_s)$$

or

$$W_s(f) = \sum_{n=-\infty}^{\infty} c_n W(f - nf_s) \tag{4-7}$$

which becomes (4-3) upon substituting (4-5b). ∎

   The PAM waveform with natural sampling is relatively easy to generate since it only requires the use of an analog switch that is readily available in CMOS hardware (e.g., the 4016-quad bilateral switch). This is shown in Fig. 4-2, where the associated waveforms $w(t)$, $s(t)$, and $w_s(t)$ are as illustrated in Fig. 4-1.
   The spectrum of the PAM signal with natural sampling is given by (4-3) in terms of the spectrum of the analog input waveform. This is illustrated in Fig. 4-3 for the case of an input waveform that has a rectangular spectrum where the duty cycle of the switching waveform is $d = \tau/T_s = \frac{1}{3}$ and the sampling rate is $f_s = 4B$. For this example, where $d = \frac{1}{3}$, the PAM spectrum is zero for $\pm 3f_s$, $\pm 6f_s$, and so on, since the spectrum in these harmonic bands is nulled out by the $(\sin x)/x$ function. From the figure it is obvious that the bandwidth of the PAM signal is much larger than the bandwidth of the original analog

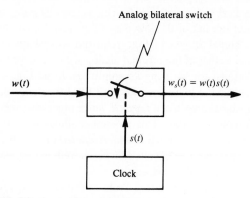

FIGURE 4-2 Generation of PAM with natural sampling (gating).

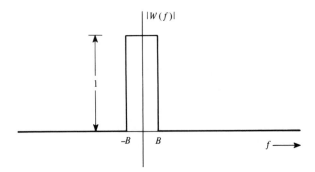

(a) Magnitude Spectrum of Input Analog Waveform

(b) Magnitude Spectrum of PAM (natural sampling) with $d = 1/3$ and $f_s = 4B$

FIGURE 4-3 Spectrum of a PAM waveform with natural sampling.

signal. In fact, for the example illustrated in Fig. 4-3b, the null bandwidth of the PAM signal is $3f_s = 12B$; that is, the null bandwidth of this PAM signal is 12 times the bandwidth of the analog signal.

At the receiver, the original analog waveform, $w(t)$, can be recovered from the PAM signal, $w_s(t)$, by passing the PAM signal through a low-pass filter where the cutoff frequency is $B < f_{\text{cutoff}} < f_s - B$. This is seen by comparing Fig. 4-3b with Fig. 4-3a. Since the spectrum out of the low-pass filter would have the same shape as that of the original analog signal shown in Fig. 4-4a, the waveshape out of the low-pass filter would be identical to that of the original analog signal except for a gain factor of d (which could be compensated for by using an amplifier). From Fig. 4-3b it is also obvious that the spectrum out of the low-pass filter will have the same shape as the spectrum of the original analog signal only when $f_s \geq 2B$, since otherwise spectral components in harmonic bands (of f_s) would overlap. This is another illustration of the Nyquist sampling rate requirement. If the analog signal is *undersampled* ($f_s < 2B$), the effect of spectral overlapping is called *aliasing*. This results in a recovered analog waveform that is distorted when compared to the original waveform.

It can also be shown (see Prob. 4-4) that the analog waveform may be recovered from the PAM signal by using *product* detection, as shown in Fig. 4-4. Here the PAM signal is

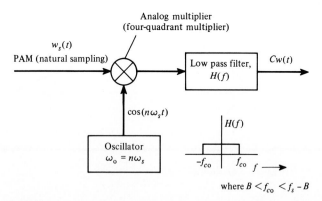

FIGURE 4-4 Demodulation of a PAM signal (naturally sampled).

multiplied with a sinusoidal signal of frequency $\omega_o = n\omega_s$. This shifts the frequency band of the PAM signal that was centered about nf_s to baseband (i.e., $f = 0$) at the multiplier output. We will study the product detector in Chapter 5. For $n = 0$ this is identical to low-pass filtering, just discussed. Of course, you might ask: Why do you need to go to the trouble of using a product detector when a simple low-pass filter will work? The answer is: Because of noise on the PAM signal. Noise due to power supply hum or noise due to mechanical circuit vibration might fall in the band corresponding to $n = 0$, and other bands might be relatively noise free. In this case, a product detector might be used to get around the noise problem.

Instantaneous Sampling (Flat-Top PAM)

Analog waveforms may also be converted to pulse signaling by the use of *flat-top* signaling with instantaneous sampling, as shown in Fig. 4-5. This is a generalization of the impulse train sampling technique that was studied in Sec. 3-5.

DEFINITION: If $w(t)$ is an analog waveform bandlimited to B hertz, the *instantaneous sampled* PAM signal is given by

$$w_s(t) = \sum_{k=-\infty}^{\infty} w(kT_s)h(t - kT_s) \tag{4-8}$$

where $h(t)$ denotes the sampling-pulse shape, and for flat-top sampling the pulse shape is

$$h(t) = \Pi\left(\frac{t}{\tau}\right) = \begin{cases} 1, & |t| < \tau/2 \\ 0, & |t| > \tau/2 \end{cases} \tag{4-9}$$

where $\tau \le T_s = 1/f_s$ and $f_s \ge 2B$.

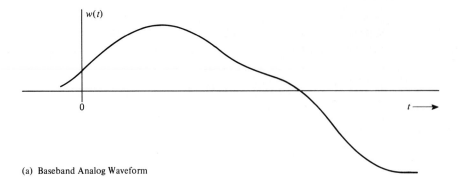

(a) Baseband Analog Waveform

(b) Impulse Train Sampling Waveform

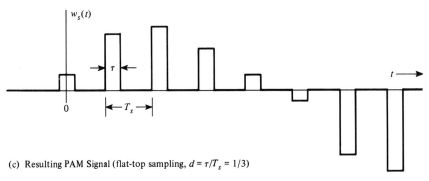

(c) Resulting PAM Signal (flat-top sampling, $d = \tau/T_s = 1/3$)

FIGURE 4-5 PAM signal with flat-top sampling.

Theorem

The spectrum for a flat-top *PAM* signal is

$$W_s(f) = \frac{1}{T_s} H(f) \sum_{k=-\infty}^{\infty} W(f - kf_s) \qquad (4\text{-}10)$$

where

$$H(f) = \mathcal{F}[h(t)] = \tau\left(\frac{\sin \pi\tau f}{\pi\tau f}\right) \qquad (4\text{-}11)$$

This type of PAM signal is said to consist of instantaneous samples since $w(t)$ is sampled at $t = kT_s$ and the sample values $w(kT_s)$ determine the amplitude of the flat-top rectangular pulses, as demonstrated in Fig. 4-5c. The flat-top PAM signal could be generated by using a sample-and-hold type of electronic circuit.

Another pulse shape, rather than the rectangular shape, could be used in (4-8), but in this case the resulting PAM waveform would not be flat-topped. The only restriction on the pulse shape is that it be zero outside $T_s/2$ [i.e., $h(t) = 0$ for $|t| \geq T_s/2$] so that the pulses do not overlap. Note that if the $h(t)$ is of the $(\sin x)/x$ type, then (4-8) becomes identical to the sampling theorem of (3-29).

PROOF. The spectrum for flat-top PAM can be obtained by taking the Fourier transform of (4-8). First, rewrite (4-8), using a more convenient form involving the convolution operation.

$$w_s(t) = \sum_k w(kT_s)h(t) * \delta(t - kT_s)$$

$$= h(t) * \sum_k w(kT_s)\, \delta(t - kT_s)$$

or

$$w_s(t) = h(t) * \left[w(t) \sum_k \delta(t - kT_s) \right]$$

The spectrum is

$$W_s(f) = H(f)\left[W(f) * \sum_k e^{-j2\pi fkT_s} \right] \tag{4-12}$$

But the sum of the exponential functions is equivalent to a Fourier series expansion (in the frequency domain), where the periodic function is an impulse train. That is,

$$\frac{1}{T_s} \sum_k \delta(f - kf_s) = \frac{1}{T_s} \sum_{n=-\infty}^{\infty} c_n e^{j(2\pi nT_s)f} \tag{4-13a}$$

where

$$c_n = \frac{1}{f_s} \int_{-f_s/2}^{f_s/2} \left[\sum_k \delta(f - kf_s) \right] e^{-j2\pi nT_s f}\, df = \frac{1}{f_s} \tag{4-13b}$$

Using (4-13a), we find that (4-12) becomes

$$W_s(f) = H(f)\left[W(f) * \frac{1}{T_s} \sum_k \delta(f - kf_s) \right]$$

$$= \frac{1}{T_s} H(f)\left[\sum_k W(f) * \delta(f - kf_s) \right]$$

which reduces to (4-10). ∎

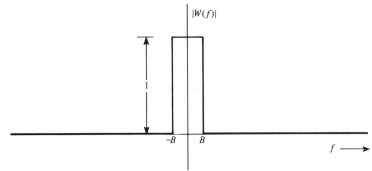

(a) Magnitude Spectrum of Input Analog Waveform

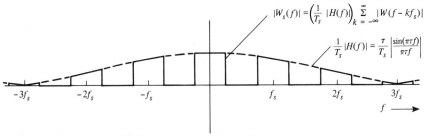

(b) Magnitude Spectrum of PAM (flat-top sampling), $\tau/T_s = 1/3$ and $f_s = 4B$

FIGURE 4-6 Spectrum of a PAM waveform with flat-top sampling.

The spectrum of the flat-topped PAM signal is illustrated in Fig. 4-6 for the case of an analog input waveform that has a rectangular spectrum. The analog signal may be recovered from the flat-topped PAM signal by the use of a low-pass filter. However, it is noted that there is some high-frequency loss in the recovered analog waveform due to the filtering effect, $H(f)$. This loss, if significant, can be reduced by decreasing τ or by using some additional gain at the high frequencies in the low-pass filter transfer function. In this case, the low-pass filter would be called an *equalization* filter and have a transfer function of $1/H(f)$ for frequencies within its passband. The pulse width τ is also called the *aperture* since τ/T_s determines the gain of recovered analog signal, which is small if τ is small relative to T_s. It is also possible to use product detection, similar to that shown in Fig. 4-4, except that now some prefilter might be needed before the multiplier (to make the spectrum flat in a band centered on $f = nf_s$), to compensate for the spectral loss due to the aperture effect.

The transmission of either naturally or instantaneously sampled PAM over a channel requires a very wide frequency response because of the narrow pulse width. This imposes stringent requirements on the magnitude and phase response of the channel. The bandwidth required is much larger than that of the original analog signal, and the noise performance of the PAM system can never be better than that achieved by transmitting the analog signal directly. Consequently, PAM is not very good for long-distance transmission. It does provide a means for converting an analog signal to a PCM signal (as discussed in the next section). PAM also provides a means for breaking a signal into time slots so that multiple PAM signals carrying information from different sources can be interleaved to transmit all of the information over a single channel. This is called time-division multiplexing and will be studied in Sec. 4-8.

4-3 Pulse Code Modulation

DEFINITION: *Pulse code modulation* (PCM) is essentially analog-to-digital conversion of a special type where the information contained in the instantaneous samples of an analog signal is represented by digital words in a serial bit stream.

If we assume that each of the digital words has n binary digits, there are $M = 2^n$ unique code words that are possible, each code word corresponding to a certain amplitude level. However, each sample value from the analog signal can be any one of an infinite number of levels, so that the digital word that represents the amplitude closest to the actual sampled value is used. This is called *quantizing*. That is, instead of using the exact sample value of the analog waveform $w(kT_s)$, the sample is replaced by the closest allowed value, where there are M allowed values, and each allowed value corresponds to one of the code words. Other popular types of analog-to-digital conversion, such as delta modulation (DM) and differential pulse code modulation (DPCM), are discussed in later sections.

PCM is very popular because of the many advantages it offers. Some of these advantages are as follows.

- Relatively inexpensive digital circuitry may be used extensively in the system.
- PCM signals derived from all types of analog sources (audio, video, etc.) may be merged with data signals (e.g., from digital computers) and transmitted over a common high-speed digital communication system. This merging is called time-division multiplexing and is discussed in detail in a later section.
- In long-distance digital telephone systems requiring repeaters, a *clean* PCM waveform can be regenerated at the output of each repeater, where the input consists of a noisy PCM waveform. However, the noise at the input may cause bit errors in the regenerated PCM output signal.
- The noise performance of a digital system can be superior to that of an analog system. In addition, the probability of error for the system output can be reduced even further by the use of appropriate coding techniques as discussed in Chapter 1.

These advantages usually outweigh the main disadvantage of PCM: a much wider bandwidth than that of the corresponding analog signal.

Sampling, Quantizing, and Encoding

The PCM signal is generated by carrying out three basic operations: sampling, quantizing, and encoding (see Fig. 4-7). The sampling operation generates a flat-top PAM signal.

The quantizing operation is illustrated in Fig. 4-8 for the $M = 8$-level case. This quan-

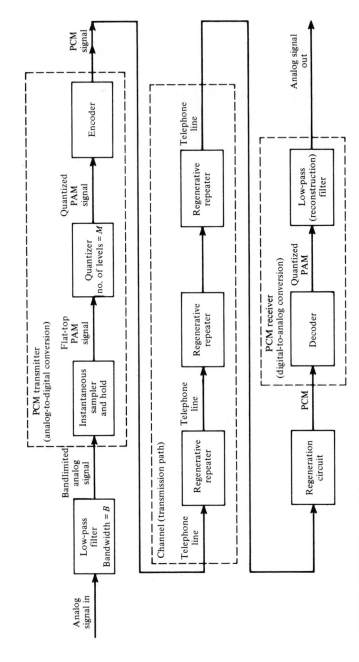

FIGURE 4-7 PCM transmission system.

(a) Quantizer Output-Input Characteristics

(b) Analog Signal, Flat-top PAM Signal, and Quantized PAM Signal

(d) PCM Signal

FIGURE 4-8 Illustration of waveforms in a PCM system.

tizer is said to be *uniform* since all of the steps are of equal size. Since we are approximating the analog sample values by using a finite number of levels ($M = 8$ in this illustration), *error* is introduced into the recovered output analog signal because of the quantizing effect. The error waveform is illustrated in Fig. 4-8c. The quantizing error consists of the difference between the analog signal at the sampler input and the output of the quantizer. Note that the peak value of the error (± 1) is one half of the quantizer step size (2). If we

TABLE 4-1 Three-Bit Gray Code for $M = 8$ Levels

Quantized Sample Voltage	Gray Code Word (PCM Output)	
+7	110	
+5	111	
+3	101	
+1	100	
		Mirror image except for sign bit
−1	000	
−3	001	
−5	011	
−7	010	

sample at the Nyquist rate ($2B$) or faster, and there is negligible channel noise, there will still be noise, called *quantizing noise,* on the recovered analog waveform due to this error. The quantizing noise can also be thought of as a round-off error. The quantizer output is a *quantized* PAM signal.

The PCM signal is obtained from the quantized PAM signal by encoding each quantized sample value into a digital word. It is up to the system designer to specify the exact code word that will represent a particular quantized level. If a Gray code of Table 4-1 is used, the resulting PCM signal is shown in Fig. 4-8d, where the PCM word for each quantized sample is strobed out of the encoder by the next clock pulse. The Gray code was chosen because it has only one bit change for each step change in the quantized level. Consequently, single errors in the received PCM code word will cause minimum errors in the recovered analog level, provided that the sign bit is not in error.

Here we have described PCM systems that represent the quantized analog sample values by *binary* code words. Of course, it is possible to represent the quantized analog samples by digital words using other than base 2. That is, for base q, the number of quantized levels allowed is $M = q^n$, where n is the number of q base digits in the code word. We will not pursue this topic since binary ($q = 2$) digital circuits are most commonly used.

Practical PCM Circuits

Three techniques are used to implement the analog-to-digital converter (ADC) encoding operation. These are the *counting or ramp, serial or successive approximation,* and *parallel or flash* encoders.

In the counting encoder, at the same time that the sample is taken, a ramp generator is energized and a binary counter is started. The output of the ramp generator is continuously compared to the sample value; when the value of the ramp becomes equal to the sample value, the binary value of the counter is read. This count is taken to be the PCM word. The binary counter and the ramp generator are then reset to zero and are ready to be reenergized at the next sampling time. This technique requires only a few components, but the speed of this type of ADC is usually limited by the speed of the counter. The Intersil ICL7126 CMOS ADC integrated circuit uses this technique.

The serial encoder compares the value of the sample with trial quantized values. Successive trials depend on whether the past comparator outputs are positive or negative. The trial values are chosen first in large steps and then in small steps so that the process will converge rapidly. The trial voltages are generated by a series of voltage dividers that are configured by (on-off) switches. These switches are controlled by digital logic. After the process converges, the value of the switch settings is read out as the PCM word. This technique requires more precision components (for the voltage dividers) than the ramp technique. The speed of the feedback ADC technique is determined by the speed of the switches. The National Semiconductor ADC0804 8-bit ADC uses this technique.

The parallel encoder uses a set of parallel comparators with reference levels that are the permitted quantized values. The sample value is fed into all of the parallel comparators simultaneously. The high or low level of the comparator outputs determines the binary PCM word with the aid of some digital logic. This is a fast ADC technique but requires more hardware than the other two methods. The RCA CA3318 8-bit ADC integrated circuit is an example of this technique.

All of the integrated circuits listed as examples above have parallel digital outputs that correspond to the digital word that represents the analog sample value. For generation of PCM, the parallel output (digital word) needs to be converted to serial form for transmission over a two-wire channel. This is accomplished by using a parallel-to-serial converter integrated circuit, which is also usually known as a *serial-input-output* (SIO) chip. The SIO chip includes a shift register that is set to contain the parallel data (from, usually, 8 or 16 input lines). Then the data are shifted out of the last stage of the shift register bit-by-bit onto a single output line to produce the serial format. Furthermore, the SIO chips are usually full duplex; that is, they have two sets of shift registers, one that functions for data flowing in each direction. One shift register converts parallel input data to serial output data for transmission over the channel, and, simultaneously, the other shift register converts received serial data from another input to parallel data that are available at another output. Three types of SIO chips are available: the *universal asynchronous receiver/transmitter* (UART), the *universal synchronous receiver/transmitter* (USRT), and the *universal synchronous/asynchronous receiver transmitter* (USART). The UART transmits and receives asynchronous serial data, the USRT transmits and receives synchronous serial data, and the USART combines both a UART and a USRT on one chip. (See Sec. 4-8 for a discussion of asynchronous and synchronous serial data lines.)

At the receiving end the PCM signal is decoded back into an analog signal by using a digital-to-analog converter (DAC) chip. If the DAC chip has a parallel data input, the received serial PCM data are first converted to a parallel form using a SIO chip as described above. The parallel data are then converted to an approximation of the analog sample value by the DAC chip. This conversion is usually accomplished by using the parallel digital word to set the configuration of electronic switches on a resistive current (or voltage) divider network so that the analog output is produced. This is called a *multiplying* DAC since the "analog" output voltage is directly proportional to the divider reference voltage multiplied by the value of the digital word. The Motorola MC1408 and the National Semiconductor DAC0808 8-bit DAC chips are examples of this technique. The DAC chip outputs samples of the quantized analog signal that approximates the analog sample values. Consequently, as the DAC chip is clocked, it generates a quantized PAM signal. This may be smoothed by a low-pass reconstruction filter to produce the analog output as illustrated in Fig. 4-7. A recently published EE handbook [Dorf, 1993, pp. 771–782] gives more details on ADC, DAC, and PCM circuits.

Bandwidth of PCM

A good question to ask is: What is the spectrum of a PCM signal? For the case of PAM signaling, the spectrum of the PAM signal could be obtained as a function of the spectrum of the input analog signal because the PAM signal is a linear function of the analog signal. This is not the case for PCM. As shown in Figs. 4-7 and 4-8, the PCM signal is a *nonlinear* function of the input analog signal. Consequently, the spectrum of the PCM signal is not directly related to the spectrum of the input analog signal. However, our study of the digital signaling in Chapter 3 shows that the bandwidth of (serial) digital signals depends on the bit rate and the pulse shape. From Fig. 4-8, the bit rate is

$$R = nf_s \tag{4-14}$$

where n is the number of bits in the PCM word ($M = 2^n$) and f_s is the sampling rate. For no aliasing we require $f_s \geq 2B$ where B is the bandwidth of the analog signal (that is to be converted to the PCM signal). Using (3-59), (3-50), and (4-14), we see that the dimensionality theorem shows that the bandwidth of the PCM waveform is bounded by

$$B_{PCM} \geq \tfrac{1}{2}R = \tfrac{1}{2}nf_s \tag{4-15a}$$

where equality is obtained if a $(\sin x)/x$ type of pulse shape is used to generate the PCM waveform. The exact spectrum for the PCM waveform will depend on the pulse shape that is used as well as on the type of line encoding. This will be studied in Sec. 4-4. For example, if one uses a rectangular pulse shape with polar NRZ line coding, Fig. 4-12b shows that the first null bandwidth is simply

$$B_{PCM} = R = nf_s \quad \text{(first null bandwidth)} \tag{4-15b}$$

Table 4-2 presents a tabulation of this result for the case of the minimum sampling rate, $f_s = 2B$. Note that the dimensionality theorem of (4-15a) demonstrates that the bandwidth of the PCM signal has a lower bound given by

$$B_{PCM} \geq nB \tag{4-15c}$$

where $f_s \geq 2B$ and B is the bandwidth of the corresponding analog signal. Thus, for reasonable values of n, *the bandwidth of the PCM signal will be significantly larger than the bandwidth of the corresponding analog signal* that it represents. For the example shown in Fig. 4-8 where $n = 3$, the PCM signal bandwidth will be at least three times wider than that of the corresponding analog signal. Furthermore, if the bandwidth of the

TABLE 4-2 Performance of a PCM System with Uniform Quantizing and No Channel Noise

Number of Quantizer Levels Used, M	Length of the PCM Word, n (bits)	Bandwidth of PCM Signal (First Null Bandwidth)[a]	Recovered Analog Signal Power-to-Quantizing Noise Power Ratios (dB)	
			$(S/N)_{pk\ out}$	$(S/N)_{out}$
2	1	$2B$	10.8	6.0
4	2	$4B$	16.8	12.0
8	3	$6B$	22.8	18.1
16	4	$8B$	28.9	24.1
32	5	$10B$	34.9	30.1
64	6	$12B$	40.9	36.1
128	7	$14B$	46.9	42.1
256	8	$16B$	52.9	48.2
512	9	$18B$	59.0	54.2
1,024	10	$20B$	65.0	60.2
2,048	11	$22B$	71.0	66.2
4,096	12	$24B$	77.0	72.2
8,192	13	$26B$	83.0	78.3
16,384	14	$28B$	89.1	84.3
32,768	15	$30B$	95.1	90.3
65,536	16	$32B$	101.1	96.3

[a] B is the absolute bandwidth of the input analog signal.

PCM signal is reduced by improper filtering, or by passing the PCM signal through a system that has a poor frequency response, the filtered pulses will be elongated (stretched in width) so that pulses corresponding to any one bit will smear into adjacent bit slots. If this condition becomes too serious, it will cause errors in the detected bits. This pulse smearing effect is called *intersymbol interference* (ISI). The filtering specifications for no ISI are discussed in Sec. 4-5.

Effects of Noise

The analog signal that is recovered at the PCM system output is corrupted by noise. Two main effects produce this noise or distortion:

1. Quantizing noise that is caused by the M-step quantizer at the PCM transmitter.
2. Bit errors in the recovered PCM signal. The bit errors are caused by *channel noise* as well as improper channel filtering, which causes ISI.

In addition, if the input analog signal that is sampled is not strictly bandlimited, there will be some aliasing noise on the recovered analog signal [Spilker, 1977]. Under certain assumptions, it can be shown that the recovered analog *peak* signal power to total *average* noise power is given by [Couch, 1993]

$$\left(\frac{S}{N}\right)_{\text{pk out}} = \frac{3M^2}{1 + 4(M^2 - 1)P_e} \tag{4-16a}$$

and the *average* signal power to the average noise power is

$$\left(\frac{S}{N}\right)_{\text{out}} = \frac{M^2}{1 + 4(M^2 - 1)\ P_e} \tag{4-16b}$$

where M is the number of quantized levels used in the PCM system and P_e is the probability of bit error in the recovered binary PCM signal at the receiver DAC before it is converted back into an analog signal. In Chapter 1 it was shown how channel coding could be used to correct some of the bit errors and, consequently, reduce P_e. Therefore, in many practical systems P_e is negligible. If we assume that there are no bit errors due to channel noise (i.e., $P_e = 0$) and no ISI, then, from (3-16a), the peak S/N due only to quantizing errors is

$$\left(\frac{S}{N}\right)_{\text{pk out}} = 3M^2 \tag{4-17a}$$

and from (4-16b) the average S/N due only to quantizing errors is

$$\left(\frac{S}{N}\right)_{\text{out}} = M^2 \tag{4-17b}$$

Numerical values for these S/N ratios are given in Table 4-2.

To realize these S/N ratios, one critical assumption is that the peak-to-peak level of the analog waveform at the input to the PCM encoder is set to the design level of the quantizer. For example, referring to Fig. 4-8a, this corresponds to the input traversing the range $-V$ to $+V$ volts where $V = 8$ volts is the design level of the quantizer. Equations (4-16) and (4-17) were derived for waveforms with equally likely values, such as a triangle waveshape, that have a peak-to-peak value of $2V$ and an rms value of $V/\sqrt{3}$, where V is the design peak level of the quantizer.

From a practical viewpoint, the quantizing noise at the output of the PCM decoder can be categorized into four types depending on the operating conditions. The four types are overload noise, random noise, granular noise, and hunting noise. As discussed earlier, the level of the analog waveform at the input of the PCM encoder needs to be set so that its peak level does not exceed the design peak of V volts. If the peak input does exceed V, then the recovered analog waveform at the output of the PCM system will have flat-tops near the peak values. This produces *overload noise.* The flat-tops are easily seen on an oscilloscope, and the recovered analog waveform sounds distorted since the flat-topping produces unwanted harmonic components. For example, this type of distortion can be heard on PCM telephone systems (as described in Chapter 8) when there are high levels such as dial tones, busy signals, or off-hook signals.

The second type of noise, *random noise,* is produced by the random quantization errors in the PCM system under normal operating conditions when the input level is properly set. This type of condition is assumed in (4-17). Random noise has a "white" hissing sound. If the input level is not sufficiently large, the S/N will deteriorate from that given by

(4-17) to one that will be described later by (4-25) and (4-26a); however, the quantizing noise will still be more or less random.

If the input level is reduced further to a relatively small value with respect to the design level, the error values are not equally likely from sample to sample, and the noise has a harsh sound resembling gravel being poured into a barrel. This is called *granular noise*. This type of noise can be randomized (noise power decreased) by increasing the number of quantization levels, and, consequently, increasing the PCM bit rate. Alternatively, granular noise can be reduced by using a nonuniform quantizer, such as the μ-law or A-law quantizers that are described in the next section.

The fourth type of quantizing noise that may occur at the output of a PCM system is *hunting noise*. It can occur when the input analog waveform is nearly constant, including when there is no signal (i.e., zero level). For these conditions the sample values at the quantizer output (see Fig. 4-8) can oscillate between two adjacent quantization levels, causing an undesired sinusoidal type tone of frequency $\frac{1}{2}f_s$ at the output of the PCM system. Hunting noise can be reduced by filtering out the tone or by designing the quantizer so that there is no vertical step at the ''constant'' value of the inputs—such as at zero volts input for the no signal case. For the no signal case, the hunting noise is also called *idle channel noise*. Idle channel noise can be reduced by using a horizontal step at the origin of the quantizer output-input characteristic instead of a vertical step as shown in Fig. 4-8a.

Recalling that $M = 2^n$, we may express Eqs. (4-17a) and (4-17b) in decibels as

$$\left(\frac{S}{N}\right)_{dB} = 6.02n + \alpha \tag{4-18}$$

where n is the number of bits in the PCM word, $\alpha = 4.77$ for the peak S/N, and $\alpha = 0$ for the average S/N. This equation—called the *6-dB rule*—points out the significant performance characteristic for PCM: *an additional 6-dB improvement in S/N is obtained for each bit added to the PCM word.* This is illustrated in Table 4-2. Equation (4-18) is valid for a wide variety of assumptions (such as various types of input waveshapes and quantization characteristics), although the value of α will depend on these assumptions [Jayant and Noll, 1984]. Of course, it is assumed that there are no bit errors and that the input signal level is large enough to range over a significant number of quantizing levels.

Example 4-1   Design of a PCM System

Assume that an analog voice-frequency signal, which occupies a band from 300 to 3400 Hz, is to be transmitted over a binary PCM system. The minimum sampling frequency would be $2 \times 3.4 = 6.8$ kHz. In practice the signal would be oversampled, and in the United States a sampling frequency of 8 kHz is the standard used for voice-frequency signals in telephone communication systems. Assume that each sample value is represented by 7 information bits plus 1 parity bit; then the bit rate of the PCM signal is

$$R = (f_s \text{ samples/sec})(n \text{ bits/sample})$$

$$= (8k \text{ samples/sec})(8 \text{ bits/sample}) = 64 \text{ kbits/sec} \tag{4-19}$$

Since the signaling is binary (i.e., two possible levels), each dimension[†] (or symbol) is carrying one bit of data, so that the baud rate is equal to the bit rate, or $D = R = 64k$ symbols/sec. Referring to the dimensionality theorem (4-15a), we realize that the theoretically minimum absolute bandwidth of the PCM signal is

$$(B)_{\min} = \tfrac{1}{2}D = 32 \text{ kHz} \tag{4-20}$$

and this is realized if the PCM waveform consists of $(\sin x)/x$ pulse shapes. If rectangular pulse shaping is used, the absolute bandwidth is infinity and the first null bandwidth, as shown in Fig. 4-12b, is

$$(B)_{\text{null}} = R = \frac{1}{T_b} = 64 \text{ kHz} \tag{4-21}$$

That is, we require a bandwidth of 64 kHz to transmit this digital voice PCM signal where the bandwidth of the original analog voice signal was, at most, 4 kHz. (In Sec. 4-5 we will see that the bandwidth of this binary PCM signal may be reduced somewhat by filtering without introducing ISI.) Using (4-17a), we observe that the peak signal-to-quantizing noise power ratio is

$$\left(\frac{S}{N}\right)_{\text{pk out}} = 3(2^7)^2 = 46.9 \text{ dB} \tag{4-22}$$

where $M = 2^7$. Note that the inclusion of a parity bit does not affect the quantizing noise. However, coding (parity bits) may be used to decrease the decoded errors caused by channel noise or ISI. In this example, these effects were assumed to be negligible since P_e was assumed to be zero.

The performance of a PCM system for the most optimistic case (i.e., $P_e = 0$) can easily be obtained as a function of M, the number of quantizing steps used. The results are shown in Table 4-2. In obtaining the (S/N), no parity bits were used in the PCM word.

One might use this table to look at the design requirements in a proposed PCM system. For example, high-fidelity enthusiasts are turning to digital audio recording techniques. Here PCM signals are recorded instead of the analog audio signal to produce superb sound reproduction. For a dynamic range of 90 dB, it is seen that at least 15-bit PCM words would be required. Furthermore, if the analog signal had a bandwidth of 20 kHz, the first null bandwidth for rectangular bit-shape PCM would be $2 \times 20 \text{ kHz} \times 15 = 600 \text{ kHz}$. With an allowance for some oversampling and a wider bandwidth to minimize ISI, the bandwidth needed would be around 1.5 MHz. Consequently, video-type tape recorders are needed to record and reproduce high-quality digital audio signals. Although this type of recording technique might seem ridiculous at first, it is realized that expensive high-quality analog recording devices are hard pressed to reproduce a dynamic range of 70 dB.

[†] See Fig. 3-7 for an illustration of a three-dimensional signal expansion. In this example we have an eight-dimensional signal expansion.

Thus digital audio is one way to achieve improved performance. This is being proven in the marketplace with the popularity of the digital compact disk (CD). The CD uses a 16-bit PCM word and a sampling rate of 44.1 kHz on each stereo channel [Miyaoka, 1984; Peek, 1985]. Reed–Solomon coding with interleaving is used to correct burst errors that occur as a result of scratches and fingerprints on the compact disk.

Nonuniform Quantizing: μ-Law and A-Law Companding

Voice analog signals are more likely to have amplitude values near zero than at the extreme peak values allowed. For example, when digitizing voice signals, if the peak value allowed is 1 V, weak passages may have voltage levels on the order of 0.1 V (20 dB down). For signals such as these with nonuniform amplitude distribution, the granular quantizing noise will be a serious problem if the step size is not reduced for amplitude values near zero and increased for extremely large values. This is called *nonuniform quantizing* since a variable step size is used. An example of a nonuniform quantizing characteristic is shown in Fig. 4-9a.

The effect of nonuniform quantizing can be obtained by first passing the analog signal through a compression (nonlinear) amplifier and then into the PCM circuit that uses a uniform quantizer. In the United States a μ-*law* type of *compression* characteristic is used. It is defined [Smith, 1957] by

$$|w_2(t)| = \frac{\ln(1 + \mu|w_1(t)|)}{\ln(1 + \mu)} \tag{4-23}$$

where the allowed peak values of $w_1(t)$ are ± 1 (i.e., $|w_1(t)| \leq 1$), μ is a positive constant that is a parameter, and ln is the natural logarithm. This compression characteristic is shown in Fig. 4-9b, for several values of μ, and it is noted that $\mu \to 0$ corresponds to linear amplification (uniform quantization overall). In the United States, Canada, and Japan, the telephone companies use a $\mu = 255$ compression characteristic in their PCM systems [Dammann, McDaniel, and Maddox, 1972].

Another compression law, used mainly in Europe, is the A-*law* characteristic. It is defined [Cattermole, 1969] by

$$|w_2(t)| = \begin{cases} \dfrac{A|w_1(t)|}{1 + \ln A}, & 0 \leq |w_1(t)| \leq \dfrac{1}{A} \\[3mm] \dfrac{1 + \ln(A|w_1(t)|)}{1 + \ln A}, & \dfrac{1}{A} \leq |w_1(t)| \leq 1 \end{cases} \tag{4-24}$$

where $|w_1(t)| \leq 1$ and A is a positive constant. The A-law compression characteristic is shown in Fig. 4-9c. The typical value for A is 87.6.

When compression is used at the transmitter, *expansion* (i.e., decompression) must be used at the receiver output to restore signal levels to their correct relative values. The *expandor* characteristic is the inverse of the compression characteristic, and the combination of a compressor and an expandor is called a *compandor*.

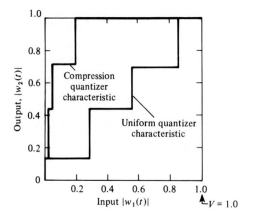

(a) $M = 8$ Quantizer Characteristic

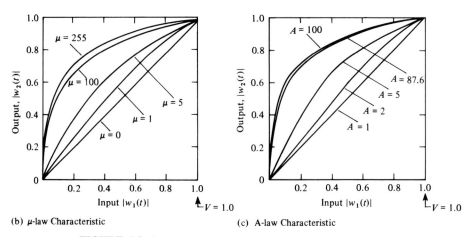

(b) μ-law Characteristic

(c) A-law Characteristic

FIGURE 4-9 Compression characteristics (first quadrant shown).

Once again, it can be shown that the output S/N follows the 6-dB law [Couch, 1993].

$$\left(\frac{S}{N}\right)_{dB} = 6.02n + \alpha \tag{4-25}$$

where

$$\alpha = 4.77 - 20\log(V/x_{rms}) \qquad \text{uniform quantizing} \tag{4-26a}$$

and for sufficiently large input levels

$$\alpha \approx 4.77 - 20\log[\ln(1 + \mu)] \qquad \mu\text{-law companding} \tag{4-26b}$$

and [Jayant and Noll, 1984]

$$\alpha \approx 4.77 - 20\log[1 + \ln A] \qquad A\text{-law companding} \tag{4-26c}$$

FIGURE 4-10 Output S/N of 8-bit PCM systems with and without companding.

n is the number of bits used in the PCM word, V is the peak design level of the quantizer, and x_{rms} is the rms value of the input analog signal. Notice that the output S/N is a function of the input level for the uniform quantizing (no companding) case but is relatively insensitive to input level for μ-law and A-law companding, as shown in Fig. 4-10. The ratio V/x_{rms} is called the *loading factor*. The input level is often set for a loading factor of $4 = 12$ dB to ensure that the overload quantizing noise will be negligible. In practice this gives $\alpha = -7.3$ for the case of uniform encoding as compared to $\alpha = 0$ that was obtained for the ideal conditions associated with (4-17b).

4-4 Digital Signaling Formats

Binary Line Coding

Binary 1's and 0's such as in PCM signaling may be represented in various serial-bit signaling formats called *line codes*. Some of the more popular line codes are shown in Fig. 4-11.[†] There are two major categories: *return-to-zero* (RZ) and *nonreturn-to-zero* (NRZ).

[†] Strictly speaking, punched paper tape is a storage medium, not a line code. However, it is included for historical purposes to illustrate the origin of the terms *mark* and *space*. In punched paper tape the binary 1 corresponds to a hole (mark), and a binary 0 corresponds to no hole (space). In current loop signaling (see Appendix C), the presence of loop current denotes a mark and the absence of loop current denotes a space.

FIGURE 4-11 Binary signaling formats.

With RZ coding, the waveform returns to a zero-volt level for a portion (usually one half) of the bit interval. The waveforms for the line code may be further classified according to the rule that is used to assign voltage levels to represent the binary data. Some examples follow.

Unipolar Signaling In positive logic unipolar signaling the binary 1 is represented by a high level (+A volts) and a binary 0 by a zero level. This type of signaling is also called *on-off keying.*

Polar Signaling Binary 1's and 0's are represented by equal positive and negative levels.

Bipolar (Pseudoternary) Signaling   Binary 1's are represented by alternately positive or negative values. The binary 0 is represented by a zero level. The term *pseudoternary* refers to the use of three encoded signal levels to represent two-level (binary) data. This is also called *alternate mark inversion* (AMI) signaling.

Manchester Signaling   Each binary 1 is represented by a positive half-bit period pulse followed by a negative half-bit period pulse. Similarly, a binary 0 is represented by a negative half-bit period pulse followed by a positive half-bit period pulse. This type of signaling is also called *split-phase encoding.*

Later in this book we will often use shortened notations. *Unipolar NRZ will be denoted simply by unipolar, polar NRZ by polar, and bipolar RZ as bipolar.* It should also be pointed out that, unfortunately, the term *bipolar* has two different conflicting definitions as used in practice. The meaning is usually made clear by the context in which it is used: (1) In the space communication industry polar NRZ is sometimes called bipolar NRZ, or simply bipolar (this meaning will not be used in this book); and (2) in the telephone industry the term *bipolar* denotes pseudoternary signaling (used in this book) as in T1 bipolar RZ signaling described in Sec. 4-8.

The line codes shown in Fig. 4-11 are also known by alternate names [Deffeback and Frost, 1971; Sklar, 1988]. For example, polar NRZ is also called NRZ-L, where L denotes the normal logical level assignment. Bipolar RZ is also called RZ-AMI, where AMI denotes alternate mark inversion. Bipolar NRZ is called NRZ-M, where M denotes inversion on mark. Negative logic bipolar NRZ is called NRZ-S, where S denotes inversion on space. Manchester NRZ is called Bi-φ-L for bi-phase with normal logic level.

Other line codes, too numerous to list here, can also be found in the literature [Bic, Duponteil, and Imbeaux, 1991; Bylanski and Ingram, 1976]. For example, the bipolar (pseudoternary) type may be extended into several subclasses as discussed briefly following (4-41).

Each of the line codes shown in Fig. 4-11 has advantages and disadvantages. For example, the unipolar NRZ line code has the advantage of using circuits that require only one power supply (e.g., a single +5-V power supply for TTL circuits), but this line code has the disadvantage of requiring channels that are dc coupled (i.e., frequency response down to $f = 0$) since the waveform has a nonzero dc value. The polar NRZ line code does not require a dc-coupled channel, *provided that* the data toggles between binary 1's and 0's often and equal numbers of binary 1's and 0's are sent. However, the circuitry that produces the polar NRZ signal requires a negative-voltage power supply as well as a positive-voltage power supply. The Manchester NRZ line code has the advantage of always having a 0 dc value, regardless of the data sequence, but it has twice the bandwidth of the unipolar NRZ or polar NRZ codes since the pulses are half the width (see Fig. 4-11).

Some desirable properties of a line code are as follows:

• *Self-synchronization.* There is enough timing information built into the code so that bit synchronizers can be designed to extract the timing or clock signal. A long series of binary 1's and 0's should not cause a problem in time recovery.

- *Low probability of bit error.* Receivers can be designed that will recover the binary data with a low probability of bit error when the input data signal is corrupted by noise or ISI. The ISI problem is discussed in Sec. 4-5.
- *A spectrum that is suitable for the channel.* For example, if the channel is ac coupled, the PSD of the line code signal should be negligible at frequencies near zero. In addition the signal bandwidth needs to be sufficiently small compared to the channel bandwidth so that ISI will not be a problem.
- *Transmission bandwidth.* It should be as small as possible.
- *Error detection capability.* It should be possible to implement this feature easily by the addition of channel encoders and decoders, or it should be incorporated into the line code.
- *Transparency.* The data protocol and line code are designed so that *every possible sequence of data* is faithfully and *transparently* received.

A protocol is not transparent if certain words are reserved for control sequences so that, for example, a certain word instructs the receiver to send all data that follows to the printer. This feature causes a problem when a random data file (such as a machine language file) is transferred over the link since some of the words in the file might be control character sequences. These sequences would be intercepted by the receiving system, and the defined action would be carried out, instead of passing the word on to the intended destination. In addition, a code is not transparent if some sequence will result in a loss of clocking signal out of the bit synchronizer at the receiver. The bipolar format is not transparent since a string of zeros will result in a loss of the clocking signal.

The particular type of waveform used for binary signaling depends on the application. For example, unipolar or polar signaling is usually found in most digital circuits, but these waveshapes may have a nonzero dc level; furthermore, the dc level depends on the exact data being represented. On the other hand, bipolar and Manchester-type signaling will always have a zero dc level regardless of the data being represented. More discussion of the advantages and disadvantages of each signal format will be given after their spectra have been derived.

Power Spectra of Line Codes

The power spectral density (PSD) can be evaluated by using either deterministic or stochastic techniques. This was discussed first in Chapter 1 and later illustrated in Example 3-6. To evaluate the PSD using the deterministic technique, the waveform for a line code that results from a particular data sequence is used. The approximate PSD is then evaluated by using (2-66) or, if the line code is periodic, by (2-122). Work Prob. 4-23 to apply this deterministic approach. Alternatively, the PSD may be evaluated by using the stochastic approach.

The stochastic approach will be used to obtain PSD of line codes that are shown in Fig. 4-11. The stochastic approach is used because it gives the PSD for the line code with a random data sequence (instead of that for a particular data sequence). Consequently, the PSD obtained by the stochastic approach is typical of those obtained for most deterministic calculations (where a different spectrum is obtained for each possible data sequence).

As discussed and illustrated in Sec. 3-6, a digital signal (or line code) can be represented by

$$s(t) = \sum_{n=-\infty}^{\infty} a_n f(t - nT_s) \tag{4-27}$$

where $f(t)$ is the symbol pulse shape and T_s is the duration of one symbol. For binary signaling $T_s = T_b$ where T_b is the time that it takes to send 1 bit. For multilevel signaling, $T_s = \ell T_b$. $\{a_n\}$ is the set of random data. For example, for the unipolar NRZ line code, $f(t) = \Pi(t/T_b)$; and $a_n = +A$ volts, where a binary 1 is sent during the bit interval corresponding to nT_b seconds and $a_n = 0$ V when a binary 0 is sent.

As proven in Sec. 4-11 (Appendix), it can be shown by using (4-27) that the general expression for the PSD of a digital signal is

$$\mathcal{P}_s(f) = \frac{|F(f)|^2}{T_s} \sum_{k=-\infty}^{\infty} R(k)e^{j2\pi kfT_s} \tag{4-28}$$

where $F(f)$ is the Fourier transform of the pulse shape, $f(t)$, and $R(k)$ is the autocorrelation of the data. This autocorrelation is given by

$$R(k) = \sum_{i=1}^{I} (a_n a_{n+k})_i P_i \tag{4-29}$$

where a_n and a_{n+k} are the (voltage) levels of the data pulses at the nth and $n + k$th symbol positions, respectively, and P_i is the probability of having the ith $a_n a_{n+k}$ product. Note that (4-28) shows that the spectrum of the digital signal depends on two things: (1) the pulse shape used, and (2) statistical properties of the data.

Using (4-28), which is the stochastic approach, the PSD for the various line codes shown in Fig. 4-11 will now be evaluated.

Unipolar NRZ Signaling For unipolar signaling the possible levels for the a's are $+A$ and 0 V. Assume that these values are equally likely to occur and that the data are independent. Now evaluate $R(k)$ as defined by (4-29). For $k = 0$ the possible products of $a_n a_n$ are $A \times A = A^2$ and $0 \times 0 = 0$, and consequently, $I = 2$. For random data, the probability of having A^2 is $\frac{1}{2}$ and the probability of having 0 is $\frac{1}{2}$, so that

$$R(0) = \sum_{i=1}^{2} (a_n a_n)_i P_i = A^2 \cdot \tfrac{1}{2} + 0 \cdot \tfrac{1}{2} = \tfrac{1}{2} A^2$$

For $k \neq 0$ there are $I = 4$ possibilities for the product values: $A \times A, A \times 0, 0 \times A, 0 \times 0$. They all occur with a probability of $\frac{1}{4}$. Thus, for $k \neq 0$,

$$R(k) = \sum_{i=1}^{4} (a_n a_{n+k}) P_i = A^2 \cdot \tfrac{1}{4} + 0 \cdot \tfrac{1}{4} + 0 \cdot \tfrac{1}{4} + 0 \cdot \tfrac{1}{4} = \tfrac{1}{4} A^2$$

Thus

$$R_{\text{unipolar}}(k) = \begin{cases} \tfrac{1}{2}A^2, & k = 0 \\ \tfrac{1}{4}A^2, & k \neq 0 \end{cases} \tag{4-30}$$

For rectangular NRZ pulse shapes, the Fourier transform pair is

$$f(t) = \Pi\left(\frac{t}{T_b}\right) \leftrightarrow F(f) = T_b \frac{\sin \pi f T_b}{\pi f T_b} \qquad (4\text{-}31)$$

Using (4-28) with $T_s = T_b$, the PSD for the unipolar NRZ line code is

$$\mathscr{P}_{\text{unipolar NRZ}}(f) = \frac{A^2 T_b}{4}\left(\frac{\sin \pi f T_b}{\pi f T_b}\right)^2\left[1 + \sum_{k=-\infty}^{\infty} e^{j2\pi k f T_b}\right] \qquad (4\text{-}32)$$

But[†]

$$\sum_{k=-\infty}^{\infty} e^{jk2\pi f T_b} = \frac{1}{T_b}\sum_{n=-\infty}^{\infty} \delta\left(f - \frac{n}{T_b}\right) \qquad (4\text{-}33)$$

Thus

$$\mathscr{P}_{\text{unipolar NRZ}}(f) = \frac{A^2 T_b}{4}\left(\frac{\sin \pi f T_b}{\pi f T_b}\right)^2\left[1 + \frac{1}{T_b}\sum_{n=-\infty}^{\infty} \delta\left(f - \frac{n}{T_b}\right)\right] \qquad (4\text{-}34)$$

But since $[\sin(\pi f T_b)/(\pi f T_b)] = 0$ at $f = n/T_b$, $n \neq 0$; this reduces to

$$\mathscr{P}_{\text{unipolar NRZ}}(f) = \frac{A^2 T_b}{4}\left(\frac{\sin \pi f T_b}{\pi f T_b}\right)^2\left[1 + \frac{1}{T_b}\delta(f)\right] \qquad (4\text{-}35)$$

If A is selected so that the normalized average power of the unipolar NRZ signal is unity, then[‡] $A = \sqrt{2}$. This PSD is plotted in Fig. 4-12a, where $1/T_b = R$, the bit rate of the line code. The obvious disadvantage of unipolar NRZ is the waste of power due to the dc level and the fact that the spectrum is not approaching zero near dc. Of course, dc coupled circuits are needed for this type of signaling. The advantages of unipolar signaling are that it is easy to generate (i.e., TTL and CMOS circuits) and it requires the use of only one power supply.

Polar NRZ Signaling For polar NRZ signaling the possible levels for the a's are $+A$ and $-A$ volts. For equally likely occurrences of $+A$ and $-A$ and assuming that the data are independent from bit to bit, we get

$$R(0) = \sum_{i=1}^{2} (a_n a_n)_i P_i = A^2 \tfrac{1}{2} + (-A)^2 \tfrac{1}{2} = A^2$$

For $k \neq 0$,

$$R(k) = \sum_{i=1}^{4} (a_n a_{n+k}) P_i = A^2 \tfrac{1}{4} + (-A)(A)\tfrac{1}{4} + (A)(-A)\tfrac{1}{4} + (-A)^2\tfrac{1}{4} = 0$$

[†] Equation (4-33) is known as the Poisson sum formula as derived in (2-110).

[‡] This can be demonstrated easily using a line code with periodic data 10101010. Then setting

$$P_s = \frac{1}{T_0}\int_0^{T_0} s^2(t)\,dt = \frac{1}{2T_b}A^2 T_b$$

equal to unity, we get $A = \sqrt{2}$.

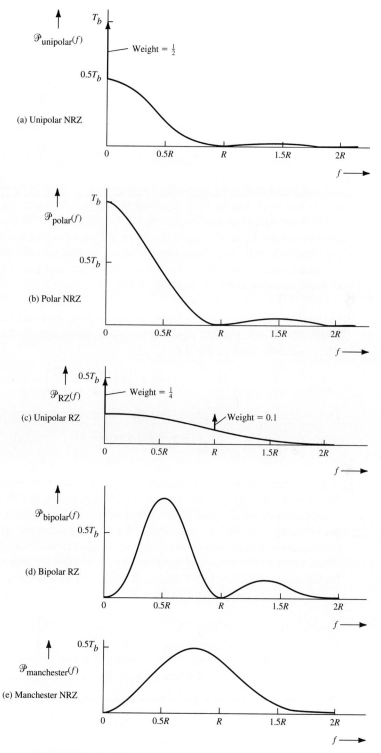

FIGURE 4-12 PSD for line codes (positive frequencies shown).

Thus

$$R_{polar}(k) = \begin{cases} A^2, & k = 0 \\ 0, & k \neq 0 \end{cases} \tag{4-36}$$

Then substituting (4-36) and (4-31) in (4-28), the PSD for the polar NRZ signal is

$$\mathcal{P}_{polar\ NRZ}(f) = A^2 T_b \left(\frac{\sin \pi f T_b}{\pi f T_b} \right)^2 \tag{4-37}$$

If A is selected so that the normalized average power of the polar NRZ signal is unity, then $A = 1$, and the resulting PSD is shown in Fig. 4-12b, where the bit rate is $R = 1/T_b$.

The polar signal has the disadvantage of having a large PSD near dc. On the other hand, polar signals are relatively easy to generate, although positive and negative power supplies are required unless special-purpose integrated circuits are used that generate dual supply voltages from a single supply. The probability of bit error performance is superior to that of other signaling methods (see Fig. 4-16).

Unipolar RZ The autocorrelation for the unipolar data was calculated previously and is given by (4-30). For RZ signaling the pulse duration is $T_b/2$ instead of T_b as used in NRZ signaling. That is, for RZ,

$$F(f) = \frac{T_b}{2} \left(\frac{\sin(\pi f T_b/2)}{\pi f T_b/2} \right) \tag{4-38}$$

Then, referring to (4-31) and (4-34), the PDF for the unipolar RZ line code is

$$\mathcal{P}_{unipolar\ RZ}(f) = \frac{A^2 T_b}{16} \left(\frac{\sin(\pi f T_b/2)}{\pi f T_b/2} \right)^2 \left[1 + \frac{1}{T_b} \sum_{n=-\infty}^{\infty} \delta\left(f - \frac{n}{T_b} \right) \right] \tag{4-39}$$

If A is selected so that the normalized average power of the unipolar RZ signal is unity, then $A = 2$. The PSD for this unity power case is shown in Fig. 4-12c, where $R = 1/T_b$.

As expected, the first null bandwidth is twice that for unipolar or polar signaling since the pulse width is half as wide. Note that there is a discrete (impulse) term at $f = R$. Consequently, this periodic component can be used for recovery of the clock signal. One disadvantage of this scheme is that it requires 3 dB more signal power than polar signaling for the same probability of bit error as shown in the next section. Moreover, the spectrum is not negligible for frequencies near dc.

Bipolar RZ Signaling The PSD for a bipolar signal can also be obtained from (4-28). The permitted values for a_n are $+A$, $-A$, and 0 where binary 1's are represented by alternating $+A$ and $-A$ values and a binary 0 is represented by $a_n = 0$. For $k = 0$ the products $a_n a_n$ are A^2 and 0 where each of these products occurs with a probability of $\frac{1}{2}$. Thus

$$R(0) = \frac{A^2}{2}$$

For $k = 1$ (the adjacent bit case) and the data sequences $(1,1)$, $(1,0)$, $(0,1)$, and $(0,0)$, the possible $a_n a_{n+1}$ products are $-A^2$, 0, 0, 0. Each of these sequences occurs with a probability of $\frac{1}{4}$. Consequently,

$$R(1) = \sum_{i=1}^{4} (a_n a_{n+1})_i P_i = -\frac{A^2}{4}$$

For $k > 1$, the bits being considered are not adjacent, and the $a_n a_{n+k}$ products are $\pm A^2$, 0, 0, 0; these occur with a probability of $\frac{1}{4}$. Then

$$R(k > 1) = \sum_{i=1}^{5} (a_n a_{n+k})_i P_i = A^2 \cdot \tfrac{1}{8} - A^2 \cdot \tfrac{1}{8} = 0$$

Thus

$$R_{\text{bipolar}}(k) = \begin{cases} \dfrac{A^2}{2}, & k = 0 \\[2mm] -\dfrac{A^2}{4}, & |k| = 1 \\[2mm] 0, & |k| > 1 \end{cases} \qquad (4\text{-}40)$$

Using (4-40) and (4-38) in (4-28) where $T_s = T_b$, the PSD for the bipolar RZ line code is

$$\mathscr{P}_{\text{bipolar RZ}}(f) = \frac{A^2 T_b}{8} \left(\frac{\sin(\pi f T_b/2)}{\pi f T_b/2} \right)^2 [1 - \cos(2\pi f T_b)]$$

or

$$\mathscr{P}_{\text{bipolar RZ}}(f) = \frac{A^2 T_b}{4} \left(\frac{\sin(\pi f T_b/2)}{\pi f T_b/2} \right)^2 \sin^2(\pi f T_b) \qquad (4\text{-}41)$$

where $A = 2$ if the normalized average power is unity. This PSD is plotted in Fig. 4-12d. Bipolar signaling has a spectral null at dc so that ac coupled circuits may be used in the transmission path.

The clock signal can be easily extracted from the bipolar waveform by converting the bipolar format to a unipolar RZ format by the use of full-wave rectification. The resulting (unipolar) RZ signal has a periodic component at the clock frequency (see Fig. 4-12c). Bipolar signals are not transparent. That is, a string of zeros will cause a loss in the clocking signal. This difficulty can be prevented by using *high-density bipolar n* (HDBn) signaling where a string of more than n consecutive zeros is replaced by a "filling" sequence that contains some pulses [Benedetto, Biglieri, and Castellani, 1987].[†] The cal-

---

[†] For example, for HDB3, the filling sequences used to replace $n + 1 = 4$ zeros are the alternating sequences 000V and 100V, where the 1 bit is encoded according to the bipolar rule and the V is a 1 pulse of such polarity as to violate the bipolar rule. The alternating filling sequences are designed so that consecutive V pulses alternate in sign. Consequently, there will be a 0 dc value in the line code and the PSD will have a null at $f = 0$. To decode the HDB3 code, the bipolar decoder has to detect the bipolar violations and to count the number of zeros preceding each violation so that the substituted 1's can be deleted.

culation of the PSD for HBDn codes is difficult since the $R(k)$ have to be individually evaluated for large values of k [Davis and Barber, 1973].

Bipolar signals also have single-error detection capabilities built in since a single error will cause a violation of the bipolar line code rule. Any violations can easily be detected by receiver logic.

Some disadvantages of bipolar signals are that the receiver has to distinguish between three levels ($+A$, $-A$, and 0) instead of just two levels in the other signaling formats previously discussed. The bipolar signal also requires approximately 3 dB more signal power than a polar signal for the same probability of bit error (see Fig. 4-16).

Manchester NRZ Signaling The Manchester signal uses the pulse shape

$$f(t) = \Pi\left(\frac{t + T_b/4}{T_b/2}\right) - \Pi\left(\frac{t - T_b/4}{T_b/2}\right) \tag{4-42}$$

and the resulting pulse spectrum is

$$F(f) = \frac{T_b}{2}\left[\frac{\sin(\pi f T_b/2)}{\pi f T_b/2}\right]e^{j\omega T_b/4} - \frac{T_b}{2}\left[\frac{\sin(\pi f T_b/2)}{\pi f T_b/2}\right]e^{-j\omega T_b/4}$$

or

$$F(f) = jT_b\left[\frac{\sin(\pi f T_b/2)}{\pi f T_b/2}\right]\sin\left(\frac{\omega T_b}{4}\right) \tag{4-43}$$

Substituting (4-43) and (4-36) into (4-28), the PSD for the Manchester NRZ becomes

$$\mathscr{P}_{\text{Manchester NRZ}}(f) = A^2 T_b\left(\frac{\sin(\pi f T_b/2)}{\pi f T_b/2}\right)^2 \sin^2(\pi f T_b/2) \tag{4-44}$$

where $A = 1$ if the normalized average power is unity.

This spectrum is plotted in Fig. 4-12e. The null bandwidth of the Manchester format is twice that of the bipolar bandwidth. However, the Manchester code has a zero dc level on a bit-by-bit basis. Moreover, a string of zeros will not cause a loss of the clocking signal.

In reviewing our study of PSD for digital signals, it should be emphasized that the spectrum is a function of the bit pattern (via the bit autocorrelation) as well as the pulse shape.

Differential Coding

When serial data are passed through many circuits along a communication channel, the waveform is often unintentionally inverted (i.e., data complemented). This result can occur in a twisted-pair transmission line channel just by switching the two leads at a connection point when a line code such as polar signaling is used. (Note that this would not affect the data on a bipolar signal.) To ameliorate this problem, *differential coding*, as illustrated in Fig. 4-13, is often employed. The encoded differential data are generated by

$$e_n = d_n \oplus e_{n-1} \tag{4-45}$$

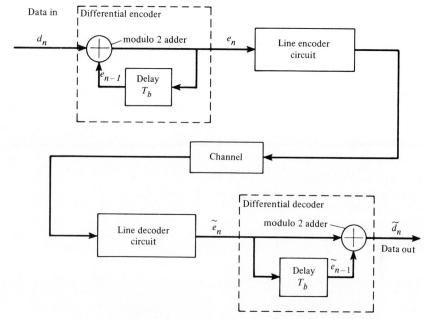

FIGURE 4-13 Differential coding system.

where $\oplus$ is a modulo 2 adder or exclusive OR gate (XOR) operation. The received encoded data are decoded by

$$\tilde{d}_n = \tilde{e}_n \oplus \tilde{e}_{n-1} \tag{4-46}$$

where the tilde denotes receiving-end data.

Each digit in the encoded sequence is obtained by comparing the present input bit with the past encoded bit. A binary 1 is encoded if the present input bit and the past encoded bit are of opposite state, and a binary 0 is encoded if the states are the same. This is equivalent to the truth table of an XOR (exclusive OR) gate or a modulo 2 adder. An example of an encoded sequence is shown in Table 4-3, where the beginning reference digit is a binary 1. At the receiver the encoded signal is decoded by comparing the state of adjacent bits. If the present received encoded bit has the same state as the past encoded bit, a binary 0 is the decoded output. Similarly, a binary 1 is decoded for opposite states. As shown in the table, the polarity of the differentially encoded waveform may be inverted without affecting the decoded data. This is a great advantage when the waveform is passed through thousands of circuits in a communication system and the positive sense of the output is lost or changes occasionally as the network changes, such as switching between several data paths. As will be seen in Sec. 6-1, differential coding can be used to eliminate the problem of 180° phase ambiguity that occurs when a Costas loop or a squaring loop is turned on.

TABLE 4-3 Example of Differential Coding

Encoding									
Input sequence	d_n		1	1	0	1	0	0	1
Encoded sequence	e_n	1	0	1	1	0	0	0	1
Reference digit ⎯⎯⎯⎯⎯⎯⎯		↑							
Decoding (with correct channel polarity)									
Received sequence (correct polarity)	$\tilde{e}_n$	1	0	1	1	0	0	0	1
Decoded sequence	$\tilde{d}_n$		1	1	0	1	0	0	1
Decoding (with inverted channel polarity)									
Received sequence (inverted polarity)	$\tilde{e}_n$	0	1	0	0	1	1	1	0
Decoded sequence	$\tilde{d}_n$		1	1	0	1	0	0	1

Eye Patterns

The effect of channel filtering and channel noise can be seen by observing the received line code on an oscilloscope. The left side of Fig. 4-14 shows received corrupted polar NRZ waveforms for the cases of (a) ideal channel filtering, (b) filtering that produces intersymbol interference (ISI), and (c) noise plus ISI. (ISI is described in Sec. 4-5.) On the right side of the figure, corresponding oscilloscope presentations of the corrupted signal are shown with multiple sweeps where each sweep is triggered by a clock signal and the sweep width is slightly larger than T_b. These displays on the right are called *eye patterns* because they resemble the picture of a human eye. Under normal operating conditions (i.e., for no detected bit errors), the eye will be open. If there is a great deal of noise or ISI, the eye will close; this indicates that bit errors will be produced at the receiver output. The eye pattern provides an excellent way of assessing the quality of the received line code and the ability of the receiver to combat bit errors. As shown in the figure, the eye pattern provides the following information.

- The *timing error* allowed on the sampler at the receiver is given by the width inside the eye, called the *eye opening*. Of course, the preferred time for sampling is at the point where the vertical opening of the eye is the largest.
- The *sensitivity* to timing error is given by the slope of the open eye (evaluated at, or near, the zero-crossing point).
- The *noise margin* of the system is given by the height of the eye opening.
- The *maximum distortion* is given by the vertical width of the upper (or lower) portion of the eye at the sampling time.

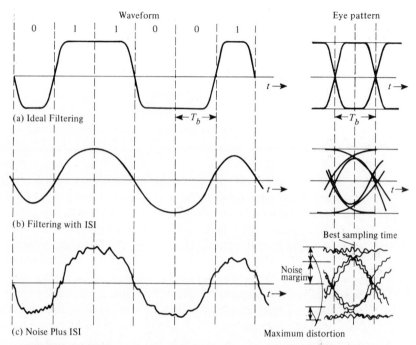

FIGURE 4-14 Distorted polar NRZ waveform and corresponding eye pattern.

Regenerative Repeaters and Probability of Bit Error for Line Codes

When a line code digital signal (such as PCM) is transmitted over a hardwire channel (such as a twisted-pair telephone line), it is attenuated, filtered, and corrupted by noise. Consequently, for long lines, the data cannot be recovered at the receiving end unless repeaters are placed in cascade along the line and at the receiver as illustrated in Fig. 4-7. These repeaters amplify and "clean up" the signal periodically. If the signal was analog instead of digital, only linear amplifiers with appropriate filters could be used since relative amplitude values would need to be preserved. In this case in-band distortion would accumulate from linear repeater to linear repeater. This is one of the disadvantages of analog signaling. However, with digital signaling, nonlinear processing can be used to regenerate a "noise-free" digital signal. This type of nonlinear processing is called a *regenerative repeater*. A simplified block diagram of a regenerative repeater for unipolar NRZ signaling is shown in Fig. 4-15. The amplifying filter increases the amplitude of the low-level input signal to a level that is compatible with the remaining circuitry and filters the signal in such a way as to minimize the effects of channel noise and ISI. (The filter that reduces ISI is called an *equalizing filter* and is discussed in Sec. 4-5.) The bit synchronizer generates a clocking signal at the bit rate that is synchronized so that the amplified

FIGURE 4-15 Regenerative repeater for unipolar NRZ signaling.

distorted signal is sampled at a point where the eye opening is at maximum. (Bit synchronizers are discussed in detail in the next section.) For each clock pulse, the sample-and-hold circuit produces the sample value that is held (for T_b, one bit interval) until the next clock pulse occurs. The comparator produces a high-level output only when the sample value is larger than the threshold level, V_T. V_T is usually selected to be one-half the expected peak-to-peak variation of the sample values.[†] If the input noise is small and there is negligible ISI, the comparator output will be high only when there is a binary 1(i.e., a high level) on the corrupted unipolar NRZ line code at the input to the repeater. The comparator—a threshold device—acts as a decision-making device. Thus the unipolar NRZ line code is regenerated "noise free" except for bit errors that are caused when the input noise and ISI alter the sample values sufficiently so that the sample values occur on the wrong side of V_T.

For minimum probability of bit error, the sample-and-hold circuit of Fig. 4-15 is replaced by an optimum sample-detection circuit called a *matched filter* (MF). If the noise has a white spectrum—that is, $\mathcal{P}_n(f) = N_0/2$ where N_0 is a constant—the MF may be described by (3-51) [Couch, 1993]. That is, over each bit interval, the sample value, $\tilde{s}_k$, is obtained by evaluating the integral

$$\tilde{s}_k = K \int_{kT_b}^{(k+1)T_b} r(t)f(t - kT_b) \, dt \qquad (4\text{-}47)$$

where $r(t)$ is the amplified and filtered received waveform that is present at the input to the MF, $f(t)$ is the (known) filtered pulse shape embodied in $r(t)$, and K is the gain of the MF. The clock pulses from the bit synchronizer circuit are used to start and stop the integrator, and to hold the past sample value, $\tilde{s}_{k-1}$, at the output of the MF circuit while the present sample value, $\tilde{s}_k$, is being evaluated (by integration).

The error performance of the regenerative repeater with MF processing is given in Table 4-4, where it is assumed that (1) the 1's and 0's are equally likely, (2) the signal is corrupted by additive white Gaussian noise (AWGN), and (3) matched filter detection is used. These results are plotted in Fig. 4-16. P_e is the probability of bit error, which is also called the *bit error rate* (BER) by communication engineers. E_b/N_0 is a measure of the signal-to-noise ratio (S/N) at the MF input. In particular, E_b is the energy in the signal (at the MF input) over a 1-bit interval and N_0 is related to the PSD of the noise (at the MF

[†]This is the optimum V_T when the binary ones and zeros are equally likely.

TABLE 4-4 Error Performance of Line Codes[a]

Line Code	Probability of Error, P_e
Unipolar NRZ or Unipolar RZ	$Q[\sqrt{(E_b/N_0)}]$
Polar NRZ or Polar RZ	$Q[\sqrt{2(E_b/N_0)}]$
Bipolar NRZ or Bipolar RZ	$\frac{3}{2}Q[\sqrt{(E_b/N_0)}]$, $E_b N_0 > 2$
Manchester NRZ or Manchester RZ	$Q[\sqrt{2(E_b/N_0)}]$

[a]$Q(z)$ is the Q function as defined in (A-112) and plotted in Fig. B-7.
SOURCE: L. W. Couch, *Digital and Analog Communication Systems,*
4th ed., Macmillan, New York, 1993.

input), $\mathcal{P}_n(f)$ by $\mathcal{P}_n(f) = N_0/2$. From Fig. 4-16 it is seen that polar or Manchester signaling gives the lowest P_e. That is, a polar or Manchester line code should be selected if error performance (and not spectral characteristics) is the prime consideration.

In long-distance digital communication systems, many repeaters may be used in cascade, as shown in Fig. 4-7. Of course, the spacing between the repeaters is governed by the path loss of the transmission medium and the amount of noise that is added. A repeater is required when the S/N at a point along the channel becomes lower than the value that is needed to maintain the overall probability-of-bit-error specification. Assume that the repeaters are spaced so that each of them has the same probability of bit error, P_e, and that there are m repeaters in the system, including the end receiver. Then, for m repeaters in cascade, the overall probability of bit error, P_{me}, can be evaluated by the use of the binomial distribution from Appendix B. Using (B-33), we see that the probability of i out of the m repeaters producing a bit error is

$$P_i = \binom{m}{i} P_e^i (1 - P_e)^{m-i} \tag{4-48}$$

However, there is a bit error at the system output only when each of an *odd* number of the cascaded repeaters produces a bit error. Consequently, the overall probability of a bit error for m cascaded repeaters is

$$P_{me} = \sum_{\substack{i=1 \\ i=\text{odd}}}^{m} P_i = \sum_{\substack{i=1 \\ i=\text{odd}}}^{m} \binom{m}{i} P_e^i (1 - P_e)^{m-i}$$

$$= mP_e(1 - P_e)^{m-1} + \frac{m(m-1)(m-2)}{3!} P_e^3 (1 - P_e)^{m-3} + \cdots \tag{4-49}$$

Under useful operating conditions, $P_e \ll 1$, so only the first term of this series is significant. Thus the overall probability of bit error is approximated by

$$P_{me} \approx mP_e \tag{4-50}$$

where P_e is the probability of bit error for a single repeater.

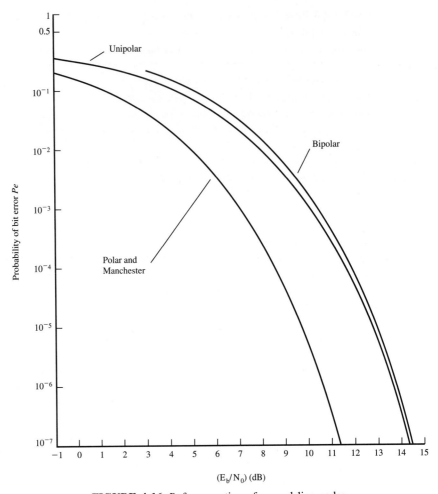

FIGURE 4-16 P_e for reception of several line codes.

Bit Synchronization

As discussed earlier, synchronization signals are clock-type signals that are necessary within a receiver (or repeater) for detection (or regeneration) of the data from the corrupted input signal. These clock signals have a precise frequency and phase relationship with respect to the *received* input signal, and they are delayed when compared to the clock signals at the transmitter since there is propagation delay through the channel.

Digital communications usually need at least three types of synchronization signals: (1) *bit sync* to distinguish one bit interval from another, as discussed in this section; (2) *frame sync* to distinguish groups of data, as discussed in Sec. 4-8 in regard to time-division multiplexing; and (3) *carrier sync* for bandpass signaling with coherent detection, as discussed in Chapters 5, 6, and 7. Systems are designed so that the sync is derived either directly from the corrupted signal or from a separate channel that is used only to transmit the sync information.

We will concentrate on systems with bit synchronizers that derive the sync directly from the corrupted signal since it is usually not economically feasible to send sync over a separate channel and since it is relatively easy to derive the bit sync for the separate channel case. The complexity of the bit synchronizer circuit depends on the sync properties of the line code. For example, the bit synchronizer for a unipolar RZ code with a sufficient number of alternating binary 1's and 0's is almost trivial since the PSD of that code has a delta function at the bit rate, $f = R$, as shown in Fig. 4-12c. Consequently, the bit sync clock signal can be obtained by passing the received unipolar RZ waveform through a narrow-band bandpass filter that is tuned to $f_0 = R = 1/T_b$. This is illustrated by Fig. 4-17 if the square-law device is deleted. Alternatively, as described in Sec. 5-3, a phase-locked-loop (PLL) can be used to extract the sync signal from the unipolar RZ line code by locking the PLL to the discrete spectral line at $f = R$. For a polar NRZ line code, the bit synchronizer is slightly more complicated as shown in Fig. 4-17. Here the filtered polar NRZ waveform (Fig. 4-17b) is converted to a unipolar RZ waveform (Fig. 4-17c) by using a square-law (or, alternatively, a full-wave rectifier) circuit. As described previously, the clock signal is easily recovered by using a filter or a PLL since the unipolar RZ code has a delta function in its spectrum at $f = R$. All of the bit synchronizers discussed thus far use some technique for detecting the spectral line at $f = R$.

Another technique utilizes the symmetry property of the line code itself [Carlson, 1986]. Referring to Fig. 4-14 which illustrates the eye pattern for a polar NRZ code, we realize that a properly filtered line code has a pulse shape that is symmetrical about the optimum clocking (sampling) time, provided that the data are alternating between 1's and 0's. Referring to Fig. 4-18, let $w_1(t)$ denote the filtered polar NRZ line code and let $w_1(\tau_0 + nT_b)$ denote a sample value of the line code at the maximum (positive or negative) of the eye opening where n is an integer, $R = 1/T_b$ is the bit rate, τ is the relative clocking time (i.e., clock phase), and τ_0 is the optimum value corresponding to samples at the maximum of the eye opening. Since the pulse shape of the line code is approximately symmetrical about the optimum clocking time for alternating data,

$$\left| w_1(\tau_0 + nT_b - \Delta) \right| \approx \left| w_1(\tau_0 + nT_b + \Delta) \right|$$

where τ_0 is the optimum clocking phase and $0 < \Delta < \frac{1}{2}T_b$. $w_1(\tau + nT_b - \Delta)$ is called the *early sample* and $w_1(\tau + nT_b + \Delta)$ is called the *late sample*. These samples can be used to derive the optimum clocking signal as illustrated in the *early–late bit synchronizer* shown in Fig. 4-18. The control voltage, $w_3(t)$, for the voltage-controlled clock (VCC) is a smoothed (averaged) version of $w_2(t)$. That is,

$$w_3(t) = \langle w_2(t) \rangle \tag{4-51a}$$

where

$$w_2(t) = \left| w_1(\tau + nT_b - \Delta) \right| - \left| w_1(\tau + nT_b + \Delta) \right| \tag{4-51b}$$

(The averaging operation is needed so that the bit synchronizer will remain synchronized even if the data do not alternate for every bit interval.) If the VCC is producing clocking pulses with the optimum relative clocking time $\tau = \tau_0$ so that samples are taken at the

(a) Block Diagram of Bit Synchronizer

(b) Filtered Polar NRZ Input Waveform

(c) Output of Square Law Device (Unipolar RZ)

(d) Output of Narrow Band Filter

(e) Clocking Output Signal

FIGURE 4-17 Square-law bit synchronizer for polar NRZ signaling.

maximum of the eye opening, equation (4-51) demonstrates that the control voltage $w_3(t)$ will be zero. If τ is late $w_3(t)$ will be a positive correction voltage, and if τ is early $w_3(t)$ will be negative. A positive (negative) control voltage will increase (decrease) the frequency of the VCC. Thus, the bit synchronizer will produce an output clock signal that is synchronized to the input data stream. That is, $w_4(t)$ will be a pulse train with narrow clock

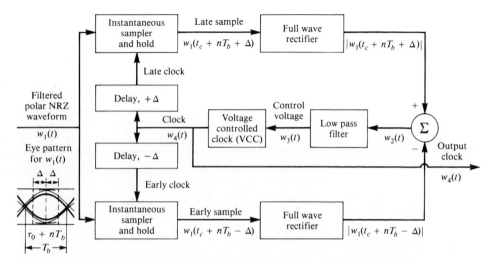

FIGURE 4-18 Early–late bit synchronizer for polar NRZ signaling.

pulses occurring at the time $t = \tau + nT_b$, where n is any integer and τ approximates τ_0, the optimum clock phase that corresponds to sampling at the maximum of the eye opening. It is interesting to realize that the early–late bit synchronizer of Fig. 4-18 has the same canonical form as the Costas carrier synchronization loop of Fig. 5-34.

As explained in previous sections, unipolar, polar, and bipolar bit synchronizers will work only when there are a sufficient number of alternating 1's and 0's in the data. The loss of synchronization because of strings of all 1's or all 0's can be prevented by adopting one of two possible alternatives. One alternative, as discussed in Chapter 1, is to use bit interleaving (i.e., scrambling). In this case the source data with strings of 1's or 0's are scrambled to produce data with alternating 1's and 0's which are transmitted over the channel using a unipolar, polar, or bipolar line code. At the receiving end scrambled data are first recovered using the usual receiving techniques with bit synchronizers as just described; then the scrambled data are unscrambled. The other alternative is to use a completely different type of line code that does not require alternating data for bit synchronization. For example, Manchester NRZ encoding can be used, but it will require a channel with twice the bandwidth of that needed for a polar NRZ code.

For further study of the overall synchronization problem, the reader is referred to Chapter 7 of Feher [1981], which was written by L. E. Franks, and to Chapter 8 of Sklar [1988], which was written by M. A. King. A special issue of the *IEEE Transactions on Communications* gives tutorial as well as detailed analysis papers on synchronization [Gardner and Lindsey, 1980]. Details about bit synchronization can be found in a number of books [Holmes, 1982; Stiffler, 1971; Ziemer and Peterson, 1985].

Multilevel Signaling

As we have seen, the bandwidth of *binary* digital waveforms may be very large. In fact, the bandwidth of the binary waveform may well exceed the bandwidth allowed. If this is

(a) ℓ Bit Digital-to-Analog Converter

(b) Input Binary Waveform, $w_1(t)$

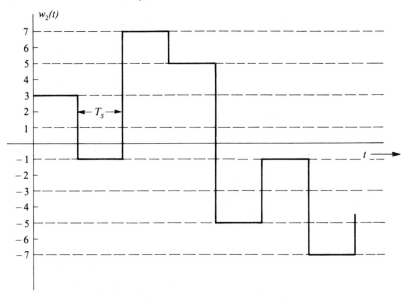

(c) $L = 8 = 2^3$ Level Waveform Out

FIGURE 4-19 Binary-to-multilevel digital signal conversion.

the case, the bandwidth of the digital signal can be reduced by converting it from a binary signal to a multilevel signal as illustrated in Fig. 4-19, where an ℓ-bit digital-to-analog converter (DAC) is used to produce a $L = 2^\ell$ multilevel signal.

For example, assume that an $\ell = 3$-bit DAC is used, so that $L = 2^3 = 8$ levels. Figure 4-19b illustrates a typical input waveform, and Fig. 4-19c shows the corresponding eight-level multilevel output waveform where T_s is the time it takes to send one multilevel symbol. To obtain this waveform, the code shown in Table 4-5 was used. From the figure,

TABLE 4-5 Three-Bit DAC Code

Digital Word	Output Level, $(a_n)_i$
000	+7
001	+5
010	+3
011	+1
100	−1
101	−3
110	−5
111	−7

we see that $D = 1/T_s = 1/(3T_b) = R/3$, or, in general, the baud rate is

$$D = \frac{R}{\ell} \tag{4-52}$$

This relationship between the output baud rate D and the associated bit rate R is identical to (3-61).

The PSD of the multilevel waveform shown in Fig. 4-19c can be obtained by the use of (4-28). Evaluating $R(k)$ for the case of equally likely levels a_n, as shown in Table 4-5, for the $k = 0$ case we have

$$R(0) = \sum_{i=1}^{8} (a_n)_i^2 P_i = 21$$

where $P_i = \frac{1}{8}$ for all of the eight possible values. For $k \neq 0$, $R(k) = 0$. Then, from (4-28), the PSD for $w_2(t)$ is

$$\mathscr{P}_{w_2}(f) = \frac{|F(f)|^2}{T_s} (21 + 0)$$

where the pulse width (or symbol width) is now $T_s = 3T_b$. For the rectangular pulse shape of width $3T_b$, this becomes

$$\mathscr{P}_{w_2}(f) = 63T_b \left(\frac{\sin 3\pi f T_b}{3\pi f T_b} \right)^2 \tag{4-53}$$

for this case where $l = 3$. Consequently, the first null bandwidth for this multilevel signal is $B_{\text{null}} = 1/(3T_b) = R/3$, or one third the bandwidth of the input binary signal.

For example, if the polar binary signal had a data rate of $R = 9600$ bits/sec, such as on an RS-232C-type line from a computer terminal (see Appendix C), the first null bandwidth of this binary signal would be 9.6 kHz, but the corresponding 8-level multilevel signal would have a bandwidth of only 3.2 kHz. Note that the multilevel signal would have a baud rate of $D = 3200$ symbols/sec and a bit rate of $R = 9600$ bits/sec, whereas the baud rate and bit rate of the binary signal are both equal to 9600.

In general, for multilevel signaling with rectangular pulse shapes, the null bandwidth is

$$B_{\text{null}} = R/\ell \tag{4-54}$$

In summary, multilevel signaling, where $L > 2$, is used to reduce the bandwidth of a digital signal when compared to the bandwidth required for binary signaling. In practice, filtered multilevel signals are often used to modulate a carrier for transmission of digital information over a communication channel. This provides a relatively narrowband digital signal.

Spectral Efficiency

DEFINITION: The *spectral efficiency* of a digital signal is given by the number of bits per second of data that can be supported by each hertz of bandwidth:

$$\eta = \frac{R}{B} \quad \text{(bits/sec)/Hz} \tag{4-55}$$

where R is the data rate and B is the bandwidth.

In applications where the bandwidth is limited by physical and regulatory constraints, the job of the communication engineer is to choose a signaling technique that gives the highest spectral efficiency while achieving given cost constraints and meeting specifications for low probability of bit error at the system output. Moreover, the maximum possible spectral efficiency is limited by the channel noise if the error is to be small. This maximum spectral efficiency is given by Shannon's channel capacity formula, (1-10),

$$\eta_{\text{max}} = \frac{C}{B} = \log_2\left(1 + \frac{S}{N}\right) \tag{4-56}$$

Shannon's theory does not tell us how to achieve a system with this maximum theoretical spectral efficiency; however, practical systems that approach this spectral efficiency usually incorporate error correction coding and multilevel signaling.

The spectral efficiency for multilevel NRZ signaling is obtained by substituting (4-54) into (4-55):

$$\eta = \ell \quad \text{(bits/sec)/Hz} \qquad \text{(multilevel NRZ signaling)} \tag{4-57}$$

where ℓ is the number of bits used in the DAC. Of course, ℓ cannot be increased without limit to an infinite efficiency because it is limited by the signal-to-noise ratio as given in (4-56).

The spectral efficiencies for all the line codes studied in the previous sections can be easily evaluated from their PSDs. The results are shown in Table 4-6. Unipolar NRZ, polar NRZ, and bipolar RZ are twice as efficient as unipolar or Manchester NRZ.

All of these binary line codes have $\eta \leq 1$. Multilevel signaling can be used to achieve much greater spectral efficiency, but multilevel circuits are more costly. In practice, multilevel signaling is used in the T1G digital telephone lines as described in Sec. 4-8.

TABLE 4-6 Spectral Efficiencies of Line Codes

Code Type	First-Null Bandwidth (Hz)	Spectral Efficiency $\eta = R/B$ [(bits/sec)/Hz]
Unipolar NRZ	R	1
Polar NRZ	R	1
Unipolar RZ	$2R$	$\frac{1}{2}$
Bipolar RZ	R	1
Manchester NRZ	$2R$	$\frac{1}{2}$
Multilevel NRZ	R/ℓ	ℓ

4-5 Intersymbol Interference

The absolute bandwidth of flat-top multilevel pulses is infinity. If these pulses are filtered improperly as they pass through a communication system, they will spread in time, and the pulse for each symbol may be smeared into adjacent time slots and cause *intersymbol interference* (ISI), as illustrated in Fig. 4-20. The question is: How can we restrict the bandwidth and still not introduce ISI? Of course, with restricted bandwidth, the pulses would have rounded tops (instead of flat tops). This problem was first studied by Nyquist in 1928 [Nyquist, 1928]. He discovered three different methods for pulse shaping that could be used to eliminate ISI. Each of these methods will be studied in the sections that follow.

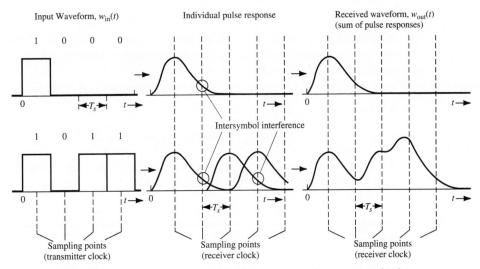

FIGURE 4-20 Examples of ISI on received pulses in a binary communication system.

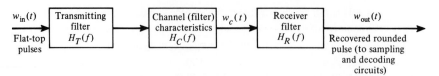

FIGURE 4-21 Baseband pulse transmission system.

Consider a digital signaling system as shown in Fig. 4-21. In general, multilevel signaling will be assumed where the flat-topped multilevel signal at the input is

$$w_{in}(t) = \sum_n a_n h(t - nT_s) \tag{4-58}$$

where $h(t) = \Pi(t/T_s)$ and a_n may take on any of the allowed L multilevels ($L = 2$ for binary signaling). The symbol rate is $D = 1/T_s$ pulses/sec. Then (4-58) may be written as

$$w_{in}(t) = \sum_n a_n h(t) * \delta(t - nT_s)$$

$$= \left[\sum_n a_n \delta(t - nT_s) \right] * h(t) \tag{4-59}$$

The output of the linear system of Fig. 4-21 would be just the input impulse train convolved with the equivalent impulse response of the overall system

$$w_{out}(t) = \left[\sum_n a_n \delta(t - nT_s) \right] * h_e(t) \tag{4-60}$$

where the equivalent impulse response is

$$h_e(t) = h(t) * h_T(t) * h_C(t) * h_R(t) \tag{4-61}$$

Note that $h_e(t)$ is also the pulse shape that will appear at the output of the receiver filter when a single flat-top pulse is fed into the transmitting filter (Fig. 4-21). The equivalent system transfer function is

$$H_e(f) = H(f)H_T(f)H_C(f)H_R(f) \tag{4-62}$$

where

$$H(f) = \mathscr{F}\left[\Pi\left(\frac{t}{T_s} \right) \right] = T_s \left(\frac{\sin \pi T_s f}{\pi T_s f} \right) \tag{4-63}$$

Equation (4-63) is used so that flat-top pulses will be present at the input to the transmitting filter. The receiving filter, $H_R(f)$, is given by

$$H_R(f) = \frac{H_e(f)}{H(f)H_T(f)H_C(f)} \tag{4-64}$$

where $H_e(f)$ is the desired overall filtering characteristic.

When $H_e(f)$ is chosen to minimize the ISI, then $H_R(f)$, obtained from (4-64), is called an *equalizing filter*. The equalizing filter characteristic depends on $H_C(f)$, the channel frequency response, as well as on the required $H_e(f)$. When the channel consists of dial-up telephone lines, the channel transfer function changes from call to call and the equalizing filter may need to be an *adaptive filter*. In this case, the equalizing filter adjusts itself to minimize the ISI (e.g., see Fig. 4-24). In some adaptive schemes, each communication session is preceded by a test bit pattern that is used to adapt the filter electronically for the maximum eye opening (i.e., minimum ISI). Such sequences are called *learning* or *training sequences* and *preambles*.

If we rewrite (4-60), the rounded pulse train at the output of the receiving filter is

$$w_{\text{out}}(t) = \sum_n a_n h_e(t - nT_s) \tag{4-65}$$

The output pulse shape is affected by the input pulse shape (flat-topped in this case), the transmitter filter, the channel filter, and the receiving filter. Since, in practice, the channel filter is already specified, the problem is to determine the transmitting filter and the receiving filter that will minimize the ISI on the rounded pulse at the output of the receiving filter.

From an applications point of view, it is realized that when the required transmitter filter and/or receiving filter transfer functions are found, they can each be multiplied by $Ke^{-j\omega T_d}$, where K is a convenient gain factor and T_d is a convenient time delay. These parameters are chosen to make the filters easier to build. The $Ke^{-j\omega T_d}$ factor(s) would not affect the zero ISI result but, of course, would modify the level and delay of the output waveform.

Nyquist's First Method (Zero ISI)

Nyquist's first method for elimination of ISI is to use an equivalent transfer function, $H_e(f)$, such that the impulse response satisfies the following condition:

$$h_e(kT_s + \tau) = \begin{cases} C, & k = 0 \\ 0, & k \neq 0 \end{cases} \tag{4-66}$$

where k is an integer, T_s is the symbol (sample) clocking period, τ is the offset in the receiver sampling clock times when compared to the clocking times of the input symbols, and C is a nonzero constant. That is, for a single flat-top pulse of level a present at the input to the transmitting filter at $t = 0$, the received pulse would be $ah_e(t)$. It would have a value of aC at $t = \tau$ but would not cause interference at other sampling times because $h_e(kT_s + \tau) = 0$ for $k \neq 0$ (e.g., see Fig. 4-20).

Now suppose that we choose a $(\sin x)/x$ function for $h_e(t)$. In particular, let $\tau = 0$ and choose

$$h_e(t) = \frac{\sin \pi f_s t}{\pi f_s t} \tag{4-67}$$

where $f_s = 1/T_s$. This impulse response satisfies Nyquist's first criterion for zero ISI, (4-66). Consequently, if the transmit and receive filters are designed so that the overall transfer function is

$$H_e(f) = \frac{1}{f_s} \Pi\left(\frac{f}{f_s}\right) \tag{4-68}$$

there will be no ISI. Furthermore, the absolute bandwidth of this transfer function is $B = f_s/2$. From our study of the sampling theorem and the dimensionality theorem in Chapter 2, we realize that this is the optimum filtering to produce a minimum bandwidth system. It will allow signaling at a baud rate of $D = 1/T_s = 2B$ pulses/sec, where B is the absolute bandwidth of the system. However, the $(\sin x)/x$ type of overall pulse shape has two practical difficulties.

1. The overall amplitude transfer characteristic $H_e(f)$ has to be flat over $-B < f < B$ and zero elsewhere. This is physically unrealizable (i.e., the impulse response is noncausal and of infinite duration). $H_e(f)$ is difficult to approximate because of the steep skirts in the filter transfer function at $f = \pm B$.
2. The synchronization of the clock in the decoding sampling circuit has to be almost perfect since the $(\sin x)/x$ pulse decays only as $1/x$ and is zero in adjacent time slots only when t is at the exactly correct sampling time. Thus, inaccurate sync will cause ISI.

Because of these difficulties, we are forced to consider other pulse shapes that have a slightly wider bandwidth. The idea is to find pulse shapes that go through zero at adjacent sampling points and yet have an envelope that decays much faster than $1/x$ so that clock jitter in the sampling times does not cause appreciable ISI. One solution for the equivalent transfer function, which has many desirable features, is the raised cosine-rolloff filter.

Raised Cosine-Rolloff Filtering

DEFINITION: The *raised cosine-rolloff filter* has the transfer function

$$H_e(f) = \begin{cases} 1, & |f| < f_1 \\ \frac{1}{2}\left\{1 + \cos\left[\frac{\pi(|f| - f_1)}{2f_\Delta}\right]\right\}, & f_1 < |f| < B \\ 0, & |f| > B \end{cases} \quad (4\text{-}69)$$

where B is the *absolute bandwidth* and the parameters f_1 and f_Δ are

$$f_\Delta = B - f_0 \quad (4\text{-}70)$$
$$f_1 \triangleq f_0 - f_\Delta \quad (4\text{-}71)$$

f_0 is the *6-dB bandwidth* of the raised cosine-rolloff filter. The *rolloff factor* is defined to be

$$r = \frac{f_\Delta}{f_0} \quad (4\text{-}72)$$

This filter characteristic is illustrated in Fig. 4-22. The corresponding impulse response is

$$h_e(t) = \mathscr{F}^{-1}[H_e(f)] = 2f_0\left(\frac{\sin 2\pi f_0 t}{2\pi f_0 t}\right)\left[\frac{\cos 2\pi f_\Delta t}{1 - (4f_\Delta t)^2}\right] \quad (4\text{-}73)$$

Plots of the frequency response and the impulse response are shown in Fig. 4-23 for rolloff factors $r = 0$, $r = 0.5$, and $r = 1.0$. The $r = 0$ characteristic is the minimum bandwidth

FIGURE 4-22 Raised cosine-rolloff filter characteristics.

(a) Magnitude Frequency Response

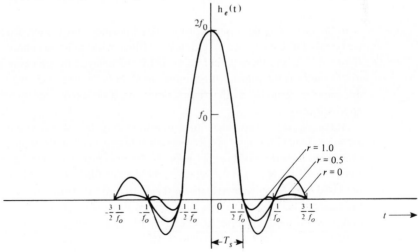

(b) Impulse Response

FIGURE 4-23 Frequency and time response for different rolloff factors.

case where $f_0 = B$ and the impulse response is the $(\sin x)/x$ pulse shape. From this figure it is seen that *as the absolute bandwidth is increased* (e.g., $r = 0.5$ and $r = 1.0$), (1) *the filtering requirements are relaxed,* although $h_e(t)$ is still noncausal; and (2) *the clock timing requirements are relaxed* also since the envelope of the impulse response decays faster than $1/|t|$ (on the order of $1/|t|^3$ for large values of t).

The baud rate that the communication system can support without ISI can be related to the absolute bandwidth of the system and the rolloff factor of the raised cosine-rolloff filter characteristic. From Fig. 4-23b, the zeros in the system impulse response occur at $t = n/2f_0$, $n \neq 0$. Thus, the raised cosine-rolloff filter satisfies Nyquist's first criterion for no ISI as described by (4-66) if we use $\tau = 0$ and sample with a period of $T_s = 1/2f_0$. The corresponding baud rate is $D = 1/T_s = 2f_0$ symbols/sec. Using (4-70) and (4-72), we see that the baud rate that can be supported by the system is

$$D = \frac{2B}{1 + r} \tag{4-74}$$

where B is the absolute bandwidth of the system and r is the system rolloff factor.

Example 4-1 (continued)

Assume that a binary PCM signal, with polar NRZ signaling, is passed through a communication system with a raised cosine-rolloff filtering characteristic and that the rolloff factor is 0.25. The bit rate of the PCM signal is 64 kbits/sec. Determine the absolute bandwidth of the filtered PCM signal.

Using (4-74), the absolute bandwidth is $B = 40$ kHz, which is less than the unfiltered PCM signal zero-crossing bandwidth of 64 kHz.

In the preceding description of the raised cosine-rolloff filter, we assumed that $H_e(f)$ was real. Of course, we could use a filter with a linear phase characteristic [i.e., $H_e(f)e^{-j\omega T_d}$], and there would be no ISI if we delayed the clocking by T_d sec, since the $e^{-j\omega T_d}$ factor is the transfer function of an ideal delay line. This would move the peak of the impulse response to the right (along the time axis), and then the filter would be approximately causal.

At the digital receiver, in addition to minimizing the ISI, we would like to minimize the effect of channel noise by proper receiver filtering. As discussed previously, the filter that minimizes the effect of channel noise is the *matched filter.* Unfortunately, if a matched filter is used for $H_R(f)$ at the receiver, the overall filter characteristic, $H_e(f)$, will usually not satisfy the Nyquist characteristic for minimum ISI. However, it can be shown that for the case of Gaussian noise into the receiver, the effects of both ISI and channel noise are minimized if the transmitter and receiver filters are designed so that [Shanmugan, 1979; Sunde, 1969; Ziemer and Peterson, 1985]

$$|H_T(f)| = \frac{\sqrt{|H_e(f)|}\,[\mathscr{P}_n(f)]^{1/4}}{\alpha\,|H(f)|\,\sqrt{|H_c(f)|}} \tag{4-75a}$$

and

$$|H_R(f)| = \frac{\alpha\sqrt{|H_e(f)|}}{\sqrt{H_c(f)}\,[\mathscr{P}_n(f)]^{1/4}} \tag{4-75b}$$

where $\mathscr{P}_n(f)$ is the PSD for the noise at the receiver input and α is an arbitrary positive constant (e.g., choose $\alpha = 1$ for convenience). $H_e(f)$ is selected from any appropriate frequency response characteristic that satisfies Nyquist's first criterion as discussed previously and $H(f)$ is given by (3-63). Any appropriate phase response can be used for $H_T(f)$ and $H_R(f)$ as long as the overall system phase response is linear. This results in a constant time delay versus frequency.

Zero-Forcing Transversal Filter Equalizers

The equalizing (i.e., receiving) filter can be realized by using a transversal filter design, as shown in Fig. 4-24. As shown, the transversal filter consists of a tapped delay line where the tap outputs are multiplied by gain factors. The resulting products are summed to produce the filter output. Although other types of realizations are possible, the transversal structure is very popular for this application because (1) it is relatively easy to analyze and design and (2) it is easy to build using *charge coupled devices* (CCD) for the tapped analog delay line [Gersho, 1975]. As described in Fig. 4-21, the input, $w_c(t)$, is from the channel and the equalizer is designed to provide an output waveform, $w_{out}(t)$, that has zero ISI.

The design problem consists of finding the values for the tap gains such that there will be no ISI on the output waveform. This can be accomplished by finding the b_n's that will satisfy Nyquist's first method for zero ISI. That is, the b_n's are found that give zeros for

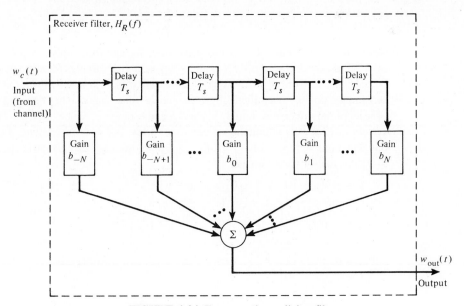

FIGURE 4-24 Transversal equalizing filter.

the impulse response, $h_e(t)$, at all sampling times except the present. To find the design equation, the system is analyzed using the impulse response technique described in the previous sections. As seen in Fig. 4-21, a single impulse into the pulse shaping filter $H(f)$ produces a single flat-topped pulse at the input to the transmit filter, $H_T(f)$. Then the corresponding output of the *channel* [i.e., the $H_c(f)$ filter] will be the response $w_c(t)$, and the overall system will have the equivalent impulse response of $h_e(t)$. For the transversal filter of Fig. 4-24, the response is related to its input by

$$h_e(t) = b_{-N} w_c(t) + b_{-N+1} w_c(t - T_s) + \cdots + b_N w_c(t - 2NT_s)$$

or

$$h_e(t) = \sum_{n=-N}^{N} b_n w_c(t - (n + N)T_s) \tag{4-76}$$

Evaluating the samples of $h_e(t)$ at the sampling times $t = (k + N)T_s = kT_s + \tau$ where the receiving clock offset time is $\tau = NT_s$, we get

$$h_e(kT_s + \tau) = \sum_{n=-N}^{N} b_n w_c((k + N)T_s - (n + N)T_s)$$

or

$$h_e(kT_s + \tau) = \sum_{n=-N}^{N} b_n w_c((k - n)T_s) \tag{4-77}$$

Using Nyquist's first method for zero ISI as described by (4-66), we realize that (4-77) becomes

$$\sum_{n=-N}^{N} b_n w_c((k - n)T_s) = \begin{cases} 1, & k = 0 \\ 0, & k = \pm 1, \pm 2, \ldots, \pm N \end{cases} \tag{4-78}$$

where, for convenience, $C = 1$ has been used. We can force only $2N$ points of the output impulse response to zero (i.e., N samples before and N samples after the peak of the pulse) because there are only $(2N + 1)$ taps on the transversal filter. However, the ISI beyond the $\pm N$ sample points is usually negligible since the time response has decayed to an insignificant amplitude over that range. Since k has the range $-N \leq k \leq N$, (4-78) represents a system of $(2N + 1)$ simultaneous equations with $(2N + 1)$ unknowns. These simultaneous equations may be solved for the $\{b_n\}$ unknowns by using matrix theory. Rewriting (4-78) in matrix form, we get

$$
\begin{matrix}
k = -N \\
k = -N + 1 \\
\vdots \\
\vdots \\
k = -1 \\
k = 0 \\
k = 1 \\
\vdots \\
\vdots \\
k = N
\end{matrix}
\begin{bmatrix}
0 \\
0 \\
\vdots \\
\vdots \\
0 \\
1 \\
0 \\
\vdots \\
\vdots \\
0
\end{bmatrix}
=
\begin{bmatrix}
w_c(0) & w_c(-T_s) & \cdots & & w_c(-2NT_s) \\
w_c(T_s) & w_c(0) & & & \\
\vdots & & & & \\
& & & & \\
& & & & \\
& & & & \\
& & & & \\
& & & & \\
& & & w_c(0) & w_c(-T_s) \\
w_c(2NT_s) & & & w_c(T_s) & w_c(0)
\end{bmatrix}
\begin{bmatrix}
b_{-N} \\
b_{-N+1} \\
\vdots \\
\vdots \\
b_{-1} \\
b_0 \\
b_1 \\
\vdots \\
\vdots \\
b_N
\end{bmatrix}
$$

If we use matrix notation, this is

$$\mathbf{H}_e = \mathbf{W}_c \mathbf{B} \qquad (4\text{-}79)$$

where the column vectors $\mathbf{H}_e$ and $\mathbf{B}$ are

$$\mathbf{H}_e = \begin{bmatrix} 0 \\ \cdot \\ \cdot \\ \cdot \\ 0 \\ 1 \\ 0 \\ \cdot \\ \cdot \\ \cdot \\ 0 \end{bmatrix}, \qquad \mathbf{B} = \begin{bmatrix} b_{-N} \\ \cdot \\ \cdot \\ \cdot \\ b_{-1} \\ b_0 \\ b_1 \\ \cdot \\ \cdot \\ \cdot \\ b_N \end{bmatrix} \qquad (4\text{-}80\text{a,b})$$

and the $(2N + 1) \times (2N + 1)$ matrix $\mathbf{W}_c$ is

$$\mathbf{W}_c = \begin{bmatrix} w_c(0) & w_c(-T_s) & \cdots & w_c(-2NT_s) \\ w_c(T_s) & w_c(0) & & \vdots \\ \vdots & & & \vdots \\ \vdots & & w_c(0) & w_c(-T_s) \\ w_c(2NT_s) & \cdots & w_c(T_s) & w_c(0) \end{bmatrix} \qquad (4\text{-}80\text{c})$$

Solving (4-79) for $\mathbf{B}$, we find that the values for the tap coefficients of the transversal filter that gives zero ISI are

$$\mathbf{B} = \mathbf{W}_c^{-1} \mathbf{H}_e \qquad (4\text{-}81)$$

Note that the b_n's that are specified by (4-81) depend on $H(f)$, $H_T(f)$, and $H_c(f)$ since $w_c(t)$ depends on all of these filters.

The transversal filter has the advantage that its transfer characteristic can be altered easily just by changing the tap coefficients. For example, in a "training mode," one or more flat-top test pulses could be fed into the transmit filter and, based on receiving the corresponding waveform $w_c(t)$ at the receiver input, the receiver could automatically compute the required tap gains for zero ISI as specified by (4-81). In the "run mode," the receiver could use these computed tap gains to detect the data with zero ISI. In practice, the channel transfer characteristic changes from time to time, so that this procedure could be repeated periodically to maintain the correct equalization. This type of automatic adjustment is called *preset equalization*. If we use another approach, it is possible to adjust the tap gains continuously by using a low-level reference signal or by computing the tap gains iteratively from the received data waveform, $w_c(t)$. This latter type of automatic equalization is called *adaptive equalization*. Both of these automatic equalization techniques can be used in practice [Lucky and Rudin, 1966; Lucky, Salz, and Weldon, 1968]. For medium-speed (2400 bits/sec) modems used for computer communications over switched (dial-up) telephone lines, it is usually adequate to use a fixed equalizer based on the expected average channel transfer characteristic. For higher speeds (larger than 2400 bits/sec), the variation in the characteristics from line to line is so large that some type of automatic equalization is usually required.

Equalizers can also be built that minimize the mean square error (MSE) on the equalizer output where the actual output due to a training signal is compared with the desired output. This type of equalizer has the advantage of minimizing the effect of channel noise as well as minimizing ISI. This approach is popular in applications of high-speed modems used on telephone lines because of the superior noise performance and because the tap gains for the adaptive equalizers can be made to converge rapidly to their desired values. A discussion of the theory of minimum MSE equalizers is beyond the scope of this book. For further study on this subject, the reader is referred to an excellent tutorial paper with its associated references [Qureshi, 1982].

Nyquist's Second and Third Methods for Control of ISI

Nyquist's *second method* of ISI control allows some ISI to be introduced in a *controlled* way so that it can be canceled out at the receiver and the data can be recovered without error if no noise is present [Couch, 1993]. This technique also allows for the possibility of doubling the bit rate or, alternatively, halving the channel bandwidth. This phenomenon was observed by telegraphers in the 1900s and is known as ''doubling the dotting speed'' [Bennett and Davey, 1965].

In *Nyquist's third method* of ISI control, the effect of ISI is eliminated by choosing $h_e(t)$ so that the area under the $h_e(t)$ pulse within the desired symbol interval, T_s, is not zero but the areas under $h_e(t)$ in adjacent symbol intervals are zero. For data detection, the receiver evaluates the area under the receiver waveform over each T_s interval. Pulses have been found that satisfy Nyquist's third criterion, but their performance in the presence of noise is inferior to the examples that have been discussed previously [Sunde, 1969].

4-6 Differential Pulse Code Modulation

When audio or video signals are sampled, it is usually found that adjacent samples are close to the same value. This means that there is a lot of redundancy in the signal samples and, consequently, that the bandwidth and the dynamic range of a PCM system are wasted when redundant sample values are retransmitted. One way to minimize redundant transmission and reduce the bandwidth is to transmit PCM signals corresponding to the difference in adjacent sample values. This, crudely speaking, is *differential pulse code modulation* (DPCM). At the receiver the present sample value is regenerated by using the past value plus the update differential value that is received over the differential system.

Moreover, the present value can be estimated from the past values by using a *prediction filter.* The filter may be realized by using a tapped delay line (bucket brigade device) to form a *transversal filter,* as shown in Fig. 4-25. When the tap gains $\{a_l\}$ are set so that the filter output will predict the present value from past values, the filter is said to be a *linear prediction filter* [Spilker, 1977]. The optimum tap gains are a function of the correlation properties of the audio or video signal [Jayant and Noll, 1984]. The output samples are

$$z(nT_s) = \sum_{l=1}^{K} a_l y(nT_s - lT_s) \qquad (4\text{-}82a)$$

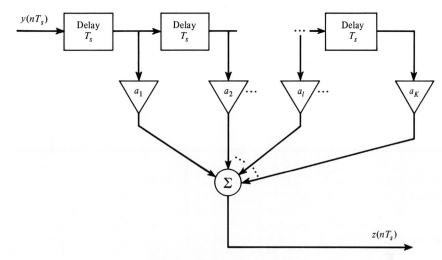

FIGURE 4-25 Transversal filter.

or, in simplified notation,

$$z_n = \sum_{l=1}^{K} a_l y_{n-l} \tag{4-82b}$$

where y_{n-l} denotes the sample value at the filter input at time $t = (n - l)T_s$ and there are K delay devices in the transversal filter.

The linear prediction filter may be used in a differential configuration to produce DPCM. Two possible configurations will be examined.

The first DPCM configuration, shown in Fig. 4-26, uses the predictor to obtain a differential pulse amplitude modulated (DPAM) signal that is quantized and encoded to produce the DPCM signal. The recovered analog signal at the receiver output will be the same as that at the system input plus *accumulated* quantizing noise. We may eliminate the accumulation effect by using the transmitter configuration of Fig. 4-27.

In the second DPCM configuration shown in Fig. 4-27, the predictor operates on quantized values at the transmitter as well as at the receiver in order to minimize the quantization noise on the recovered analog signal. The analog output at the receiver is the same as the input analog signal at the transmitter except for quantizing noise; furthermore, the quantizing noise does not accumulate, as was the case in the first configuration.

It can be shown that DPCM, like PCM, follows the 6-dB rule [Jayant and Noll, 1984]

$$\left(\frac{S}{N}\right)_{dB} = 6.02n + \alpha \tag{4-83a}$$

where

$$-3 < \alpha < 15 \quad \text{for DPCM speech} \tag{4-83b}$$

and n is the number of quantizing bits ($M = 2^n$). Unlike companded PCM, the α for DPCM varies over a wide range depending on the properties of the input analog signal.

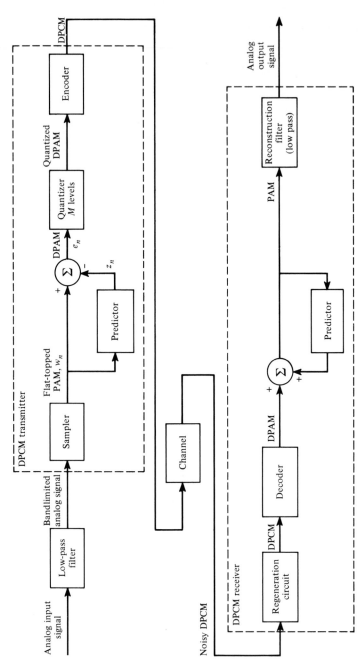

FIGURE 4-26 DPCM using prediction from samples of input signal.

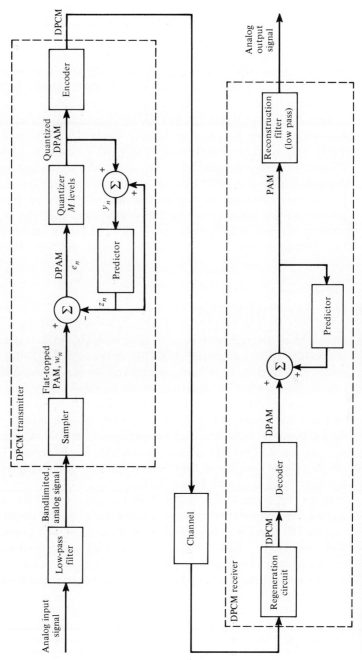

FIGURE 4-27 DPCM using prediction from quantized differential signal.

Equation (4-83b) gives the range of α for voice-frequency (300 to 3400 Hz) telephone-quality speech. This DPCM performance may be compared to that for PCM. Equation (4-26) indicates that $\alpha = -10$ dB for μ-law companded PCM with $\mu = 255$. Thus there may be a S/N improvement as large as 25 dB when DPCM is used instead of $\mu = 255$ PCM. Alternatively, for the same S/N, DPCM could require 3 or 4 fewer bits per sample than companded PCM. This is why telephone DPCM systems often operate at a bit rate of $R = 32$ kbits/sec or $R = 24$ kbits/sec instead of the standard 64 kbits/sec as needed for companded PCM.

The CCITT has adopted a 32-kbit/sec DPCM standard that uses 4-bit quantization at an 8-ksample/sec rate for encoding 3.2-kHz bandwidth VF signals [Decina and Modena, 1988]. Moreover, a 64-kbit/sec DPCM CCITT standard (4-bit quantization and 16 ksamples/sec) has been adopted for encoding audio signals that have a 7-kHz bandwidth. A detailed analysis of DPCM systems is difficult and depends on the type of input signal present, the sample rate, the number of quantizing levels used, the number of stages in the prediction filter, and the predictor gain coefficients. This type of analysis is beyond the scope of this text, but for further study the reader is referred to published work on this topic [Flanagan et al., 1979; Jayant, 1974; Jayant and Noll, 1984; O'Neal, 1966b].

4-7 Delta Modulation

From a block diagram point of view, *delta modulation* (DM) is a special case of DPCM where there are two quantizing levels. As shown in Fig. 4-27, for the case of $M = 2$, the quantized DPAM signal is *binary* and the encoder is not needed since the function of the encoder is to convert the multilevel DPAM signal to binary code words. For the case of $M = 2$, the DPAM signal is a DPCM signal where the code words are one bit long. The cost of a DM system is less than that of a DPCM system ($M > 2$) since the analog-to-digital converter (ADC) and digital-to-analog converter (DAC) are not needed. This is the main attraction of the DM scheme—it is relatively inexpensive. In fact, the cost may be further reduced by replacing the predictor by a low-cost integration circuit (such as an RC low-pass filter), as shown in Fig. 4-28.

In the DM circuit shown in Fig. 4-28, the operations of the subtractor and two-level quantizer are implemented by using a comparator so that the output is $\pm V_c$ (binary). In this case the DM signal is a polar signal. A set of waveforms associated with the delta modulator is shown in Fig. 4-29. In Fig. 4-29a an assumed analog input waveform is illustrated. If the instantaneous samples of the flat-topped PAM signal are taken at the beginning of each sampling period, the corresponding accumulator output signal is shown.[†] Here the integra-

---

[†] The sampling frequency, $f_s = 1/T_s$, is selected to be within the range $2B_{in} < f_s < 2B_{channel}$, where B_{in} is the bandwidth of the input analog signal and $B_{channel}$ is the bandwidth of the channel. The lower limit prevents aliasing of the analog signal and the upper limit prevents ISI in the DM signal at the receiver. See Example 4-2 for further restrictions on the selection of f_s.

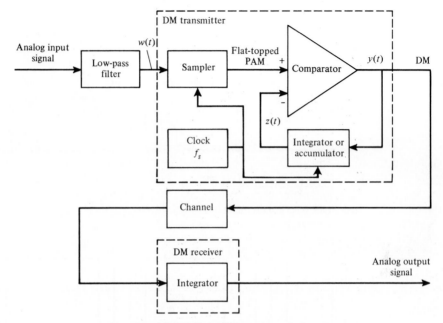

FIGURE 4-28 DM system.

tor is assumed to act as an accumulator (such as integrating impulses) so that the integrator output at time $t = nT_s$ is given by

$$z_n = \frac{1}{V_c} \sum_{i=0}^{n} \delta y_i \qquad (4\text{-}84)$$

where $y_i = y(iT)$ and δ is the accumulator gain or step size. The corresponding DM output waveform is shown in Fig. 4-29b.

At the receiver the DM signal may be converted back to an analog signal approximation to the analog signal at the system input. This is accomplished by using an integrator for the receiver that produces a smoothed waveform corresponding to a smoothed version of the accumulator output waveform that is present in the transmitter (Fig. 4-29a).

Granular Noise and Slope Overload Noise

From Fig. 4-29a it is seen that the accumulator output signal does not always track the analog input signal. The quantizing noise error signal may be classified into two types of noise—*slope overload noise* and *granular noise.* Slope overload noise occurs when the step size δ is too small for the accumulator output to follow quick changes in the input waveform. Granular noise occurs for any step size but is smaller for a small step size. Thus we would like to have δ as small as possible to minimize the granular noise. The granular noise in a DM system is similar to the granular noise in a PCM system, whereas slope

(a) Analog Input and Accumulator Output Waveforms

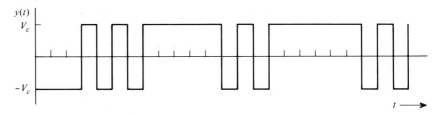

(b) Delta Modulation Waveform

FIGURE 4-29 DM system waveforms.

overload noise is a new phenomenon due to a differential signal being encoded (instead of the original signal itself). Both phenomena are also present in the DPCM system discussed earlier.

It is clear that there should be an optimum value for the step size, δ, since if δ is increased, the granular noise will increase but the slope overload noise will decrease. This is illustrated in Fig. 4-30.

Example 4-2   Design of a DM System

Find the step size δ required to prevent slope overload noise for the case when the input signal is a sine wave.

The maximum slope that can be generated by the accumulator output is

$$\frac{\delta}{T_s} = \delta f_s \qquad (4\text{-}85)$$

For the case of the sine-wave input where $w(t) = A \sin \omega_a t$, the slope is

$$\frac{dw(t)}{dt} = A\omega_a \cos \omega_a t \qquad (4\text{-}86)$$

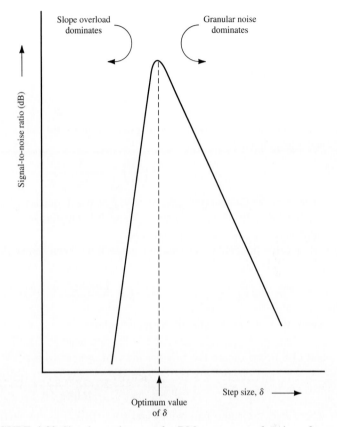

FIGURE 4-30 Signal-to-noise out of a DM system as a function of step size.

and the maximum slope of the input signal is $A\omega_a$. Consequently, for no slope overload we require that $\delta f_s > A\omega_a$, or

$$\delta > \frac{2\pi f_a A}{f_s} \tag{4-87}$$

However, we do not want to make δ too much larger than this value or the granular noise will become too large.

The resulting detected signal-to-noise ratio can also be calculated. It has been determined experimentally that the spectrum of the granular noise is uniformly distributed over the frequency band $|f| \le f_s$. That is, the PSD for the noise is $\mathscr{P}_n(f) = \delta^2/(6f_s)$. Then granular noise power in the analog signal band, $|f| \le B$, is

$$N = \langle n^2 \rangle = \int_{-B}^{B} \mathscr{P}_n(f)\,df = \frac{\delta^2 B}{3f_s} \tag{4-88}$$

or, using (4-87), with equality

$$N = \frac{4\pi^2 A^2 f_a^2 B}{3 f_s^3}$$

The signal power is

$$S = \langle w^2(t) \rangle = \frac{A^2}{2} \tag{4-89}$$

The resulting average signal to quantizing noise ratio out of a DM system with a sine-wave test signal is

$$\left(\frac{S}{N} \right)_{\text{out}} = \frac{3}{8\pi^2} \frac{f_s^3}{f_a^2 B} \tag{4-90}$$

where f_s is the DM sampling frequency, f_a is the frequency of the sinusoidal input, and B is the bandwidth of the receiving system. It is emphasized that (4-90) was shown to be valid only for sinusoidal-type signals.

For voice-frequency (VF) audio signals, it has been shown that (4-87) is too restrictive if $f_a = 4$ kHz and that slope overload is negligible if [DeJager, 1952]

$$\delta \geq \frac{2\pi 800 W_p}{f_s} \tag{4-91}$$

where W_p is the peak value of the input audio waveform, $w(t)$. (This is due to the fact that the midrange frequencies around 800 Hz dominate in the VF signal.) Combining (4-91) and (4-88), we obtain the S/N for the DM system with a VF-type signal

$$\left(\frac{S}{N} \right)_{\text{out}} = \frac{\langle w^2(t) \rangle}{N} = \frac{3 f_s^3}{(1600\pi)^2 B} \left(\frac{\langle w^2(t) \rangle}{W_p^2} \right) \tag{4-92}$$

where B is the audio bandwidth and $(\langle w^2(t) \rangle / W^2)$ is the average-audio-power to peak-audio-power ratio.

This result can be used to design a VF DM system. For example, suppose that we desire an S/N of at least 30 dB. Assume that the VF bandwidth is 4 kHz and the average-to-peak audio power is $\frac{1}{2}$. Then (4-92) gives a required sampling frequency of 40.7 kbits/sec or $f_s = 10.2B$. It is also interesting to compare this DM system with a PCM system that has the same bandwidth (i.e., bit rate). The number of bits, n, required for each PCM word is determined by $R = (2B)n = 10.2B$ or $n \approx 5$. Then the average-signal to quantizing-noise ratio of the comparable PCM system is 30.1 dB (see Table 4-2). Thus, under these conditions, the PCM system with a comparable bandwidth has about the same S/N performance as the DM system. Furthermore, repeating the preceding procedure, it can be shown that if an S/N larger than 30 dB was desired, the PCM system would have a larger S/N than that of a DM system with comparable bandwidth; on the other hand, if an S/N less than 30 dB was sufficient, the DM system would outperform (i.e., have a larger S/N than) the PCM system of the same bandwidth. Note that the S/N for DM increases as f_s^3 or 9 dB per octave increase of f_s.

It is also possible to improve the S/N performance of a DM system by using double integration instead of single integration, as was studied here. With a double integration system the S/N increases as f_s^5 or 15 dB per octave [Jayant and Noll, 1984].

Adaptive Delta Modulation and Continuously Variable Slope Delta Modulation

To minimize the slope overload noise while holding the granular noise at a reasonable value, *adaptive delta modulation* (ADM) is used. Here the step size is varied as a function of time as the input waveform changes. The step size is kept small to minimize the granular noise until the slope overload noise begins to dominate. Then the step size is increased to reduce the slope overload noise. The step size may be adapted, for example, by examining the DM pulses at the transmitter output. When the DM pulses consist of a string of pulses with positive polarity, the step size is increased (see Fig. 4-29) until the DM pulses begin to alternate in polarity, then decreased, and so on. One possible algorithm for varying the step size is shown in Table 4-7, where the step size changes with discrete variation. Here the step size is normally set to a value δ when the ADM signal consists of data with alternating 1's and 0's or when two successive binary 1's or 0's occur. However, if three successive binary 1's occur, the step size is increased to 2δ, and 4δ for four successive binary 1's. Figure 4-31 gives a block diagram for this ADM system.

Papers have been published with demonstration records that illustrate the quality of ADM and other digital techniques when voice signals are sent over digital systems and recovered [Flanagan et al., 1979; Jayant, 1974]. Another variation of ADM is *continuously variable slope delta modulation* (CVSD). Here the step size is made continuously variable instead of stepped in discrete increments.

The Motorola MC3417 is a CVSD integrated circuit which varies the slope (step size) as a function of the last three bits of the encoded data sequence; the MC3418 has a similar 4-bit algorithm [Motorola, 1985]. Both of these CVSD codec chips can be connected either as modulators (encoders) or as demodulators (decoders) and may be operated with bit rates ranging from 9.4 to 64 kbits/sec. Of course, a better S/N is obtained at the decoder output if a higher bit rate is used. For example, if MC3417 codecs are used for encoding and decoding in a 16-kbit/sec CVSD system, the S/N at the output will be 16 dB. This is called "communication quality." If MC3418s are used in a 37.7-kbit/sec system, the output S/N will be 30 dB. This performance is similar to that obtained for the DM and PCM systems discussed after equation (4-92).

TABLE 4-7 Step-Size Algorithm

Data Sequence[a]				Number of Successive Binary 1's or 0's	Step-Size Algorithm, $f(d)$
×	×	0	1	1	δ
×	0	1	1	2	δ
0	1	1	1	3	2δ
1	1	1	1	4	4δ

[a] ×, don't care.

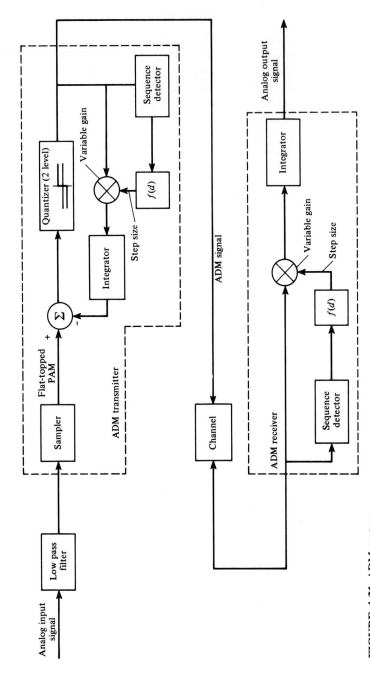

FIGURE 4-31 ADM system.

The question might be asked: Which is better, PCM or DM? The answer, of course, depends on the criterion used for comparison and the type of message. If the objective is to have a relatively simple, low-cost system, delta modulation may be the best. However, the cost of ADCs is dropping, so this may not be a factor in the future. If high output S/N is the criterion, PCM is probably the best [O'Neal, 1966a]. If one is interfacing to existing equipment, compatibility, of course, would be a prime consideration. In this regard, PCM has the advantage because it was adopted first and is widely used.

Speech Coding

Digital speech coders can be classified into two categories: waveform coders and vocoders. *Waveform coders* use algorithms to encode and decode so that the system output is an approximation to the input waveform. *Vocoders* encode the speech by extracting a set of parameters. These parameters are digitized and transmitted to the receiver where they are used to set values for parameters in function generators and filters which, in turn, synthesize the output speech sound. Usually, the vocoder output waveform does not approximate the input waveform and has an artificial, unnatural sound. Although the words of the speaker may be clearly understandable, the speaker may not be identifiable. That is, the speaker may ''sound like a robot.'' For this reason and because of space limitations, only waveform encoders (e.g., PCM, DPCM, DM, and CVSD) are covered in this book. It was demonstrated that VF-quality speech may be encoded at bit rates as low as 24 kbits/sec. More advanced techniques reduce the required bit rate to 16 or 8 kbits/sec, and some researchers believe that speech coding may be possible even at 2 kbits/sec. Some techniques that are available to achieve waveform coders at low bit rates are: linear prediction (already discussed as applied to DPCM), adaptive subband coding, and vector quantization. Adaptive subband coding allocates bits according to the input speech spectrum and the properties of hearing. With vector quantization, whole blocks of samples are encoded at a time instead of encoding on a sample-by-sample basis. An example is the vector sum excited linear prediction filter (VSELF) technique that is used in digital cellular telephones and described at the end of Sec. 8-8. Of course, these advanced techniques require more complex circuits and a larger delay while the output is being computed. For more details about this interesting topic of speech coders, the reader is referred to the literature [Aoyama, Daumer, and Modena, 1988; Flanagan et al., 1979; Jayant, 1986].

4-8 Time-Division Multiplexing[†]

> **DEFINITION:** *Time-division multiplexing* (TDM) is the time interleaving of samples from several sources so that the information from these sources can be transmitted serially over a single communication channel.

[†]This is a method in which a common channel or system is shared by many users. Other methods for sharing a common communication system are discussed under the topic of multiple access techniques in Sec. 8-5.

FIGURE 4-32 Three-channel TDM PCM system.

Figure 4-32 illustrates the TDM concept as applied to three analog sources that are multiplexed over a PCM system. For convenience, natural sampling is shown together with the corresponding gated TDM PAM waveform. In practice, an electronic switch is used for the commutation (sampler). In this example the pulse width of the TDM PAM signal is $T_s/3 = 1/(3f_s)$, and the pulse width of the TDM PCM signal is $T_s/(3n)$, where n is the number of bits used in the PCM word. Here $f_s = 1/T_s$ denotes the frequency of rotation for the commutator, and f_s satisfies the Nyquist rate for the analog source with the largest bandwidth. In some applications where the bandwidth of the sources is markedly different, the larger bandwidth sources may be connected to several switch positions on the sampler so that they will be sampled more often than the smaller bandwidth sources.

At the receiver the decommutator (sampler) has to be synchronized with the incoming waveform so that the PAM samples corresponding to source 1, for example, will appear on the channel 1 output. This is called frame synchronization. Low-pass filters are used to reconstruct the analog signals from the PAM samples. ISI resulting from poor channel filtering would cause PCM samples from one channel to appear on another channel, even though perfect bit and frame synchronization were maintained. This feedthrough of one channel's signal into another channel is called *crosstalk*.

Frame Synchronization

Frame synchronization is needed at the TDM receiver so that the received multiplexed data can be sorted and directed to the appropriate output channel. The frame sync can be provided to the receiver demultiplexer (demux) circuit either by sending a frame sync signal from the transmitter over a separate channel or by deriving the frame sync from the TDM signal itself. Because the implementation of the first approach is obvious, we will concentrate on implementation of the latter approach. In addition, the latter approach is usually more economical since a separate sync channel is not needed. As illustrated in Fig. 4-33, frame sync may be multiplexed along with the information words in an N channel TDM system by transmitting a unique K-bit sync word at the beginning of each frame. As illustrated in Fig. 4-34, the frame sync is recovered from the corrupted TDM signal by using a frame synchronizer circuit which crosscorrelates the regenerated TDM signal with the expected unique sync word $\mathbf{s} = (s_1, s_2, \ldots, s_K)$ that is specified by the fixed tap gains $s_1, s_2, \ldots, s_K$. Here, assume that the bits of the sync word s_j's, are in a polar format (± 1). The present bit of the regenerated TDM signal is clocked into the first stage of the shift register and then shifted to the next stage on the next clock pulse so that the most immedi-

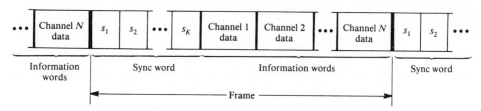

FIGURE 4-33 TDM frame sync format.

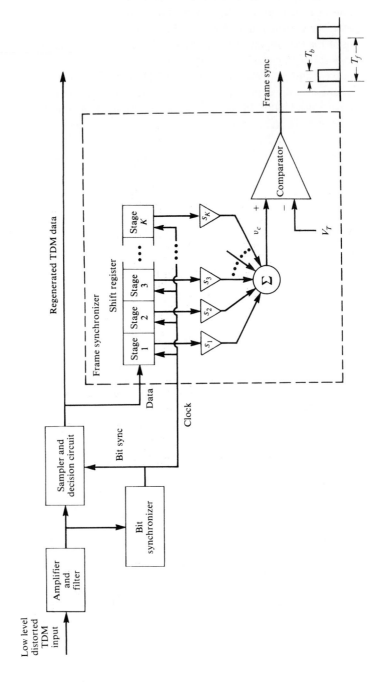

FIGURE 4-34 Frame synchronizer with TDM receiver front end.

ate K bits are always stored in the shift register. The contents of the shift register are multiplied by the tap gains which correspond to the bits (± 1) of the sync word. These are *algebraically* summed and fed into the comparator input. When the unique K bit sync word appears in the data stream and is exactly aligned in the shift register so that s_1 is in stage 1, s_2 is in stage 2, and so on, then the voltage at the input to the comparator will be

$$v_c = s_1^2 + s_2^2 + \cdots + s_K^2 = K \tag{4-93}$$

K is also the maximum voltage that is possible for v_c for any possible data sequence that could be stored in the shift register. Furthermore, if the data in the shift register happen to differ in sign at any one-bit position compared to the bits in the sync word, then $v_c = K - 2$. Consequently, if the comparator threshold voltage, V_T, is set slightly smaller than K volts, say $V_T = K - 1$, then the comparator output will go high only during the T_b-second interval when the sync word is perfectly aligned in the shift register. Thus the frame synchronizer recovers the frame sync signal.

False sync output pulses will occur if K successive information bits happen to match the bits in the sync word. For equally likely TDM data and $V_T = K - 1$, the probability of this false sync occurring is

$$P_f = \left(\frac{1}{2}\right)^K = 2^{-K} \tag{4-94}$$

In frame synchronizer design, this equation may be used to determine the number of bits, K, needed in the sync word so that the false lock probability will meet specifications. Alternatively, more sophisticated techniques such as aperture windows can be used to suppress false lock pulses [Ha, 1986]. The information words may also be encoded so that they are not allowed to have the bit strings that match the unique sync word.

Since the input to the comparator, v_c, is the crosscorrelation of the sync word with the passing K-bit word stored in the shift register, the sync word needs to be chosen so that its autocorrelation function, $R_s(k)$, has the desirable properties: $R_s(0) = 1$ and $R(k) \approx 0$ for $k \neq 0$. The PN codes (studied in Sec. 7-5) are almost ideal in this regard. For example, if $P_f = 4 \times 10^{-5}$ is the allowed probability of false sync, then from (4-94) a ($K = 15$)-bit sync word is required. Consequently, a 15-stage shift register is needed for the frame synchronizer in the receiver. The 15-bit PN sync word can be generated at the transmitter using a four-stage shift register. For further study of frame synchronizers the reader is referred to Ziemer and Peterson [1985] and Ha [1986].

Synchronous and Asynchronous Lines

For bit sync, data transmission systems are designed to operate with either synchronous or asynchronous serial data lines. In a *synchronous* system, each device is designed so that its internal clock is relatively stable for a long period of time, and it is synchronized to a system master clock. Each bit of data is clocked in synchronism with the master clock. The synchronizing signal may be provided by a separate clocking line or may be embedded in the data signal (e.g., by the use of Manchester line codes). In addition, synchronous transmission requires a higher level of synchronization to allow the receiver to determine the beginning and end of blocks of data. This is achieved by the use of frame sync as discussed previously and data link protocols as described in Appendix C.

In *asynchronous* systems, the timing is precise only for the bits within each character (or word). This is also called *start-stop* signaling because each character consists of a "start bit" that starts the receiver clock and concludes with one or two "stop bits" that terminate the clocking. Usually, two stop bits are used with terminals that signal at rates less than 300 bits/sec, and one stop bit is used if $R \geq 300$ bits/sec. Thus, with asynchronous lines, the receiver clock is started aperiodically and no synchronization with a master clock is required. This is ideal for keyboard terminals where the typist does not type at an even pace and the input rate is much slower than that of the data communication system. These asynchronous terminals often use a 7-bit ASCII code (see Appendix C), and the complete character consists of one start bit, 7 bits of the ASCII code, one parity bit, and one stop bit (for $R \geq 300$ bits/sec). This gives a total character length of 10 bits. In TDM of the asynchronous type, the different sources are multiplexed on a *character-interleaved* (i.e., character-by-character) basis instead of interleaving on a bit-by-bit basis. The synchronous transmission system is more efficient because start and stop bits are not required. However, the synchronous mode of transmission requires that the clocking signal be passed along with the data and that the receiver synchronize to the clocking signal.

"Intelligent" TDMs may be used to *concentrate* data arriving from many different terminals or sources. They are capable of providing speed, code, and protocol conversion. At the input to a large mainframe computer, these devices are called *front-end processors.* The hardware in the intelligent TDM consists of microprocessors or minicomputers. Usually, they connect "on the fly" to the input data lines that have data present and momentarily disconnect the lines that do not have data present. For example, the user of a keyboard terminal is disconnected from the system while he or she is thinking (although to the user it does not appear to be disconnected) but is connected as each character or block of data is sent. Thus the output data rate of the multiplexer is much less than the sum of the data capacities of the input lines. This technique is called *statistical* multiplexing; it allows many more terminals to be connected on line to the system.

Multiplexers can also be classified into three general types. The first TDM type consists of those that connect to synchronous lines. The second TDM type consists of those that connect to quasi-synchronous lines. In this case, the individual clocks of the input data sources are not exactly synchronized in frequency. Consequently, there will be some variation in the bit rates between the data arriving from different sources. In addition, in some applications the clock rates of the input data streams are not related by a rational number. In these cases, the TDM output signal will have to be clocked at an increased rate above the nominal value to accommodate those inputs that are not synchronous. When a new input bit is not available at the multiplexer clocking time (due to nonsynchronization), *stuff bits,* which are dummy bits, are inserted in the TDM output data stream. This is illustrated by the bit-interleaved multiplexer shown in Fig. 4-35. The stuff bits may be binary 1's, 0's, or some alternating pattern, depending on the choice of the system designer. The third TDM type consists of those that operate with asynchronous sources and produce a high-speed asynchronous output (no stuff bits required) or high-speed synchronous output (stuff bits required).

FIGURE 4-35 Two-channel bit-interleaved TDM with pulse stuffing.

Example 4-3   Design of a Time-Division Multiplexer

Design a time-division multiplexer that will accommodate 11 sources. Assume that the sources have the following specifications.

Source 1.   Analog, 2-kHz bandwidth.
Source 2.   Analog, 4-kHz bandwidth.
Source 3.   Analog, 2-kHz bandwidth.
Sources 4–11.   Digital, synchronous at 7200 bits/sec.

Also assume that the analog sources will be converted into 4-bit PCM words and, for simplicity, that frame sync will be provided via a separate channel and synchronous TDM lines are used. To satisfy the Nyquist rate for the analog sources, sources 1, 2, and 3 need to be sampled at 4, 8, and 4 kHz, respectively. As shown in Fig. 4-36, this can be accomplished by rotating the first commutator at $f_1 = 4$ kHz and sampling source 2 twice on each revolution. This produces a 16-kilosample/sec TDM PAM signal on the commutator output. Each of the analog sample values is converted into a 4-bit PCM word, so that the rate of the TDM PCM signal on the ADC output is 64 kbits/sec. The digital data on the ADC output may be merged with the data from the digital sources

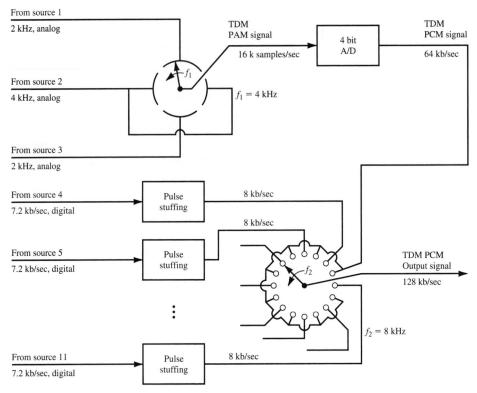

FIGURE 4-36 TDM with analog and digital inputs as described in Example 4-3.

by using a second commutator rotating at $f_2 = 8$ kHz and wired so that the 64-kbit/sec PCM signal is present on 8 of 16 terminals. This provides an effective sampling rate of 64 kbits/sec. On the other eight terminals the digital sources are connected to provide a data transfer rate of 8 kbits/sec for each source. Since the digital sources are supplying a 7.2-kbit/sec data stream, pulse stuffing is used to raise the source rate to 8 kbits/sec.

This example illustrates the main advantage of TDM: it can easily accommodate both analog and digital sources. Unfortunately, when analog signals are converted to digital signals without redundancy reduction, they consume a great deal of digital system capacity.

TDM Hierarchy

In practice, TDMs may be grouped into two categories. The first category consists of multiplexers used in conjunction with digital computer systems to merge digital signals from several sources for TDM transmission over a high-speed line to a digital computer. The output rate of these multiplexers has been standardized to 1.2, 2.4, 3.6, 4.8, 7.2, 9.6, and 19.2 kbits/sec.

The second category of time-division multiplexers is used by the common carriers, such as the American Telephone and Telegraph Company (AT&T), to combine different sources into a high-speed digital TDM signal for transmission over toll networks. Unfortunately, the standards adopted by North America and Japan are different from those that have been adopted in other parts of the world. Of course, this leads to complications at the boundaries of two systems with different standards. The North America/Japan standards were first adopted by AT&T, and another set of standards has been adopted by the International Telegraph and Telephone Consultative Committee (CCITT) under the auspices of the International Telecommunications Union (ITU). The North American TDM hierarchy is shown in Fig. 4-37 [James and Muench, 1972].[†] The telephone industry has standardized the bit rates to 1.544 Mbits/sec, 6.312 Mbits/sec, etc., and designates them as DS-1 for digital signal, type 1; DS-2 for digital signal, type 2; etc. as listed in Table 4-8. In Fig. 4-37 all input lines are assumed to be digital (binary) streams, and the number of voice-frequency (VF) analog signals that can be represented by these digital signals is shown in parentheses. The higher multiplexing level inputs are not always derived from lower level multiplexers. For example, one analog television signal can be converted directly to a DS-3 data stream (44.73 Mbits/sec). Similarly, the DS streams can carry a mixture of information from a variety of sources such as video, VF, and computers.

The transmission medium that is used for the multiplex levels depends on the DS level involved and on the economics of using a particular type of medium at a particular location (see Table 4-8). For example, higher DS levels may be transmitted over coaxial cables, fiber optic cable, microwave radio, or via satellite. A single DS-1 signal is usually transmitted over one pair of twisted wires. (One pair is used for each direction.) This type of DS-1 transmission over a twisted-pair medium is known (from its development in 1962 by AT&T) as the *T1 carrier system*. DS-1 signaling over a T1 system is very popular because of its relatively low cost and its excellent maintenance record. (T1 will be discussed in more detail in the following section.) Table 4-9 shows the specifications for the T-carrier digital baseband systems. Table 8-2 is a similar table for the capacity of common carrier bandpass systems. The corresponding CCITT TDM standard that is used throughout the world except for North America and Japan[†] is shown in Fig. 4-38 [Irmer, 1975].

With the development of high-bit-rate fiber optic systems, it has become apparent that the original TDM standards are not adequate. A new TDM standard called SONET (Synchronous Optical Network) was proposed by Bellcore (Bell Communications Research) around 1985 and has evolved into an international standard that was adopted by the CCITT in 1989. This SONET standard is shown in Table 4-10. The OC-1 signal is an optical (light) signal that is turned on and off (modulated) by an electrical binary signal

---

[†] The Japanese TDM hierarchy is the same as that for North America for multiplex levels 1 and 2, but differs for levels 3, 4, and 5. For level 3 the Japanese standard is 32.064 Mbits/sec (480 VF), level 4 is 97.728 Mbits/sec (1440 VF), and level 5 is 397.200 Mbits/sec (5760 VF). Dissimilarities between standards used are briefly discussed and summarized by Jacobs [1986].

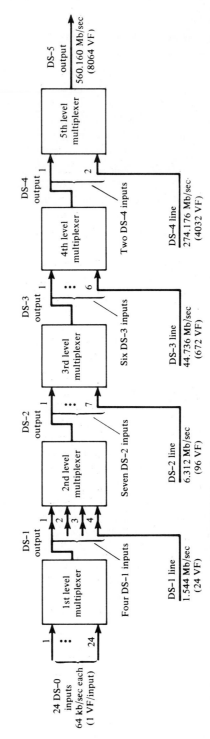

FIGURE 4-37 North American digital TDM hierarchy.

TABLE 4-8 TDM Standards for North America

Digital Signal Number	Bit Rate, R (Mbits/sec)	No. of 64-kbit/sec PCM VF Channels	Transmission Media Used
DS-0	0.064	1	Wire pairs
DS-1	1.544	24	Wire pairs
DS-1C	3.152	48	Wire pairs
DS-2	6.312	96	Wire pairs, fiber
DS-3	44.736	672	Coax., radio, fiber
DS-3C	90.254	1344	Radio, fiber
DS-4E	139.264	2016	Radio, fiber, coax.
DS-4	274.176	4032	Coax., fiber
DS-432	432.00	6048	Fiber
DS-5	560.160	8064	Coax., fiber

that has a line rate of 51.84 Mbits/sec. The electrical signal is called the STS-1 signal (Synchronous Transport Signal—level 1). Other OC-N signals have line rates of exactly N times the OC-1 rate and are formed by modulating a light signal with a STS-N electrical signal. The STS-N signal is obtained by byte-interleaving (scrambling) N STS-1 signals. (More details about fiber optic systems are given in Sec. 8-7.)

The telephone industry is moving toward an all-digital network that integrates voice and data over a single telephone line from each user to the telephone company equipment. This approach is called the *integrated service digital network* (ISDN). The standard implementation of *"basic rate"* ISDN service uses an overall data rate of 144 kbits/sec which is broken down into two B channels (64 kbits/sec each) and one D channel (16 kbits/sec). The two B channels carry PCM-encoded telephone conversations or data and the D channel is used for signaling to set up calls, disconnect calls, and route data for the B channels [Pandhi, 1987]. Basic rate ISDN is also called *narrowband ISDN* (N-ISDN). The *"primary rate"* ISDN service is in the development stage, but one implementation has an aggregate data rate of 1536 kbits/sec and consists of twenty-three 64-kbit/sec B channels and one 64-kbit/sec D channel. Primary rate ISDN is also called *broadband ISDN* (B-ISDN). A more detailed discussion of ISDN will be delayed until Sec. 8-3 since material covered in the intervening chapters is useful for a better understanding of ISDN and its applications.

The T1 PCM System

For telephone voice service the first-level TDM multiplexer in Fig. 4-37 is replaced by a TDM PCM system, which will convert 24 VF analog telephone signals to a DS-1 (1.544 Mbits/sec) data stream. In AT&T terminology this is either a D-type channel bank or a

TABLE 4-9 Specifications for T-Carrier Baseband Digital Transmission Systems

System	Rate (Mbits/sec)	System Capacity			Medium	Line Code	Repeater Spacing (miles)	Maximum System Length (miles)	System Error Rate
		Digital Signal No.	Voice Channels	TV					
T1	1.544	DS-1	24	—	Wire pair	Bipolar RZ	1	50	10^{-6}
T1C	3.152	DS-1C	48	—	Wire pair	Bipolar RZ	1	—	10^{-6}
T1D	3.152	DS-1C	48	—	Wire pair	Duobinary NRZ	1	—	10^{-6}
T1G	6.443	DS-2	96	—	Wire pair	4-level NRZ	1	200	10^{-6}
T2	6.312	DS-2	96	—	Wire pair[a]	B6ZS[b] RZ	2.3	500	10^{-7}
T3	44.736	DS-3	672	1	Coax.	B3ZS[b] RZ	[c]	[c]	[c]
T4	274.176	DS-4	4032	6	Coax.	Polar NRZ	1	500	10^{-6}
T5	560.160	DS-5	8064	12	Coax.	Polar NRZ	1	500	4×10^{-7}

[a] Special two-wire cable is required for 12,000-ft repeater spacing. Since T2 cannot use standard exchange cables, it is not as popular as T1.

[b] BnZS denotes *binary n-zero substitution*, where a string of n zeros in the bipolar line code is replaced with a special three-level code word so that synchronization can be maintained [Bic, Duponteil, and Imbeaux, 1991; Fike and Friend, 1984].

[c] Used in central telephone office for building multiplex levels; not used for transmission from office to office.

FIGURE 4-38 CCITT digital TDM hierarchy.

30 digital inputs 64 Kb/sec each

1st level multiplexer

Four 2.048 Mb/sec inputs

2.048 Mb/sec (30 VF)

2nd level multiplexer

Four 8.448 Mb/sec inputs

8.448 Mb/sec (120 VF)

3rd level multiplexer

Four 34.368 Mb/sec inputs

34.368 Mb/sec (480 VF)

4th level multiplexer

Four 139.264 Mb/sec inputs

139.264 Mb/sec (1920 VF)

5th level multiplexer

565.148 Mb/sec (7680 VF)

TABLE 4-10 SONET Signal Hierarchy

OC Level	Line Rate (MBits/sec)	Equivalent Number of:		
		DS-3s	DS-1s	DS-0s
OC-1	51.84	1	28	672
OC-3	155.52	3	84	2,016
OC-9	466.56	9	252	6,048
OC-12	622.08	12	336	8,064
OC-18	933.12	18	504	12,096
OC-24	1,244.16	24	672	16,128
OC-36	1,866.24	36	1,008	24,192
OC-48	2,488.32	48	1,344	32,256

digital carrier trunk (DCT) unit. ITT Telecommunications manufactures the T324 system, equivalent to the D3 channel bank, which also converts 24 VF signals into a DS-1 TDM data stream. A *T1 line span* is a twisted-pair telephone line that is used to carry the DS-1 (1.544-Mbit/sec) data stream. Two lines, one for transmit and one for receive, are used in the system. If the T1 line is connecting telephone equipment at different sites, repeaters are required about every mile.

The T1 system was developed by Bell Laboratories for short-haul digital communication of VF traffic up to 50 mi. The sampling rate used on each of the 24 VF analog signals is 8 kHz, which means that one frame length is $1/(8 \text{ kHz}) = 125 \ \mu\text{sec}$, as shown in Fig. 4-39. Presently, each analog sample is nominally encoded into an 8-bit PCM word so that there are $8 \times 24 = 192$ bits of data, plus one bit that is added for frame synchronization, yielding a total of 193 bits per frame. The T1 data rate is then (193 bits/frame)(8000 frames/sec) = 1.544 Mbits/sec, and the corresponding duration of each bit is 0.6477 μsec. The signaling is incorporated into the T1 format by replacing the eighth bit (the least significant bit) in each of the 24 channels of the T1 signal by a signaling bit in every sixth frame. Thus the signaling data rate for each of the 24 input channels is (1 bit/6 frames)(8000 frames/sec) = 1.333 kbits/sec. The framing bit used in the even-numbered frames follows the sequence 001110, and in the odd-numbered frames it follows the sequence 101010, so that the frames with the signaling information in the eighth bit position (for each channel) may be identified. The digital signaling on the T1 line is represented by a bipolar RZ waveform format (see Fig. 4-11) with peak levels of ± 3 V across a 100-Ω load. Consequently, there is no dc component on the T1 line regardless of the data pattern. In encoding the VF PAM samples, a $\mu = 255$ type compression characteristic is used, as described earlier in this chapter. Since the T1 data rate is 1.544 Mbits/sec and the line code is bipolar, the first zero-crossing bandwidth is 1.544 MHz and the spectrum peaks at 772 kHz, as shown in Fig. 4-12d. If the channel filtering transfer function was of the raised cosine-rolloff type with $r = 1$, the absolute channel bandwidth would be 1.544 MHz. In the past, when twisted-pair lines were used for analog transmis-

FIGURE 4-39 T1 TDM format for one frame.

sion only, *loading* coils (inductors) were used to improve the frequency (amplitude) response. However, they cause the line to have a phase response that is not linear with frequency, resulting in ISI. Thus they must be removed when the line is used for T1 service.

The T1G carrier, is described in Table 4-9. Instead of binary levels, it uses $M = 4$ (quaternary) multilevel signaling, where $+3$ V represents the two binary bits 11, $+1$ V represents 01, -1 V represents 00, and -3 V represents 10 [Azaret et al., 1985]. Thus a data rate of 6.443 Mbits/sec is achieved via 3.221-Mbaud signaling. This gives a 3.221-MHz zero-crossing bandwidth, which is close to the 3.152 zero-crossing bandwidth of the T1C system. This bandwidth can be supported by standard twisted-pair wires (one pair for each direction) with repeaters spaced at one-mile intervals. To achieve reliable signaling, the T1G equipment inserts additional parity and framing bits into the input stream DS-2 (6.312-Mbit/sec) signal so that a bit rate of 6.443 Mbits/sec is needed. For the first time the T1G system allows DS-2 (96 VF) capacity using standard twisted-pair cable that is common in existing telephone systems. In addition, old T1C-type systems can be upgraded to DS-2 capacity by replacing the old repeaters with T1G repeaters. The T1G system is also designed for economical operation, with the low-power repeaters having a mean time between failures of 1000 years and automated detection of faulty repeaters.

When considering the TDM approach for toll telephone transmission, one must consider the disadvantages as well as the advantages in comparison with frequency-division multiplexing (FDM). FDM is discussed in Chapter 6 (Fig. 6-16) and Chapter 8 (Fig. 8-1). It *was* the dominant multiplexing technique used in telephone toll service and for good reason—it *was* cheaper before the advent of low-cost ICs and fiber optic systems. The main difficulty with TDM is that it requires very wide bandwidth when compared to FDM, and it is difficult to obtain wide bandwidth with conventional wire transmission facilities. For example, the AT&T L5 coaxial cable transmission system can carry 10,800 VF channels in an FDM format using an overall bandwidth of 60 MHz. To transmit the same number of VF signals using TDM PCM, we need a bandwidth of about (10,800 VF channels)(64 kHz/VF channel) = 691 MHz, which is about 11 times the bandwidth required when using FDM. However, fiber optic cable systems have phenomenal bandwidth and are relatively inexpensive on a per-channel basis. For example, the FTG1.7 fiber optic TDM system (see Table 8-2) has a capacity of 24,192 VF channels. Digital circuits are also much cheaper and more compact than analog circuits. Consequently, TDM systems are favored over FDM systems. Nevertheless, toll transmission facilities are very expensive, and it may be years before all FDM equipment can be economically replaced by TDM equipment.

4-9 Pulse Time Modulation: Pulse Width Modulation and Pulse Position Modulation

Pulse time modulation (PTM) is a class of signaling techniques that encodes the sample values of an analog signal onto the *time axis* of a digital signal, and it is analogous to angle modulation techniques, which are described in Chapter 6. (As we have seen, PAM, PCM, and DM techniques encode the sample values into the amplitude characteristics of the digital signal.)

The two main types of pulse time modulation are *pulse width modulation* (PWM) and *pulse position modulation* (PPM) (see Fig. 4-40). In PWM, which is also called *pulse duration modulation* (PDM), sample values of the analog waveform are used to determine

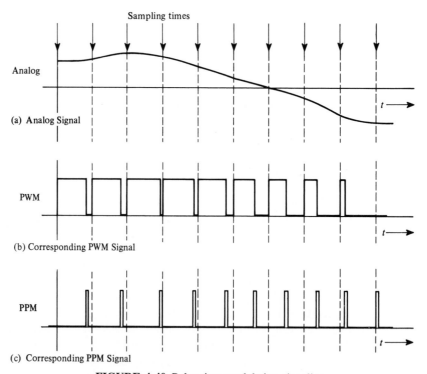

FIGURE 4-40 Pulse time modulation signaling.

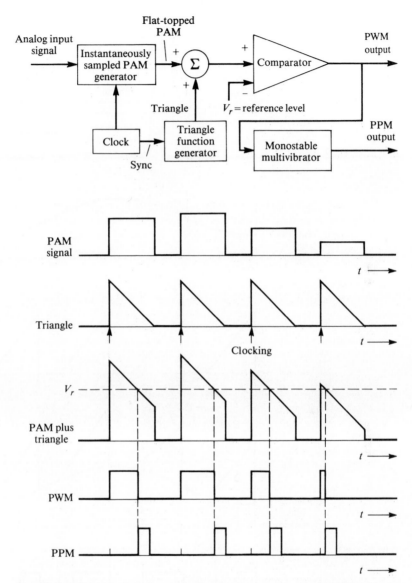

FIGURE 4-41 Technique for generating instantaneously sampled PTM signals.

the *width* of the pulse signal. Either *instantaneous* sampling or *natural* sampling can be used. Figure 4-41 shows a technique for generating PWM signals with instantaneous sampling, and Fig. 4-42 displays PWM with natural sampling. In PPM the analog sample value determines the *position* of a narrow pulse relative to the clocking time. Techniques for generating PPM are also shown in the figures, and it is seen that PPM is easily

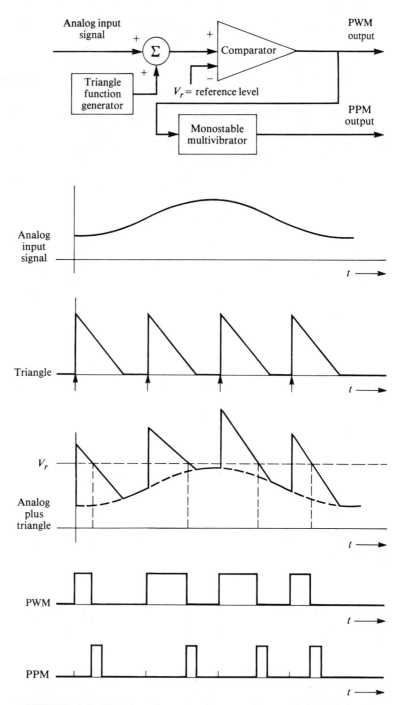

FIGURE 4-42 Technique for generating naturally sampled PTM signals.

obtained from PWM by using a monostable multivibrator circuit. In the literature on PTM signals, the comparator level V_r is often called the *slicing level*.

PWM or PPM signals may be converted back to the corresponding analog signal by a receiving system (Fig. 4-43). For PWM detection the PWM signal is used to start and stop the integration of an integrator; that is, the integrator is reset to zero, and integration is begun when the PWM pulse goes from a low level to a high level and the integrator integrates until the PWM pulse goes low. If the integrator input is connected to a constant

FIGURE 4-43 Detection of PWM and PPM signals.

voltage source, the output will be a truncated ramp. After the PWM signal goes low, the amplitude of the truncated ramp signal will be equal to the corresponding PAM sample value. At clocking time, the output of the integrator is then gated to a PAM output line (slightly before the integrator is reset to zero) using a sample-and-hold circuit. The PAM signal is then converted to the analog signal by low-pass filtering. In a similar way, PPM may be converted to PAM by using the clock pulse to reset the integrator to zero and start the integration. The PPM pulse is then used to stop the integration. The final value of the ramp is the PAM sample that is used to regenerate the analog signal.

Pulse time modulation signaling is not widely used to communicate across channels because a relatively wide bandwidth channel is needed, especially for PPM. However, PTM signals may be found internally in digital communications terminal equipment. The spectra of PTM signals are quite difficult to evaluate because of the nonlinear nature of the modulation [Rowe, 1965]. The main advantage of PTM signals is that they have a great immunity to additive noise when compared to PAM signaling, and they are easier to generate and detect than PCM, since PCM requires ADCs.

4-10 Summary

In this chapter we have studied baseband pulse and digital signaling techniques. It was found that the analog signal could be represented exactly by using pulse signaling techniques such as pulse amplitude modulation (PAM), pulse width modulation (PWM), or pulse position modulation (PPM). Furthermore, it was shown that analog signals could be approximated as accurately as desired by using digital signaling techniques such as pulse code modulation (PCM).

In our study of baseband digital signaling we concentrated on four major topics: (1) how the information in analog waveforms can be represented by digital signaling; (2) how to compute the spectrum for line codes and evaluate their probability of bit error at the receiver output; (3) how filtering of the digital signal, due to the communication channel, affects our ability to recover the digital information at the receiver [i.e., the intersymbol interference (ISI) problem]; and (4) how we can merge the information from several sources into one digital signal by using time-division multiplexing (TDM). U.S. and worldwide standards for TDM telecommunications systems were given.

Digital signaling techniques were found to be very efficient because (1) binary digital circuitry could be used, (2) the signals could be easily regenerated, (3) digital formats could be adopted that would handle information from both analog and digital sources, (4) many sources could be easily merged using TDM, and (5) binary signaling is very noise resistant.

PCM is an analog-to-digital conversion scheme that involves three basic operations: (1) *sampling* a bandlimited analog signal, (2) *quantizing* the analog samples into M discrete values, and (3) *encoding* each sample value into an n-bit word where $M = 2^n$. There are two sources of noise in the signal that is recovered at the receiver output: (1) quantizing noise due to the approximation of the sample values using the M allowed values, and (2) noise due to receiver bit detection errors caused by channel noise or by ISI that arises because of improper channel frequency response. If the original analog signal is not strictly bandlimited, there will be a third noise component on the receiver output due to aliasing.

In studying the effect of improper channel filtering in producing ISI, the raised cosine-type rolloff filter was examined. Here it was found that the minimum bandwidth required to pass a PCM signal without ISI was equal to one half of the baud rate. However, this leads to technical difficulties since the overall filter characteristic is that for an ideal low-pass filter ($r = 0$) that is not causal. In addition, the sampling time at the receiver becomes very critical. A channel bandwidth equal to the baud rate ($r = 1$), which is also the zero-crossing bandwidth of a polar NRZ signal, was found to be more realistic.

The channel bandwidth may be reduced if multilevel signal techniques are used(for a given data rate, R) or if differential pulse code modulation (DPCM) is used. In DPCM the difference between the actual and predicted sample values is transmitted over the system. Assuming that past values of the analog signal are related to the present value, we can obtain a bandwidth reduction over that needed when PCM is used. If equipment simplicity is of prime importance, delta modulation (DM) is the usual choice.

In this chapter we have been concerned with *baseband* signaling. In other words, the information is represented by a signal that has a spectrum concentrated about $f = 0$. In the next chapter we will be concerned with modulating baseband signals onto a carrier so that the spectrum will be concentrated about some desired frequency called the *carrier fre-quency*.

4-11 Appendix: PSD for Digital Signaling

The expression for the PSD of a digital signal, as given by (4-28), will now be derived. Referring to (4-27), a digital signal can be represented by

$$s(t) = \sum_{n=-\infty}^{\infty} a_n f(t - nt_s) \tag{4-95}$$

where $f(t)$ is the symbol pulse shape and T_s is the duration of one symbol as illustrated in Fig. 4-19c.[†] $\{a_n\}$ is a set of random variables that represent the digital data.

The PSD for $s(t)$, (4-28), will now be derived using the definition for PSD as given by (2-66). The truncated version of (4-95) is

$$s_T(t) = \sum_{n=-N}^{N} a_n f(t - nT_s) \tag{4-96}$$

where $T = 2(N + \frac{1}{2})T_s$. Then

$$X_T(f) = \mathcal{F}[x_T(t)] = \sum_{n=-N}^{N} a_n \mathcal{F}[f(t - nT_s)]$$

or

$$X_T(f) = \sum_{n=-N}^{N} a_n F(f)e^{-j\omega nT_s} \tag{4-97}$$

[†] If the digital signal is a binary signal, then $T_s = T_b$ as shown in Fig. 4-19b.

where $F(f) = \mathcal{F}[f(t)]$. Substituting (4-97) into (2-66), the PSD is

$$\mathcal{P}_s(f) = \lim_{T \to \infty} \left(\frac{1}{T} |F(f)|^2 \overline{\left| \sum_{n=-N}^{N} a_n e^{-j\omega n T_s} \right|^2} \right) \tag{4-98}$$

where the ensemble average (as indicated by the overbar and described in App. B) has been employed since the data are random variables. Equation (4-98) becomes

$$\mathcal{P}_s(f) = |F(f)|^2 \lim_{T \to \infty} \left(\frac{1}{T} \sum_{n=-N}^{N} \sum_{m=-N}^{N} \overline{a_n a_m} e^{j(m-n)\omega T_s} \right) \tag{4-99}$$

where the autocorrelation of the data is

$$R(k) = \overline{a_n a_{n+k}} = \sum_{i=1}^{I} (a_n a_{n+k})_i P_i \tag{4-100}$$

P_i is the probability of getting the product $(a_n a_{n+k})_i$, and there are I possible values for the $a_n a_{n+k}$ product. Now, make a change in one index of (4-99), letting $m = n + k$. Then, by using (4-100) and $T = (2N + 1)T_s$, (4-99) becomes

$$\mathcal{P}_s(f) = |F(f)|^2 \lim_{n \to \infty} \left[\frac{1}{(2N+1)T_s} \sum_{n=-N}^{N} \sum_{k=-N-n}^{k=N-n} R(k) e^{jk\omega T_s} \right] \tag{4-101}$$

Replacing the outer sum over the index n by $2N + 1$, we obtain the following expression. (This procedure is not strictly correct since the inner sum is also a function of n. The correct procedure would be to exchange the order of summation. That procedure would produce the same result as obtained below when $N \to \infty$.)

$$\mathcal{P}_s(f) = \frac{|F(f)|^2}{T_s} \lim_{N \to \infty} \left[\frac{2N+1}{2N+1} \sum_{k=-N-n}^{k=N-n} R(k) e^{jk\omega T_s} \right] \tag{4-102}$$

or

$$\mathcal{P}_s(f) = \frac{|F(f)|^2}{T_s} \sum_{k=-\infty}^{\infty} R(k) e^{jk\omega T_s} \tag{4-103}$$

This is identical to (4-28).

PROBLEMS

4-1 Demonstrate that the Fourier series coefficients for the switching waveform shown in Fig. 4-1b are given by (4-5b).

4-2 (a) Sketch the naturally sampled PAM waveform that results from sampling a 1-kHz sine wave at a 4-kHz rate.
     (b) Repeat part (a) for the case of a flat-topped PAM waveform.

4-3 The spectrum of an analog audio signal is shown in Fig. P4-3. The waveform is to be sampled at a 10-kHz rate with a pulse width of $\tau = 50\ \mu\text{sec}$.

FIGURE P4-3

(a) Find an expression for the spectrum of the naturally sampled PAM waveform. Sketch your result.

(b) Find an expression for the spectrum of the flat-topped PAM waveform. Sketch your result.

4-4 (a) Show that an analog output waveform (which is proportional to the original input analog waveform) may be recovered from a naturally sampled PAM waveform using the demodulation technique shown in Fig. 4-4.

(b) Find the constant of proportionality C that is obtained using this demodulation technique where $w(t)$ is the original waveform and $Cw(t)$ is the recovered waveform. Note that C is a function of n where the oscillator frequency is nf_s.

4-5 Figure 4-4 illustrates how a naturally sampled PAM signal can be demodulated to recover the analog waveform by use of a product detector. Show that the product detector can also be used to recover $w(t)$ from an instantaneously sampled PAM signal provided that the appropriate filter, $H(f)$, is used. Find the required $H(f)$ characteristic.

4-6 Starting with the PAM signal of Prob. 4-3:

(a) Design a PAM product demodulator with an oscillator operating at 30 kHz to recover the analog waveform from the naturally sampled PAM waveform.

(b) Design a PAM product demodulator with an oscillator operating at 30 kHz to demodulate the flat-topped PAM waveform.

(c) Discuss whether any synchronization signals are needed to operate these demodulators. Be sure to show the characteristics of any filters that are needed in your demodulator designs.

4-7 An analog waveform, $w(t)$, is converted into a flat-topped PAM signal using a sampling rate of 8 kHz and a pulse width of 100 μsec. Assume that $W(f) = 2\Lambda(f/B)$, where $B = 3$ kHz.

(a) Find and sketch the magnitude spectrum for the PAM signal.

(b) Find a numerical value for the first-null bandwidth of the PAM signal.

4-8 Assume that an analog signal with a spectrum shown in Fig. P4-3 is to be transmitted over a PAM system that has ac coupling. Thus a PAM pulse shape of the Manchester type as given by (4-42) is used. The PAM sampling frequency is 10 kHz. Find the spectrum for the Manchester encoded flat-topped PAM waveform. Sketch your result.

4-9 In a binary PCM system, if the quantizing noise is not to exceed $\pm P$ percent of the peak-to-peak analog level, show that the number of bits in each PCM word needs to be

$$n \geq [\log_2 10]\left[\log_{10}\left(\frac{50}{P}\right)\right] = 3.32 \log_{10}\left(\frac{50}{P}\right)$$

(*Hint:* Look at Fig. 4-8c.)

4-10 The information in an analog voltage waveform is to be transmitted over a PCM system with a $\pm 0.1\%$ accuracy (full scale). The analog waveform has an absolute bandwidth of 100 Hz and an amplitude range of -10 to $+10$ V.
(a) Determine the minimum sampling rate needed.
(b) Determine the number of bits needed in each PCM word.
(c) Determine the minimum bit rate required in the PCM signal.
(d) Determine the minimum absolute channel bandwidth required for transmission of this PCM signal.

4-11 A 40-Mbyte hard disk is used to store PCM data. Suppose that a VF (voice-frequency) signal is sampled at 8 ksamples/sec and the encoded PCM is to have an average S/N of at least 30 dB. How many minutes of VF conversation (i.e., PCM data) can be stored on the hard disk?

4-12 An analog signal with a bandwidth of 4.2 MHz is to be converted into binary PCM and transmitted over a channel. The peak-signal/quantizing-noise ratio at the receiver output must be at least 55 dB.
(a) If we assume $P_e = 0$ and no ISI, what will be the word length and the number of levels needed?
(b) What will be the equivalent bit rate?
(c) What will be the channel null bandwidth required if rectangular pulse shapes are used?

4-13 Modern compact disk (CD) players use 16-bit PCM, including one parity bit with 8 times oversampling of the analog signal. The analog signal bandwidth is 20 kHz.
(a) What is the null bandwidth of this PCM signal?
(b) Using (4-18), find the peak (S/N) in decibels.

4-14 Given an audio signal with spectral components in the frequency band 300 to 3000 Hz, assume that a sampling rate of 7 kHz will be used to generate a PCM signal. Design an appropriate PCM system, as follows.
(a) Draw a block diagram of the PCM system including the transmitter, channel, and receiver.
(b) Specify the number of uniform quantization levels needed and the zero-crossing channel bandwidth required, assuming that the peak signal-to-noise ratio at the receiver output needs to be at least 30 dB and that polar NRZ signaling is used.
(c) Discuss how nonuniform quantization can be used to improve the performance.

4-15 The S/N as given by (4-17a) and (4-17b) assume no ISI and no bit errors due to channel noise (i.e., $P_e = 0$). How large can P_e become before (4-17a) and (4-17b) are in error by 0.1% if $M = 4$, 8, or 16.

4-16 In a PCM system the bit error rate due to channel noise is 10^{-4}. Assume that the peak signal-to-noise ratio on the recovered analog signal needs to be at least 30 dB.
   (a) Find the minimum number of quantizing levels that can be used to encode the analog signal into a PCM signal.
   (b) If the original analog signal had an absolute bandwidth of 2.7 kHz, what is the zero-crossing bandwidth of the PCM signal for the polar NRZ signaling case?

4-17 Referring to Fig. 4-17 for a bit synchronizer using a square-law device, draw some typical waveforms that will appear in the bit synchronizer if a Manchester encoded PCM signal is present at the input. Discuss whether you would expect this bit synchronizer to work better for the Manchester encoded PCM signal or for a polar NRZ-encoded PCM signal.

4-18 (a) Sketch the complete $\mu = 10$ compressor characteristic that will handle input voltages over the range -5 to $+5$ V.
   (b) Plot the corresponding expandor characteristic.
   (c) Draw a 16-level nonuniform quantizer characteristic that corresponds to the $\mu = 10$ compression characteristic.

4-19 For a 4-bit PCM system, calculate and sketch a plot of the output S/N (in decibels) as a function of the relative input level, $20 \log(x_{rms}/V)$ for
   (a) A PCM system that uses $\mu = 10$ law companding.
   (b) A PCM system that uses uniform quantization (no companding).
   Which of these systems is better to use in practice? Why?

4-20 The performance of a $\mu = 255$ law companded PCM system is to be examined when the input consists of a sine wave having a peak value of V volts. Assume that $M = 256$.
   (a) Find an expression that describes the output S/N for this companded PCM system.
   (b) Plot the $(S/N)_{out}$ (in decibels) as a function of the relative input level, $20 \log(x_{rms}/V)$. Compare this result with that shown in Fig. 4-10.

4-21 Assume a typical binary sequence and show that if the corresponding polar NRZ signal and unipolar NRZ signal have the same peak-to-peak amplitude, the polar signal has less power (an advantage) than the unipolar signal. If noise is added to these signals, how do the probabilities of bit errors compare for these two signaling techniques?

4-22 The RS-232 serial port on a personal computer is transmitting 2400-bit/sec data using a polar NRZ line code that has a peak value of 12 V. Assume that binary 1's and 0's are equally likely to occur. Compute and plot the PSD for this RS-232 signal.

4-23 Consider a deterministic test pattern consisting of alternating binary 1's and binary 0's. Determine the magnitude spectra (not the PSD) for the following types of signaling formats as a function of T_b, where T_b is the time needed to send one bit of data.

(a) Unipolar NRZ signaling.

(b) Unipolar RZ signaling where the pulse width τ is $\tau = \frac{3}{4}T_b$.

How would each of these magnitude spectra change if the test pattern was changed to an alternating sequence of four binary 1's followed by four binary 0's?

4-24 Consider a random data pattern consisting of binary 1's and 0's where the probability of obtaining either a binary 1 or a binary 0 is $\frac{1}{2}$. Calculate the PSD function for the following types of signaling formats as a function of T_b, where T_b is the time needed to send one bit of data.

(a) Unipolar NRZ signaling.

(b) Unipolar RZ signaling where the pulse width τ is $\tau = \frac{3}{4}T_b$.

How do these PSDs for the random data cases compare to the magnitude spectra for the deterministic case of Prob. 4-23? What is the spectral efficiency for each of these cases?

4-25 Consider a deterministic data pattern consisting of alternating binary 1's and 0's. Determine the magnitude spectra (not the PSD) for the following types of signaling formats as a function of T_b, where T_b is the time needed to send one bit of data.

(a) Polar NRZ signaling.

(b) Manchester NRZ signaling.

How would each of these magnitude spectra change if the test pattern was changed to an alternating sequence of four binary 1's followed by two binary 0's?

4-26 Consider a random data pattern consisting of binary 1's and 0's, where the probability of obtaining either a binary 1 or a binary 0 is $\frac{1}{2}$. Calculate the PSD for the following types of signaling formats as a function of T_b, where T_b is the time needed to send 1 bit of data.

(a) Polar RZ signaling where the pulse width is $\tau = \frac{1}{2}T_b$.

(b) Manchester RZ signaling where the pulse width is $\tau = \frac{1}{4}T_b$. What is the first-null bandwidth of these signals? What is the spectral efficiency for each of these signaling cases?

4-27 Obtain the equations for the PSD of the bipolar NRZ and bipolar RZ (pulse width $\frac{1}{2}T_b$) line codes assuming peak values of ± 3 V. Plot these PSD results for the case of $R = 1.544$ Mbits/sec.

4-28 In Fig. 4-12 the PSDs for several line codes are shown. These PSDs were plotted assuming unity power for each signal so that the PSDs could be compared on an equal transmission power basis. Rederive the PSDs for these line codes assuming that the peak level is unity (i.e., $A = 1$). Plot these PSDs so that the spectra can be compared on an equal peak-signal-level basis.

4-29 Using (4-28), determine the conditions required so that there are delta functions in the PSD for line codes. Discuss how this affects the design of bit synchronizers for these line codes. [*Hint:* Examine (4-39).]

4-30 Consider a random data pattern consisting of binary 1's and 0's where the probability of obtaining either a binary 1 or a binary 0 is $\frac{1}{2}$. Assume that these data are encoded into a polar-type waveform where the pulse shape of each bit is given by

$$f(t) = \begin{cases} \cos\left(\dfrac{\pi t}{T_b}\right), & |t| < T_b/2 \\[2mm] 0, & |t| \text{ elsewhere} \end{cases}$$

T_b is the time needed to send one bit.
(a) Sketch a typical example of this waveform.
(b) Find the expression for the PSD of this waveform and sketch it.
(c) What is the spectral efficiency of this type of binary signal?

4-31 The data stream 01101000101 appears at the input of a differential encoder. Depending on the initial startup condition of the encoder, find two possible differentially encoded data streams that can appear at the output.

4-32 Create a practical block diagram for a differential encoding and decoding system. Explain how it works by showing the encoding and decoding for the sequence 001111010001. Assume that the reference digit is a binary 1. Show that error propagation cannot occur.

4-33 Design a regenerative repeater with its associated bit synchronizer for a polar RZ line code. Explain how your design works. (*Hint:* See Fig. 4-15 and the discussion on bit synchronizers.)

4-34 The approximate overall bit error for m cascaded repeaters is given by (4-50), which is valid when $P_e \ll 1$. This approximation is the dominant (first) term in (4-49). Assume that this approximation is considered to be valid when the first term of (4-49) dominates the second term by three orders of magnitude (i.e., 1000). Under this assumption, how small does P_e need to be for (4-50) to be valid? Give answers for $m = 5$, 10, and 30. Comment on the usefulness of (4-50) when typical systems have overall error rates of 10^{-5} or less.

4-35 Design a bit synchronizer for a Manchester NRZ line code by completing the following steps:
(a) Give a simplified block diagram.
(b) Explain how it works.
(c) Specify filter or phase-locked-loop (PLL) requirements.
(d) Explain the advantages and disadvantages of using this design for the Manchester NRZ line code as compared to using a polar NRZ line code and its associated bit synchronizer.

4-36 Figure 4-19c illustrates an eight-level multilevel signal. Assume that this line code is passed through a channel that filters this signal and adds some noise.
(a) Draw a picture of the eye pattern for the received waveform.
(b) Design a possible receiver with its associated symbol synchronizer for this line code.
(c) Explain how your receiver works.

4-37 Multilevel data with an equivalent bit rate of 2400 bits/sec is sent over a channel using a four-level line code which has a rectangular pulse shape at the output of the

transmitter. The overall transmission system (i.e., the transmitter, channel, and receiver) has a $r = 0.5$ raised cosine-rolloff filter characteristic.
(a) Find the baud rate of the received signal.
(b) Find the 6-dB bandwidth for this transmission system.
(c) Find the absolute bandwidth for this transmission system.

4-38 The information in an analog waveform is to be transmitted over a multilevel PCM system where the number of multilevels is eight. Assume that an accuracy of $\pm 1\%$ is required (full scale) and that the absolute bandwidth is 2700 Hz. The analog voltage has a range of -1 to $+1$ V.
(a) Determine the minimum bit rate of the PCM signal.
(b) Determine the minimum baud rate of the PCM signal.
(c) Determine the minimum absolute channel bandwidth required for transmission of this PCM signal.

4-39 A binary waveform of 9600 bits/sec is converted into an octal (multilevel) waveform that is passed through a channel with a raised cosine-rolloff filter characteristic. The channel has a conditioned (equalized) phase response out to 2.4 kHz.
(a) What is the baud rate of the multilevel signal?
(b) What is the rolloff factor of the filter characteristic?

4-40 Assume that the spectral properties of an $L = 64$ level multilevel waveform with rectangular RZ-type pulse shapes are to be examined. The pulse shape is given by

$$f(t) = \Pi\left(\frac{2t}{T_s}\right)$$

T_s is the time needed to send one of the multilevel symbols.
(a) Determine the expression for the PSD for the case of equally likely levels where the peak signal levels for this multilevel waveform are ± 10 V.
(b) What is the null bandwidth?
(c) What is the spectral efficiency?

4-41 A binary communication system uses polar signaling. The overall impulse response is designed to be of the $(\sin x)/x$ type as given by (4-67) so that there will be no ISI. The bit rate is $R = f_s = 300$ bits/sec.
(a) What is the bandwidth of the polar signal?
(b) Plot the waveform of the polar signal at the system output when the input binary data is 01100101. Can you discern the data by looking at this polar waveform?

4-42 Equation (4-67) gives one possible noncausal impulse response for a communication system that will have no ISI. For a causal approximation, select

$$h_e(t) = \frac{\sin \pi f_s(t - 4 \times 10^{-3})}{\pi f_s(t - 4 \times 10^{-3})}\Pi\left(\frac{t - 4 \times 10^{-3}}{8 \times 10^{-3}}\right)$$

where $f_s = 1000$.
(a) Using a PC, calculate $H_e(f)$ by use of the Fourier transform integral and plot $|H_e(f)|$.
(b) What is the bandwidth of this causal approximation, and how does it compare to the bandwidth of the noncausal filter described by (4-67) and (4-68)?

4-43 Starting with (4-69), prove that the impulse response of the raised cosine-rolloff filter is given by (4-73).

4-44 Consider the raised cosine-rolloff filter given by (4-69) and (4-73).
(a) Plot $|H_e(f)|$ for the case of $r = 0.75$, indicating f_1, f_0, and B on your sketch, similar to Fig. 4-22.
(b) Plot $h_e(t)$ for the case of $r = 0.75$ in terms of $1/f_0$, similar to Fig. 4-23.

4-45 Find the PSD of the waveform out of an $r = 0.5$ raised cosine-rolloff channel when the input is a polar NRZ signal. Assume that equally likely binary signaling is used and the channel bandwidth is just large enough to prevent ISI.

4-46 An analog signal is to be converted into a polar PCM signal and transmitted over a channel that is absolutely bandlimited to 4 kHz. Assume that 16 quantization levels are used and that the overall equivalent system transfer function is of the raised cosine-rolloff type with $r = 0.5$.
(a) Find the maximum PCM bit rate that can be supported by this system without introducing ISI.
(b) Find the maximum bandwidth that can be permitted for the analog signal.

4-47 Rework Prob. 4-46 for the case of a multilevel PCM signal when the number of levels is four.

4-48 Find the tap coefficients required for a zero-forcing transversal equalizing filter for the case of a three-tap filter. For a single flat-topped pulse into the transmit filter the response of the channel at the sampling times is $w_c(-2T_s) = -0.08$, $w_c(-T_s) = 0.25$, $w_c(0) = 1.0$, $w_c(T_s) = 0.30$, and $w_c(2T_s) = -0.06$.

4-49 Find the three tap coefficients for a zero-forcing transversal filter equalizer with $w_c(-2T_s) = -0.01$, $w_c(-T_s) = 0.1$, $w_c(0) = 0.8$, $w_c(T_s) = -0.2$, and $w_c(2T_s) = 0.05$.

4-50 A 1-bit/sec unipolar NRZ signal (rectangular bit shape) is sent over a bandlimited channel. The channel has the impulse response $h_c(t) = e^{-1000t}u(t)$. Design a five-tap zero-forcing transversal filter to equalize the channel response. Assume that $h_c(t)$ has significant values only over the first three bit intervals.

4-51 Assume that an analog signal is to be encoded into either PCM or DPCM. Discuss how the resulting spectra for the PCM and DPCM signals would be alike or different. (*Hint:* The number of bits needed in the DPCM word is less than the number of bits needed for the PCM word.)

4-52 Assume that a PCM-type system is to be designed such that an audio signal can be delivered at the receiver output. This audio signal is to have a bandwidth of 3400 Hz and a S/N of at least 40 dB. Determine the bit rate requirements for a design that uses:
(a) $\mu = 255$ companded PCM signaling.
(b) DPCM signaling.
Discuss which of the systems above would be used in your design and why.

4-53 A DM binary sequence 101011100001010110 is received. Referring to Fig. 4-28, plot the detected analog signal that appears at the output of the integrator.

4-54 Refer to Fig. 4-29, which shows typical DM waveforms. Draw an analog waveform that is different from the one shown in the figure. Draw the corresponding DM and integrator output waveforms. Denote the regions where slope overload noise dominates and where granular noise dominates.

4-55 A DM system is tested with a 10-kHz sinusoidal signal, 1 V peak to peak, at the input. It is sampled at 10 times the Nyquist rate.
(a) What is the step size required to prevent slope overload and to minimize granular noise?
(b) What is the PSD for the granular noise?
(c) If the receiver input is bandlimited to 200 kHz, what is the average-signal/quantizing-noise power ratio?

4-56 Assume that the input to a DM is $0.1t^8 - 5t + 2$. The step size of the DM is 1 V, and the sampler operates at 10 samples/sec. Over a time interval of 0 to 2 sec, sketch the input waveform, the delta modulator output, and the integrator output. Denote the granular noise and slope overload regions.

4-57 Rework Prob. 4-56 for the case of an adaptive delta modulator where the step size is selected according to the number of successive binary 1's or 0's on the DM output. Assume that the step size is 1.5 V when there are four or more binary digits of the same sign, 1 V for the case of three successive digits, and 0.5 V for the case of two or fewer successive digits.

4-58 A delta modulator is to be designed to transmit the information of an analog waveform that has a peak-to-peak level of 1 V and a bandwidth of 3.4 kHz. Assume that the waveform is to be transmitted over a channel where the frequency response is extremely poor above 1 MHz.
(a) Select the appropriate step size and sampling rate for a sine-wave test signal and discuss the performance of the system using the parameter values you have selected.
(b) If the DM system is to be used to transmit the information of a voice (analog) signal, select the appropriate step size when the sampling rate is 25 kHz. Discuss the performance of the system under these conditions.

4-59 A binary sequence 111010100000101000000101 is transmitted by DM. Evaluate and sketch the resulting analog waveform that appears at the receiver output.

4-60 One analog waveform $w_1(t)$ is bandlimited to 3 kHz, and another, $w_2(t)$, is bandlimited to 9 kHz. These two signals are to be sent by TDM over a PAM-type system.
(a) Determine the minimum sampling frequency for each signal and design a TDM commutator and decommutator to accommodate these signals.
(b) Draw some typical waveforms for $w_1(t)$ and $w_2(t)$, and sketch the corresponding TDM PAM waveform.

4-61 Three waveforms are time-division multiplexed over a channel using instantaneously sampled PAM. Assume that the PAM pulse width is very narrow and that each of the analog waveforms are sampled every 0.15 sec. Plot the (composite) TDM waveform when the input analog waveforms are

$$w_1(t) = 3 \sin(2\pi t)$$
$$w_2(t) = \Pi\left(\frac{t-1}{2}\right)$$
$$w_3(t) = -\Lambda(t-1)$$

4-62 Twenty-three analog signals, each with a bandwidth of 3.4 kHz, are sampled at an 8-kHz rate and multiplexed together with a synchronization channel (8 kHz) into a TDM PAM signal. This TDM signal is passed through a channel with an overall raised cosine-rolloff filter characteristic of $r = 0.75$.
   (a) Draw a block diagram for the system indicating the f_s of the commutator and the overall pulse rate of the TDM PAM signal.
   (b) Evaluate the absolute bandwidth required for the channel.

4-63 Two flat-topped PAM signals are time-division multiplexed together to produce a composite TDM PAM signal that is transmitted over a channel. The first PAM signal is obtained from an analog signal that has a rectangular spectrum, $W_1(f) = \Pi(f/2B)$. The second PAM signal is obtained from an analog signal that has a triangular spectrum, $W_2(f) = \Lambda(f/B)$ where $B = 3$ kHz.
   (a) Determine the minimum sampling frequency for each signal and design a TDM commutator and decommutator to accommodate these signals.
   (b) Calculate and sketch the magnitude spectrum for the composite TDM PAM signal.

4-64 Rework Prob. 4-62 for a TDM pulse code modulation system where an 8-bit quantizer is used to generate the PCM words for each of the analog inputs and an 8-bit synchronization word is used in the synchronization channel.

4-65 Design a TDM PCM system that will accommodate four 300-bit/sec (synchronous) digital inputs and one analog input that has a bandwidth of 500 Hz. Assume that the analog samples will be encoded into 4-bit PCM words. Draw a block diagram for your design, analogous to Fig. 4-36, indicating the data rates at the various points on the diagram. Explain how your design works.

4-66 Design a TDM system that will accommodate two 2400-bit/sec synchronous digital inputs and an analog input that has a bandwidth of 2700 Hz. Assume that the analog input is sampled at 1.11111 times the Nyquist rate and converted into 4 bit PCM words. Draw a block diagram for your design and indicate the data rate at various points on your diagram. Explain how your TDM scheme works.

4-67 A character-interleaved TDM is used to combine the data streams of a number of 110-bit/sec asynchronous terminals for data transmission over a 2400-bit/sec digital line. Each terminal sends characters consisting of 7 data bits, 1 parity bit, 1 start bit, and 2 stop bits. Assume that one synchronization character is sent after every 19 data characters and, in addition, at least 3% of the line capacity is reserved for pulse stuffing to accommodate speed variations from the various terminals.
   (a) Determine the number of bits per character.

  (b) Determine the number of terminals that can be accommodated by the multiplexer.

  (c) Sketch a possible framing pattern for the multiplexer.

4-68 Assume that two 600-bit/sec terminals, five 300-bit/sec terminals, and a number of 150-bit/sec terminals are to be time-multiplexed in a character-interleaved format over a 4800-bit/sec digital line. The terminals send 10 bits/character, and one synchronization character is inserted for every 99 data characters. All the terminals are asynchronous, and 3% of the line capacity is allocated for pulse stuffing to accommodate variations in the terminal clock rates.

  (a) Determine the number of 150-bit/sec terminals that can be accommodated.

  (b) Sketch a possible framing pattern for the multiplexer.

4-69 In designing a TDM system, a frame synchronizer identical to that shown in Fig. 4-34 is to be used. It is desired to choose a threshold so that frame sync can be detected even when one bit of the received sync word is in error. Thus, choose $V_T = K - 2$.

  (a) Find the expression for the probability of false sync, P_f, assuming equally likely data into the synchronizer.

  (b) Draw a block diagram for your design of the frame synchronizer including the number of shift register stages needed if $P_f \le 10^{-3}$ is required. Choose a sync word that will satisfy this specification and show inverters or no inverters on your diagram, as needed, in place of the gains $s_1, s_2, \ldots, s_K$. Explain how your frame synchronizer works.

  (c) Design a circuit (i.e., block diagram) that is used at the transmitter end to generate your unique frame sync word. Explain how your circuit works.

4-70 Find the number of the following devices that could be accommodated by a T1-type TDM line if 1% of the line capacity were reserved for synchronization purposes.

  (a) 110-bit/sec teleprinter terminals.

  (b) 300-bit/sec computer terminals.

  (c) 1200-bit/sec computer terminals.

  (d) 9600-bit/sec computer output ports.

  (e) 64-kbit/sec PCM voice-frequency lines.

How would these numbers change if each of the sources were operational an average of 10% of the time?

4-71 A TDM system has four 300-bit/sec and one 1200-bit/sec computer terminals connected to its input, and 3% of the line capacity is used for pulse stuffing to accommodate speed variations among the terminals. No statistical multiplexing is used.

  (a) Find the expression for the PSD of the polar NRZ signal at the TDM output. Assume that the binary 1's and 0's are equally likely and that the TDM signal levels are ± 12 V.

  (b) Sketch the PSD of this TDM signal and compare it with the sketch of the PSD for the signals that are emitted from the computer terminals (polar signal with ± 12-V levels).

4-72 Still black-and-white video data are sent over a basic rate ISDN system using 2B + D channels. The video data are sent over the two B channels, and the D channel is used for control and other data. Assume that each still picture consists of 480×500 pixels and that each pixel is encoded into one of eight allowed gray levels. How many pictures can be sent per second?

4-73 Assume that a sine wave is sampled at four times the Nyquist rate using instantaneous sampling.
  (a) Sketch the corresponding PWM signal.
  (b) Sketch the corresponding PPM signal.

4-74 Repeat Prob. 4-73, but assume that natural sampling is used.

4-75 Discuss why a PPM system requires a synchronizing signal, whereas PAM and PWM can be detected without the need for a synchronizing signal.

4-76 Assume that $w(t) = 10 \sin 2\pi t$ is instantaneously sampled every 0.1 sec, starting at $t = 0$.
  (a) Evaluate the exact spectrum for the PWM signal, assuming that the maximum pulse width is obtained if the sample value is 10 V and the pulse width is zero if the sample value is -10 V.
  (b) Evaluate the exact PPM spectrum, assuming that a pulse width of 0.01 sec is used.

4-77 Compare the bandwidth required to send a message by using PPM and PCM signaling. Assume that the digital source sends out 8 bits/character, so that the digital source can send 256 different messages (characters). Assume that the source rate is 10 characters/sec. Use the dimensionality theorem, $N/T_0 = 2B$, to determine the minimum bandwidth required, B.
  (a) Determine the minimum bandwidth required for a PCM signal that will encode the source information.
  (b) Determine the minimum bandwidth required for a PPM signal that will encode the source information.

Bandpass Signaling Principles and Circuits

This chapter is concerned with *bandpass* signaling techniques. As indicated in Chapter 1, the bandpass communication signal is obtained by modulating a baseband analog or digital signal onto a carrier. Here the basic principles of bandpass signal representation and the modulation process will be developed by use of the complex envelope. The complex envelope principle is then used to deduce techniques for evaluating the spectra and the power of bandpass signals.

The second half of this chapter, which begins with Sec. 5-8, uses this bandpass theory to analyze and design component blocks and circuits that are used in communication systems. These are filters, linear and nonlinear amplifiers, up-and-down converters, modulators, detectors, and phase-locked loops.

5-1 Complex Envelope Representation of Bandpass Waveforms

What is a general representation for bandpass digital and analog signals? How do we represent a modulated signal? How do we represent bandpass noise? These are some of the questions that are answered in this section.

Definitions: Baseband, Bandpass, and Modulation

DEFINITION: A *baseband* waveform has a spectral magnitude that is nonzero for frequencies in the vicinity of the origin (i.e., $f = 0$) and negligible elsewhere.

DEFINITION: A *bandpass* waveform has a spectral magnitude that is nonzero for frequencies in some band concentrated about a frequency $f = \pm f_c$, where $f_c \gg 0$. The spectral magnitude is negligible elsewhere. f_c is called the *carrier frequency*.

For bandpass waveforms the value of f_c may be arbitrarily assigned for mathematical convenience in *some* problems. In others, namely, modulation problems, f_c is the frequency of an oscillatory signal in the transmitter circuit and is the assigned frequency of the transmitter, such as, for example, 850 kHz for an AM broadcasting station.

In communication problems, the information source signal is usually a baseband signal: for example, a transistor-transistor logic (TTL) waveform from a digital circuit or an audio (analog) signal from a microphone. The communication engineer has the job of building a system that will transfer the information in this source signal $m(t)$ to the desired destination. As shown in Fig. 5-1, this usually requires the use of a bandpass signal, $s(t)$, which has a bandpass spectrum that is concentrated at $\pm f_c$ where f_c is selected so that $s(t)$ will propagate across the communication channel (either a softwire or a hardwire channel).

DEFINITION: *Modulation* is the process of imparting the source information onto a bandpass signal with a carrier frequency f_c by the introduction of amplitude and/or phase perturbations. This bandpass signal is called the *modulated* signal $s(t)$, and the baseband source signal is called the *modulating* signal $m(t)$.

Examples of exactly how modulation is accomplished are given later in this chapter. This definition indicates that modulation may be visualized as a mapping operation that maps the source information onto the bandpass signal $s(t)$ that will be transmitted over the channel.

As the modulated signal passes through the channel, noise corrupts it. The result is a bandpass signal-plus-noise waveform that is available at the receiver input, $r(t)$ (see Fig. 5-1). The receiver has the job of trying to recover the information that was sent from the source. $\tilde{m}$ denotes the corrupted version of m.

Complex Envelope Representation

All bandpass waveforms, whether they arise from a modulated signal, interfering signals, or noise, may be represented in a convenient form given by the following theorem. $v(t)$ will be used to denote the bandpass waveform canonically; specifically, $v(t)$ can represent

FIGURE 5-1 Communication system.

the signal when $s(t) \equiv v(t)$, the noise when $n(t) \equiv v(t)$, the filtered signal plus noise at the channel output when $r(t) \equiv v(t)$, or any other type of bandpass waveform.[†]

Theorem

Any physical bandpass waveform can be represented by

$$v(t) = \text{Re}\{g(t)e^{j\omega_c t}\} \tag{5-1a}$$

$\text{Re}\{\cdot\}$ denotes the real part of $\{\cdot\}$, $g(t)$ is called the *complex envelope* of $v(t)$, and f_c is the associated carrier frequency (hertz) where $\omega_c = 2\pi f_c$. Furthermore, two other equivalent representations are

$$v(t) = R(t) \cos[\omega_c t + \theta(t)] \tag{5-1b}$$

and

$$v(t) = x(t) \cos \omega_c t - y(t) \sin \omega_c t \tag{5-1c}$$

where

$$g(t) = x(t) + jy(t) = |g(t)|e^{j\underline{/g(t)}} \equiv R(t)e^{j\theta(t)} \tag{5-2}$$

$$x(t) = \text{Re}\{g(t)\} \equiv R(t) \cos \theta(t) \tag{5-3a}$$

$$y(t) = \text{Im}\{g(t)\} \equiv R(t) \sin \theta(t) \tag{5-3b}$$

$$R(t) \overset{\triangle}{=} |g(t)| \equiv \sqrt{x^2(t) + y^2(t)} \tag{5-4a}$$

$$\theta(t) \overset{\triangle}{=} \underline{/g(t)} = \tan^{-1}\left(\frac{y(t)}{x(t)}\right) \tag{5-4b}$$

The waveforms $g(t)$, $x(t)$, $y(t)$, $R(t)$, and $\theta(t)$ are all baseband waveforms, and, except for $g(t)$, they are all real waveforms. $R(t)$ is a nonnegative real waveform. Thus, (5-1) is a low-pass-to-bandpass transformation. $R(t)$ is called the *real envelope* of $v(t)$.

PROOF. Any physical waveform (it does *not* have to be periodic) may be represented over all time, $T_0 \to \infty$, by the complex Fourier series:

$$v(t) = \sum_{n=-\infty}^{n=\infty} c_n e^{jn\omega_0 t}, \qquad \omega_0 = 2\pi/T_0 \tag{5-5}$$

Furthermore, since the physical waveform is real $c_{-n} = c_n^*$ and using $\text{Re}\{\cdot\} = \frac{1}{2}\{\cdot\} + \frac{1}{2}\{\cdot\}^*$,

$$v(t) = \text{Re}\left\{c_0 + 2\sum_{n=1}^{\infty} c_n e^{jn\omega_0 t}\right\} \tag{5-6}$$

Furthermore, since $v(t)$ is a bandpass waveform, the c_n have negligible magnitudes for n in the vicinity of 0 and, in particular, $c_0 = 0$. Thus, with the introduction of an arbitrary parameter f_c, (5-6) becomes[‡]

$$v(t) = \text{Re}\left\{\left(2\sum_{n=1}^{n=\infty} c_n e^{j(n\omega_0 - \omega_c)t}\right)e^{j\omega_c t}\right\} \tag{5-7}$$

[†] The symbol $\equiv$ denotes an equivalence and the symbol $\overset{\triangle}{=}$ denotes a definition.

[‡] Since the frequencies involved in the argument of $\text{Re}\{\cdot\}$ are all positive, it can be shown that the complex function $2\sum_{n=1}^{\infty} c_n e^{jn\omega_0 t}$ is analytic in the upper-half complex t plane. Many interesting properties result because this function is an analytic function of a complex variable.

so that (5-1a) follows where

$$g(t) \equiv 2 \sum_{n=1}^{\infty} c_n e^{j(n\omega_0 - \omega_c)t} \qquad (5\text{-}8)$$

■

Since $v(t)$ is a bandpass waveform with nonzero spectrum concentrated near $f = f_c$, the Fourier coefficients c_n are nonzero only for values of n in the range $\pm n f_0 \approx f_c$. Therefore, from (5-8) $g(t)$ has a spectrum that is concentrated near $f = 0$. That is, $g(t)$ is a *baseband* waveform. It is also obvious from (5-8) that $g(t)$ may be a complex function of time. Representing the complex envelope in terms of two real functions in Cartesian coordinates, we have

$$g(t) \equiv x(t) + jy(t)$$

where $x(t) = \text{Re}\{g(t)\}$ and $y(t) = \text{Im}\{g(t)\}$. $x(t)$ is said to be the *in-phase modulation* associated with $v(t)$, and $y(t)$ is said to be the *quadrature modulation* associated with $v(t)$. Alternatively, the polar form of $g(t)$, represented by $R(t)$ and $\theta(t)$, is given by (5-2), where the identities between Cartesian and polar coordinates are given by (5-3) and (5-4). $R(t)$ and $\theta(t)$ are real waveforms and, in addition, $R(t)$ is always nonnegative. $R(t)$ is said to be the *amplitude modulation* (AM) on $v(t)$, and $\theta(t)$ is said to be the *phase modulation* (PM) on $v(t)$. It is also realized that if $v(t)$ is a deterministic waveform, $x(t)$, $y(t)$, $R(t)$, and $\theta(t)$ are also deterministic. If $v(t)$ is stochastic, for example, representing bandpass noise, $x(t)$, $y(t)$, $R(t)$, and $\theta(t)$ are stochastic baseband processes. Thus, in general, bandpass noise includes both AM, $R(t)$, and PM, $\theta(t)$, noise components. The usefulness of the complex envelope representation for bandpass waveforms cannot be overemphasized. In modern communication systems, the bandpass signal is often partitioned into two channels, one for $x(t)$ called the I (in-phase) channel and one for $y(t)$ called the Q (quadrature-phase) channel.

5-2 Representation of Modulated Signals

As defined earlier, modulation is the process of encoding the source information $m(t)$ (modulating signal) into a bandpass signal $s(t)$ (modulated signal). Consequently, the modulated signal is just a special application of the bandpass representation. The *modulated signal* is given by

$$s(t) = \text{Re}\{g(t)e^{j\omega_c t}\} \qquad (5\text{-}9)$$

where $\omega_c = 2\pi f_c$. f_c is the carrier frequency. The complex envelope $g(t)$ is a function of the modulating signal $m(t)$. That is,

$$g(t) = g[m(t)] \qquad (5\text{-}10)$$

Thus $g[\,\cdot\,]$ performs a mapping operation on $m(t)$. This was shown in Fig. 5-1.

Table 5-1 gives an overview on the *big picture* for the modulation problem. Examples of the mapping function $g[m]$ are given for amplitude modulation (AM), double-sideband suppressed carrier (DSB-SC), phase modulation (PM), frequency modulation (FM),

TABLE 5-1 Complex Envelope Functions for Various Types of Modulation[a]

Type of Modulation	Mapping Functions $g[m]$	Corresponding Quadrature Modulation	
		$x(t)$	$y(t)$
AM	$A_c[1 + m(t)]$	$A_c[1 + m(t)]$	0
DSB-SC	$A_c m(t)$	$A_c m(t)$	0
PM	$A_c e^{jD_p m(t)}$	$A_c \cos[D_p m(t)]$	$A_c \sin[D_p m(t)]$
FM	$A_c e^{jD_f \int_{-\infty}^{t} m(\sigma)\,d\sigma}$	$A_c \cos\left[D_f \int_{-\infty}^{t} m(\sigma)\,d\sigma\right]$	$A_c \sin\left[D_f \int_{-\infty}^{t} m(\sigma)\,d\sigma\right]$
SSB-AM-SC[b]	$A_c[m(t) \pm j\hat{m}(t)]$	$A_c m(t)$	$\pm A_c \hat{m}(t)$
SSB-PM[b]	$A_c e^{jD_p[m(t)\pm j\hat{m}(t)]}$	$A_c e^{\mp D_p \hat{m}(t)} \cos[D_p m(t)]$	$A_c e^{\mp D_p \hat{m}(t)} \sin[D_p m(t)]$
SSB-FM[b]	$A_c e^{jD_f \int_{-\infty}^{t}[m(\sigma)\pm j\hat{m}(\sigma)]d\sigma}$	$A_c e^{\mp D_f \int_{-\infty}^{t}\hat{m}(\sigma)\,d\sigma} \cos\left[D_f \int_{-\infty}^{t} m(\sigma)\,d\sigma\right]$	$A_c e^{\mp D_f \int_{-\infty}^{t}\hat{m}(\sigma)\,d\sigma} \sin\left[D_f \int_{-\infty}^{t} m(\sigma)\,d\sigma\right]$
SSB-EV[b]	$A_c e^{\ln[1+m(t)]\pm j\hat{\ln}[1+m(t)]}$	$A_c[1 + m(t)] \cos\{\hat{\ln}[1 + m(t)]\}$	$\pm A_c[1+m(t)] \sin\{\hat{\ln}[1 + m(t)]\}$
SSB-SQ[b]	$A_c e^{(1/2)\{\ln[1+m(t)]\pm j\hat{\ln}[1+m(t)]\}}$	$A_c \sqrt{1+m(t)} \cos\{\tfrac{1}{2}\hat{\ln}[1 + m(t)]\}$	$\pm A_c \sqrt{1+m(t)} \sin\{\tfrac{1}{2}\hat{\ln}[1 + m(t)]\}$
QM	$A_c m_1(t) + jm_2(t)$	$A_c m_1(t)$	$A_c m_2(t)$

Type of Modulation	Corresponding Amplitude and Phase Modulation		Linearity	Remarks
	$R(t)$	$\theta(t)$		
AM	$A_c\lvert 1 + m(t)\rvert$	$\begin{cases}0, & m(t) > -1 \\ 180°, & m(t) < -1\end{cases}$	L[c]	$m(t) > -1$ required for envelope detection
DSB-SC	$A_c\lvert m(t)\rvert$	$\begin{cases}0, & m(t) > 0 \\ 180°, & m(t) < 0\end{cases}$	L	Coherent detection required
PM	A_c	$D_p m(t)$	NL	D_p is the phase deviation constant (rad/volt)
FM	A_c	$D_f\displaystyle\int_{-\infty}^{t} m(\sigma)\,d\sigma$	NL	D_f is the frequency deviation constant (rad/volt-sec)
SSB-AM-SC[b]	$A_c\sqrt{[m(t)]^2 + [\hat{m}(t)]^2}$	$\tan^{-1}[\pm\hat{m}(t)/m(t)]$	L	Coherent detection required
SSB-PM[b]	$A_c e^{\mp D_p\hat{m}(t)}$	$D_p m(t)$	NL	
SSB-FM[b]	$A_c e^{\mp D_f\int_{-\infty}^{t}\hat{m}(\sigma)\,d\sigma}$	$D_f\displaystyle\int_{-\infty}^{t} m(\sigma)\,d\sigma$	NL	
SSB-EV[b]	$A_c[1 + m(t)]$	$\pm\hat{\ln}[1 + m(t)]$	NL	$m(t) > -1$ is required so that the ln(·) will have a real value
SSB-SQ[b]	$A_c\sqrt{1 + m(t)}$	$\pm\tfrac{1}{2}\hat{\ln}[1 + m(t)]$	NL	$m(t) > -1$ is required so that the ln(·) will have a real value
QM	$A_c\sqrt{m_1^2(t) + m_2^2(t)}$	$\tan^{-1}[m_2(t)/m_1(t)]$	L	Used in NTSC color television; requires coherent detection

[a] $A_c > 0$ is a constant that sets the power level of the signal as evaluated by use of (5-17); L, linear; NL, nonlinear; $[\cdot]$ is the Hilbert transform (i.e., $-90°$ phase-shifted version) of $[\cdot]$ (see Sec. 6-5 and Sec. A-7, Appendix A).

[b] Use upper signs for upper sideband signals and lower signs for lower sideband signals.

[c] In the strict sense, AM signals are not linear because the carrier term does not satisfy the linearity (superposition) condition.

235

single-sideband AM suppressed carrier (SSB-AM-SC), single-sideband PM (SSB-PM), single-sideband FM (SSB-FM), single-sideband envelope detectable (SSB-EV), single-sideband square-law detectable (SSB-SQ), and quadrature modulation (QM). Modulated signals are discussed in detail in Chapter 6. Obviously, it is possible to use other $g[m]$ functions that are not listed in Table 5-1. The question is: Are they useful? $g[m]$ functions are desired that are easy to implement and that will give desirable spectral properties. Furthermore, in the receiver the inverse function $m[g]$ is required. The inverse should be single valued over the range used and should be easily implemented. The mapping should suppress as much noise as possible so that $m(t)$ can be recovered with little corruption.

5-3 Spectrum of Bandpass Signals

The spectrum of a bandpass signal is directly related to the spectrum of its complex envelope.

Theorem

If a bandpass waveform is represented by

$$v(t) = \text{Re}\{g(t)e^{j\omega_c t}\} \tag{5-11}$$

then the spectrum of the bandpass waveform is

$$V(f) = \tfrac{1}{2}[G(f - f_c) + G^*(-f - f_c)] \tag{5-12}$$

and the PSD of the waveform is

$$\mathcal{P}_v(f) = \tfrac{1}{4}[\mathcal{P}_g(f - f_c) + \mathcal{P}_g(-f - f_c)] \tag{5-13}$$

where $G(f) = \mathcal{F}[g(t)]$ and $\mathcal{P}_g(f)$ is the PSD of $g(t)$.

PROOF

$$v(t) = \text{Re}\{g(t)e^{j\omega_c t}\} = \tfrac{1}{2}g(t)e^{j\omega_c t} + \tfrac{1}{2}g^*(t)e^{-j\omega_c t}$$

Thus

$$V(f) = \mathcal{F}[v(t)] = \tfrac{1}{2}\mathcal{F}[g(t)e^{j\omega_c t}] + \tfrac{1}{2}\mathcal{F}[g^*(t)e^{-j\omega_c t}] \tag{5-14}$$

If we use $\mathcal{F}[g^*(t)] = G^*(-f)$ from Table 2-1 and the frequency translation property of Fourier transforms from Table 2-1, this equation becomes

$$V(f) = \tfrac{1}{2}\{G(f - f_c) + G^*[-(f + f_c)]\} \tag{5-15}$$

which reduces to (5-12).

The PSD for $v(t)$ is obtained by first evaluating the autocorrelation for $v(t)$.

$$R_v(\tau) = \langle v(t)v(t + \tau) \rangle = \langle \text{Re}\{g(t)e^{j\omega_c t}\} \, \text{Re}\{g(t + \tau)e^{j\omega_c(t+\tau)}\} \rangle$$

Using the identity (see Prob. 2-67),

$$\text{Re}(c_2)\,\text{Re}(c_1) = \tfrac{1}{2}\,\text{Re}(c_2^* c_1) + \tfrac{1}{2}\,\text{Re}(c_2 c_1)$$

where $c_2 = g(t)e^{j\omega_c t}$ and $c_1 = g(t + \tau)e^{j\omega_c(t+\tau)}$, we get

$$R_v(\tau) = \langle \tfrac{1}{2}\,\text{Re}\{g^*(t)g(t + \tau)e^{-j\omega_c t}e^{j\omega_c(t+\tau)}\}\rangle + \langle \tfrac{1}{2}\,\text{Re}\{g(t)g(t + \tau)e^{j\omega_c t}e^{j\omega_c(t+\tau)}\}\rangle$$

Realizing that both $\langle\ \rangle$ and Re{ } are linear operators, we may exchange the order of the operators without affecting the result, and the autocorrelation becomes

$$R_v(\tau) = \tfrac{1}{2}\,\text{Re}\{\langle g^*(t)g(t+\tau)e^{j\omega_c\tau}\rangle\} + \tfrac{1}{2}\,\text{Re}\{\langle g(t)g(t+\tau)e^{j2\omega_c t}e^{j\omega_c\tau}\rangle\}$$

or

$$R_v(\tau) = \tfrac{1}{2}\,\text{Re}\{\langle g^*(t)g(t+\tau)\rangle e^{j\omega_c\tau}\} + \tfrac{1}{2}\,\text{Re}\{\langle g(t)g(t+\tau)e^{j2\omega_c t}\rangle e^{j\omega_c\tau}\}$$

But $\langle g^*(t)g(t+\tau)\rangle = R_g(\tau)$. The second term on the right is negligible because $e^{j2\omega_c t} = \cos 2\omega_c t + j\sin 2\omega_c t$ oscillates much faster than variations in $g(t)g(t+\tau)$. In other words, f_c is much larger than the frequencies in $g(t)$, so the integral is negligible. This is an application of the Riemann–Lebesque lemma from integral calculus [Olmsted, 1961]. Thus the autocorrelation reduces to

$$R_v(\tau) = \tfrac{1}{2}\,\text{Re}\{R_g(\tau)e^{j\omega_c\tau}\} \tag{5-16}$$

The PSD is obtained by taking the Fourier transform of (5-16) (i.e., applying the Wiener–Khintchine theorem). Note that (5-16) has the same mathematical form as (5-11) when t is replaced by τ, so the Fourier transform has the same form as (5-12). Thus

$$\mathcal{P}_v(f) = \mathcal{F}[R_v(\tau)] = \tfrac{1}{4}[\mathcal{P}_g(f-f_c) + \mathcal{P}_g^*(-f-f_c)]$$

But $\mathcal{P}_g^*(f) = \mathcal{P}_g(f)$ since the PSD is a real function. Thus the PSD is given by (5-13).

■

5-4 Evaluation of Power

Theorem

The total average normalized power of a bandpass waveform, $v(t)$, is

$$P_v = \langle v^2(t)\rangle = \int_{-\infty}^{\infty} \mathcal{P}_v(f)\,df = R_v(0) = \tfrac{1}{2}\langle |g(t)|^2\rangle \tag{5-17}$$

where "normalized" implies that the load is equivalent to one ohm.

PROOF.   Substituting $v(t)$ into (2-67), we get

$$P_v = \langle v^2(t)\rangle = \int_{-\infty}^{\infty} \mathcal{P}_v(f)\,df$$

But $R_v(\tau) = \mathcal{F}^{-1}[\mathcal{P}_v(f)] = \int_{-\infty}^{\infty} \mathcal{P}_v(f)e^{j2\pi f\tau}\,df$, so

$$R_v(0) = \int_{-\infty}^{\infty} \mathcal{P}_v(f)\,df$$

Also, from (5-16),

$$R_v(0) = \tfrac{1}{2}\,\text{Re}\{R_g(0)\} = \tfrac{1}{2}\,\text{Re}\{\langle g^*(t)g(t+0)\rangle\}$$

or

$$R_v(0) = \tfrac{1}{2}\,\text{Re}\{\langle |g(t)|^2\rangle\}$$

But $|g(t)|$ is always real, so

$$R_v(0) = \tfrac{1}{2} \langle |g(t)|^2 \rangle$$ ∎

Another type of power rating, called the *peak envelope power* (PEP), is useful for transmitter specifications.

> **DEFINITION:** The *peak envelope power* (PEP) is the average power that would be obtained if $|g(t)|$ were to be held constant at its peak value.

This is equivalent to evaluating the average power in an unmodulated RF sinusoid that has a peak value of $A_p = \max[v(t)]$, as is readily seen from Fig. 6-1.

Theorem

The normalized PEP is given by

$$P_{\text{PEP}} = \tfrac{1}{2} [\max|g(t)|]^2 \tag{5-18}$$

A proof of this theorem follows by applying the definition to (5-17). As described in Chapter 6, the PEP is useful for specifying the power capability of AM, SSB, and television transmitters.

Example 5-1   Amplitude-Modulated Signal

Evaluate the magnitude spectrum for an amplitude-modulated (AM) signal. From Table 5-1, the complex envelope of an AM signal is

$$g(t) = A_c[1 + m(t)]$$

so that the spectrum of the complex envelope is

$$G(f) = A_c \delta(f) + A_c M(f) \tag{5-19}$$

Using (5-9), we obtain the AM signal waveform

$$s(t) = A_c[1 + m(t)] \cos \omega_c t$$

and, using (5-12), the AM spectrum

$$S(f) = \tfrac{1}{2} A_c [\delta(f - f_c) + M(f - f_c) + \delta(f + f_c) + M(f + f_c)] \tag{5-20a}$$

where, since $m(t)$ is real, $M^*(f) = M(-f)$, and $\delta(f) = \delta(-f)$ (the delta function was defined to be even) were used. Suppose that the magnitude spectrum of the modulation happens to be a triangular function, as shown in Fig. 5-2a. This spectrum might arise from an analog audio source where the bass frequencies are emphasized. The resulting AM spectrum, using (5-21), is shown in Fig. 5-2b. Note that since $G(f - f_c)$ and $G^*(-f - f_c)$ do not overlap, the magnitude spectrum is

$$|S(f)| = \begin{cases} \tfrac{1}{2} A_c \delta(f - f_c) + \tfrac{1}{2} A_c |M(f - f_c)|, & f > 0 \\ \tfrac{1}{2} A_c \delta(f + f_c) + \tfrac{1}{2} A_c |M(-f - f_c)|, & f < 0 \end{cases} \tag{5-20b}$$

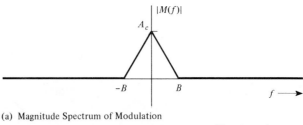

(a) Magnitude Spectrum of Modulation

(b) Magnitude Spectrum of AM Signal

FIGURE 5-2 Spectrum of an AM signal.

The "1" in $g(t) = A_c[1 + m(t)]$ causes delta functions to occur in the spectrum at $f = \pm f_c$, where f_c is the assigned carrier frequency. Using (5-17), we obtain the total average signal power

$$P_s = \tfrac{1}{2}A_c^2 \langle |1 + m(t)|^2 \rangle = \tfrac{1}{2}A_c^2 \langle 1 + 2m(t) + m^2(t) \rangle$$
$$= \tfrac{1}{2}A_c^2 [1 + 2\langle m(t) \rangle + \langle m^2(t) \rangle]$$

If we assume that the dc value of the modulation is zero, as shown in Fig. 5-2a, the average signal power becomes

$$P_s = \tfrac{1}{2}A_c^2 [1 + P_m] \tag{5-21}$$

where $P_m = \langle m^2(t) \rangle$ is the power in the modulation, $m(t)$, $\tfrac{1}{2}A_c^2$ is the carrier power, and $\tfrac{1}{2}A_c^2 P_m$ is the power in the sidebands of $s(t)$.

5-5 Bandpass Filtering and Linear Distortion

Equivalent Low-Pass Filter

In Sec. 3-3 the general transfer function technique was described for the treatment of linear filter problems. Now a shortcut technique will be developed for modeling a bandpass filter by using an equivalent low-pass filter that has a complex valued impulse response (see Fig. 5-3a). $v_1(t)$ and $v_2(t)$ are the input and output bandpass waveforms with

$v_1(t) = \text{Re } [g_1(t)e^{j\omega_c t}]$

Bandpass filter
$h(t) = \text{Re } [k(t)e^{j\omega_c t}]$
$H(f) = \frac{1}{2}K(f - f_c) + \frac{1}{2}K^*(-f - f_c)$

$v_2(t) = \text{Re } [g_2(t)e^{j\omega_c t}]$

(a) Bandpass Filter

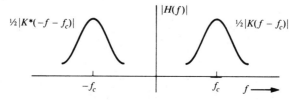

$\frac{1}{2}|K^*(-f - f_c)|$

$|H(f)|$

$\frac{1}{2}|K(f - f_c)|$

$-f_c$

f_c $f \longrightarrow$

(b) Typical Bandpass Filter Frequency Response

$\frac{1}{2}g_1(t)$

$\frac{1}{2}G_1(f)$

Equivalent lowpass filter
$\frac{1}{2}k(t)$
$\frac{1}{2}K(f)$

$\frac{1}{2}g_2(t)$

$\frac{1}{2}G_2(f)$

(c) Equivalent (Complex Impulse Response) Lowpass Filter

$\frac{1}{2}|K(f)|$

$f \longrightarrow$

(d) Typical Equivalent Lowpass Filter Frequency Response

FIGURE 5-3 Bandpass filtering.

the corresponding complex envelopes $g_1(t)$ and $g_2(t)$. The impulse response of the bandpass filter, $h(t)$, can also be represented by its corresponding complex envelope $k(t)$. In addition, as shown in Fig. 5-3a, the frequency domain description, $H(f)$, can be expressed in terms of $K(f)$ with the help of (5-11) and (5-12). Figure 5-3b shows a typical bandpass frequency response characteristic $|H(f)|$.

Theorem

The complex envelopes for the input, output, and impulse response of a bandpass filter are related by

$$\frac{1}{2}g_2(t) = \frac{1}{2}g_1(t) * \frac{1}{2}k(t) \tag{5-22}$$

where $g_1(t)$ is the complex envelope of the input and $k(t)$ is the complex envelope of the impulse response. It also follows that

$$\frac{1}{2}G_2(f) = \frac{1}{2}G_1(f)\frac{1}{2}K(f) \tag{5-23}$$

PROOF. Using (3-5), we know that the spectrum of the output is

$$V_2(f) = V_1(f)H(f) \tag{5-24}$$

Since $v_1(t)$, $v_2(t)$, and $h(t)$ are all bandpass waveforms, the spectra of these waveforms are related to the spectra of their complex envelopes by (5-15); thus (5-24) becomes

$$\frac{1}{2}[G_2(f-f_c) + G_2^*(-f-f_c)]$$
$$= \frac{1}{2}[G_1(f-f_c) + G_1^*(-f-f_c)]\frac{1}{2}[K(f-f_c) + K^*(-f-f_c)]$$
$$= \frac{1}{4}[G_1(f-f_c)K(f-f_c) + G_1(f-f_c)K^*(-f-f_c)$$
$$+ G_1^*(-f-f_c)K(f-f_c) + G_1^*(-f-f_c)K^*(-f-f_c)] \tag{5-25}$$

But $G_1(f-f_c)K^*(-f-f_c) = 0$ since the spectrum of $G_1(f-f_c)$ is zero in the region of frequencies around $-f_c$ where $K^*(-f-f_c)$ is nonzero. That is, there is no spectral overlap of $G_1(f-f_c)$ and $K^*(-f-f_c)$ because $G_1(f)$ and $K(f)$ have nonzero spectra only around $f = 0$ (i.e., baseband, as illustrated in Fig. 4-2d). Similarly, $G_1^*(-f-f_c)K(f-f_c) = 0$. Consequently, (5-25) becomes

$$[\frac{1}{2}G_2(f-f_c)] + [\frac{1}{2}G_2^*(-f-f_c)]$$
$$= [\frac{1}{2}G_1(f-f_c)\frac{1}{2}K(f-f_c)] + [\frac{1}{2}G_2^*(-f-f_c)\frac{1}{2}K^*(-f-f_c)] \tag{5-26}$$

Thus $\frac{1}{2}G_2(f) = \frac{1}{2}G_1(f)\frac{1}{2}K(f)$, which is identical to (5-23). Taking the inverse Fourier transform of both sides of (5-23), (5-22) is obtained. ∎

This theorem indicates that any bandpass filter system may be described and analyzed by using an *equivalent low-pass filter* as shown in Fig. 5-3c. A typical equivalent low-pass frequency response characteristic is shown in Fig. 5-3d. Since equations for equivalent low-pass filters are usually much less complicated than those for bandpass filters, the equivalent low-pass filter system model is very useful. This is the basis for computer programs that simulate bandpass communication systems by using equivalent low-pass models and use the bandpass sampling theorem.

It is realized that the linear bandpass filter can produce variations in the phase modulation at the output, $\theta_2(t)$, where $\theta_2(t) = \underline{/g_2(t)}$, as a function of the amplitude modulation on the input complex envelope, $R_1(t)$, where $R_1(t) = |g_1(t)|$. This is called *AM-to-PM conversion*. Similarly, the filter can also cause variations on the AM at the output, $R_2(t)$, because of the PM on the input, $\theta_1(t)$. This is called *PM-to-AM conversion*.

Since $h(t)$ represents a linear filter, $g_2(t)$ will be a linear filtered version of $g_1(t)$; however, $\theta_2(t)$ and $R_2(t)$—the PM and AM components of $g_2(t)$—will be a *nonlinear* filtered version of $g_1(t)$ since $\theta_2(t)$ and $R_2(t)$ are nonlinear functions of $g_2(t)$. The analysis of the nonlinear distortion is very complicated. Although many analysis techniques have been published in the literature, none has been entirely satisfactory. Panter [1965] gives a three-chapter summary of some of these techniques, and a classical paper is also recommended [Bedrosian and Rice, 1968]. Furthermore, nonlinearities that occur in a practical system will also cause nonlinear distortion and AM-to-PM conversion effects. Nonlinear effects can be analyzed by several techniques, including power-series analysis; this is discussed in the section on amplifiers that follows later in this chapter. If a nonlinear effect in a *bandpass* system is to be analyzed, a Fourier series technique that uses the Chebyshev transform has been found to be useful [Spilker, 1977].

Linear Distortion

In Sec. 3-4 the general conditions were found for distortionless transmission. For linear *bandpass filters* (channels), a less restrictive set of conditions will now be shown to be satisfactory. For distortionless transmission of bandpass signals, the channel transfer function, $H(f) = |H(f)|e^{j\theta(f)}$, needs to satisfy the following requirements:

- The amplitude response is constant. That is,

$$|H(f)| = A \tag{5-27a}$$

  where A is a positive (real) constant.
- The derivative of the phase response is a constant. That is,

$$-\frac{1}{2\pi}\frac{d\theta(f)}{df} = T_g \tag{5-27b}$$

  where T_g is a constant called the complex *envelope delay* or, more concisely, the *group delay* and $\theta(f) = \underline{/H(f)}$.

  This is illustrated in Fig. 5-4. Note that (5-27a) is identical to the general requirement of (3-21a), but (5-27b) is less restrictive than (3-21b). That is, if (3-21b) is satisfied, (5-27b)

(a) Magnitude Response

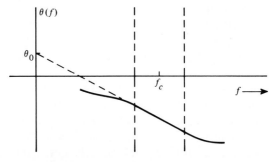

(b) Phase Response

FIGURE 5-4 Transfer characteristics of a distortionless bandpass channel.

is satisfied where $T_d = T_g$; however, if (5-27b) is satisfied, (3-21b) is not necessarily satisfied because the integral of (5-27b) is

$$\theta(f) = -2\pi f T_g + \theta_0 \qquad (5\text{-}28)$$

where θ_0 is a phase-shift constant, as shown in Fig. 5-4b. If θ_0 happens to be nonzero, (3-21b) is not satisfied.

Now it will be shown that (5-27a) and (5-27b) are sufficient requirements for distortionless transmission of bandpass signals. From (5-27a) and (5-28) the channel (or filter) transfer function is

$$H(f) = Ae^{j(-2\pi f T_g + \theta_0)} = (Ae^{j\theta_0})e^{-j2\pi f T_g} \qquad (5\text{-}29)$$

over the bandpass of the signal. If the input to the bandpass channel is represented by

$$v_1(t) = x(t)\cos\omega_c t - y(t)\sin\omega_c t$$

then, using (5-29) and realizing that $e^{-j2\pi f T_g}$ causes a delay of T_g, the output of the channel is

$$v_2(t) = Ax(t - T_g)\cos[\omega_c(t - T_g) + \theta_0] - Ay(t - T_g)\sin[\omega_c(t - T_g) + \theta_0]$$

Using (5-28), we obtain

$$v_2(t) = Ax(t - T_g)\cos[\omega_c t + \theta(f_c)] - Ay(t - T_g)\sin[\omega_c t + \theta(f_c)]$$

where, by use of (3-21b) evaluated at $f = f_c$,

$$\theta(f_c) = -\omega_c T_g + \theta_0 = -2\pi f_c T_d$$

Thus the output bandpass signal can be described by

$$v_2(t) = Ax(t - T_g)\cos[\omega_c(t - T_d)] - Ay(t - T_g)\sin[\omega_c(t - T_d)] \qquad (5\text{-}30)$$

where the modulation on the carrier (i.e., the x and y components) has been delayed by the *group time delay,* T_g, and the carrier has been delayed by the *carrier time delay,* T_d. Since $\theta(f_c) = -2\pi f_c T_d$, where $\theta(f_c)$ is the carrier phase shift, T_d is also called the *phase delay.* Equation (5-30) demonstrates that the bandpass filter delays the input complex envelope (i.e., the input information) by T_g seconds, whereas the carrier is delayed by T_d seconds. This is distortionless transmission, which is obtained when (5-27a) and (5-27b) are satisfied. Note that T_g will differ from T_d unless θ_0 happens to be zero.

In summary, the general requirements for distortionless transmission of either baseband or bandpass signals are given by (3-21a) and (3-21b). However, for the bandpass case (3-21b) is overly restrictive and may be replaced by (5-27b). (In this case $T_d \neq T_g$ unless $\theta_0 = 0$.) That is, for distortionless *bandpass* transmission, it is only necessary to have a transfer function with a *constant amplitude* and a *constant phase derivative* over the bandwidth of the signal.

5-6 Bandpass Sampling Theorem

Computer simulation is often used to analyze the performance of complicated communication systems, especially when coding schemes are used. This requires that the RF signal and noise for the system under test be sampled so that the data can be obtained for processing by digital computer simulation. If the sampling were carried out at the Nyquist rate or larger ($f_s \geq 2B$, where B is the highest frequency involved in the spectrum of the RF signal), the sampling rate would be ridiculous. For example, consider a satellite communication system with a carrier frequency of $f_c = 6$ GHz. The sampling rate required would be at least 12 GHz. Fortunately, for the signals of this type (bandpass signals), it can be shown that the sampling rate depends only on the *bandwidth* of the signal, not on the absolute frequencies involved. This is equivalent to saying that we can reproduce the signal from samples of the complex envelope.

Bandpass Sampling Theorem

If a (real) bandpass waveform has a nonzero spectrum only over the frequency interval $f_1 < |f| < f_2$ where the transmission bandwidth B_T is taken to be the absolute bandwidth given by $B_T = f_2 - f_1$, then the waveform may be reproduced from sample values, if the sampling rate is

$$f_s \geq 2B_T \tag{5-31}$$

This theorem may be demonstrated by using the quadrature bandpass representation

$$v(t) = x(t) \cos \omega_c t - y(t) \sin \omega_c t \tag{5-32}$$

Let f_c be the center of the bandpass so that $f_c = (f_2 + f_1)/2$. Then, from (5-8) it is seen that both $x(t)$ and $y(t)$ are baseband signals and absolutely bandlimited to $B = B_T/2$. From the baseband sampling theorem the sampling rate required to represent these baseband signals is $f_b \geq 2B = B_T$. Equation (5-32) becomes

$$v(t) = \sum_{n=-\infty}^{n=\infty} \left[x\left(\frac{n}{f_b}\right) \cos \omega_c t - y\left(\frac{n}{f_b}\right) \sin \omega_c t \right] \left[\frac{\sin\{\pi f_b[t - (n/f_b)]\}}{\pi f_b[t - (n/f_b)]} \right] \tag{5-33}$$

For the general case, where the $x(n/f_b)$ and $y(n/f_b)$ samples are independent, two real samples are obtained for each value of n so that the overall sampling rate for $v(t)$ is $f_s = 2f_b \geq 2B_T$. This is the bandpass sampling frequency requirement of (5-31). In most engineering applications, $f_c \gg B_T$. Thus the x and y samples can be obtained by sampling $v(t)$ at $t \approx (n/f_b)$, but adjusting t slightly, so that $\cos \omega_c t = 1$ and $\sin \omega_c t = 1$ at the *exact* sampling time for x and y, respectively. That is, for $t \approx n/f_s$, $v(n/f_b) = x(n/f_b)$ when $\cos \omega_c t = 1$ (i.e., $\sin \omega_c t = 0$) and $v(n/f_b) = y(n/f_b)$ when $\sin \omega_c t = 1$ (i.e., $\cos \omega_c t = 0$). If f_c is not large enough for the x and y samples to be obtained directly from $v(t)$, then $x(t)$ and $y(t)$ can first be obtained by the use of two quadrature product detectors as described by (5-76). The $x(t)$ and $y(t)$ baseband signals can then be individually sampled at a rate of f_b, and it is seen that the overall equivalent sampling rate is still $f_s = 2f_b \geq 2B_T$.

In the application of this theorem, it is assumed that the bandpass signal $v(t)$ is reconstructed by use of (5-33). This implies that *nonuniformly* spaced time samples of $v(t)$ are used since the samples are taken in pairs (for the x and y components) instead of being uniformly spaced T_s seconds apart. *Uniformly* spaced samples of $v(t)$ itself can be used with a minimum sampling frequency of $2B_T$, *provided* that either f_1 or f_2 is a harmonic of f_s [Taub and Schilling, 1986]. Otherwise, a minimum sampling frequency larger than $2B_T$

but not larger than $4B_T$ is required [Haykin, 1983; Peebles, 1976; Taub and Schilling, 1986]. This phenomenon also occurs with impulse sampling [eq. (3-45)] because f_s needs to be selected so that there is no spectral overlap in the $f_1 < f < f_2$ band when the band-pass spectrum is translated to harmonics of f_s.

Bandpass Dimensionality Theorem

Assume that a bandpass waveform has a nonzero spectrum only over the frequency interval $f_1 < |f| < f_2$ where the transmission bandwidth B_T is taken to be the absolute bandwidth given by $B_T = f_2 - f_1$ and $B_T \ll f_1$. The waveform may be completely specified over a T_0-second interval by

$$N = 2B_T T_0 \tag{5-34}$$

independent pieces of information. N is said to be the number of dimensions required to specify the waveform.

The bandpass dimensionality theorem is similar to the dimensionality theorem discussed earlier, (3-46), and may be demonstrated by the use of the complex Fourier series to represent the bandpass waveform over a T_0-second interval. The number of nonzero Fourier coefficients required to produce a line spectrum over the B_T hertz frequency interval is B_T/f_0 since f_0 is the frequency spacing between adjacent lines. Since $c_n = |c_n|e^{j\angle c_n}$ and $c_{-n} = c_n^*$, the number of independent (real value) samples is $2B_T/f_0 = 2B_T T_0$.

As mentioned earlier, computer simulation is often used to analyze communication systems. The bandpass dimensionality theorem tells us that a bandpass signal B_T hertz wide can be represented over a T_0-second interval provided that at least $N = 2B_T T_0$ samples are used.

5-7 Received Signal Plus Noise

Using the representation of bandpass signals and including the effects of channel filtering, a model for the received signal plus noise will now be obtained. Referring to Fig. 5-1, the signal out of the transmitter is

$$s(t) = \text{Re}[g(t)e^{j\omega_c t}]$$

where $g(t)$ is the complex envelope for the particular type of modulation used (see Table 5-1).

A good mathematical model for the received signal plus noise, $r(t)$, may or may not be easy to obtain, depending on the complexity of the channel. If the channel is linear and time invariant, then

$$r(t) = s(t) * h(t) + n(t) \tag{5-35}$$

where $h(t)$ is the impulse response of the channel and $n(t)$ is the noise at the receiver input. Furthermore, if the channel is distortionless, its transfer function is given by (5-29), and consequently, the signal plus noise at the receiver input is

$$r(t) = \text{Re}[Ag(t - T_g)e^{j\omega_c t + j\theta(f_c)} + n(t)] \tag{5-36}$$

where A is the gain of the channel (a positive number and usually less than 1), T_g is the channel group delay, and $\theta(f_c)$ is the carrier phase shift caused by the channel. In practice, the values for T_g and $\theta(f_c)$ are often not known, so that if values for T_g and $\theta(f_c)$ are needed by the receiver to detect the information that was transmitted, receiver circuits are devised to recover (i.e., estimate) the received carrier phase $\theta(f_c)$ and the group delay (e.g., a bit synchronizer for the case of digital signaling). To carry out a detailed analysis of the receiver performance when there are errors due to poor estimates of received carrier phase and group delay is beyond the scope of this book. (These topics are appropriate for advanced graduate courses.) Consequently, we will assume that the receiver circuits are designed to make these effects negligible, and therefore we can consider the signal plus noise at the receiver input to be

$$r(t) = \text{Re}[g(t)e^{j\omega_c t}] + n(t) \qquad (5\text{-}37)$$

where the effects of channel filtering, if any, are taken into account by some modification of the complex envelope, $g(t)$, and the constant A_c that is implicit within $g(t)$ (see Table 5-1) is adjusted to reflect the effect of channel attenuation. Details of this approach are worked out in Sec. 8-6.

Given that (5-37) models the receiver input, the receiver output, $\tilde{m}(t)$, depends on the type of functional blocks used within the receiver, such as filters, limiters, and detectors. These blocks are described in Sections 5-8 through 5-14 and their effects are summarized Table 5-4.

5-8 Classification of Filters and Amplifiers

Filters

Filters are devices that take an input waveshape and modify the frequency spectrum to produce the output waveshape. Filters may be classified in several ways. One is by the type of construction used, such as LC elements or quartz crystal elements. Another is by the type of transfer function that is realized, such as the Butterworth or Chebyshev response (defined subsequently). These two topics of construction types and transfer function characteristics are discussed in this section.

Filters use energy storage elements to obtain frequency discrimination. In any physical filter the energy storage elements are imperfect. For example, a physical inductor has some series resistance as well as inductance, and a physical capacitor has some shunt (leakage) resistance as well as capacitance. A natural question, then, is: What is the quality, Q, of a circuit element or filter? Unfortunately, two different measures of filter quality are used in the technical literature. The first definition is concerned with the efficiency of *energy storage* in a circuit; it is [Ramo, Whinnery, and vanDuzer, 1984]

$$Q = \frac{2\pi(\text{maximum energy stored during one cycle})}{\text{energy dissipated per cycle}} \qquad (5\text{-}38)$$

Of course, a larger value for Q corresponds to a more perfect storage element. That is, a perfect L or C element would have infinite Q. The second definition is concerned with the *frequency selectivity* of a circuit; it is

$$Q = \frac{f_0}{B} \tag{5-39}$$

where f_0 is the resonant frequency and B is the 3-dB bandwidth. Here the larger the value of Q, the better the frequency selectivity, since for a given f_0, the bandwidth would be smaller.

In general, the value of Q as evaluated using (5-38) is different from the value of Q obtained from (5-39). However, these two definitions give identical values for an *RLC* series resonant circuit driven by a voltage source or for an *RLC* parallel resonant circuit driven by a current source [Nilsson, 1990]. For bandpass filtering applications, frequency selectivity is the desired characteristic, so (5-39) is used. Also, (5-39) is easy to evaluate from laboratory measurements. If we are designing a passive filter (not necessarily a single-tuned circuit) of center frequency f_0 and 3-dB bandwidth B, the individual circuit elements will each need to have much larger Q's than f_0/B. Thus, for a practical filter design we first need to answer the question: What are the Q's needed for the filter elements, and what kind of elements will give these values of Q? This question is answered in Table 5-2.

Table 5-2 lists filters as classified by the type of energy storage elements used in their construction and gives typical values for the Q of the elements. Filters that use lumped[†] L and C elements become impractical to build above 300 MHz because the parasitic capacitance and inductance of the leads significantly affect the frequency response at high frequencies. Active filters, which use operational amplifiers with *RC* circuit elements, are practical only below 500 kHz since the op amps need to have a large open-loop gain over the operating band. For very-low-frequency filters, *RC* active filters are usually preferred to *LC* passive filters because the size of the *LC* components becomes large and the Q of the inductors becomes small in this frequency range.

Crystal filters are manufactured from quartz crystal elements. These act as a series resonant circuit in parallel with a shunt capacitance caused by the holder (mounting). Thus a parallel resonant as well as a series resonant mode of operation is possible. Above 100 MHz the quartz element becomes physically too small to manufacture, and below 1 kHz the size of the element becomes prohibitively large. Crystal filters have excellent performance because of the inherently high Q of the elements, but they are more expensive than *LC* and ceramic filters.

Mechanical filters use the vibrations of a resonant mechanical system to obtain the filtering action. The mechanical system usually consists of a series of disks spaced along a rod. Transducers are mounted on each end of the rod to convert the electrical signals to mechanical vibrations at the input, and vice versa at the output. Each disk is the mechani-

---

[†] A lumped element is a discrete *R*-, *L*-, or *C*-type element as compared to a continuously distributed *RLC* element such as that found in a transmission line.

TABLE 5-2 Filter Construction Techniques

Construction Type	Description of Elements or Filter	Center Frequency Range	Unloaded Q (Typical)	Filter Application[a]
LC (passive)		dc–300 MHz	100	Audio, video, IF, and RF
Active		dc–500 kHz	200[b]	Audio
Crystal	Quartz crystal	1 kHz–100 MHz	100,000	IF
Mechanical	Transducers, Rod, Disk	50–500 kHz	1,000	IF
Ceramic	Ceramic disk Electrodes	10 kHz–10.7 MHz	1,000	IF
Surface acoustic waves (SAW)	One section Fingers Piezoelectric substrate, Finger overlap region	10–800 MHz	c	IF and RF
Transmission line	$\leftarrow \lambda/4 \rightarrow$	UHF and microwave	1,000	RF
Cavity		Microwave	10,000	RF

[a] IF, intermediate frequency; RF, radio frequency (see Sec. 5-15).

[b] Bandpass Q's.

[c] Depends on design: $N = f_0/B$ where N is the number of sections, f_0 is the center frequency, and B is the bandwidth. Loaded Q's of 18,000 have been achieved.

cal equivalent of a high-Q electrical parallel resonant circuit. The mechanical filter usually has a high insertion loss resulting from the inefficiency of the input and output transducers.

Ceramic filters are constructed from piezoelectric ceramic disks with plated electrode connections on opposite sides of the disk. The behavior of the ceramic element is similar to that of the crystal filter element, as discussed earlier, except that the Q of the ceramic element is much lower. The advantage of the ceramic filter is that it often provides adequate performance at a cost that is low when compared to that for crystal filters.

Surface acoustic wave (SAW) filters utilize acoustic waves that are launched and travel on the surface of a piezoelectric substrate (slab). Metallic interleaved "fingers" have been deposited on the substrate. They help convert the electric signal to an acoustic wave (and vice versa) by providing an electric field pattern between the fingers that creates the acoustic wave as the result of the piezoelectric effect. The geometry of the fingers determines the frequency response of the filter as well as providing the input and output coupling [Dorf, 1993, pp. 1073–1074]. The insertion loss is somewhat larger than that for crystal or ceramic filters. However, the ease of shaping the transfer function and the wide bandwidth that can be obtained with controlled attenuation characteristics make the SAW filters very attractive. This new technology is being used to provide excellent IF amplifier characteristics in modern television sets.

SAW devices can also be tapped so that they are useful for transversal filter configurations operating in the RF range. At lower frequencies, charge transfer devices (CTDs) can be used to implement transversal filters [Gersho, 1975].

Transmission line filters utilize the resonant properties of open-circuited or short-circuited transmission lines. These are useful at UHF and microwave frequencies where wavelengths are small enough so that filters of reasonable size can be constructed. Similarly, the resonant effect of cavities is useful in building filters for microwave frequencies where the cavity size becomes small enough to be practical.

Filters are also characterized by the type of transfer function that is realized. The transfer function of a linear filter with lumped circuit elements may be written as the ratio of two polynomials

$$H(f) = \frac{b_0 + b_1(j\omega) + b_2(j\omega)^2 + \cdots + b_k(j\omega)^k}{a_0 + a_1(j\omega) + a_2(j\omega)^2 + \cdots + a_n(j\omega)^n} \qquad (5\text{-}40)$$

where the constants a_i and b_i are functions of the element values and $\omega = 2\pi f$. The parameter n is said to be the *order* of the filter. By adjusting the constants to certain values, desirable transfer function characteristics can be obtained. Table 5-3 lists three different filter characteristics and the optimization criterion that defines each one. The Chebyshev filter is used when a sharp attenuation characteristic is required when using a minimum number of circuit elements. The Bessel filter is often used in data transmission when the pulse shape is to be preserved since it attempts to maintain a linear phase response in the passband. The Butterworth filter is often used as a compromise between the Chebyshev and Bessel characteristics.

The topic of filters is immense, and all aspects of filtering cannot possibly be covered here. For example, with the advent of inexpensive microprocessors, *digital filtering* and

TABLE 5-3 Some Filter Characteristics

Type	Optimization Criterion	Transfer Characteristic for the Low-Pass Filter[a]
Butterworth	Maximally flat: as many derivatives of $|H(f)|$ as possible go to zero as $f \to 0$	$|H(f)| = \dfrac{1}{\sqrt{1 + (f/f_b)^{2n}}}$
Chebyshev	For a given peak-to-peak ripple in the passband of the $|H(f)|$ characteristic, the $|H(f)|$ attenuates the fastest for any filter of nth order	$|H(f)| = \dfrac{1}{\sqrt{1 + \epsilon^2 C_n^2(f/f_b)}}$ ϵ = a design constant; $C_n(f)$ is the nth-order Chebyshev polynomial defined by the recursion relation $$C_n(x) = 2xC_{n-1}(x) - C_{n-2}(x)$$ where $C_0(x) = 1$ and $C_1(x) = x$
Bessel	Attempts to maintain linear phase in the passband	$H(f) = \dfrac{K_n}{B_n(f/f_b)}$ K_n is a constant chosen to make $H(0) = 1$ and the Bessel recursion relation is $$B_n(x) = (2n - 1)\, B_{n-1}(x) - x^2 B_{n-2}(x)$$ where $B_0(x) = 1$ and $B_1(x) = 1 + jx$

[a] f_b is the cutoff frequency of the filter.

digital signal processing is becoming very important [Childers and Durling, 1975; Oppenheim and Schafer, 1975, 1989]. Here the analog waveform is sampled, and the sample values are processed by using digital techniques. Difference equations (as opposed to differential equations) describe this type of filtering operation. By changing the software, different filter characteristics can be realized. This technique of filter realization by software programming instead of hardware programming has many advantages. However, for real-time filtering, this technique is limited to realizing filters in the audio and video frequency range. For additional reading on analog filters with emphasis on communication system applications, the reader is referred to the literature [Bowron and Stephenson, 1979].

Amplifiers

For analysis purposes, electronic circuits and, more specifically, amplifiers can be classified into two main categories:

- Nonlinear circuits.
- Linear circuits.

(Linearity was defined in Sec. 3-1.) In practice all circuits are nonlinear to some degree, even at low (voltage and current) signal levels, and become highly nonlinear for high signal levels. Linear circuit analysis is often used for the low signal level case since it greatly simplifies the mathematics and it gives accurate answers if the signal level is sufficiently small.

The main categories of nonlinear and linear analysis can be further classified into subcategories of circuits with

- Memory.
- No memory.

Circuits with memory contain inductive and capacitive effects which cause the present output value to be a function of previous input values as well as the present input value. If a circuit has no memory, its present output value is a function only of its present input value.

In introductory electrical engineering courses, it is first assumed that circuits are linear with no memory (resistive circuits) and, later, linear with memory (*RLC* circuits). It follows that linear amplifiers with memory may be described by a transfer function that is the ratio of the Fourier transform of the output signal divided by the Fourier transform of the input signal. As discussed in Sec. 3-4, the transfer function of a distortionless amplifier is given by $Ke^{-j\omega T_d}$, where K is the voltage gain of the amplifier and T_d is the delay between the output and input waveforms. If the transfer function of the linear amplifier is not of this form, the output signal will be a *linearly* distorted version of the input signal.

5-9 Nonlinear Distortion

In addition to linear distortion, practical amplifiers also produce nonlinear distortion. In order to examine the effects of nonlinearity and yet keep a mathematical model that is tractable, we will assume that there is *no memory* in the following analysis. Thus, we will look at the present output as a function of the present input in the time domain. If the amplifier is linear, this relationship is

$$v_0(t) = Kv_i(t) \tag{5-41}$$

where K is the voltage gain of the amplifier. In practice, the output of the amplifier saturates at some value as the amplitude of the input signal is increased. This is illustrated by the nonlinear output-to-input characteristic shown in Fig. 5-5. The output-to-input characteristic may be modeled by a Taylor's expansion about $v_i = 0$ (i.e., a Maclaurin series):

$$v_0 = K_0 + K_1 v_i + K_2 v_i^2 + \cdots = \sum_{n=0}^{\infty} K_n v_i^n \tag{5-42}$$

where

$$K_n = \frac{1}{n!} \left(\frac{d^n v_0}{dv_i^n} \right) \bigg|_{v_i=0} \tag{5-43}$$

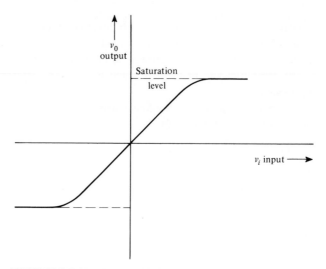

FIGURE 5-5 Nonlinear amplifier output-to-input characteristic.

It is seen that there will be nonlinear distortion on the output signal if $K_2, K_3, \ldots$, are not zero. K_0 is the output dc offset level, $K_1 v_i$ is the first-order (linear) term, $K_2 v_i^2$ is the second-order (square-law) term, and so on. Of course, K_1 will be larger than $K_2, K_3, \ldots$, if the amplifier is anywhere near to being linear.

The *harmonic distortion* associated with the amplifier output is determined by applying a single sinusoidal test tone to the amplifier input. Let the input test tone be represented by

$$v_i(t) = A_0 \sin \omega_0 t \tag{5-44}$$

Then the second-order output term is

$$K_2(A_0 \sin \omega_0 t)^2 = \frac{K_2 A_0^2}{2} (1 - \cos 2\omega_0 t) \tag{5-45}$$

This indicates that the second-order distortion creates a dc level $K_2 A_0^2/2$ (in addition to any dc bias) and second harmonic distortion with amplitude $K_2 A_0^2/2$. In general, for a single tone input the output will be

$$v_{out}(t) = V_0 + V_1 \cos(\omega_0 t + \phi_1) + V_2 \cos(2\omega_0 t + \phi_2)$$
$$+ V_3 \cos(3\omega_0 t + \phi_3) + \cdots \tag{5-46}$$

where V_n is the peak value of the output at the frequency $n f_0$ hertz. Then the percentage of *total harmonic distortion* (THD) is defined by

$$\text{THD (\%)} = \frac{\sqrt{\sum_{n=2}^{\infty} V_n^2}}{V_1} \times 100 \tag{5-47}$$

The THD of an amplifier can be measured by using a distortion analyzer, or it can be evaluated by (5-47), with the V_n's obtained from a spectrum analyzer.

The *intermodulation distortion* (IMD) of the amplifier is obtained by using a two-tone test. If the input (tone) signals are

$$v_i(t) = A_1 \sin \omega_1 t + A_2 \sin \omega_2 t \qquad (5\text{-}48)$$

then the second-order output term is

$$K_2(A_1 \sin \omega_1 t + A_2 \sin \omega_2 t)^2$$
$$= K_2(A_1^2 \sin^2 \omega_1 t + 2A_1 A_2 \sin \omega_1 t \sin \omega_2 t + A_2^2 \sin^2 \omega_2 t)$$

The first and last terms on the right side of this equation produce harmonic distortion at frequencies $2f_1$ and $2f_2$. The cross-product term produces IMD. This term is present only when *both* input terms are present—thus the name "intermodulation distortion." Then the second-order IMD is

$$2K_2 A_1 A_2 \sin \omega_1 t \sin \omega_2 t = K_2 A_1 A_2 \{\cos[(\omega_1 - \omega_2)t] - \cos[(\omega_1 + \omega_2)t]\}$$

It is clear that IMD generates sum and difference frequencies.

The third-order term is

$$K_3 v_i^3 = K_3(A_1 \sin \omega_1 t + A_2 \sin \omega_2 t)^3$$
$$= K_3(A_1^3 \sin^3 \omega_1 t + 3A_1^2 A_2 \sin^2 \omega_1 t \sin \omega_2 t$$
$$+ 3A_1 A_2^2 \sin \omega_1 t \sin^2 \omega_2 t + A_2^3 \sin^3 \omega_2 t) \qquad (5\text{-}49)$$

The first and last terms on the right side of this equation will produce harmonic distortion and the second term, a cross product, becomes

$$3K_3 A_1^2 A_2 \sin^2 \omega_1 t \sin \omega_2 t = \tfrac{3}{2} K_3 A_1^2 A_2 \sin \omega_2 t(1 - \cos 2\omega_1 t)$$
$$= \tfrac{3}{2} K_3 A_1^2 A_2 \{\sin \omega_2 t - \tfrac{1}{2}[\sin(2\omega_1 + \omega_2)t$$
$$- \sin(2\omega_1 - \omega_2)t]\} \qquad (5\text{-}50)$$

Similarly, the third term of (5-49) is

$$3K_3 A_1 A_2^2 \sin \omega_1 t \sin^2 \omega_2 t$$
$$= \tfrac{3}{2} K_3 A_1 A_2^2 \{\sin \omega_1 t - \tfrac{1}{2}[\sin(2\omega_2 + \omega_1)t - \sin(2\omega_2 - \omega_1)t]\} \quad (5\text{-}51)$$

The last two terms in (5-50) and (5-51) are intermodulation terms at nonharmonic frequencies. For the case of *bandpass* amplifiers where f_1 and f_2 are within the bandpass with f_1 close to f_2 (i.e., $f_1 \approx f_2 \gg 0$), the distortion products at $2f_1 + f_2$ and $2f_2 + f_1$ will usually fall outside the passband and, consequently, may not be a problem. However, the terms at $2f_1 - f_2$ and $2f_2 - f_1$ will fall inside the passband and will be close to the desired frequencies f_1 and f_2. These will be the main distortion products for bandpass amplifiers, such as those used for RF amplification in transmitters and receivers.

As (5-50) and (5-51) show, if either A_1 or A_2 is increased sufficiently, the IMD will become significant since the desired output varies linearly with A_1 or A_2 and the IMD output varies as $A_1^2 A_2$ or $A_1 A_2^2$. Of course, the exact input level required for the intermodulation products to be a problem depends on the relative values of K_3 and K_1. This may be specified by the amplifier third-order *intercept point,* which is evaluated by applying two equal test tones (i.e., $A_1 = A_2 = A$). The desired linearly amplified outputs will have amplitudes of K_1A, and each of the third-order intermodulation products will have amplitudes of $3K_3A^3/4$. The ratio of the desired output to the IMD output is then

$$R_{\text{IMD}} = \frac{4}{3}\left(\frac{K_1}{K_3A^2}\right) \tag{5-52}$$

The input intercept point is defined as the input level that causes R_{IMD} to be unity (see Fig. 5-6). The solid curves are obtained by measurement using two sinusoidal signal generators to generate the tones and measuring the level of the desired output (at f_1 or f_2) and the IMD products (at $2f_1 - f_2$ or $2f_2 - f_1$) using a spectrum analyzer. The intercept point is a fictitious point that is obtained by extrapolation of the linear portion (decibel plot) of the desired output and IMD curves until they intersect. It is seen that the desired output (output at either f_1 or f_2) actually saturates when measurements are made since the higher order terms in the Taylor series have components at f_1 and f_2 that subtract from the linearly amplified output. For example, with K_3 being negative, the leading term in (5-51) occurs at f_1 and will subtract from the linearly amplified component at f_1, thus producing a

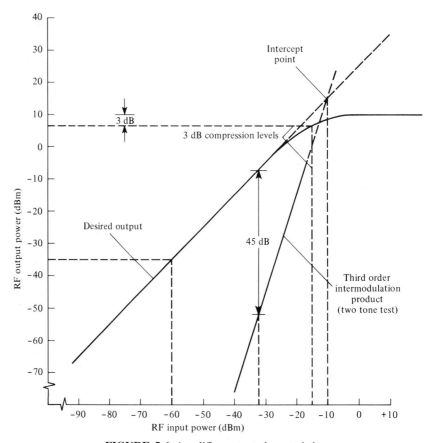

FIGURE 5-6 Amplifier output characteristics.

saturated characteristic for the sinusoidal component at f_1. For an amplifier that happens to have the particular nonlinear characteristic shown in Fig. 5-6, the intercept point occurs for an RF input level of -10 dBm. Other properties of the amplifier are also illustrated in the figure. The gain of the amplifier is 25 dB in the linear region since a -60 dBm input produces a -35 dBm output level. The desired output is compressed by 3 dB for an input level of -15 dBm. Consequently, the amplifier might be considered to be linear only if the input level is less than -15 dBm. Furthermore, if the third-order IMD products are to be down by at least 45 dBm, the input level will have to be kept lower than -32 dBm.

Another term in the distortion products at the output of a nonlinear amplifier is called *cross modulation*. Cross-modulation terms are obtained when examining the third-order products resulting from a two-tone test. As shown in (5-50) and (5-51), the terms $\frac{3}{2}K_3 A_1^2 A_2 \sin \omega_2 t$ and $\frac{3}{2}K_3 A_1 A_2^2 \sin \omega_1 t$ are cross-modulation terms. Let us examine the term $\frac{3}{2}K_3 A_1^2 A_2 \sin \omega_2 t$. If we allow some amplitude variation on the input signal $A_1 \sin \omega_1 t$ so that it looks like an AM signal $A_1[1 + m_1(t)] \sin \omega_1 t$, where $m_1(t)$ is the modulating signal, a third-order distortion product becomes

$$\tfrac{3}{2}K_3 A_1^2 A_2 [1 + m_1(t)]^2 \sin \omega_2 t \qquad (5\text{-}53)$$

Thus the AM on the signal at carrier frequency f_1 will produce a signal at frequency f_2 with distorted modulation. That is, if two signals are passed through an amplifier having third-order distortion products in the output, and if either input signal has some AM, the amplified output of the *other* signal will be amplitude modulated to some extent by a distorted version of the modulation. This phenomenon is cross modulation.

Of course, passive as well as active circuits may have nonlinear characteristics and, consequently, will produce distortion products. For example, suppose that two AM broadcast stations have strong signals in the vicinity of a barn or house that has a metal roof with rusted joints. The roof may act as an antenna to receive and reradiate the RF energy, and the rusted joints may act as a diode (a nonlinear passive circuit). Signals at harmonics and intermodulation frequencies may be radiated and cause interference to other communication signals. In addition, cross-modulation products may be radiated. That is, distorted modulation of one station is heard on radios (located in the vicinity of the rusted roof) that are tuned to the other station's frequency.

When amplifiers are used to produce high-power signals, such as in transmitters, it is desirable to have amplifiers with high efficiency in order to reduce the costs of power supplies, cooling equipment, and energy consumed. The efficiency is the ratio of the output signal power to the dc input power. Amplifiers may be grouped into several categories, depending on the biasing levels and circuit configurations used. Some of these are Class A, B, C, D, E, F, G, H, and S [Krauss, Bostian, and Raab, 1980; Smith, 1986]. For Class A operation, the bias on the amplifier stage is adjusted so that current flows all during the complete cycle of an applied input test tone. For Class B operation, the amplifier is biased so that current flows for 180° of the applied signal cycle. Therefore, if a Class B amplifier is to be used for a baseband linear amplifier, such as an audio power amplifier in a hi-fi system, two devices are wired in push-pull configuration so that each one alternately conducts current over half of the input signal cycle. In *bandpass* Class B linear amplification, where the bandwidth is a small percentage of the operating frequency, only one active device is needed since tuned circuits may be used to supply the output current over the other half of the signal cycle. For Class C operation, the bias is set so that (collector or plate) current flows in pulses, each one having a pulse width that is usually much less than half of the input cycle. Unfortunately, with Class C operation, it is not possible to have linear amplification even if the amplifier is a bandpass RF amplifier with tuned circuits providing current over the nonconducting portion of the cycle. If one tries to amplify an AM signal with a Class C amplifier or other types of nonlinear amplifiers, the AM on the output will be distorted. However, RF signals with a constant real envelope, such as FM signals, may be amplified without distortion since a nonlinear amplifier preserves the zero-crossings of the input signal.

The efficiency of a Class C amplifier is determined essentially by the conduction angle of the active device since poor efficiency is caused by signal power being wasted in the device itself during the conduction time. The Class C amplifier is most efficient, having an efficiency factor of 100% for an ideal Class C amplifier. Class B amplifiers have an efficiency of $\pi/4 \times 100 = 78.5\%$ or less, and Class A amplifiers have an efficiency of 50% or less [Krauss, Bostian, and Raab, 1980]. Since Class C amplifiers are the most efficient, they are generally used to amplify constant envelope signals, such as FM signals used in FM broadcasting. Class D, E, F, G, H, and S amplifiers usually employ switching techniques in specialized circuits to obtain high efficiency [Krauss, Bostian, and Raab, 1980; Smith, 1986].

Many types of microwave amplifiers, such as traveling-wave tubes (TWT), operate on the velocity modulation principle. The input microwave signal is fed into a slow-wave structure. Here the velocity of propagation of the microwave signal is reduced so that it is slightly below the velocity of the dc electron beam. This enables a transfer of kinetic energy from the electron beam to the microwave signal, thereby amplifying the signal. In this type of amplifier, the electron current is *not* turned on and off to provide the amplifying mechanism; thus it is not classified in terms of Class B or C operation. The TWT is a linear amplifier when operated at the appropriate drive level. If the drive level is increased, the efficiency (RF output/dc input) is improved, but the amplifier becomes nonlinear. In this case constant envelope signals, such as PSK or PM, need to be used so that the intermodulation distortion will not cause a problem. This is often the mode of operation for satellite transponders (transmitters in communication satellites), where solar cells are costly and have limited power output. This subject is discussed in more detail in Sec. 8-5.

5-10 Limiters

A *limiter* is a nonlinear circuit with an output saturation characteristic. A soft saturating limiter characteristic is shown in Fig. 5-5. Figure 5-7 shows a hard (ideal) limiter characteristic, together with an illustration of the unfiltered output waveform obtained for an input waveform. The ideal limiter transfer function is essentially identical to the output-to-input characteristic of an ideal comparator with a zero reference level. The waveforms shown in Fig. 5-7 illustrate how amplitude variations on the input signal are eliminated on

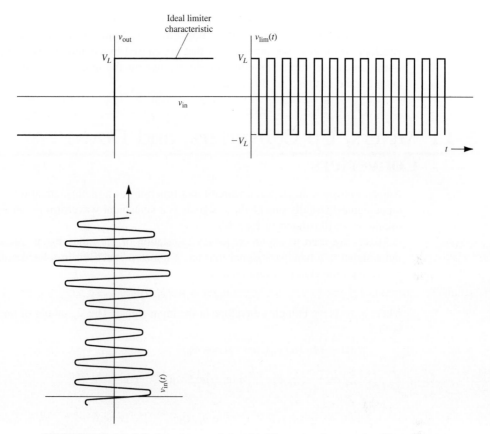

FIGURE 5-7 Ideal limiter characteristic with illustrative input and unfiltered output waveforms.

the output signal. A *bandpass limiter* is a nonlinear circuit with a saturating characteristic followed by a bandpass filter. For the case of an ideal bandpass limiter, the filter output waveform would be sinusoidal since the harmonics of the square wave would be filtered out. In general, any bandpass input (it might be a modulated signal plus noise) can be represented, using (5-1b), by

$$v_{in}(t) = R(t) \cos[\omega_c t + \theta(t)] \qquad (5\text{-}54)$$

where $R(t)$ is the equivalent real envelope and $\theta(t)$ is the equivalent phase function. The corresponding output of an ideal bandpass limiter becomes

$$v_{out}(t) = KV_L \cos[\omega_c t + \theta(t)] \qquad (5\text{-}55)$$

where K is the level of the fundamental component of the square wave, $4/\pi$, multiplied by the gain of the output (bandpass) filter. This equation indicates that any AM that was present on the limiter input does not appear on the limiter output but that the phase function is preserved (i.e., the zero-crossings of the input are preserved on the limiter output). Limiters are often used in receiving systems designed for angle modulated signaling—such as PSK, FSK, and analog FM—to eliminate any variations in the real envelope of the receiver input signal that are caused by channel noise or signal fading. These amplitude variations could produce noise on the detected signal at the receiver output if the limiter was not used.

5-11 Mixers, Up Converters, and Down Converters

An *ideal mixer* is an electronic circuit that functions as a mathematical multiplier of two input signals. Usually one of these signals is a sinusoidal waveform produced by a local oscillator, as illustrated in Fig. 5-8.

Mixers are used to obtain frequency translation of the input signal. Assume that the input signal is a bandpass signal that has a nonzero spectrum in a band around or near $f = f_c$, then the signal is represented by

$$v_{\text{in}}(t) = \text{Re}\{g_{\text{in}}(t)e^{j\omega_c t}\} \tag{5-56}$$

where $g_{\text{in}}(t)$ is the complex envelope of the input signal. The signal out of the ideal mixer is then

$$v_1(t) = [A_0 \, \text{Re}\{g_{\text{in}}(t)e^{j\omega_c t}\}] \cos \omega_0 t$$

$$= \frac{A_0}{4} [g_{\text{in}}(t)e^{j\omega_c t} + g_{\text{in}}^*(t)e^{-j\omega_c t}](e^{j\omega_0 t} + e^{-j\omega_0 t})$$

$$= \frac{A_0}{4} [g_{\text{in}}(t)e^{j(\omega_c + \omega_0)t} + g_{\text{in}}^*(t)e^{-j(\omega_c + \omega_0)t} + g_{\text{in}}(t)e^{j(\omega_c - \omega_0)t} + g_{\text{in}}^*(t)e^{-j(\omega_c - \omega_0)t}]$$

or

$$v_1(t) = \frac{A_0}{2} \text{Re}\{g_{\text{in}}(t)e^{j(\omega_c + \omega_0)t}\} + \frac{A_0}{2} \text{Re}\{g_{\text{in}}(t)e^{j(\omega_c - \omega_0)t}\} \tag{5-57}$$

This equation illustrates that the input bandpass signal with a spectrum near $f = f_c$ has been converted (i.e., frequency translated) into two output bandpass signals, one at the up-conversion frequency band, where $f_u = f_c + f_0$, and one at the down-conversion band, where $f_d = f_c - f_0$. A filter, as illustrated in Fig. 5-8, may be used to select either the up-conversion component or the down-conversion component. A *bandpass* filter is used to select the up-conversion component, but the down-conversion component is selected by either a *baseband* filter or a *bandpass* filter, depending on the location of $f_c - f_0$. For example, if $f_c - f_0 = 0$, a low-pass filter would be needed and the resulting output spectrum would be a baseband spectrum. If $f_c - f_0 > 0$, where $f_c - f_0$ was larger than the bandwidth of $g_{\text{in}}(t)$, a bandpass filter would be used and the filter output would be

$$v_2(t) = \text{Re}\{g_2(t)e^{j(\omega_c - \omega_0)t}\} = \frac{A_0}{2} \text{Re}\{g_{\text{in}}(t)e^{j(\omega_c - \omega_0)t}\} \tag{5-58}$$

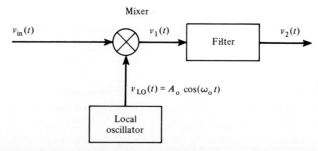

FIGURE 5-8 Mixer followed by a filter for either up or down conversion.

For this case of $f_c > f_0$, it is seen that the modulation on the mixer input signal $v_{in}(t)$ is preserved on the mixer up- or down-converted signals.

If $f_c < f_0$, we rewrite (5-57), obtaining

$$v_1(t) = \frac{A_0}{2} \text{Re}\{g_{in}(t)e^{j(\omega_c + \omega_0)t}\} + \frac{A_0}{2} \text{Re}\{g_{in}^*(t)e^{j(\omega_0 - \omega_c)t}\} \tag{5-59}$$

since the frequency in the exponent of the bandpass signal representation needs to be positive for easy physical interpretation of the location of spectral components. For this case of $f_0 > f_c$, the complex envelope of the down-converted signal has been conjugated when compared to the complex envelope of the input signal. This is equivalent to saying that the sidebands have been exchanged; that is, the upper sideband of the input signal spectrum becomes the lower sideband of the down-converted output signal, and so on. This is demonstrated mathematically by looking at the spectrum of $g^*(t)$. The spectrum is

$$\mathscr{F}[g_{in}^*(t)] = \int_{-\infty}^{\infty} g_{in}^*(t)e^{-j\omega t} \, dt = \left[\int_{-\infty}^{\infty} g_{in}(t)e^{-j(-\omega)t} \, dt\right]^*$$

$$= G_{in}^*(-f) \tag{5-60}$$

The $-f$ indicates that the upper and lower sidebands have been exchanged, and the conjugate indicates that the phase spectrum has been inverted.

In summary, the complex envelope for the signal out of an *up converter* is

$$g_2(t) = \frac{A_0}{2} g_{in}(t) \tag{5-61a}$$

where $f_u = f_c + f_0 > 0$. Thus the same modulation is on the output signal as was on the input signal, but the amplitude has been changed by the $A_0/2$ scale factor.

For the case of *down conversion* there are two possibilities. For $f_d = f_c - f_0 > 0$ where $f_0 < f_c$,

$$g_2(t) = \frac{A_0}{2} g_{in}(t) \tag{5-61b}$$

This is called down conversion with *low-side injection* since the LO frequency is below that of the incoming signal (i.e., $f_0 < f_c$). Here the output modulation is the same as that of the input except for the $A_0/2$ scale factor. The other possibility is $f_d = f_0 - f_c > 0$, where $f_0 > f_c$, which produces the output complex envelope

$$g_2 = \frac{A_0}{2} g_{in}^*(t) \tag{5-61c}$$

This is down conversion with *high-side* injection since $f_0 > f_c$. This is the case where the sidebands on the down-converted output signal are reversed from those on the input (e.g., a LSSB input signal becomes a USSB output signal).

Ideal mixers act as linear time-varying circuit elements since

$$v_1(t) = (A \cos \omega_0 t) v_{in}(t)$$

where $A \cos \omega_0 t$ is the time-varying gain of the linear circuit. It should also be recognized that mixers used in communication circuits are essentially mathematical multipliers. They should not be confused with the audio mixers that are used in radio and TV broadcasting studios. An *audio mixer* is a summing amplifier with multiple inputs so that several inputs from several sources—such as microphones, tape decks, and turntables—can be ''mixed'' (added) to produce one output signal. Unfortunately, the term *mixer* means entirely different things depending on the context used. As used in transmitters and receivers, it means a multiplying operation that produces a frequency translation of the input signal. In audio systems it means a summing operation to add several inputs to produce one output signal.

In practice, the multiplying operation needed for mixers may be realized by using one of the following.

1. A continuously variable transconductance device such as a dual-gate FET.
2. A nonlinear device.
3. A linear device with time-varying discrete gain.

In the first method, when a dual-gate FET is used to obtain multiplication, $v_{in}(t)$ is usually connected to gate 1 and the local oscillator is connected to gate 2. The resulting output is

$$v_1(t) = K v_{in}(t) v_{LO}(t) \tag{5-62}$$

over the operative region, where $v_{LO}(t)$ is the local oscillator voltage. The multiplier is said to be of a *single-quadrant* type if the multiplier action of (5-62) is obtained only when both the input waveforms, v_{in} and $v_{LO}(t)$, have either nonnegative or nonpositive values [i.e., a plot of the values of $v_{in}(t)$ versus $v_{LO}(t)$ falls within a single quadrant]. The multiplier is of the *two-quadrant* type if multiplier action is obtained when either $v_{in}(t)$ or $v_{LO}(t)$ is nonnegative or nonpositive and the other is arbitrary. The multiplier is said to be of the *four-quadrant* type when multiplier action is obtained regardless of the signs of $v_{in}(t)$ and $v_{LO}(t)$.

In the second technique, a nonlinear device can be used to obtain multiplication by summing the two inputs as illustrated in Fig. 5-9. Looking at the square-law component at the output, we have

$$v_1(t) = K_2(v_{in} + v_{LO})^2 + \text{other terms}$$
$$= K_2(v_{in}^2 + 2v_{in}v_{LO} + v_{LO}^2) + \text{other terms} \tag{5-63}$$

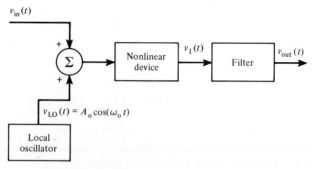

FIGURE 5-9 Nonlinear device used as a mixer.

The cross-product term gives the desired multiplier action:

$$2K_2 v_{in} v_{LO} = 2K_2 A_0 v_{in}(t) \cos \omega_0 t \qquad (5\text{-}64)$$

If we assume that $v_{in}(t)$ is a bandpass signal, the filter can be used to pass either the up- or down-conversion terms. However, some distortion products may also fall within the output passband if ω_c and ω_0 are not chosen carefully.

In the third method, a linear device with time-varying discrete gain is used to obtain multiplier action. This is demonstrated in Fig. 5-10, where the time-varying device is an analog switch (such as a CMOS 4016 integrated circuit) that is activated by a square-wave oscillator signal, $v_0(t)$. The discrete gain of the switch is either unity or zero. The waveform at the output of the analog switch is

$$v_1(t) = v_{in}(t)s(t) \qquad (5\text{-}65)$$

where $s(t)$ is a unipolar switching square wave that has unity peak amplitude. (This is analogous to PAM with natural sampling that was studied in Chapter 4.) Thus (5-65) becomes

$$v_1(t) = v_{in}(t)\left[\frac{1}{2} + \sum_{n=1}^{\infty} \frac{2 \sin(n\pi/2)}{n\pi} \cos n\omega_0 t\right] \qquad (5\text{-}66)$$

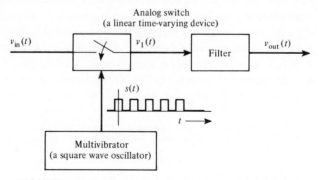

FIGURE 5-10 Linear time-varying device used as a mixer.

The multiplying action is obtained from the $n = 1$ term, which is

$$\frac{2}{\pi} v_{in}(t) \cos \omega_0 t \tag{5-67}$$

This would generate up- and down-conversion signals at $f_c + f_0$ and $f_c - f_0$ if $v_{in}(t)$ were a bandpass signal with a nonzero spectrum in the vicinity of $f = f_c$. However, (5-66) shows that other frequency bands are also present in the output signal, namely, at frequencies $f = |f_c \pm nf_0|$, $n = 3, 5, 7, \ldots$ and, in addition, there is the feed-through term $\frac{1}{2}v_{in}(t)$ appearing at the output. Of course, a filter may be used to pass either the up- or down-conversion component appearing in (5-66).

Mixers are often classified as being *unbalanced, single balanced,* or *double balanced.* That is, in general we obtain at the output of mixer circuits

$$v_1(t) = C_1 v_{in}(t) + C_2 v_0(t) + C_3 v_{in}(t)v_0(t) + \text{other terms} \tag{5-68}$$

When C_1 and C_2 are not zero, the mixer is said to be *unbalanced* since $v_{in}(t)$ and $v_0(t)$ feed through to the output. An example of an unbalanced mixer was illustrated in Fig. 5-9, where a nonlinear device was used to obtain mixing action. In the Taylor's expansion of the nonlinear device output-to-input characteristics, the linear term would provide feedthrough of both $v_{in}(t)$ and $v_0(t)$. A *single-balanced mixer* has feedthrough for only one of the inputs; that is, either C_1 or C_2 of (5-68) is zero. An example of a single-balanced mixer is shown in Fig. 5-10, which uses sampling to obtain mixer action. In this example, (5-66) demonstrates that $v_0(t)$ is balanced out (i.e., $C_2 = 0$) and $v_{in}(t)$ feeds through with a gain of $C_1 = \frac{1}{2}$. A *double-balanced mixer* has no feedthrough from either input; that is, both C_1 and C_2 of (5-68) are zero. An example of a double-balanced mixer is discussed in the next paragraph.

Figure 5-11a exhibits the circuit for a double-balanced mixer. This circuit is popular because it is relatively inexpensive and it has excellent performance. The third-order IMD is typically down at least 50 dB compared to the desired output components. It is usually designed for source and load impedances of 50 Ω and has broadband input and output ports. The RF [i.e., $v_{in}(t)$] port and the LO (local oscillator) port are often usable over a frequency range of 1000:1, say 1 to 1000 MHz; and the IF (intermediate frequency) output port, $v_1(t)$, is typically usable from dc to 600 MHz. The transformers are made by using small toroidal cores, and the diodes are matched hot carrier diodes. The input signal level at the RF port is relatively small, usually less than -5 dBm, and the local oscillator level at the LO port is relatively large, say $+5$ dBm. The LO signal is large, so that this signal, in effect, turns the diodes on and off so that the diodes will act as switches. The LO provides the switching control signal. This circuit thus acts as a time-varying linear circuit (with respect to the RF input port), and the analysis is very similar to that used for the analog-switch mixer of Fig. 5-10. During the portion of the cycle when $v_{LO}(t)$ has a positive voltage, the output voltage is proportional to $+v_{in}(t)$ as seen from the equivalent circuit shown in Fig. 5-11b. When $v_{LO}(t)$ is negative, the output voltage is proportional to $-v_{in}(t)$, as seen from the equivalent circuit shown in Fig. 5-11c. Thus the output of this double-balanced mixer is

$$v_1(t) = Kv_{in}(t)s(t) \tag{5-69}$$

(a) A Double Balanced Mixer Circuit

(b) Equivalent Circuit When $v_{LO}(t)$ Is Positive   (c) Equivalent Circuit When $v_{LO}(t)$ Is Negative

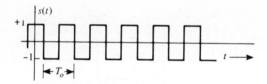

(d) Switching Waveform Due to the Local Oscillator Signal

FIGURE 5-11 Analysis of a double-balanced mixer circuit.

where $s(t)$ is a bipolar switching waveform as shown in Fig. 5-11d. Since the switching waveform arises from the LO signal, its period is $T_0 = 1/f_0$. The switching waveform is described by

$$s(t) = 4 \sum_{n=1}^{\infty} \frac{\sin(n\pi/2)}{n\pi} \cos n\omega_0 t \qquad (5\text{-}70)$$

so that the mixer output is

$$v_1(t) = [v_{in}(t)] \left[4K \sum_{n=1}^{\infty} \frac{\sin(n\pi/2)}{n\pi} \cos n\omega_0 t \right] \qquad (5\text{-}71)$$

If the input is a bandpass signal with nonzero spectrum in the vicinity of f_c, this equation shows that the spectrum of the input will be translated to the frequencies $|f_c \pm nf_0|$, where $n = 1, 3, 5, \ldots$. In practice, the value K is such that the conversion gain (which is defined as the desired output level divided by the input level) at the frequency $|f_c \pm f_0|$ is about -6 dB. Of course, an output filter may be used to select the up-converted or down-converted frequency band.

In addition to up- or down-conversion applications, mixers (i.e., multipliers) may be used for modulators to translate a baseband signal to an RF frequency band, and mixers may be used as product detectors to translate RF signals to baseband. These applications will be discussed in later sections that deal with transmitters and receivers.

5-12 Frequency Multipliers

Frequency multipliers consist of a nonlinear circuit followed by a tuned circuit, as illustrated in Fig. 5-12. If a bandpass signal is fed into a frequency multiplier, the output will appear in a frequency band at the nth harmonic of the input frequency. Since the device is nonlinear, the bandwidth of the nth harmonic output is larger than that of the input signal. In general, the bandpass input signal is represented by

$$v_{in}(t) = R(t) \cos[\omega_c t + \theta(t)] \tag{5-72}$$

The transfer function of the nonlinear device may be expanded in a Taylor's series, so that the nth order output term is

$$v_1(t) = K_n v_{in}^n(t) = K_n R^n(t) \cos^n[\omega_c t + \theta(t)]$$

(a) Block Diagram of a Frequency Multiplier

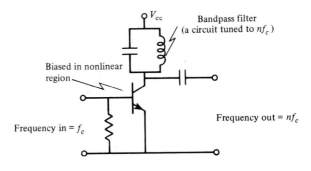

(b) Circuit Diagram for a Frequency Multiplier

FIGURE 5-12 Frequency multiplier.

or[†]

$$v_1(t) = CR^n(t) \cos[n\omega_c t + n\theta(t)] + \text{other terms}$$

Since the bandpass filter is designed to pass frequencies in the vicinity of nf_c, the output is

$$v_{\text{out}}(t) = CR^n(t) \cos[n\omega_c t + n\theta(t)] \tag{5-73}$$

This illustrates that the input *amplitude* variation $R(t)$ *appears distorted* on the output signal since the real envelope on the output is $R^n(t)$. The waveshape of the *angle* variation, $\theta(t)$, is *not distorted* by the frequency multiplier, but the frequency multiplier does increase the magnitude of the angle variation by a factor of n. Thus frequency multiplier circuits are not used on signals where the AM is to be preserved; but as we will see, the frequency multiplier is very useful in PM and FM problems since it effectively "amplifies" the angle variation waveform, $\theta(t)$. The $n = 2$ multiplier is called a *doubler stage*, and the $n = 3$ frequency multiplier is said to be a *tripler stage*.

The frequency multiplier should not be confused with a mixer. The frequency multiplier acts as a nonlinear device. The mixer circuit (which uses a mathematical multiplier operation) acts as a linear circuit with time-varying gain (due to the LO signal). The bandwidth of the signal at the output of a frequency multiplier is larger than that of the input signal, and it appears in a frequency band located at the nth harmonic of the input. The bandwidth of a signal at the output of a mixer is the same as that of the input, but the input spectrum has been translated either up or down depending on the LO frequency and the bandpass of the output filter. Of course, it is realized that a frequency multiplier is essentially a nonlinear amplifier followed by a bandpass filter that is designed to pass the nth harmonic.

5-13 Detector Circuits

As indicated in Fig. 5-1, the receiver contains carrier circuits that convert the input bandpass waveform into an output baseband waveform. These carrier circuits are called detector circuits. The following sections will show how detector circuits can be designed to produce $R(t)$, $\theta(t)$, $x(t)$, or $y(t)$ at their output for the corresponding bandpass signal that is fed into the detector input.

Envelope Detector

An *ideal envelope detector* is a circuit that produces a waveform at its output that is proportional to the real envelope, $R(t)$, of its input. From (5-1b) the bandpass input may be represented by $R(t) \cos[\omega_c t + \theta(t)]$, where $R(t) \geq 0$; then the output of the ideal envelope detector is

$$v_{\text{out}}(t) = KR(t) \tag{5-74}$$

where K is the proportionality constant.

[†] mth-order output terms, where $m > n$, may also contribute to the nth harmonic output provided that K_m is sufficiently large with respect to K_n. This is illustrated by (A-18), where $m = 4$ and $n = 2$.

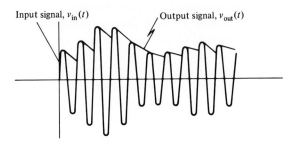

(a) A Diode Envelope Detector

(b) Waveforms Associated with the Diode Envelope Detector

FIGURE 5-13 Envelope detector.

A simple diode detector circuit that approximates an ideal envelope detector is shown in Fig. 5-13a. The diode current occurs in pulses proportional to the positive part of the input waveform. The current pulses charge the capacitor to produce the output voltage waveform, as illustrated in Fig. 5-13b. The RC time constant is chosen so that the output signal will follow the real envelope, $R(t)$, of the input signal. Consequently, the cutoff frequency of the low-pass filter needs to be much smaller than the carrier frequency f_c and much larger than the bandwidth of the (detected) modulation waveform, B. That is,

$$B \ll \frac{1}{2\pi RC} \ll f_c \tag{5-75}$$

where RC is the time constant of the filter.

Product Detector

A *product detector* (Fig. 5-14) is a mixer circuit that down-converts the input (bandpass signal plus noise) to baseband. The output of the multiplier is

$$v_1(t) = R(t) \cos[\omega_c t + \theta(t)] A_0 \cos(\omega_c t + \theta_0)$$
$$= \tfrac{1}{2} A_0 R(t) \cos[\theta(t) - \theta_0] + \tfrac{1}{2} A_0 R(t) \cos[2\omega_c t + \theta(t) + \theta_0]$$

where the frequency of the oscillator is f_c and the phase is θ_0. The low-pass filter passes only the down-conversion term, so that the output is

$$v_{out}(t) = \tfrac{1}{2} A_0 R(t) \cos[\theta(t) - \theta_0] = \tfrac{1}{2} A_0 \mathrm{Re}\{g(t)e^{-j\theta_0}\} \tag{5-76}$$

where the complex envelope of the input is denoted by

$$g(t) = R(t)e^{j\theta(t)} = x(t) + jy(t)$$

and $x(t)$ and $y(t)$ are the quadrature components [see (5-2)]. Since the frequency of the oscillator is the same as the carrier frequency of the incoming signal, the oscillator has

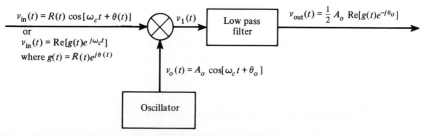

FIGURE 5-14 Product detector.

been *frequency synchronized* with the input signal. Furthermore, if, in addition, $\theta_0 = 0$, the oscillator is said to be *phase synchronized* with the in-phase component and the output becomes

$$v_{\text{out}}(t) = \tfrac{1}{2}A_0 x(t) \tag{5-77a}$$

If $\theta_0 = 90°$,

$$v_{\text{out}} = \tfrac{1}{2}A_0 y(t) \tag{5-77b}$$

Equation (5-76) also indicates that a product detector is sensitive to AM and/or PM. For example, if the input contains no angle modulation so that $\theta(t) = 0$ and if the reference phase is set to zero (i.e., $\theta_0 = 0$), then

$$v_{\text{out}}(t) = \tfrac{1}{2}A_0 R(t) \tag{5-78a}$$

which implies that $x(t) \geq 0$ and the real envelope is obtained on the product detector output, just as for the case of the envelope detector discussed previously. However, if an angle-modulated signal $A_c \cos[\omega_c t + \theta(t)]$ is present at the input and $\theta_0 = 90°$, the product detector output is

$$v_{\text{out}}(t) = \tfrac{1}{2}A_0 \operatorname{Re}\{A_c e^{j[\theta(t)-90°]}\}$$

or

$$v_{\text{out}}(t) = \tfrac{1}{2}A_0 A_c \sin \theta(t) \tag{5-78b}$$

In this case, the product detector acts like a *phase detector* with a *sinusoidal characteristic* since the output voltage is proportional to the sine of the phase difference between the input signal and the oscillator signal. Phase detector circuits are also available that yield triangle and sawtooth characteristics [Krauss, Bostian, and Raab, 1980]. Referring to (5-78b) for the phase detector with a sinusoidal characteristic, and assuming that the phase difference is small [i.e., $|\theta(t)| \ll \pi/2$], we see that $\sin \theta(t) \approx \theta(t)$ and

$$v_{\text{out}}(t) \approx \tfrac{1}{2}A_0 A_c \theta(t) \tag{5-79}$$

which is a linear characteristic (for small angles). Thus the output of this phase detector is directly proportional to the phase differences when the difference angle is small, as illustrated in Fig. 5-20.

It should be realized that the product detector acts as a linear time-varying device with respect to the input $v_{\text{in}}(t)$, in contrast to the envelope detector, which is a nonlinear device. The property of being either linear or nonlinear significantly affects the results when two or more components, such as a signal plus noise, are applied to the input.

Detectors may also be classified as being either coherent or noncoherent. A *coherent* detector has two inputs—one for a reference signal, such as the synchronized oscillator signal, and one for the modulated signal that is to be demodulated. The product detector is an example of a coherent detector. A *noncoherent* detector has only one input, namely, the modulated signal port. The envelope detector is an example of a noncoherent detector.

Frequency Modulation Detector

An *ideal frequency modulation (FM) detector* is a device that produces an output that is proportional to the instantaneous frequency of the input. That is, if the bandpass input is represented by $R(t) \cos[\omega_c t + \theta(t)]$, the output of the ideal FM detector is

$$v_{out}(t) = \frac{Kd[\omega_c t + \theta(t)]}{dt} = K\left[\omega_c + \frac{d\theta(t)}{dt}\right] \tag{5-80}$$

Usually, the FM detector is *balanced.* This means that the dc voltage $K\omega_c$ does not appear on the output if the detector is tuned to (or designed for) the carrier frequency f_c. In this case the output is

$$v_{out}(t) = K\frac{d\theta(t)}{dt} \tag{5-81}$$

There are many ways to build FM detectors, but almost all of them are based on one of three principles:

- FM-to-AM conversion.
- Phase-shift or quadrature detection.
- Zero-crossing detection.

A *slope detector* is one example of the FM-to-AM conversion principle. A block diagram is shown in Fig. 5-15. A bandpass limiter is needed to suppress any amplitude variations on the input signal since these would distort (produce noise in) the desired output signal.

The slope detector may be analyzed as follows. Assume that the input is a fading signal with frequency modulation. From Table 5-1, this FM signal may be represented by

$$v_{in}(t) = A(t) \cos[\omega_c t + \theta(t)] \tag{5-82}$$

where

$$\theta(t) = K_f \int_{-\infty}^{t} m(t_1) \, dt_1 \tag{5-83}$$

$A(t)$ represents the envelope that is fading and $m(t)$ is the modulation (e.g., audio) signal. It follows that the limiter output is

$$v_1(t) = \frac{4}{\pi} V_L \cos[\omega_c t + \theta(t)] \tag{5-84}$$

FIGURE 5-15 Frequency demodulation using slope detection.

and the output of the differentiator becomes

$$v_2(t) = -\frac{4}{\pi} V_L \left[\omega_c + \frac{d\theta(t)}{dt} \right] \sin[\omega_c t + \theta(t)] \tag{5-85}$$

The output of the envelope detector is the magnitude of the complex envelope for $v_2(t)$:

$$v_{out}(t) = \left| -\frac{4}{\pi} V_L \left[\omega_c + \frac{d\theta(t)}{dt} \right] \right|$$

and since $\omega_c \gg d\theta/dt$ in practice, this becomes

$$v_{out}(t) = \frac{4}{\pi} V_L \left[\omega_c + \frac{d\theta(t)}{dt} \right]$$

Using (5-83), we obtain

$$v_{out}(t) = \frac{4}{\pi} V_L \omega_c + \frac{4}{\pi} V_L K_f m(t) \tag{5-86}$$

which indicates that the output consists of a dc voltage, $\frac{4}{\pi} V_L \omega_c$, plus the ac voltage

$\frac{4}{\pi} V_L K_f m(t)$, which is proportional to the modulation on the FM signal. Of course, a

(a) Circuit Diagram of a Slope Detector

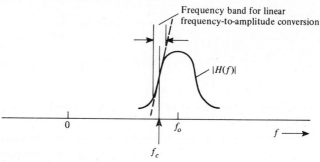

(b) Magnitude of Filter Transfer Function

FIGURE 5-16 Slope detection using a single-tuned circuit for frequency-to-amplitude conversion.

(a) Block Diagram

(b) Circuit Diagram

FIGURE 5-17 Balanced discriminator.

capacitor could be placed in series with the output so that only the ac voltage would be passed to the load.

The differentiation operation can be obtained by any circuit that acts like a frequency-to-amplitude converter. For example, a single-tuned resonant circuit can be used as illustrated in Fig. 5-16, where the magnitude transfer function is $|H(f)| = K_1 f + K_2$ over the linear (useful) portion of the characteristic. A balanced FM detector, which is also called a *balanced discriminator,* is shown in Fig. 5-17. Two tuned circuits are used to balance out the dc when the input has a carrier frequency of f_c and to provide an extended linear frequency-to-voltage conversion characteristic.

Balanced discriminators can also be built that function because of the phase-shift properties of a double-tuned RF transformer circuit with primary and secondary windings [Stark, Tuteur, and Anderson, 1988]. In practice, discriminator circuits have been replaced by integrated circuits that operate on the quadrature principle.

The *quadrature detector* is described as follows: A quadrature signal is first obtained from the FM signal; then, using a product detector, the quadrature signal is multiplied with the FM signal to produce the demodulated signal, $v_{out}(t)$. The quadrature signal can be produced by passing the FM signal through a capacitor (large) reactance that is connected in series with a parallel resonant circuit which is tuned to f_c. The quadrature signal voltage appears across the parallel resonant circuit. The series capacitance provides a 90° phase shift and the resonant circuit provides an additional phase shift that is proportional to the instantaneous frequency deviation (from f_c) of the FM signal. Using (5-84) and (5-83), the FM signal is

$$v_{in}(t) = \frac{4}{\pi} V_L \cos[\omega_c t + \theta(t)] \tag{5-87}$$

and the quadrature signal is

$$v_{quad}(t) = \frac{4}{\pi} K_1 V_L \sin\left[\omega_c t + \theta(t) + K_2 \frac{d\theta(t)}{dt}\right] \tag{5-88}$$

where K_1 and K_2 are constants that depend on component values used for the series capacitor and in the parallel resonant circuit. These two signals, (5-87) and (5-88), are multiplied together by a product detector (e.g., see Fig. 5-14) to produce the output signal

$$v_{out}(t) = \tfrac{1}{2}K_1 \left(\frac{4}{\pi}\right)^2 V_L^2 \sin\left[K_2 \frac{d\theta(t)}{dt}\right] \tag{5-89}$$

where the sum-frequency term is eliminated by the low-pass filter. For K_2 sufficiently small, $\sin x \approx x$, and by use of (5-83), the output becomes

$$v_{out} = \tfrac{1}{2}K_1 K_2 \left(\frac{4}{\pi}\right)^2 V_L^2 K_f m(t) \tag{5-90}$$

This demonstrates that the quadrature detector detects the modulation on the input FM signal. The MC 1357 IF amplifier/detector and the LM 1868 AM/FM radio integrated circuits use a quadrature detector. The quadrature detector principle is also used by phase-locked loops that are configured to detect FM—see (5-110).

As indicated by (5-80), the output of an ideal FM detector is directly proportional to the instantaneous frequency of the input. This linear frequency-to-voltage characteristic may be obtained directly by counting the zero-crossings of the input waveform. An FM detector utilizing this technique is called a *zero-crossing detector.* A hybrid circuit (i.e., consisting of both digital and analog devices) that is a balanced FM zero-crossing detector is shown in Fig. 5-18. The limited (square-wave) FM signal, denoted by $v_1(t)$, is shown in

(a) Circuit

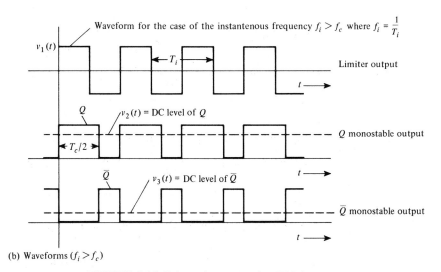

(b) Waveforms ($f_i > f_c$)

FIGURE 5-18 Balanced zero-crossing FM detector.

Fig. 5-18b. For illustration purposes, it is assumed that $v_1(t)$ is observed over that portion of the modulation cycle when the instantaneous frequency

$$f_i(t) = f_c + \frac{1}{2\pi} \frac{d\theta(t)}{dt} \qquad (5\text{-}91)$$

is larger than the carrier frequency, f_c. That is, $f_i > f_c$ in the illustration. Since the modulation voltage varies slowly with respect to the input FM signal oscillation, $v_1(t)$ appears (in the figure) to have a constant frequency, although it is actually varying in frequency according to $f_i(t)$. The monostable multivibrator (one shot) is triggered on the positive slope zero-crossings of $v_1(t)$. For balanced FM detection, the pulse width of the Q output is set to $T_c/2 = 1/2f_c$, where f_c is the carrier frequency of the FM signal at the input. Thus the differential amplifier output voltage is zero if $f_i = f_c$. For $f_i > f_c$ [as illustrated by the $v_1(t)$ waveform in the figure] the output voltage is positive and for $f_i < f_c$ the output voltage will be negative. Thus a linear frequency-to-voltage characteristic, $C[f_i(t) - f_c]$, is obtained where, for an FM signal at the input, $f_i(t) = f_c + (1/2\pi)K_f m(t)$.

Another circuit that can be used for FM demodulation as well as for other purposes is the phase-locked loop.

5-14 Phase-Locked Loops

A phase-locked loop (PLL) consists of three basic components: (1) a phase detector, (2) a low-pass filter, and (3) a voltage-controlled oscillator (VCO) (see Fig. 5-19). The VCO is an oscillator that produces a periodic waveform, the frequency of which may be varied about some free-running frequency, f_0, according to the value of the applied voltage $v_2(t)$. The free-running frequency, f_0, is the frequency of the VCO output when the applied voltage $v_2(t)$ is zero. The phase detector produces an output signal $v_1(t)$ that is a function of the phase difference between the incoming signal $v_{in}(t)$ and the oscillator signal $v_0(t)$. The filtered signal $v_2(t)$ is the control signal that is used to change the frequency of the VCO output. The PLL configuration may be designed so that it acts as a narrowband tracking filter when the low-pass filter (LPF) is a narrowband filter. In this operating mode the frequency of the VCO will become that of one of the line components of the input signal spectrum, so that, in effect, the VCO output signal is a periodic signal with a frequency equal to the average frequency of this input signal component. Once the VCO has acquired this frequency component, the frequency of the VCO will track this input signal component if it changes slightly in frequency. In another mode of operation, the bandwidth of the LPF is wider so that the VCO can track the instantaneous frequency of the input signal. When the PLL tracks the input signal in either of these ways, the PLL is said to be "locked."

If the applied signal has an initial frequency of f_0, the PLL will acquire lock and the VCO will track the input signal frequency over some range, provided that the input frequency changes slowly. However, the loop will remain locked only over some finite range of frequency shift. This range is called the *hold-in* (or *lock*) *range*. The hold-in range depends on the overall dc gain of the loop, which includes the dc gain of the LPF. On the other hand, if the applied signal has an initial frequency not equal to f_0, the loop may not acquire lock even though the input frequency is within the hold-in range. The frequency range over which the applied input will cause the loop to lock is called the *pull-in (or capture) range*. This range is primarily determined by the loop filter characteristics, and it is never greater than the hold-in range. (This is illustrated in Fig. 5-23.) Another important PLL specification is the *maximum locked sweep rate*. It is defined as the maximum rate of

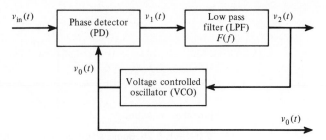

FIGURE 5-19 Basic PLL.

change of the input frequency for which the loop will remain locked. If the input frequency changes faster than this rate, the loop will drop out of lock.

If the PLL is realized using analog circuit techniques, it is said to be an *analog phase-locked loop* (APLL). On the other hand, if digital circuits are used, it is said to be a *digital phase-locked loop* (DPLL). The phase detection (PD) characteristic depends on the exact implementation used. Some PD characteristics are shown in Fig. 5-20. The sinusoidal characteristic is obtained if an (analog circuit) multiplier is used and the periodic signals are sinusoids. The multiplier may be implemented by using a double-balanced mixer. The triangle and sawtooth PD characteristics are obtained by using digital circuits. In addition to using digital VCO and PD circuits, the DPLL may incorporate a digital loop filter and signal processing techniques that use microprocessors. Gupta published a fine tutorial paper on analog phase-locked loops in the *IEEE Proceedings* [Gupta, 1975], and Lindsey and Chie followed with a survey paper on digital PLL techniques [Lindsey and Chie, 1981]. In addition, there are excellent books available [Blanchard, 1976; Gardner, 1979]. A detailed discussion of PLLs is beyond the scope of this book, but some of the significant results will be developed here.

The PLL may be studied by examining the APLL, as shown in Fig. 5-21. In this figure a multiplier (sinusoidal PD characteristic) is used. Assume that the input signal is

$$v_{\text{in}}(t) = A_i \sin[\omega_0 t + \theta_i(t)] \tag{5-92}$$

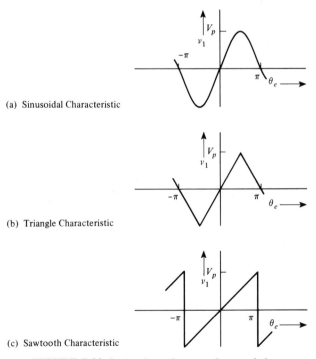

(a) Sinusoidal Characteristic

(b) Triangle Characteristic

(c) Sawtooth Characteristic

FIGURE 5-20 Some phase detector characteristics.

FIGURE 5-21 Analog PLL.

and that the VCO output signal is

$$v_0(t) = A_0 \cos[\omega_0 t + \theta_0(t)] \tag{5-93}$$

where

$$\theta_0(t) = K_v \int_{-\infty}^{t} v_2(\tau) \, d\tau \tag{5-94}$$

K_v is the VCO gain constant (rad/V-sec). The PD output is

$$v_1(t) = K_m A_i A_0 \sin[\omega_0 t + \theta_i(t)] \cos[\omega_0 t + \theta_0(t)]$$

$$= \frac{K_m A_i A_0}{2} \sin[\theta_i(t) - \theta_0(t)] + \frac{K_m A_i A_0}{2} \sin[2\omega_0 t + \theta_i(t) + \theta_0(t)] \tag{5-95}$$

where K_m is the gain of the multiplier circuit. The sum frequency term does not pass through the LPF, so the LPF output is

$$v_2(t) = K_d[\sin \theta_e(t)] * f(t) \tag{5-96}$$

where

$$\theta_e(t) \triangleq \theta_i(t) - \theta_0(t) \tag{5-97}$$

$$K_d = \frac{K_m A_i A_0}{2} \tag{5-98}$$

and $f(t)$ is the impulse response of the LPF. $\theta_e(t)$ is called the *phase error*; K_d is the equivalent PD constant, which for the multiplier-type PD depends on the levels of the input signal, A_i, and the level of the VCO signal, A_0.

The overall equation describing the operation of the PLL may be obtained by taking the derivative of (5-94) and (5-97), and combining the result by use of (5-96). The resulting nonlinear equation that describes the PLL becomes

$$\frac{d\theta_e(t)}{dt} = \frac{d\theta_i(t)}{dt} - K_d K_v \int_0^t [\sin \theta_e(\lambda)] f(t - \lambda) \, d\lambda \tag{5-99}$$

where $\theta_e(t)$ is the unknown and $\theta_i(t)$ is the forcing function.

In general, this PLL equation is difficult to solve. However, it may be reduced to a linear equation if the gain K_d is large so that the error $\theta_e(t)$ is small. In this case, $\sin \theta_e(t) \approx \theta_e(t)$, and the resulting linear equation is

$$\frac{d\theta_e(t)}{dt} = \frac{d\theta_i(t)}{dt} - K_d K_v \theta_e(t) * f(t) \tag{5-100}$$

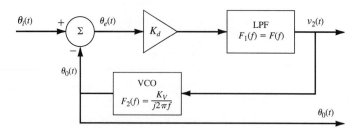

FIGURE 5-22 Linear model of the analog PLL.

A block diagram that follows from this linear equation is shown in Fig. 5-22. It should be realized that in this linear PLL model, the *phase* of the input signal and the *phase* of the VCO output signal are used instead of actual signals themselves. The closed-loop transfer function $\Theta_0(f)/\Theta_i(f)$ is

$$H(f) = \frac{\Theta_0(f)}{\Theta_i(f)} = \frac{K_d K_v F(f)}{j2\pi f + K_d K_v F(f)} \tag{5-101}$$

where $\Theta_0(f) = \mathcal{F}[\theta_0(t)]$ and $\Theta_i(f) = \mathcal{F}[\theta_i(t)]$. Of course, the design and analysis techniques used to evaluate linear feedback control systems, such as Bode plots, which will indicate phase gain and phase margins, are applicable. In fact, they are extremely useful in describing the performance of *locked* PLLs.

The equation for the *hold-in range* may be obtained by examining the nonlinear behavior of the PLL. From (5-94) and (5-96), the instantaneous frequency deviation of the VCO from ω_0 is

$$\frac{d\theta_0(t)}{dt} = K_v v_2(t) = K_v K_d[\sin \theta_e(t)] * f(t) \tag{5-102}$$

To obtain the hold-in range, the input frequency is changed very slowly from f_0. Here the dc gain of the filter is the controlling parameter, and (5-102) becomes

$$\Delta\omega = K_v K_d F(0) \sin \theta_e \tag{5-103}$$

The maximum and minimum values of $\Delta\omega$ give the hold-in range, and these are obtained when $\sin \theta_e = \pm 1$. Thus the maximum hold-in range (no noise case) is

$$\Delta f_h = \frac{1}{2\pi} K_v K_d F(0) \tag{5-104}$$

A typical lock-in characteristic is illustrated in Fig. 5-23. The solid curve shows the VCO control signal $v_2(t)$ as the sinusoidal testing signal is swept from a low frequency to a high frequency (with the free-running frequency of the VCO, f_0, being within the swept band). The dashed curve shows the result when sweeping from high to low. The hold-in range Δf_h is related to the dc gain of the PLL as described by (5-104).

The *pull-in range* Δf_p is determined primarily by the loop filter characteristics. For example, assume that the loop has not acquired lock and that the testing signal is swept slowly toward f_0. At the PD output there will be a beat (oscillatory) signal, and its frequency $|f_{\text{in}} - f_0|$ will vary from a large value to a small value as the test signal frequency sweeps toward f_0. As the testing signal frequency comes closer to f_0, the beat-

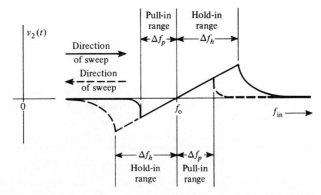

FIGURE 5-23 PLL VCO control voltage for a swept sinusoidal input signal.

frequency waveform will become nonsymmetrical so that it will have a nonzero dc value. This dc value tends to change the frequency of the VCO to that of the input signal frequency so that the loop will tend to lock. The pull-in range, Δf_p, where the loop acquires lock will depend on exactly how the loop filter $F(f)$ processes the PD output to produce the VCO control signal. Furthermore, even if the input signal is within the pull-in range, it may take a fair amount of time for the loop to acquire lock since the LPF acts as an integrator and it takes some time for the control voltage (filter output) to build up to a value large enough for lock to occur. The analysis of the pull-in phenomenon is complicated. It is actually statistical in nature since it depends on the initial phase relationship of the input and VCO signals and on noise that is present in the circuit. Consequently, in the measurement of Δf_p, several repeated trials may be needed to obtain a typical value.

The locking phenomenon is not peculiar to PLL circuits but occurs in other types of circuits as well. For example, if an external signal is injected into the output port of an oscillator (i.e., a plain oscillator, not a VCO), the oscillator signal will tend to change frequency and will eventually lock onto the external signal frequency if the external signal is within the pull-in range of the oscillator. This phenomenon is called *injection locking* or *synchronization* of an oscillator. This injection-locking phenomenon may be modeled by a PLL model [Couch, 1971].

The PLL has numerous applications in communication systems. Some of these are (1) FM detection, (2) generation of highly stable FM signals, (3) coherent AM detection, (4) frequency multiplication, (5) frequency synthesis, and (6) use as a building block within complicated digital systems to provide bit synchronization and data detection.

Let us now find what conditions are required for the PLL to become an FM detector. Referring to Fig. 5-21, let the PLL input signal be an FM signal:

$$v_{in}(t) = A_i \sin\left[\omega_c t + D_f \int_{-\infty}^{t} m(\lambda)\, d\lambda\right] \qquad (5\text{-}105a)$$

where

$$\theta_i(t) = D_f \int_{-\infty}^{t} m(\lambda)\, d\lambda \qquad (5\text{-}105b)$$

or

$$\Theta_i(f) = \frac{D_f}{j2\pi f} M(f) \tag{5-105c}$$

and $m(t)$ is the baseband (e.g., audio) modulation that is to be detected. That is, we would like to find the conditions such that the PLL output, $v_2(t)$, is proportional to $m(t)$. Assume that f_c is within the capture (pull-in) range of the PLL; thus, for simplicity, let $f_0 = f_c$. Then the linearized PLL model, as shown in Fig. 5-22, can be used for analysis. Working in the frequency domain, we obtain the output

$$V_2(f) = \frac{\left(j\dfrac{2\pi f}{K_v}\right) F_1(f)}{F_1(f) + j\left(\dfrac{2\pi f}{K_v K_d}\right)} \Theta_i(f)$$

which becomes, using (5-105c),

$$V_2(f) = \frac{\dfrac{D_f}{K_v} F_1(f)}{F_1(f) + j\left(\dfrac{2\pi f}{K_v K_d}\right)} M(f) \tag{5-106}$$

We now need to find the conditions such that $V_2(f)$ is proportional to $M(f)$. Assume that the bandwidth of the modulation is B hertz, and let $F_1(f)$ be a low-pass filter. Thus

$$F(f) = F_1(f) = 1, \qquad |f| < B \tag{5-107}$$

Also, let

$$\frac{K_v K_d}{2\pi} \gg B \tag{5-108}$$

Then (5-106) becomes

$$V_2(f) = \frac{D_f}{K_v} M(f) \tag{5-109}$$

or

$$v_2(t) = Cm(t) \tag{5-110}$$

where the constant of proportionality is $C = D_f/K_v$. Thus the PLL circuit of Fig. 5-21 will become a FM detector circuit where $v_2(t)$ is the detected FM output when the conditions of (5-107) and (5-108) are satisfied.

In another application, the PLL may be used to supply the coherent oscillator signal for product detection of an AM signal (see Fig. 5-24). Recall, from (5-92) and (5-93), that the VCO of a PLL locks 90° out of phase with respect to the incoming signal.[†] Then $v_0(t)$ needs to be shifted by $-90°$ so that it will be in phase with the carrier of the input AM

[†]This results from the characteristic of the phase detector circuit. This statement is correct for a PD that produces a zero dc output voltage when the two PD input signals are 90° out of phase (i.e., a multiplier-type PD). However, if the PD circuit produced a zero dc output when the two PD inputs were in phase, the VCO of the PLL would lock in phase with the incoming PLL signal.

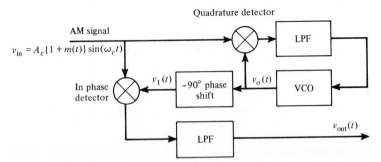

FIGURE 5-24 PLL used for coherent detection of AM.

signal. This was found to be the requirement for coherent detection of AM as given by (5-77). In this application the bandwidth of the LPF needs to be just wide enough to provide the necessary pull-in range in order for the VCO to be able to lock onto the carrier frequency, f_c.

Figure 5-25 illustrates the use of a PLL in a frequency synthesizer. This frequency synthesizer generates a periodic signal of frequency

$$f_{\text{out}} = \left(\frac{N}{M}\right) f_x \tag{5-111}$$

where f_x is the frequency of the stable oscillator and N and M are the frequency-divider parameters. This result is verified by recalling that when the loop is locked, the dc control signal $v_3(t)$ shifts the frequency of the VCO so that $v_2(t)$ will have the same frequency as $v_{\text{in}}(t)$. Thus,

$$\frac{f_x}{M} = \frac{f_{\text{out}}}{N}$$

which is equivalent to (5-111). If programmable dividers are used, the synthesizer output frequency may be changed at will, according to (5-111), by selecting appropriate values of N and M. Of course, this could be carried out by using a microprocessor under software program control. It is noted that for the case of $M = 1$, this synthesizer configuration acts like a frequency multiplier. In addition, more complicated PLL synthesizer configurations can be built that incorporate mixers and additional oscillators.

In the preceding section we have described the operating principles for communication

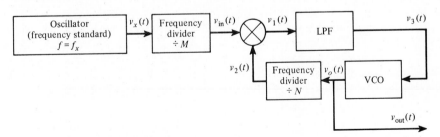

FIGURE 5-25 PLL used in a frequency synthesizer.

TABLE 5-4 Effect of Communication System Components

Device Name	Device Parameter(s)[a]	Output Complex Envelope[b]	Output Waveform
Linear bandpass amplifier	Gain = A	$Ag(t)$	$\mathrm{Re}\{Ag(t)e^{j\omega_c t}\}$
Linear bandpass filter	Impulse response = $\mathrm{Re}\{k(t)e^{j\omega_c t}\}$	$\frac{1}{2}g(t) * k(t)$	$\frac{1}{2}\,\mathrm{Re}\{g(t) * k(t)e^{j\omega_c t}\}$
Hard bandpass limiter	Limit level = V_L; $K = 4/\pi$	$KV_L e^{j\theta(t)}$	$\mathrm{Re}\{KV_L e^{j\theta(t)} e^{j\omega_c t}\}$
Down converter	Gain = A; $\omega_0 < \omega_c$	$Ag(t)$	$\mathrm{Re}\{Ag(t)e^{j(\omega_c - \omega_0)t}\}$
Down converter[c]	Gain = A; $\omega_c < \omega_0$	$Ag^*(t)$	$\mathrm{Re}\{Ag^*(t)e^{j(\omega_0 - \omega_c)t}\}$
Up converter	Gain = A	$Ag(t)$	$\mathrm{Re}\{Ag(t)e^{j(\omega_c + \omega_0)t}\}$
Frequency multiplier	Input = $\mathrm{Re}\{R(t)e^{j\theta(t)} e^{j\omega_c t}\}$; multiply by n	$CR^n(t)e^{jn\theta(t)}$	$\mathrm{Re}\{CR^n(t)e^{jn\theta(t)} e^{jn\omega_c t}\}$
Envelope detector	Gain = A	NA	$AR(t)$
Phase detector	Gain = A	NA	$A\theta(t)$
Frequency modulation detector	Gain = A	NA	$A\,d\theta(t)/dt$
Product detector	Gain = A; reference = $K\cos(\omega_c t + \theta_0)$	NA	$A\,\mathrm{Re}\{g(t)e^{-j\theta_0}\}$
Product detector	Gain = A; in-phase ref. ($\theta_0 = 0$)	NA	$Ax(t)$
Product detector	Gain = A; quad-phase ref. ($\theta_0 = 90°$)	NA	$Ay(t)$

[a] ω_0, LO frequency.
[b] NA, not applicable.
[c] For high-side injection (i.e., $\omega_c < \omega_0$), the upper and lower sidebands at the output are inverted compared to those at the input since $\mathscr{F}[g^*(t)] = G^*(-f)$.

system components such as filters, amplifiers, limiters, up/down converters, PLL, and detectors. The results are summarized in Table 5-4, which gives the output of each device as a function of the complex envelope for the input to that device. In the remainder of this book, we see how these devices are connected together to build communication systems. Space limitations do not permit further coverage of devices or detailed circuit analysis. The reader is referred to specialized books on these and related topics (such as oscillators and frequency synthesizers) [Manassewitsch, 1987; Sinnema and McPherson, 1991; Smith, 1986; Young, 1990].

5-15 Transmitters and Receivers

Generalized Transmitters

Transmitters generate the modulated signal at the carrier frequency f_c from the modulating signal $m(t)$. In Secs. 5-1 and 5-2 it was demonstrated that any type of modulated signal could be represented by

$$v(t) = \text{Re}\{g(t)e^{j\omega_c t}\} \tag{5-113}$$

or, equivalently,

$$v(t) = R(t)\cos[\omega_c t + \theta(t)] \tag{5-114}$$

and

$$v(t) = x(t)\cos \omega_c t - y(t)\sin \omega_c t \tag{5-115}$$

where the complex envelope

$$g(t) = R(t)e^{j\theta(t)} = x(t) + jy(t) \tag{5-116}$$

is a function of the modulating signal $m(t)$. The particular relationship that is chosen for $g(t)$ in terms of $m(t)$ defines the type of modulation that is used, such as AM, SSB, or FM (see Table 5-1). A generalized approach may be taken to obtain universal transmitter models that may be reduced to those used for a particular modulation type. We will also see that there are equivalent models that correspond to different circuit configurations, yet they may be used to produce the same type of modulated signal at their outputs. It is up to communications engineers to select an implementation method that will maximize performance, yet minimize cost based on the state of the art in circuit development.

There are two canonical forms for the generalized transmitter, as indicated by (5-114) and (5-115). Equation (5-114) describes an AM-PM type circuit as shown in Fig. 5-26. The baseband signal processing circuit generates $R(t)$ and $\theta(t)$ from $m(t)$. The R and θ are functions of the modulating signal $m(t)$ as given in Table 5-1 for the particular modulation type desired. The signal processing may be implemented either by using nonlinear analog circuits or a digital computer that incorporates the R and θ algorithms under software program control. In the implementation using a digital computer, one ADC will be needed at the input and two DACs will be needed at the output. The remainder of the AM-PM canonical form requires RF circuits, as indicated in the figure.

Figure 5-27 illustrates the second canonical form for the generalized transmitter. This uses in-phase and quadrature-phase (IQ) processing. Similarly, the formulas relating $x(t)$

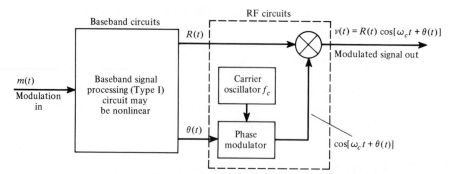

FIGURE 5-26 Generalized transmitter using the AM–PM generation technique.

and $y(t)$ to $m(t)$ are shown in Table 5-1, and the baseband signal processing may be implemented by using either analog hardware or digital hardware with software. The remainder of the canonical form utilizes RF circuits as indicated.

Once again, it is stressed that any type of signal modulation (AM, FM, SSB, QPSK, etc.) may be generated by using either of these two canonical forms. Both of these forms conveniently separate baseband processing from RF processing. Digital techniques are especially useful to realize the baseband processing portion. Furthermore, if digital computing circuits are used, any desired modulation type can be obtained by selecting the appropriate software program.

Most of the practical transmitters in use today are special variations on these canonical forms. Practical transmitters may perform the RF operations at some convenient lower RF frequency and then up-convert to the desired operating frequency. In the case of RF signals that contain no AM, frequency multipliers may be used to arrive at the operating frequency. Of course, power amplifiers are usually required to bring the output power level up to the specified value. If the RF signal contains no amplitude variations, Class C amplifiers (relatively high efficiency) may be used; otherwise, Class B amplifiers are used.

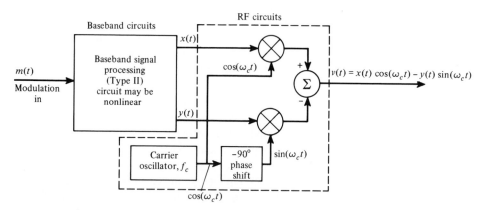

FIGURE 5-27 Generalized transmitter using the quadrature generation technique.

Generalized Receiver: The Superheterodyne Receiver

The receiver has the job of extracting the source information from the received modulated signal that has been corrupted by noise. Often it is desired that the receiver output be a replica of the modulating signal that was present at the transmitter input. There are two main classes of receivers: the *tuned radio frequency* (TRF) receiver and the *superheterodyne* receiver.

The TRF receiver consists of a number of cascaded high-gain RF bandpass stages that are tuned to the carrier frequency, f_c, followed by an appropriate detector circuit (envelope detector, product detector, FM detector, etc.). The TRF is not very popular because it is difficult to design tunable RF stages so that the desired station can be selected and yet have a narrow bandwidth so that adjacent channel stations are rejected. In addition, it is difficult to obtain high gain at radio frequencies and to have sufficiently small stray coupling between the output and input of the RF amplifying chain so that the chain will not become an oscillator at f_c. The "crystal set" that is built by the Cub Scouts is an example of a single-RF-stage TRF receiver that has no gain in the RF stage. TRF receivers are often used to measure time-dispersive (multipath) characteristics of radio channels [Rappaport, 1989].

Most receivers employ the *superheterodyne* receiving technique. This technique consists of either down-converting or up-converting the input signal to some convenient frequency band, called the *intermediate frequency* (IF) band, and then extracting the information (or modulation) by using the appropriate detector (see Fig. 5-28).[†] This basic receiver structure is used for the reception of all types of bandpass signals, such as television, FM, AM, satellite, and radar signals. The RF amplifier has a bandpass characteristic that passes the desired signal and provides amplification to override additional noise that is generated in the mixer stage. The RF filter characteristic also provides some rejection of adjacent channel signals and noise, but the main adjacent channel rejection is accomplished by the IF filter.

[†] *Dual-conversion* superheterodyne receivers can also be built. Here a second mixer and a second IF stage follow the first IF stage shown in Fig. 5-28. The MC3363 is an example of a dual-conversion receiver.

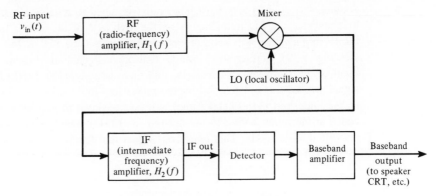

FIGURE 5-28 Superheterodyne receiver.

The IF filter is a bandpass filter that selects either the up-conversion or down-conversion component (whichever is chosen by the receiver designer). When up conversion is selected, it should be recalled that the complex envelope of the IF (bandpass) filter output is the same as the complex envelope for the RF input, except for the effect of RF filtering, $H_1(f)$, and IF filtering $H_2(f)$. However, if down conversion is used with $f_{LO} > f_c$, the complex envelope at the IF output will be the conjugate of that for the RF input [see (5-59)]. This means that the sidebands of the IF output will be inverted (i.e., the upper sideband on the RF input will become the lower sideband, etc., on the IF output). If $f_{LO} < f_c$, the sidebands are not inverted. In some special applications the LO frequency is selected to be the carrier frequency ($f_{LO} = f_c$), and then the superheterodyne receiver becomes a direct-conversion receiver.[†] In this case the IF filter is replaced by a low-pass filter so that the mixer-LPF combination becomes a product detector and the detector stage of Fig. 5-28 is deleted. Thus, the synchrodyne receiver is the same as a TRF receiver with product detection.

The center frequency selected for the IF amplifier is chosen based on three considerations.

1. The frequency should be such that a stable high-gain amplifier can be economically attained.
2. The frequency needs to be low enough so that with practical circuit elements in the IF filters, values of Q can be attained that will provide a steep attenuation characteristic outside the bandwidth of the IF signal. This decreases the noise and minimizes the interference from adjacent channels.
3. The frequency needs to be high enough so that the receiver image response can be made acceptably small.

The *image response* is the reception of an unwanted signal located at the image frequency due to insufficient attenuation of the image signal by the RF amplifier filter. The image response is best illustrated by an example.

Example 5-2 AM Broadcast Superheterodyne Receiver

Assume that an AM broadcast band radio is tuned to receive a station at 850 kHz and that the LO frequency is on the high side of the carrier frequency. If the IF frequency is 455 kHz, the LO frequency will be $850 + 455 = 1305$ kHz (see Fig. 5-29). Furthermore, assume that other signals are present at the RF input of the radio and, particularly, that there is a signal at 1760 kHz; this signal will be down-converted by the mixer to $1760 - 1305 = 455$ kHz. That is, the undesired (1760-kHz) signal will be translated to 455 kHz and will be added at the mixer output to the desired (850-kHz) signal, which was also down-converted to 455 kHz. This *undesired* signal that has been converted to the IF

[†]A direct-conversion receiver is also called a *homodyne* or a *synchrodyne* receiver.

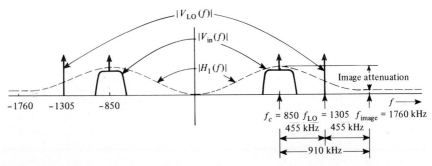

FIGURE 5-29 Spectra of signals and transfer function of an RF amplifier in a superheterodyne receiver.

band is called the *image signal*. If the gain of the RF amplifier is down by, say, 25 dB at 1760 kHz as compared to 850 kHz, and if the undesired signal is 25 dB stronger at the receiver input than the desired signal, both signals will have the same level when translated to the IF. This undesired signal will definitely interfere with the desired signal in the detection process.

For down converters (i.e., $f_{IF} = |f_c - f_{LO}|$) the image frequency is

$$f_{image} = \begin{cases} f_c + 2f_{IF}, & \text{if } f_{LO} > f_c \quad \text{(high-side injection)} \\ f_c - 2f_{IF}, & \text{if } f_{LO} < f_c \quad \text{(low-side injection)} \end{cases} \quad (5\text{-}117a)$$

where f_c is the desired RF frequency, f_{IF} is the IF frequency, and f_{LO} is the local oscillator frequency. For up converters (i.e., $f_{IF} = f_c + f_{LO}$) the image frequency is

$$f_{image} = f_c + 2f_{LO} \quad (5\text{-}117b)$$

From Fig. 5-29 it is seen that the image response will usually be reduced if the IF frequency is increased, since f_{image} will occur farther away from the main peak (or lobe) of the RF filter characteristic, $|H_1(f)|$.

Recalling our earlier discussion on mixers, we also realize that other spurious responses (in addition to the image response) will occur in practical mixer circuits. These must also be taken into account in good receiver design.

Table 5-5 illustrates some typical IF frequencies that have become de facto standards. For the intended application, the IF frequency is low enough that the IF filter will provide good adjacent channel signal rejection when circuit elements with realizable Q are used; yet the IF frequency is large enough to provide adequate image-signal rejection by the RF amplifier filter.

The type of detector selected for use in the superheterodyne receiver depends on the intended application. For example, a product detector may be used in a PSK (digital) system, and an envelope detector is used in AM broadcast receivers. If the complex envelope $g(t)$ is desired for generalized signal detection or for optimum reception in

TABLE 5-5 Some Popular IF Frequencies in the United States

IF Frequency	Application
262.5 kHz	AM broadcast radios (in automobiles)
455 kHz	AM broadcast radios
10.7 MHz	FM broadcast radios
21.4 MHz	FM two-way radios
30 MHz	Radar receivers
43.75 MHz (video carrier)	TV sets
60 MHz	Radar receivers
70 MHz	Satellite receivers

digital systems, the $x(t)$ and $y(t)$ quadrature components, where $x(t) + jy(t) = g(t)$, may be obtained by using quadrature product detectors, as illustrated in Fig. 5-30. $x(t)$ and $y(t)$ could be fed into a signal processor to extract the modulation information. Disregarding the effects of noise, the signal processor could recover $m(t)$ from $x(t)$ and $y(t)$ (and, consequently, demodulate the IF signal) by using the inverse of the complex envelope generation functions given in Table 5-1.

The superheterodyne receiver has many advantages and some disadvantages. The main advantage is that extraordinarily high gain can be obtained without instability (self-oscillation). The stray coupling between the output of the receiver and the input does not cause oscillation because the gain is obtained in disjoint frequency bands—RF, IF, and baseband. The receiver is easily tunable to another frequency by changing the frequency of the LO signal (which may be supplied by a frequency synthesizer) and by tuning the bandpass of the RF amplifier to the desired frequency. Furthermore, high-Q elements—which are needed (to produce steep filter skirts) for adjacent channel rejection—are needed only in the fixed tuned IF amplifier. The main disadvantage of the superheterodyne receiver is the response to spurious signals that will occur if one is not careful with the design.

A discussion of receivers would not be complete without considering some of the

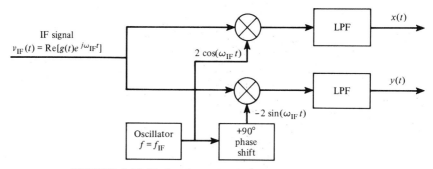

FIGURE 5-30 IQ (in-phase and quadrature-phase) detector.

causes of *interference.* Often the receiver owner thinks that a certain signal, such as an amateur radio signal, is causing the difficulty. This may or may not be the case. The origin of the interference may be at any of three locations.

1. At the interfering signal *source,* the transmitter may generate out-of-band signal components (such as harmonics) that fall in the band of the desired signal.
2. At the *receiver* itself, the front end may overload or produce spurious responses. Front-end overload occurs when the RF and/or mixer stage of the receiver is driven into the nonlinear range by the interfering signal and the nonlinearity causes cross modulation on the desired signal at the output of the receiver RF amplifier.
3. In the *channel,* a nonlinearity in the transmission medium may cause undesired signal components in the band of the desired signal.

For more discussion of receiver design and examples of practical receiver circuits, the reader is referred to the *ARRL Handbook* [ARRL, 1993].

5-16 Summary

The basic techniques used for bandpass signaling have been studied in this chapter. The complex envelope technique for representing bandpass signals and filters was found to be very useful. A description of communication circuits with performance analysis was presented for filters, amplifiers, limiters, mixers, frequency multipliers, phase-locked loops, and detector circuits. Nonlinear as well as linear circuit analysis techniques were used. The superheterodyne receiving circuit was found to be the fundamental technique used in communication receiver design, with the detector circuit determining whether the receiver is designed to detect digital or analog signals of a particular type. Generalized transmitters and receivers were developed, and practical aspects of their design, such as spurious signals, were evaluated.

PROBLEMS

5-1   If $v(t) = \text{Re}\{g(t)e^{j\omega_c t}\}$, show that (5-1b) and (5-1c) are correct where $g(t) = x(t) + jy(t) = R(t)e^{j\theta(t)}$.

5-2   A bandpass filter is shown in Fig. P5-2.

FIGURE P5-2

(a) Find the mathematical expression for the transfer function of this filter $H(f) = V_2(f)/V_1(f)$ as a function of R, L, and C. Sketch the magnitude transfer function $|H(f)|$.

(b) Find the expression for the equivalent low-pass filter transfer function and sketch the corresponding low-pass magnitude transfer function.

5-3 Let the transfer function of an ideal bandpass filter be given by

$$H(f) = \begin{cases} 1, & |f + f_c| < B_T/2 \\ 1, & |f - f_c| < B_T/2 \\ 0, & f \text{ elsewhere} \end{cases}$$

where B_T is the absolute bandwidth of the filter.

(a) Sketch the magnitude transfer function, $|H(f)|$.

(b) Find an expression for the waveform at the output, $v_2(t)$, if the input consists of the pulsed carrier:

$$v_1(t) = A\Pi(t/T)\cos(\omega_c t)$$

(c) Sketch the output waveform, $v_2(t)$, for the case when $B_T = 4/T$ and $f_c \gg B_T$. *Hint:* Use the complex envelope technique and express the answer as a function of the sine integral where the sine integral is defined by

$$\text{Si}(u) = \int_0^u \frac{\sin \lambda}{\lambda} \, d\lambda$$

The sketch can be obtained by looking up values for the sine integral from published tables [Abramowitz and Stegun, 1964] or by numerically evaluating $\text{Si}(u)$.

5-4 Examine the distortion properties of an RC low-pass filter (shown in Fig. 3-2). Assume that the filter input consists of a bandpass signal that has a bandwidth of 1 kHz and a carrier frequency of 15 kHz. Let the time constant of the filter be $\tau_0 = RC = 10^{-5}$ sec.

(a) Find the phase delay for the output carrier.

(b) Determine the group delay at the carrier frequency.

(c) Evaluate the group delay for frequencies around and within the frequency band of the signal. Plot this delay as a function of frequency.

(d) Using the results of (a) through (c), explain why the filter does or does not distort the bandpass signal.

5-5 A bandpass filter as shown in Fig. P5-5 has the transfer function

$$H(s) = \frac{Ks}{s^2 + (\omega_0/Q)s + \omega_0^2}$$

where $Q = R\sqrt{C/L}$, the resonant frequency is $f_0 = 1/(2\pi\sqrt{LC})$, $\omega_0 = 2\pi f_0$, K is a constant, and values for R, L, and C are given in the figure. Assume that a bandpass signal with $f_c = 4$ kHz and a bandwidth of 200 Hz passes through the filter, where $f_0 = f_c$.

(a) What is the bandwidth of the filter?

(b) Plot the carrier delay as a function of f about f_0.

FIGURE P5-5

(c) Plot the group delay as a function of f about f_0.

(d) Explain why the filter does or does not distort the signal.

5-6 An FM signal is of the form

$$s(t) = \cos\left[\omega_c t + D_f \int_{-\infty}^{t} m(\sigma) \, d\sigma\right]$$

where $m(t)$ is the modulating signal and $\omega_c = 2\pi f_c$, f_c being the carrier frequency. Show that the functions $g(t)$, $x(t)$, $y(t)$, $R(t)$, and $\theta(t)$ as given for FM in Table 5-1 are correct.

5-7 SSB-PM has a complex envelope given by

$$g(t) = e^{jD_p[m(t) \pm j\hat{m}(t)]}$$

where $m(t)$ is the modulating signal and $\hat{m}(t)$ is the Hilbert transform of m. Show that the functions $x(t)$, $y(t)$, $R(t)$, and $\theta(t)$ as given for SSB-PM in Table 5-1 are correct.

5-8 Given a modulated signal

$$s(t) = 100 \sin(\omega_c + \omega_a)t + 500 \cos \omega_c t - 100 \sin(\omega_c - \omega_a)t$$

where the unmodulated carrier is $500 \cos \omega_c t$.

(a) Find the complex envelope for the modulated signal. What type of modulation is it? What is the modulating signal?

(b) Find the quadrature modulation components, $x(t)$ and $y(t)$, for this modulated signal.

(c) Find the magnitude and PM components, $R(t)$ and $\theta(t)$, for this modulated signal.

(d) Find the total average power where $s(t)$ is a voltage waveform that is applied across a 50-Ω load.

5-9 Find the spectrum for the modulated signal as given in Prob. 5-8 by two methods.

(a) By direct evaluation using the Fourier transform of $s(t)$.

(b) By the use of (5-12).

5-10 Given a pulse-modulated signal of the form

$$s(t) = e^{-at} \cos[(\omega_c + \Delta\omega)t]u(t)$$

where a, ω_c, and $\Delta\omega$ are positive constants and $\omega_c \gg \Delta\omega$ (ω_c is the carrier frequency),

(a) Find the complex envelope.

(b) Find the spectrum $S(f)$.

(c) Sketch the magnitude and phase spectra $|S(f)|$ and $\theta(f) = \underline{/S(f)}$.

5-11 In a digital computer simulation of a bandpass filter, the complex envelope of the impulse response is used where $h(t) = \mathrm{Re}[k(t)e^{j\omega_c t}]$, as shown in Fig. 5-3. The complex impulse response can be expressed in terms of quadrature components: $k(t) = 2h_x(t) + j2h_y(t)$, where $h_x(t) = \frac{1}{2}\mathrm{Re}[k(t)]$ and $h_y(t) = \frac{1}{2}\mathrm{Im}[k(t)]$. The complex envelopes of the input and output are denoted, respectively, by $g_1(t) = x_1(t) + jy_1(t)$ and $g_2(t) = x_2(t) + jy_2(t)$. The bandpass filter simulation can be carried out by using four *real baseband* filters (i.e., filters having real impulse responses), as shown in Fig. P5-11. Note that although there are four filters, there are only two distinctly different impulse responses, $h_x(t)$ and $h_y(t)$.

(a) Using (5-22), show that Fig. P5-11 is correct.

(b) Show that $h_y(t) \equiv 0$ (i.e., no filter needed) if the bandpass filter has a transfer function with Hermitian symmetry about f_c, that is, if $H(-\Delta f + f_c) = H^*(\Delta f + f_c)$ where $|\Delta f| < B_T/2$ and B_T is the bounded spectral bandwidth of the bandpass filter. This Hermitian symmetry implies that the magnitude frequency response of the bandpass filter is even about f_c and the phase response is odd about f_c.

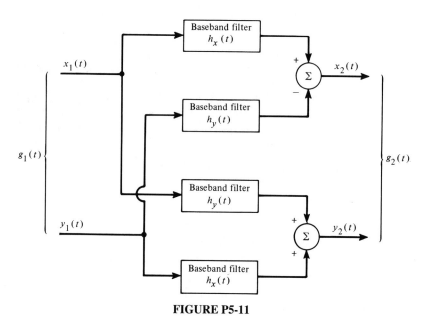

FIGURE P5-11

5-12 Evaluate and sketch the magnitude transfer function for **(a)** Butterworth, **(b)** Chebyshev, and **(c)** Bessel low-pass filters. Assume that $f_b = 10$ Hz and $\epsilon = 1$.

5-13 Plot the amplitude response, the phase response, and the phase delay as a function of frequency for the following low-pass filters where $B = 100$ Hz. Also, compare your results for these two filters.

(a) Butterworth filter, second order:

$$H(f) = \frac{1}{1 + \sqrt{2}(jf/B) + (jf/B)^2}$$

(b) Butterworth filter, fourth order:

$$H(f) = \frac{1}{[1 + 0.765(jf/B) + (jf/B)^2][1 + 1.848(jf/B) + (jf/b)^2]}$$

5-14 Assume that the output-to-input characteristic of a bandpass amplifier is described by (5-42) and that the linearity of the amplifier is being evaluated by using a two-tone test.

(a) Find the frequencies of the fifth-order intermodulation products that fall within the amplifier bandpass.

(b) Evaluate the levels for the fifth-order intermodulation products in terms of A_1, A_2, and the K's.

5-15 An amplifier is tested for total harmonic distortion (THD) by using a single-tone test. The output is observed on a spectrum analyzer. It is found that the peak values of the three measured harmonics decrease according to an exponential recursion relation, $V_{n+1} = V_n e^{-n}$, where $n = 1, 2, 3$. What is the THD?

5-16 The nonlinear output–input characteristic of an amplifier is

$$v_{\text{out}}(t) = 5v_{\text{in}}(t) + 1.5v_{\text{in}}^2(t) + 1.5v_{\text{in}}^3(t)$$

Assume that input signal consists of seven components

$$v_{\text{in}}(t) = \frac{1}{2} + \frac{4}{\pi^2} \sum_{k=1}^{6} \frac{1}{(2k-1)^2} \cos[(2k-1)\pi t]$$

(a) Plot the output signal and compare it with the linear output component $5v_{\text{in}}(t)$.

(b) Take the FFT of the output $v_{\text{out}}(t)$ and compare it with the spectrum for the linear output component.

5-17 For a bandpass limiter circuit, show that the bandpass output is given by (5-55), where $K = (4/\pi)A_0$. A_0 denotes the voltage gain of the bandpass filter, and it is assumed that the gain is constant over the frequency range of the bandpass signal.

5-18 Discuss whether or not the Taylor series nonlinear model is applicable for analysis of (a) soft limiters and (b) hard limiters.

5-19 Assume that an audio sine-wave testing signal is passed through an audio hard limiter circuit. Evaluate the total harmonic distortion (THD) on the signal at the limiter output.

5-20 Using the mathematical definition for linearity given in Chapter 3, show that the analog switch multiplier of Fig. 5-10 is a linear device.

5-21 An audio signal with a bandwidth of 10 kHz is transmitted over an AM transmitter with a carrier frequency of 1.0 MHz. The AM signal is received on a superheterodyne receiver with an envelope detector. What is the constraint on the RC time constant for the envelope detector?

5-22 Assume that an AM receiver with an envelope detector is tuned to an SSB-AM signal that has a modulation waveform given by $m(t)$. Find the mathematical expression for the audio signal that appears at the receiver output in terms of $m(t)$. Is the audio output distorted?

5-23 Evaluate the sensitivity of the zero-crossing FM detector shown in Fig. 5-18. Assume that the differential amplifier is described by $v_{out}(t) = A[v_2(t) - v_3(t)]$, where A is the voltage gain of the amplifier. In particular, show that $v_{out} = Kf_d$, where $f_d = f_i - f_c$ and find the value of the sensitivity constant K in terms of A, R, and C. Assume that the peak levels of the monostable outputs Q and $\overline{Q}$ are 4 V (TTL circuit levels).

5-24 (a) Using (5-100), show that the linearized block diagram model for a PLL is given by Fig. 5-22.

   (b) Show that (5-101) describes the linear PLL model as given in Fig. 5-22.

5-25 Using the Laplace transform and the final value theorem, find an expression for the steady-state phase error, $\lim_{t\to\infty} \theta_e(t)$, for a PLL as described by (5-100). [*Hint:* The final value theorem is $\lim_{t\to\infty} f(t) = \lim_{s\to0} sF(s)$.]

5-26 Assume that the loop filter of a PLL is a low-pass filter, as shown in Fig. P5-26.

   (a) Evaluate the closed-loop transfer function $H(f) = \dfrac{\Theta_0(f)}{\Theta_i(f)}$ for a linearized PLL.

   (b) Sketch the Bode plot $[|H(f)|]_{dB} \triangleq 20 \log |H(f)|$, for this PLL.

$F(f)$

R

C

FIGURE P5-26

5-27 Assume that the phase noise characteristic of a PLL is being examined. The internal phase noise of the VCO is modeled by the input $\theta_n(t)$, as shown in Fig. P5-27.

   (a) Find an expression for the closed-loop transfer function $\Theta_0(f)/\Theta_n(f)$, where $\theta_i(t) = 0$.

   (b) If $F_1(f)$ is a low-pass filter given in Fig. P5-26, sketch the Bode plot $[|\Theta_0(f)/\Theta_n(f)|]_{dB}$ for the phase noise transfer function.

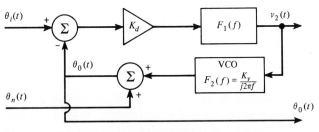

FIGURE P5-27

5-28 The input to a PLL is $v_{in}(t) = A \sin(\omega_0 t + \theta_i)$. The LPF has a transfer function $F(s) = (s + a)/s$.
   (a) What is the steady-state phase error?
   (b) What is the maximum hold-in range for the noiseless case?

5-29 (a) Refer to Fig. 5-25 for a PLL frequency synthesizer. Design a synthesizer that will cover a range of 144 to 148 MHz in 5-kHz steps starting at 144.000 MHz. Assume that the reference input frequency standard operates at 5 MHz and that the M divider is fixed at some value and the N divider is programmable so that the synthesizer will cover the desired range. Sketch a diagram of your design, indicating the frequencies present at various points of the diagram.
   (b) Modify your design so that the output signal can be frequency modulated with an audio-frequency input such that the peak deviation of the RF output is 5 kHz.

5-30 Assume that an SSB-AM transmitter is to be realized using the AM-PM generation technique, as shown in Fig. 5-26.
   (a) Sketch a block diagram for the baseband signal processing circuit.
   (b) Find expressions for $R(t)$, $\theta(t)$, and $v(t)$ when the modulation is $m(t) = A_1 \cos \omega_1 t + A_2 \cos \omega_2 t$.

5-31 Rework Prob. 5-30 for the case of generating an FM signal.

5-32 Assume that an SSB-AM transmitter is to be realized using the quadrature generation technique, as shown in Fig. 5-27.
   (a) Sketch a block diagram for the baseband signal processing circuit.
   (b) Find expressions for $x(t)$, $y(t)$, and $v(t)$ when the modulation is $m(t) = A_1 \cos \omega_1 t + A_2 \cos \omega_2 t$.

5-33 Rework Prob. 5-32 for the case of generating an FM signal.

5-34 An FM radio is tuned to receive an FM broadcasting station of frequency 96.9 MHz. The radio is of the superheterodyne type with the LO operating on the high side of the 96.9-MHz input and using a 10.7-MHz IF amplifier.
   (a) Determine the LO frequency.
   (b) If the FM signal has a bandwidth of 180 kHz, determine the filter characteristics for the RF and IF filters.
   (c) Calculate the frequency of the image response.

5-35 A 4-GHz satellite downlink signal is received on an Earth station receiver. The IF frequency is 70 MHz. What is the image frequency for the case of:
(a) High-side injection?
(b) Low-side injection?

5-36 A superheterodyne receiver is tuned to a station at 20 MHz. The local oscillator frequency is 80 MHz and the IF is 100 MHz.
(a) What is the image frequency?
(b) If the LO has appreciable second-harmonic content, what two additional frequencies are received?
(c) If the RF amplifier contains a single-tuned parallel resonant circuit with $Q = 50$ tuned to 20 MHz, what will be the image attentuation in dB?

5-37 An SSB-AM receiver is tuned to receive a 7.225-MHz lower SSB (LSSB) signal. The LSSB signal is modulated by an audio signal that has a 3-kHz bandwidth. Assume that the receiver uses a superheterodyne circuit with an SSB IF filter. The IF amplifier is centered on 3.395 MHz. The LO frequency is on the high (frequency) side of the input LSSB signal.
(a) Draw a block diagram of the single-conversion superheterodyne receiver, indicating frequencies present and typical spectra of the signals at various points within the receiver.
(b) Determine the required RF and IF filter specifications, assuming that the image frequency is to be attenuated by 40 dB.

5-38 (a) Draw a block diagram of a superheterodyne FM receiver that is designed to receive FM signals over a band from 144 to 148 MHz. Assume that the receiver is of the dual conversion type (i.e., a mixer and an IF amplifier followed by another mixer and a second IF amplifier) where the first IF frequency is 10.7 MHz and the second IF is 455 kHz. Indicate the frequencies of the signals at different points on the diagram and, in particular, show the frequencies involved when a signal at 146.82 MHz is being received.
(b) Replace the first oscillator by a frequency synthesizer such that the receiver can be tuned in 5-kHz steps from 144.000 to 148.000 MHz. Show the diagram of your synthesizer design and the frequencies involved.

5-39 An AM broadcast-band radio is tuned to receive a 1080-kHz AM signal and uses high-side LO injection. The IF is 455 kHz.
(a) Sketch the frequency response for the RF and IF filters.
(b) What is the image frequency?

5-40 Commercial AM broadcast stations operate in the 540- to 1700-kHz band with a transmission bandwidth limited to 10 kHz.
(a) What are the maximum number of stations that can be accommodated?
(b) If stations are not assigned to adjacent channels (in order to reduce interference on receivers that have poor IF characteristics), how many stations can be accommodated?
(c) For 455-kHz IF receivers, what band of image frequencies fall within the AM band for down-converter receivers with high-side injection?

AM and FM Systems

This chapter is concerned with the classical bandpass signaling techniques of amplitude modulation (AM), single-sideband (SSB), phase modulation (PM), and frequency modulation (FM). Here the theory of bandpass signaling of Chapter 5 is used to analyze and design practical bandpass communication systems. The noise performance of these systems is described. Technical standards for AM and FM broadcasting systems are presented. The results of this chapter will provide a basis for understanding digital modulation systems that are examined in Chapter 7.

6-1 Amplitude Modulation

From Sec. 5-2 it is recalled that any type of modulated signal can be represented by

$$s(t) = \text{Re}\{g(t)e^{j\omega_c t}\} \tag{6-1}$$

and that the complex envelope of an AM signal is given by

$$g(t) = A_c[1 + m(t)] \tag{6-2}$$

where the constant A_c has been included to specify the power level and $m(t)$ is the modulating signal (which may be analog or digital). These equations reduce to the representation for the AM signal:

$$s(t) = A_c[1 + m(t)] \cos \omega_c t \tag{6-3}$$

A waveform illustrating the AM signal, as seen on an oscilloscope, is shown in Fig. 6-1. For convenience it is assumed that the modulating signal $m(t)$ is a sinusoid. $A_c[1 + m(t)]$ corresponds to the in-phase component $x(t)$ of the complex envelope; it also corresponds to the real envelope $|g(t)|$ when $m(t) \geq -1$ (the usual case).

If $m(t)$ has a peak positive value of $+1$ and a peak negative value of -1, the AM signal is said to be 100% modulated.

(a) Sinusoidal Modulating Wave

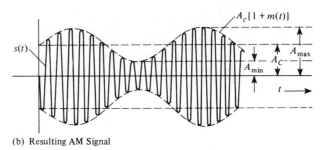

(b) Resulting AM Signal

FIGURE 6-1 AM signal waveform.

DEFINITION: The *percentage of positive modulation* on an AM signal is

$$\% \text{ positive modulation} = \frac{A_{\max} - A_c}{A_c} \times 100 = \max[m(t)] \times 100 \quad (6\text{-}4)$$

and the *percentage of negative modulation* is

$$\% \text{ negative modulation} = \frac{A_c - A_{\min}}{A_c} \times 100 = -\min[m(t)] \times 100 \quad (6\text{-}5)$$

The overall modulation percentage is

$$\% \text{ modulation} = \frac{A_{\max} - A_{\min}}{2A_c} \times 100 = \frac{\max[m(t)] - \min[m(t)]}{2} \times 100 \quad (6\text{-}6)$$

where $A_{\max}$ is the maximum value of $A_c[1 + m(t)]$, $A_{\min}$ is the minimum value, and A_c is the level of the AM envelope under the condition of no modulation [i.e., $m(t) = 0$].

Equation (6-6) may be obtained by averaging the positive and negative modulation as given by (6-4) and (6-5). $A_{\max}$, $A_{\min}$, and A_c are illustrated in Fig. 6-1b, where, in this example, $A_{\max} = 1.5A_c$ and $A_{\min} = 0.5A_c$, so that the percentages of positive and negative modulation are both 50% and the overall modulation is 50%.

The percentage of modulation can be over 100% ($A_{\min}$ will have a negative value) provided that a four-quadrant multiplier is used to generate the product of $A_c[1 + m(t)]$ and $\cos \omega_c t$ so that the true AM waveform, as given by (6-3), is obtained.[†] However, if the

---

[†] If the percentage of modulation becomes very large (approaching infinity), the AM signal becomes the double-sideband suppressed carrier signal that is described in the next section.

transmitter uses a two-quadrant multiplier that produces a zero output when $A_c[1 + m(t)]$ is negative, the output signal will be

$$s(t) = \begin{cases} A_c[1 + m(t)] \cos \omega_c t, & \text{if } m(t) \geq -1 \\ 0, & \text{if } m(t) < -1 \end{cases} \qquad (6\text{-}7)$$

which is a distorted AM signal. The bandwidth of this signal is much wider than that of the undistorted AM signal, as is easily demonstrated by spectral analysis. This is the overmodulated condition that the FCC does not allow. An AM transmitter that uses plate modulation is an example of a circuit that acts as a two-quadrant multiplier. Here, for high-power AM signal generation, the unmodulated carrier signal is applied to the grid of the tube, and the dc plate voltage is varied proportionally to $A_c[1 + m(t)]$, where $A_c[1 + m(t)] \geq 0$. This produces the product $A_c[1 + m(t)] \cos \omega_c t$, provided that $m(t) \geq -1$, but produces no output when $m(t) < -1$.

If the percentage of negative modulation is less than 100%, an envelope detector may be used to recover the modulation without distortion since the envelope, $|g(t)| = |A_c[1 + m(t)]|$, is identical to $A_c[1 + m(t)]$. If the percentage of negative modulation is over 100%, undistorted modulation can still be recovered provided that the proper type of detector—a product detector—is used. This is seen from (5-76) with $\theta_0 = 0$. Furthermore, the product detector may be used for any percentage of modulation and a product detector is superior to an envelope detector when the input signal-to-noise ratio is small.

Using (5-17), we realize that the *normalized average power* of the AM signal is

$$\langle s^2(t) \rangle = \tfrac{1}{2} \langle |g(t)|^2 \rangle = \tfrac{1}{2} A_c^2 \langle [1 + m(t)]^2 \rangle$$
$$= \tfrac{1}{2} A_c^2 \langle 1 + 2m(t) + m^2(t) \rangle$$
$$= \tfrac{1}{2} A_c^2 + A_c^2 \langle m(t) \rangle + \tfrac{1}{2} A_c^2 \langle m^2(t) \rangle \qquad (6\text{-}8)$$

If the modulation contains no dc level, $\langle m(t) \rangle = 0$ and the *normalized* power of the AM signal is

$$\langle s^2(t) \rangle = \underbrace{\tfrac{1}{2} A_c^2}_{\substack{\text{discrete} \\ \text{carrier power}}} + \underbrace{\tfrac{1}{2} A_c^2 \langle m^2(t) \rangle}_{\text{sideband power}} \qquad (6\text{-}9)$$

Note that this result is identical to that given by (5-37) if $A_c = 1$.

DEFINITION: The *modulation efficiency* is the percentage of the total power of the modulated signal that conveys information.

In AM signaling, only the sideband components convey information, so the modulation efficiency is

$$E = \frac{\langle m^2(t) \rangle}{1 + \langle m^2(t) \rangle} \times 100\% \qquad (6\text{-}10)$$

The highest efficiency that could be obtained for a 100% AM signal would be 50%, which is attained only for square-wave modulation.

Using (5-18), we obtain the normalized peak envelope power (PEP) of the AM signal:

$$P_{\text{PEP}} = \frac{A_c^2}{2}\{1 + \max[m(t)]\}^2 \tag{6-11}$$

The voltage spectrum of the AM signal was obtained in (5-20b) of Example 5-1 and is

$$S(f) = \frac{A_c}{2}\left[\delta(f - f_c) + M(f - f_c) + \delta(f + f_c) + M(f + f_c)\right] \tag{6-12}$$

(The AM spectrum is given in Fig. 5-2.) The AM spectrum is relatively easy to obtain since it is just a translated version of the modulation spectrum plus delta functions that give the carrier line spectral component. The *bandwidth* is *twice* that of the modulation. As we will see shortly, the spectrum for an FM signal is much more complicated since the modulation mapping function $g(m)$ is nonlinear.

Example 6-1   Power of an AM Signal

The FCC rates AM broadcast band transmitters by their average *carrier* power; this is common in other AM audio applications as well. Suppose that a 5000-W AM transmitter is connected to a 50-Ω load; then the constant A_c is given by $\frac{1}{2}A_c^2/50 = 5000$. Thus the peak voltage across the load will be $A_c = 707$ V during the times of no modulation. If the transmitter is then 100% modulated by a 1000-Hz test tone, the total (carrier plus sideband) average power will be, from (6-9),

$$1.5\left[\frac{1}{2}\left(\frac{A_c^2}{50}\right)\right] = (1.5) \times (5000) = 7500 \text{ W}$$

since $\langle m^2(t) \rangle = \frac{1}{2}$ for a sinusoidal modulation waveshape of unity (100%) amplitude. Note that 7500 W is the actual power, not the normalized power. The peak voltage (100% modulation) is (2)(707) = 1414 V across the 50-Ω load. From (6-11), the PEP is

$$4\left[\frac{1}{2}\left(\frac{A_c^2}{50}\right)\right] = (4)(5000) = 20,000 \text{ W}$$

The modulation efficiency would be 33% since $\langle m^2(t) \rangle = \frac{1}{2}$.

There are many ways of building AM transmitters. One might first consider generating the AM signal at a low power level (by using a multiplier) and then amplifying it. This, however, requires the use of linear amplifiers (such as Class A or B amplifiers, as discussed in Sec. 5-9) so that the AM will not be distorted. Because these linear amplifiers are not very efficient in converting the power-supply power to an RF signal, much of the energy is wasted in heat.[†] Consequently, high-power AM broadcast transmitters are built by amplifying the carrier oscillator signal to a high power level with efficient Class C or

[†] Do not confuse this conversion efficiency with modulation efficiency, which was defined by (6-10).

(a) Block Diagram

(b) Waveforms

FIGURE 6-2 Generation of high-power AM by the use of PWM.

Class D amplifiers and then amplitude modulating the last high-power stage. This is called *high-level* modulation, and an example is shown in Fig. 6-2a. For high conversion efficiency, a pulse width modulation (PWM) technique is used to achieve the AM [DeAngelo, 1982], as shown in this figure. The audio input is converted to a PWM signal that is used to control a high-power switch (tube or transistor) circuit. The switch circuit output consists of a high-level PWM signal that is filtered by a low-pass filter to produce the ''dc'' component that is used as the power supply for the power amplifier (PA) stage. The PWM switching frequency is usually chosen in the range of 70 to 80 kHz so that the fundamental and harmonic components of the PWM signal can be easily suppressed by the low-pass filter, and yet the ''dc'' can vary at an audio rate as high as 12 or 15 kHz for good AM audio frequency response. This technique provides excellent frequency response and low distortion since no high-power audio transformers are needed.

6-2 AM Broadcast Technical Standards

Some of the FCC technical standards for AM broadcast stations are shown in Table 6-1. In the United States, assigned carrier frequencies are classified according to the station's intended coverage: clear-channel, regional, or local. Clear-channel stations, also called *Class I* or *Class II* stations, are licensed to operate with a carrier power as large as 50 kW. These stations are intended to cover large areas. Moreover, to accommodate as many stations as possible, nonclear-channel stations may be assigned to operate on clear-chan-

TABLE 6-1 AM Broadcast Station Technical Standards

Item	FCC Technical Standard
Assigned frequency, f_c	In 10-kHz increments from 540 to 1700 kHz
Channel bandwidth	10 kHz
Carrier frequency stability	± 20 Hz of the assigned frequency
% modulation	Maintain 85–95%; max.: 100% neg., 125% pos.
Audio-frequency response[a]	± 2 dB from 100 Hz to 5 kHz with 1 kHz being the 0-dB reference
Harmonic distortion[a]	Less than 5% for up to 85% modulation; less than 7.5% for modulation between 85% and 95%
Noise and hum	At least 45 dB below 100% modulation in the band 30 Hz to 20 kHz
Maximum power licensed	50 kW

[a]Under the new FCC deregulation policy, these requirements are deleted from the FCC rules, although broadcasters still use them as guidelines for minimum acceptable performance.

nel frequencies when they can be implemented without interfering with the dominant clear-channel station. Often, to prevent interference, these secondary stations have to operate with directional antenna patterns such that there is a null in the direction of the dominant station. This is especially true for nighttime operation when sky-wave propagation allows the clear-channel stations to cover most of the United States. Other secondary stations are allowed to operate only in the daytime since any nighttime operation would interfere with the clear-channel station. Other frequencies are set aside for regional stations, also called *Class III* stations, which are intended to cover medium-sized areas. These stations have allowed carrier power levels as large as 5 kW. A third class of frequencies is assigned to local (also called *Class IV*) stations, which are intended to cover one city or a county area and are licensed for a maximum power of 1 kW. Detailed listings of the frequency assignments for these four classes of stations and their licensed powers are available. International broadcast AM stations, which operate in the shortwave bands (3 to 30 MHz), generally operate with higher power levels. Some of these feed 500 kW of carrier power into directional antennas. These antennas produce effective radiated power levels in the megawatt range (i.e., when the gain of the directional antenna is taken into account).

For many years, AM broadcasters have dreamed of offering stereo transmissions to their listeners. Technically, this advance has been possible for a long time, but for political reasons it was not implemented until the 1980s. In 1977 the FCC conducted evaluations of five different AM stereo systems that were proposed by the Kahn Communication/Hazeltine Corporation, Belar Electronics, the Magnavox Corporation, the Harris Corporation, and Motorola [Mennie, 1978]. Each of these proposed systems had advantages and disadvantages, and the FCC decided to allow each AM broadcaster to implement any one of them. This led to confusion in the marketplace since each system required a different type of stereo decoding circuit in the AM receiver. Receiver manufacturers did not want to build all five decoding circuits into each receiver in order to accommodate all the possibilities AM broadcasters might offer. However, now almost all AM stereo broadcasters use the Motorola technique. Nonetheless, it is claimed that the Kahn system is superior during multipath interference conditions that often occur at night when simultaneous sky waves and ground waves are received [Murphy, 1988].

The Kahn system implements AM stereo by transmitting the right-channel audio on an upper SSB-AM signal and the left-channel audio on a lower SSB-AM signal (see Table 5-1), with both SSB signals having the same carrier frequency, f_c. This is called *independent sideband* (ISB) transmission. A mono (conventional) AM receiver tuned to f_c receives both sidebands for mono (left plus right channel) reception. Two mono receivers can be used to receive stereo by tuning one slightly higher than f_c (right-channel audio output) and one slightly lower than f_c (left-channel audio output). In addition, stereo AM receivers can be built that give much better left- and right-channel separation than that obtained by using two mono receivers.

The Motorola C-QUAM[†] system uses quadrature modulation (QM) (see Table 5-1). The monaural audio, consisting of the sum of the left and right channels, is used to

---

[†]C-QUAM is the acronym used by Motorola for compatible quadrature amplitude modulation.

modulate a cosine carrier. That is, $m_1(t) = V_0 + m_L(t) + m_R(t)$, where V_0 is the dc offset used to produce the discrete carrier term in the AM spectrum, $m_L(t)$ is the left-channel audio, and $m_R(t)$ is the right-channel audio. The quadrature carrier is modulated by $m_2(t) = m_L(t) - m_R(t)$. The resulting real envelope $R(t)$ consists of a dc term and a distorted audio term. The distortion is reduced by using a limiter and a filter on the QM output and then amplitude modulating the resulting constant-amplitude signal with $m_L(t) + m_R(t)$ [Mennie, 1978]. The resulting C-QUAM signal is compatible with a mono (conventional) AM receiver for mono reception. Stereo AM receivers use an envelope detector to recover $m_L(t) +, m_R(t)$ and a quadrature product detector to recover $m_L(t) - m_R(t)$. Sum and difference networks can then be used to obtain the left- and right-channel audio, $m_L(t)$ and $m_R(t)$, respectively.

6-3 Double-Sideband Suppressed Carrier

A *double-sideband suppressed carrier* (DSB-SC) signal is essentially an AM signal that has a suppressed discrete carrier. The DSB-SC signal is given by

$$s(t) = A_c m(t) \cos \omega_c t \qquad (6\text{-}13)$$

where $m(t)$ is assumed to have a zero dc level for the suppressed carrier case. The spectrum is identical to that for AM given by (6-12), except that the delta functions at $\pm f_c$ are missing. That is, the spectrum for DSB-SC is

$$S(f) = \frac{A_c}{2}[M(f - f_c) + M(f + f_c)] \qquad (6\text{-}14)$$

When compared with an AM signal, the percentage of modulation on a DSB-SC signal is infinite since there is no carrier line component. Furthermore, the modulation efficiency of a DSB-SC signal is 100% since no power is wasted in a discrete carrier. However, a product detector (which is more expensive than an envelope detector) is required for demodulation of the DSB-SC signal. If transmitting circuitry restricts the modulated signal to a certain peak value, say A_p, it can be demonstrated (see Prob. 6-8) that the sideband power of a DSB-SC signal is *four* times that of a comparable AM signal that has the same peak level. In this sense the DSB-SC signal has a fourfold power advantage over that of an AM signal.

It is also realized that if $m(t)$ is a polar binary data signal (instead of an audio signal), then (6-13) is a BPSK signal, discussed in Example 3-6. As shown in Table 5-1, a QM signal can be generated by adding two DSB signals where there are two modulating signals, $m_1(t)$ and $m_2(t)$, modulating cosine and sine carriers, respectively.

6-4 Costas Loop and Squaring Loop

The coherent reference for product detection cannot be obtained by the use of an ordinary phase-locked tracking loop since there are no spectral line components at $\pm f_c$. However, since the DSB-SC signal has a spectrum that is symmetrical with respect to the (suppressed) carrier frequency, either one of two types of carrier recovery loops shown in Fig.

(a) Costas Phase-Locked Loop

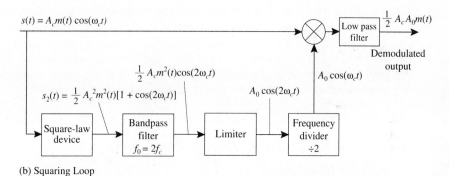

(b) Squaring Loop

FIGURE 6-3 Carrier recovery loops for DSB-SC signals.

6-3 may be used to demodulate the DSB-SC signal. Figure 6-3a shows the *Costas PLL* and Fig. 6-3b shows the *squaring loop*. It can be shown that the noise performance of these two loops are equivalent [Ziemer and Peterson, 1985], so the choice of which loop to implement depends on the relative cost of the loop components and the accuracy that can be realized when each component is built.

As shown in Fig. 6-3a, the Costas PLL is analyzed by assuming that the VCO is locked to the input suppressed carrier frequency, f_c, with a constant phase error of θ_e. Then the voltages $v_1(t)$ and $v_2(t)$ are obtained at the output of the baseband low-pass filters as shown. Since θ_e is small, the amplitude of $v_1(t)$ is relatively large compared to that of $v_2(t)$ (i.e., $\cos \theta_e \gg \sin \theta_e$). Furthermore, $v_1(t)$ is proportional to $m(t)$, so it is the demodulated (product detector) output. The product voltage $v_3(t)$ is

$$v_3(t) = \tfrac{1}{2}(\tfrac{1}{2}A_0 A_c)^2 m^2(t) \sin 2\theta_e$$

The voltage $v_3(t)$ is filtered with a LPF that has a cutoff frequency near dc so that this filter acts as an integrator to produce the dc VCO control voltage

$$v_4(t) = K \sin 2\theta_e$$

where $K = \frac{1}{2}(\frac{1}{2}A_0 A_c)^2 \langle m^2(t) \rangle$ and $\langle m^2(t) \rangle$ is the dc level of $m^2(t)$. This dc control voltage is sufficient to keep the VCO locked to f_c with a small phase error, θ_e.

The squaring loop, shown in Fig. 6-3b, is analyzed by evaluating the expression for the signal out of each component block as shown on this figure. As shown by Fig. 6-3, either the Costas PLL or the squaring loop can be used to demodulate a DSB-SC signal, since for each case the output is $Cm(t)$, where C is a constant. Furthermore, either of these loops can be used to recover (i.e., demodulate) a binary-phase-shift keyed (BPSK) signal since the BPSK signal has the same mathematical form as a DSB-SC signal, where $m(t)$ is a polar NRZ signal as given in Fig. 4-11c and the BPSK waveform is shown in Fig. 7-1d.

Both the Costas PLL and the squaring loop have one major disadvantage—a 180° phase ambiguity. For example, suppose that the input is $-A_c m(t) \cos \omega_c t$ instead of $+A_c m(t) \cos \omega_c t$. Retracing the steps in the preceding analysis, we see that the output would be described by *exactly* the same equation that was obtained before. Then, whenever the loop is energized, it is just as likely to phase lock such that the demodulated output is proportional to $-m(t)$ as it is to $m(t)$. Thus we cannot be sure of the polarity of the output. This is no problem if $m(t)$ is a monaural audio signal since $-m(t)$ sounds the same to our ears as $m(t)$. However, if $m(t)$ is a polar data signal, binary 1's might come out as binary 0's after the circuit is energized, or vice versa. As we found in Chapter 4, there are two ways of abrogating this 180° phase ambiguity: (1) a known test signal can be sent over the system after the loop is turned on so that the sense of the polarity can be determined, or (2) differential coding and decoding may be used.

6-5 Asymmetric Sideband Signals

Single Sideband

DEFINITION: An *upper single sideband* (USSB) signal has a zero-valued spectrum for $|f| < f_c$, where f_c is the carrier frequency.

A *lower single sideband* (LSSB) signal has a zero-valued spectrum for $|f| > f_c$, where f_c is the carrier frequency.

There are numerous ways in which the modulation $m(t)$ may be mapped into the complex envelope $g[m]$ such that an SSB signal will be obtained. Table 5-1 lists some of these methods.

- SSB-AM, which is detected by using a product detector.
- SSB-PM, which may be detected by using a phase detector.
- SSB-FM, which may be detected by using an FM detector.
- SSB-EV, which may be demodulated by using an envelope detector.
- SSB-SQ, which may be demodulated by using a square-law detector that squares the SSB-SQ signal and passes the result through a baseband (low-pass) filter.

SSB-AM is by far the most popular type. It is widely used by the military and by radio amateurs in high-frequency (HF) communication systems, and it is popular because the bandwidth is the same as that of the modulating signal (which is half the bandwidth of an AM or DSB-SC signal). For this reason, we will concentrate on this type of SSB signal. In the usual application, the term *SSB* refers to the SSB-AM type of signal unless otherwise denoted.

Theorem

An SSB signal (i.e., SSB-AM type) is obtained by using the complex envelope

$$g(t) = A_c[m(t) \pm j\hat{m}(t)] \tag{6-15}$$

which results in the SSB signal waveform

$$s(t) = A_c[m(t) \cos \omega_c t \mp \hat{m}(t) \sin \omega_c t] \tag{6-16}$$

where the upper $(-)$ sign is used for USSB and the lower $(+)$ sign is used for LSSB. $\hat{m}(t)$ denotes the Hilbert transform of $m(t)$, which is given by[†]

$$\hat{m}(t) \overset{\triangle}{=} m(t) * h(t) \tag{6-17}$$

where

$$h(t) = \frac{1}{\pi t} \tag{6-18}$$

and $H(f) = \mathcal{F}[h(t)]$ corresponds to a $-90°$ phase shift network:

$$H(f) = \begin{cases} -j, & f > 0 \\ j, & f < 0 \end{cases} \tag{6-19}$$

Figure 6-4 illustrates this theorem. Assume that $m(t)$ has a magnitude spectrum that is of triangular shape, as shown in Fig. 6-4a. Then for the case of USSB (upper signs), the spectrum of $g(t)$ is zero for negative frequencies, as shown in Fig. 6-4b, and $s(t)$ has the USSB spectrum shown in Fig. 6-4c. This result is proved as follows.

PROOF. We need to show that the spectrum of $s(t)$ is zero on the appropriate sideband (depending on the sign chosen). Taking the Fourier transform of (6-16) and letting $\hat{m}(t) = n(t)$ for convenience, we have

$$S(f) = A_c \int_{-\infty}^{\infty} \left[m(t) \left(\frac{e^{j\omega_c t} + e^{-j\omega_c t}}{2} \right) \right.$$

$$\left. \mp\ n(t) \left(\frac{e^{j\omega_c t} - e^{-j\omega_c t}}{2j} \right) \right] e^{-j\omega t}\ dt$$

$$= \frac{A_c}{2} \int_{-\infty}^{\infty} [m(t) \pm jn(t)]e^{-j(\omega - \omega_c)t}\ dt$$

$$+ \frac{A_c}{2} \int_{-\infty}^{\infty} [m(t) \mp jn(t)]e^{-j(\omega + \omega_c)t}\ dt \tag{6-20}$$

[†] A table of Hilbert transform pairs is given in Sec. A-7 (App. A).

(a) Baseband Magnitude Spectrum

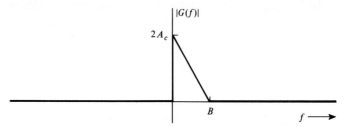

(b) Magnitude of Corresponding Spectrum of the Complex Envelope for USSB

(c) Magnitude of Corresponding Spectrum for the USSB Signal

FIGURE 6-4 Spectrum for a USSB signal.

or

$$S(f) = \frac{A_c}{2} \left[M(f - f_c) \pm jN(f - f_c)\right] + \frac{A_c}{2} \left[M(f + f_c) \mp jN(f + f_c)\right]$$

Recalling that $n(t) = \hat{m}(t) = m(t) * h(t)$, we have

$$N(f) = M(f)H(f) = M(f) \begin{cases} -j, & f > 0 \\ j, & f < 0 \end{cases} \qquad (6\text{-}21)$$

Using (6-21) in (6-20), we obtain

$$S(f) = \frac{A_c}{2} \left[M(f - f_c) \pm jM(f - f_c) \begin{cases} -j, & (f - f_c) > 0 \\ +j, & (f - f_c) < 0 \end{cases} \right]$$

$$+ \frac{A_c}{2} \left[M(f + f_c) \mp jM(f + f_c) \begin{cases} -j, & (f + f_c) > 0 \\ +j, & (f + f_c) < 0 \end{cases} \right] \qquad (6\text{-}22)$$

For the USSB result choose the upper signs, and this equation reduces to

$$S(f) = A_c \begin{Bmatrix} M(f - f_c), & f > f_c \\ 0, & f < f_c \end{Bmatrix} + A_c \begin{Bmatrix} 0, & f > -f_c \\ M(f + f_c), & f < -f_c \end{Bmatrix} \quad (6\text{-}23)$$

which is indeed a USSB signal (see Fig. 6-4).

If the lower signs were chosen, an LSSB signal would have been obtained. ∎

The *normalized average power* of the SSB signal is

$$\langle s^2(t) \rangle = \tfrac{1}{2} \langle |g(t)|^2 \rangle = \tfrac{1}{2} A_c^2 \langle m^2(t) + [\hat{m}(t)]^2 \rangle \quad (6\text{-}24)$$

But $\langle \hat{m}(t)^2 \rangle = \langle m^2(t) \rangle$, so that the SSB signal power is

$$\langle s^2(t) \rangle = A_c^2 \langle m^2(t) \rangle \quad (6\text{-}25)$$

which is the power of the modulating signal $\langle m^2(t) \rangle$ multiplied by the power gain factor A_c^2.

The *normalized peak envelope power (PEP)* is

$$\tfrac{1}{2} \max\{|g(t)|^2\} = \tfrac{1}{2} A_c^2 \max\{m^2(t) + [\hat{m}(t)]^2\} \quad (6\text{-}26)$$

Figure 6-5 illustrates two techniques for generating the SSB signal. The *phasing method* is identical to the IQ canonical form discussed earlier (Fig. 5-27) as applied to SSB signal

(a) Phasing Method

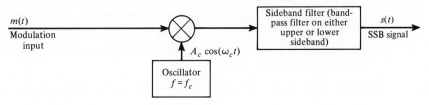

(b) Filter Method

FIGURE 6-5 Generation of SSB.

generation. The *filtering method* is a special case where RF processing (by using the sideband filter) is used to form the equivalent $g(t)$, instead of using baseband processing to generate $g[m]$ directly. The filter method is the most popular method used since excellent sideband suppression can be obtained when a crystal filter is used for the sideband filter. Crystal filters are relatively inexpensive when produced in quantity at standard IF frequencies. In addition to these two techniques for generating SSB, there is a third technique called *Weaver's method.* This is described by Fig. P6-12 and Prob. 6-12. The practical SSB transmitter would incorporate an up converter to translate the SSB signal to the desired operating frequency and use a Class B amplifier to amplify the signal to the desired power level.

SSB signals have *both* AM and PM. Using (6-15), we have for the AM component (real envelope)

$$R(t) = |g(t)| = A_c \sqrt{m^2(t) + [\hat{m}(t)]^2} \tag{6-27}$$

and for the PM component

$$\theta(t) = \underline{/g(t)} = \tan^{-1} \left[\frac{\pm \hat{m}(t)}{m(t)} \right] \tag{6-28}$$

SSB signals may be received by using a superheterodyne receiver that incorporates a product detector with $\theta_0 = 0$. Thus the receiver output is

$$v_{\text{out}}(t) = K \operatorname{Re}\{g(t)e^{-j\theta_0}\} = KA_c m(t) \tag{6-29}$$

where K depends on the gain of the receiver and the loss in the channel. In detecting SSB signals with audio modulation, the reference phase θ_0 does not have to be zero because the same intelligence is heard regardless of the value of the phase used [although the $v_{\text{out}}(t)$ waveform will be drastically different depending on the value of θ_0]. Of course, for digital modulation, the phase has to be exactly correct if the digital waveshape is to be preserved. Furthermore, SSB is a poor modulation technique to use *if* the modulating data signal consists of a line code with a *rectangular* pulse shape. The rectangular shape (zero rise time) causes the value of the SSB-AM signal to be infinite adjacent to the switching times of the data because of the Hilbert transform operation. (This result will be demonstrated in a homework problem.) Thus an SSB signal with this type of modulation cannot be generated by any practical device since a device can produce only finite peak value signals. However, if rolled-off pulse shapes are used in the line code, such as $(\sin x)/x$ pulses, the SSB signal will have a reasonable peak value, and digital data transmission can then be accommodated via SSB.

SSB has many advantages such as the superior detected signal-to-noise ratio when compared to AM (see Fig. 6-18) and the fact that SSB has one half the bandwidth of AM or DSB-SC signals. Space limitations do not permit more discussion of SSB; for more information on this topic, the reader is referred to a book that is devoted wholly to SSB [Sabin and Schoenike, 1987].

Amplitude-Companded Single Sideband

One of the main disadvantages of SSB is that, for proper detection, the frequency of the oscillator signal at the product detector mixer, f_0, must be the same as that of the incoming

SSB signal, f_c. That is, $f_0 = f_c$, as shown in Fig. 5-14. This is the assumption in (5-76) that leads to (6-29). However, the receiver operator usually does not know f_c; the operator knows only that he or she wants to tune in an SSB station. Consequently, if $f_0 \neq f_c$, the spectrum of the detected audio signal will be shifted by the frequency difference, $\Delta f = f_c - f_0$. This effect is observed when an amateur radio operator tunes in an SSB signal. That is, initially, the pitch of the audio signal out of the receiver is either too high or too low, and the operator keeps adjusting f_0 until the pitch of the output signal sounds natural (i.e., $f_0 \approx f_c$, so that $\Delta f \approx 0$). The assumption that $\Delta f \approx 0$, leading to (6-29), is now achieved, but it required the trial and error of a human operator. This trial-and-error approach is difficult, if not impossible to implement with an electronic circuit, so ''automatic tuning'' cannot be achieved. This problem of not being able to set $f_0 = f_c$ electronically can be avoided if a low-level sinusoidal signal of known frequency, called a pilot tone, is added to the modulating audio signal that is fed into the SSB transmitter. Then a phase-locked loop (PLL) (with appropriate frequency dividers) can be used at the receiver to recover the pilot tone and derive the oscillator signal where $f_0 = f_c$ for use by the product detector. This is the technique used in *amplitude-companded single sideband* (ACSSB). In 1985 the FCC approved the use of ACSSB for use in the land mobile service as an alternative to narrowband frequency modulation (as indicated in footnote c of Table 6-5). The ACSSB system uses a 3.1-kHz pilot tone that has a level 10 dB below the peak audio level [ARRL, 1993]. In addition, 6 dB of amplitude companding is used. (This is the same idea as using nonuniform quantizing, as described in Sec. 3-4.)

The ACSSB system gives a 12- to 15-dB improvement in postdetection signal-to-noise ratio when compared to a narrowband FM system for reception of fringe-area signals. In addition, this SSB technique allows four ACSSB stations to be assigned to the same bandwidth that was previously occupied by only one narrowband FM station.

Vestigial Sideband

In certain applications (such as television broadcasting) a DSB modulation technique takes too much bandwidth for the (television) channel and an SSB technique is too expensive to implement, although it takes only half the bandwidth. In this case a compromise between DSB and SSB, called *vestigial sideband* (VSB), is often chosen. VSB is obtained by partial suppression of one of the sidebands of a DSB signal. The DSB signal may be either an AM signal or a DSB-SC signal. This is illustrated by Fig. 6-6, where one sideband of the DSB signal is attenuated by using a bandpass filter, called a vestigial sideband filter, that has an asymmetrical frequency response about $\pm f_c$. The VSB signal is given by

$$s_{\text{VSB}}(t) = s(t) * h_v(t) \tag{6-30}$$

where $s(t)$ is a DSB signal described by either (6-3) with carrier or (6-13) with suppressed carrier, and $h_v(t)$ is the impulse response of the VSB filter. The spectrum of the VSB signal is

$$S_{\text{VSB}}(f) = S(f)H_v(f) \tag{6-31}$$

as illustrated in Fig. 6-6d.

The modulation on the VSB signal can be recovered by a receiver that uses product

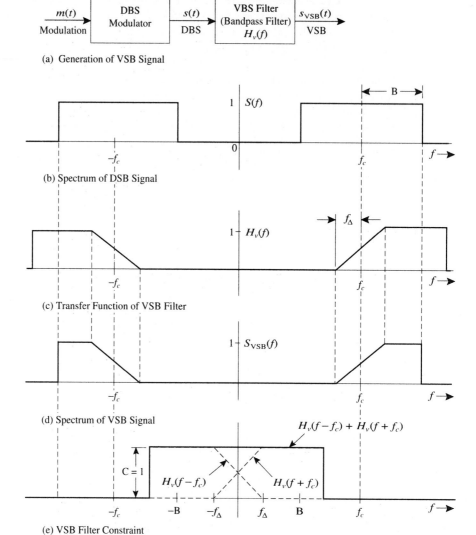

FIGURE 6-6 VSB transmitter and spectra.

detection or, if a large carrier is present, by use of envelope detection. For recovery of undistorted modulation, the transfer function for the VSB filter must satisfy the constraint

$$H_v(f - f_c) + H_v(f + f_c) = C, \qquad |f| \le B \qquad (6\text{-}32)$$

where C is a constant and B is the bandwidth of the modulation. Application of this constraint is shown in Fig. 6-6e, where it is seen that the condition specified by (6-32) is satisfied for the VSB filter characteristic shown in Fig. 6-6c.

The need for the constraint of (6-32) will now be proven. Assume that $s(t)$ is a DSB-SC signal. Then, by use of (6-14) and (6-31), the spectrum of the VSB signal is

$$S_{VSB}(f) = \frac{A_c}{2}[M(f - f_c)H_v(f) + M(f + f_c)H_v(f)]$$

Referring to Fig. 5-14, the product detector output is

$$v_{out}(t) = [A_0 s_{VSB}(t)\cos\omega_c t] * h(t)$$

where $h(t)$ is the impulse response of the low-pass filter having a bandwidth of B hertz. In the frequency domain this becomes

$$V_{out}(f) = A_0\{S_{VSB}(f) * [\tfrac{1}{2}\delta(f - f_c) + \tfrac{1}{2}\delta(f + f_c)]\}H(f)$$

where $H(f) = 1$ for $|f| < B$ and 0 for f elsewhere. Substituting for $S_{VSB}(f)$ and using the convolutional property $x(f) * \delta(f - a) = x(f - a)$, $V_{out}(f)$ is

$$V_{out}(f) = \frac{A_c A_0}{4}[M(f)H_v(f - f_c) + M(f)H_v(f + f_c)], \qquad |f| < B$$

or

$$V_{out}(f) = \frac{A_c A_0}{4}M(f)[H_v(f - f_c) + H_v(f + f_c)], \qquad |f| < B$$

If $H_v(f)$ satisfies the constraint of (6-32), this becomes

$$V_{out}(f) = KM(f)$$

or $v_{out}(t) = Km(t)$ where $K = A_c A_0/4$. This shows that the output of the product detector is undistorted when (6-32) is satisfied.

As discussed in Chapter 8, Sec. 8-9, broadcast television uses VSB to reduce the required channel bandwidth to 6 MHz. In this application, as shown in Fig. 8-31e, the frequency response of the visual TV transmitter is flat over the upper sideband out to 4.2 MHz above the visual carrier frequency and is flat over the lower sideband out to 0.75 MHz below the carrier frequency. The IF filter in the TV receiver has the VSB filter characteristic shown in Fig. 6-6c, where $f_\Delta = 0.75$ MHz. This gives an overall frequency response characteristic that satisfies the constraint of (6-32) so that the video modulation on the visual VSB TV signal can be recovered at the receiver without distortion.

6-6 Phase Modulation and Frequency Modulation

Representation of PM and FM Signals

Phase modulation (PM) and *frequency modulation* (FM) are special cases of angle-modulated signaling. In angle modulated signaling the complex envelope is

$$g(t) = A_c e^{j\theta(t)} \qquad (6\text{-}33)$$

Here the real envelope, $R(t) = |g(t)| = A_c$, is a constant, and the phase $\theta(t)$ is a linear function of the modulating signal $m(t)$. However, $g(t)$ is a *nonlinear* function of the modulation. Using (6-33), we find the resulting *angle-modulated signal* to be

$$s(t) = A_c \cos[\omega_c t + \theta(t)] \tag{6-34}$$

For PM the phase is directly proportional to the modulating signal:

$$\theta(t) = D_p m(t) \tag{6-35}$$

where the proportionality constant D_p is the phase sensitivity of the phase modulator, having units of radians per volt [assuming that $m(t)$ is a voltage waveform].

For FM the phase is proportional to the integral of $m(t)$:

$$\theta(t) = D_f \int_{-\infty}^{t} m(\sigma) \, d\sigma \tag{6-36}$$

where the frequency deviation constant D_f has units of radians/volt-second.

By comparing the last two equations, it is seen that if we have a PM signal modulated by $m_p(t)$, there is *also* FM on the signal corresponding to a *different* modulation waveshape that is given by

$$m_f(t) = \frac{D_p}{D_f} \left[\frac{dm_p(t)}{dt} \right] \tag{6-37}$$

where the subscripts f and p denote frequency and phase, respectively. Similarly, if we have an FM signal modulated by $m_f(t)$, the corresponding phase modulation on this signal is

$$m_p(t) = \frac{D_f}{D_p} \int_{-\infty}^{t} m_f(\sigma) \, d\sigma \tag{6-38}$$

By using (6-38), a PM circuit may be used to synthesize an FM circuit by inserting an integrator in cascade with the phase modulator input (see Fig. 6-7a).

Direct PM circuits are realized by passing an unmodulated sinusoidal signal through a time-varying circuit that introduces a phase shift that varies with the applied modulating voltage (see Fig. 6-8a). D_p is the gain of the PM circuit (rad/V). Similarly, a direct FM circuit is obtained by varying the tuning of an oscillator tank (resonant) circuit according to the modulation voltage. This is shown in Fig. 6-8b, where D_f is the gain of the modulator circuit (which has units of radians per volt-second).

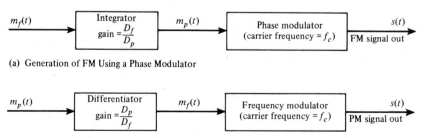

(a) Generation of FM Using a Phase Modulator

(b) Generation of PM Using a Frequency Modulator

FIGURE 6-7 Generation of FM from PM, and vice versa.

(a) A Phase Modulator Circuit

(b) A Frequency Modulator Circuit

FIGURE 6-8 Angle modulator circuits. RFC = radio-frequency choke.

DEFINITION: If a bandpass signal is represented by

$$s(t) = R(t) \cos \psi(t)$$

where $\psi(t) = \omega_c t + \theta(t)$, then the *instantaneous* frequency (hertz) of $s(t)$ is

$$f_i(t) = \frac{1}{2\pi} \omega_i(t) = \frac{1}{2\pi}\left[\frac{d\psi(t)}{dt}\right]$$

or

$$f_i(t) = f_c + \frac{1}{2\pi}\left[\frac{d\theta(t)}{dt}\right] \tag{6-39}$$

For the case of FM, using (6-36), the instantaneous frequency is

$$f_i(t) = f_c + \frac{1}{2\pi} D_f m(t) \tag{6-40}$$

Of course, this is the reason for calling this type of signaling *frequency modulation*—the instantaneous frequency varies about the assigned carrier frequency f_c directly proportional to the modulating signal $m(t)$. Figure 6-9b shows how the instantaneous frequency varies when a sinusoidal modulation (for illustrative purposes) is used. The resulting FM signal is shown in Fig. 6-9c.

The instantaneous frequency should not be confused with the term *frequency* as used in the spectrum of the FM signal. The spectrum is given by the Fourier transform of $s(t)$ and is evaluated by looking at $s(t)$ over the infinite time interval $(-\infty < t < \infty)$. Thus the

(a) Sinusoidal Modulating Signal

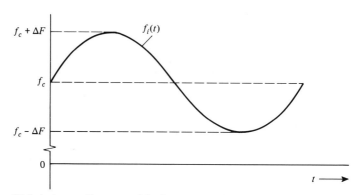

(b) Instantaneous Frequency of the Corresponding FM Signal

(c) Corresponding FM Signal

FIGURE 6-9 FM with a sinusoidal baseband modulating signal.

spectrum tells us what frequencies are present in the signal (on the average) *over all time.* The instantaneous frequency is the frequency that is present at a *particular* instant of time.

The *frequency deviation* from the carrier frequency is

$$f_d(t) = f_i(t) - f_c = \frac{1}{2\pi}\left[\frac{d\theta(t)}{dt}\right] \tag{6-41}$$

and the *peak frequency deviation* is

$$\Delta F = \max\left\{\frac{1}{2\pi}\left[\frac{d\theta(t)}{dt}\right]\right\} \tag{6-42}$$

Note that ΔF is a nonnegative number. In some applications, such as (unipolar) digital modulation, the peak-to-peak deviation is used. This is defined by

$$\Delta F_{pp} = \max\left\{\frac{1}{2\pi}\left[\frac{d\theta(t)}{dt}\right]\right\} - \min\left\{\frac{1}{2\pi}\left[\frac{d\theta(t)}{dt}\right]\right\} \tag{6-43}$$

For FM signaling the peak frequency deviation is related to the peak modulating voltage by

$$\Delta F = \frac{1}{2\pi} D_f V_p \tag{6-44}$$

where $V_p = \max[m(t)]$, as illustrated in Fig. 6-9a.

From Fig. 6-9 it is obvious that an increase in the amplitude of the modulation signal V_p will increase ΔF. This will increase the bandwidth of the FM signal but will not affect the average power level of the FM signal, which is $A_c^2/2$. As V_p is increased, spectral components will appear farther and farther away from the carrier frequency, and the spectral components near the carrier frequency will decrease in magnitude since the total power in the signal remains constant (for specific details, see Example 6-2). This is distinctly different from AM signaling, where the level of the modulation affects the power in the AM signal but does not affect its bandwidth.

In a similar way, the *peak phase deviation* may be defined by

$$\Delta\theta = \max[\theta(t)] \tag{6-45}$$

and for PM this is related to the peak modulating voltage by

$$\Delta\theta = D_p V_p \tag{6-46}$$

where $V_p = \max[m(t)]$.

DEFINITION:[†] The *phase modulation index* is given by

$$\beta_p = \Delta\theta \tag{6-47}$$

where $\Delta\theta$ is the peak phase deviation.

The *frequency modulation index* is given by

$$\beta_f = \frac{\Delta F}{B} \tag{6-48}$$

[†] For digital signals, an alternative definition of modulation index is sometimes used and is denoted by h in the literature. This digital modulation index is given by $h = 2\Delta\theta/\pi$, where $2\Delta\theta$ is the maximum peak-to-peak phase deviation change during the time that it takes to send one symbol, T_s (see Sec. 7-1).

where ΔF is the peak frequency deviation and B is the bandwidth of the modulating signal, which for the case of sinusoidal modulation is f_m, the frequency of the sinusoid.[†]

For the case of PM or FM signaling with *sinusoidal* modulation such that the PM and FM signals have the same peak frequency deviation, β_p is identical to β_f.

Spectra of Angle-Modulated Signals

Using (5-12), we find that the spectrum of an angle modulated signal is given by

$$S(f) = \tfrac{1}{2}[G(f - f_c) + G^*(-f - f_c)] \tag{6-49}$$

where

$$G(f) = \mathscr{F}[g(t)] = \mathscr{F}[A_c e^{j\theta(t)}] \tag{6-50}$$

When the spectra for AM, DSB-SC, and SSB were evaluated, we were able to obtain relatively simple formulas relating $S(f)$ to $M(f)$. For angle modulation signaling this is not the case because $g(t)$ is a nonlinear function of $m(t)$. Thus a general formula relating $G(f)$ to $M(f)$ cannot be obtained. This is unfortunate, but it is a fact of life. That is, to evaluate the spectrum for an angle-modulated signal, (6-50) must be evaluated on a case-by-case basis for the particular modulating waveshape of interest. Furthermore, since $g(t)$ is a nonlinear function of $m(t)$, superposition does not hold and the FM spectrum for the sum of two modulating waveshapes is not the same as summing the FM spectra that were obtained when the individual waveshapes were used.

One example of the spectra obtained for an angle-modulated signal is given in Chapter 3 (see Example 3-6). There a carrier was phase-modulated by a square wave where the peak-to-peak phase deviation was 180°. In this example the spectrum was easy to evaluate because this was the very special case where the PM signal reduces to a DSB-SC signal. In general, of course, the evaluation of (6-50) into a closed form is not easy, and one often has to use numerical techniques to approximate this Fourier transform integral. An example for the case of a sinusoidal modulating waveshape will now be worked out.

Example 6-2   Spectrum of a PM or FM Signal with Sinusoidal Modulation

Assume that the modulation on the PM signal is

$$m_p(t) = A_m \sin \omega_m t \tag{6-51}$$

Then

$$\theta(t) = \beta \sin \omega_m t \tag{6-52}$$

where $\beta_p = D_p A_m = \beta$ is the phase modulation index.

[†] Strictly speaking, the FM index is defined only for the case of single-tone (i.e., sinusoidal) modulation. However, it is often used for other waveshapes, where B is chosen to be the highest frequency or the dominant frequency in the modulating waveform.

The same phase function $\theta(t)$, as given by (6-52), could also be obtained if FM were used, where

$$m_f(t) = A_m \cos \omega_m t \tag{6-53}$$

and $\beta = \beta_f = D_f A_m / \omega_m$. The peak frequency deviation would be $\Delta F = D_f A_m / 2\pi$.

The complex envelope is

$$g(t) = A_c e^{j\theta(t)} = A_c e^{j\beta \sin \omega_m t} \tag{6-54}$$

which is periodic with period $T_m = 1/f_m$. Consequently, $g(t)$ could be represented by a Fourier series that is valid over all time ($-\infty < t < \infty$):

$$g(t) = \sum_{n=-\infty}^{n=\infty} c_n e^{jn\omega_m t} \tag{6-55}$$

where

$$c_n = \frac{A_c}{T_m} \int_{-T_m/2}^{T_m/2} (e^{j\beta \sin \omega_m t}) e^{-jn\omega_m t} \, dt \tag{6-56}$$

which reduces to

$$c_n = A_c \left[\frac{1}{2\pi} \int_{-\pi}^{\pi} e^{j(\beta \sin\theta - n\theta)} \, d\theta \right] = A_c J_n(\beta) \tag{6-57}$$

This integral—known as the *Bessel function of the first kind of the nth order*, $J_n(\beta)$—cannot be evaluated in closed form, but it has been evaluated numerically. Some tabulated four-place and two-place values for $J_n(\beta)$ are given in Tables 6-2 and 6-3 respectively. Extensive tables are available [Abramowitz and Stegun, 1964] or can be computed using MathCAD or MATLAB. The Bessel functions are standard function calls in mathematical personal computer programs such as MathCAD and MATLAB. Examination of the integral shows that (by making a change in variable)

$$J_{-n}(\beta) = (-1)^n J_n(\beta) \tag{6-58}$$

A plot of the Bessel functions for various orders, n, as a function of β is shown in Fig. 6-10.

Taking the Fourier transform of (6-55), we obtain

$$G(f) = \sum_{n=-\infty}^{n=\infty} c_n \, \delta(f - nf_m) \tag{6-59}$$

or

$$G(f) = A_c \sum_{n=-\infty}^{n=\infty} J_n(\beta) \, \delta(f - nf_m) \tag{6-60}$$

TABLE 6-2 Four-Place Values of the Bessel Functions $J_n(\beta)$

β: n	0.5	1	2	3	4	5	6	7	8	9	10
0	0.9385	0.7652	0.2239	-0.2601	-0.3971	-0.1776	0.1506	0.3001	0.1717	-0.09033	-0.2459
1	0.2423	0.4401	0.5767	0.3391	-0.06604	-0.3276	-0.2767	-0.004683	0.2346	0.2453	0.04347
2	0.03060	0.1149	0.3528	0.4861	0.3641	0.04657	-0.2429	-0.3014	-0.1130	0.1448	0.2546
3	0.002564	0.01956	0.1289	0.3091	0.4302	0.3648	0.1148	-0.1676	-0.2911	-0.1809	0.05838
4		0.002477	0.03400	0.1320	0.2811	0.3912	0.3576	0.1578	-0.1054	-0.2655	-0.2196
5			0.007040	0.04303	0.1321	0.2611	0.3621	0.3479	0.1858	-0.05504	-0.2341
6			0.001202	0.01139	0.04909	0.1310	0.2458	0.3392	0.3376	0.2043	-0.01446
7				0.002547	0.01518	0.05338	0.1296	0.2336	0.3206	0.3275	0.2167
8					0.004029	0.01841	0.05653	0.1280	0.2235	0.3051	0.3179
9						0.005520	0.02117	0.05892	0.1263	0.2149	0.2919
10						0.001468	0.006964	0.02354	0.06077	0.1247	0.2075
11							0.002048	0.008335	0.02560	0.06222	0.1231
12								0.002656	0.009624	0.02739	0.06337
13									0.003275	0.01083	0.02897
14										0.003895	0.01196
15										0.001286	0.004508
16											0.001567

TABLE 6-3 Two-Place Values of the Bessel Functions $J_n(\beta)$

β \ n:	0	1	2	3	4	5	6	7	8	9	10	11	12
0.0	1.00	0											
0.2	0.99	0.10	0										
0.4	0.96	0.20	0.02										
0.6	0.91	0.29	0.04	0									
0.8	0.85	0.37	0.08	0.01									
1.0	0.77	0.44	0.11	0.02	0								
1.2	0.67	0.50	0.16	0.03	0.01								
1.4	0.57	0.54	0.21	0.05	0.01								
1.6	0.46	0.57	0.26	0.07	0.01								
1.8	0.34	0.58	0.31	0.10	0.02	0							
2.0	0.22	0.58	0.35	0.13	0.03	0.01							
2.2	0.11	0.56	0.40	0.16	0.05	0.01							
2.4	0	0.52	0.43	0.20	0.06	0.02	0						
2.6	-0.10	0.47	0.46	0.24	0.08	0.02	0.01						
2.8	-0.19	0.41	0.48	0.27	0.11	0.03	0.01						
3.0	-0.26	0.34	0.49	0.31	0.13	0.04	0.01	0					
3.2	-0.32	0.26	0.48	0.34	0.16	0.06	0.02	0.01					
3.4	-0.36	0.18	0.47	0.37	0.19	0.07	0.02	0.01					
3.6	-0.39	0.10	0.44	0.40	0.22	0.09	0.03	0.01					
3.8	-0.40	0.01	0.41	0.42	0.25	0.11	0.04	0.01					
4.0	-0.40	-0.07	0.36	0.43	0.28	0.13	0.05	0.02	0				
4.2	-0.38	-0.14	0.31	0.43	0.31	0.16	0.06	0.02	0.01				
4.4	-0.34	-0.20	0.25	0.43	0.34	0.18	0.08	0.03	0.01				
4.6	-0.30	-0.26	0.18	0.42	0.36	0.21	0.09	0.03	0.01				
4.8	-0.24	-0.30	0.12	0.40	0.38	0.23	0.11	0.04	0.01	0			
5.0	-0.18	-0.33	0.05	0.36	0.39	0.26	0.13	0.05	0.02	0.01			
5.2	-0.11	-0.34	-0.02	0.33	0.40	0.29	0.15	0.07	0.02	0.01			
5.4	-0.04	-0.35	-0.09	0.28	0.40	0.31	0.18	0.08	0.03	0.01			
5.6	0.03	-0.33	-0.15	0.23	0.39	0.33	0.20	0.09	0.04	0.01	0		
5.8	0.09	-0.31	-0.20	0.17	0.38	0.35	0.22	0.11	0.05	0.02	0.01		

TABLE 6-3 Two-Place Values of the Bessel Functions $J_n(\beta)$ (*continued*)

β \ n:	0	1	2	3	4	5	6	7	8	9	10	11	12
6.0	0.15	−0.28	−0.24	0.11	0.36	0.36	0.25	0.13	0.06	0.02	0.01		
6.2	0.20	−0.23	−0.28	0.05	0.33	0.37	0.27	0.15	0.07	0.03	0.01		
6.4	0.24	−0.18	−0.30	−0.01	0.29	0.37	0.29	0.17	0.08	0.03	0.01		
6.6	0.27	−0.12	−0.31	−0.06	0.25	0.37	0.31	0.19	0.10	0.04	0.01	0	
6.8	0.29	−0.07	−0.31	−0.12	0.21	0.36	0.33	0.21	0.11	0.05	0.02	0.01	
7.0	0.30	0	−0.30	−0.17	0.16	0.35	0.34	0.23	0.13	0.06	0.02	0.01	
7.2	0.30	0.05	−0.28	−0.21	0.11	0.33	0.35	0.25	0.15	0.07	0.03	0.01	
7.4	0.28	0.11	−0.25	−0.24	0.05	0.30	0.35	0.27	0.16	0.08	0.04	0.01	
7.6	0.25	0.16	−0.21	−0.27	0	0.27	0.35	0.29	0.18	0.10	0.04	0.02	0
7.8	0.22	0.20	−0.16	−0.29	−0.06	0.23	0.35	0.31	0.20	0.11	0.05	0.02	0.01
8.0	0.17	0.23	−0.11	−0.29	−0.11	0.19	0.34	0.32	0.22	0.13	0.06	0.03	0.01
8.2	0.12	0.26	−0.06	−0.29	−0.15	0.14	0.32	0.33	0.24	0.14	0.07	0.03	0.01
8.4	0.07	0.27	0	−0.27	−0.19	0.09	0.30	0.34	0.26	0.16	0.08	0.04	0.02
8.6	0.01	0.27	0.05	−0.25	−0.22	0.04	0.27	0.34	0.28	0.18	0.10	0.04	0.02
8.8	−0.04	0.26	0.10	−0.22	−0.25	−0.01	0.24	0.34	0.29	0.20	0.11	0.05	0.02
9.0	−0.09	0.25	0.14	−0.18	−0.27	−0.06	0.20	0.33	0.31	0.21	0.12	0.06	0.03
9.2	−0.14	0.22	0.18	−0.14	−0.27	−0.10	0.16	0.31	0.31	0.23	0.14	0.07	0.03
9.4	−0.18	0.18	0.22	−0.09	−0.27	−0.14	0.12	0.30	0.32	0.25	0.16	0.08	0.04
9.6	−0.21	0.14	0.24	−0.04	−0.26	−0.18	0.08	0.27	0.32	0.27	0.17	0.10	0.05
9.8	−0.23	0.09	0.25	0.01	−0.25	−0.21	0.03	0.25	0.32	0.28	0.19	0.11	0.05

TABLE 6-3 Two-Place Values of the Bessel Functions $J_n(\beta)$ *(continued)*

β \ n:	0	1	2	3	4	5	6	7	8	9	10	11	12
10.0	−0.25	0.04	0.25	0.06	−0.22	−0.23	−0.01	0.22	0.32	0.29	0.21	0.12	0.06
10.2	−0.25	−0.01	0.25	0.10	−0.19	−0.25	−0.06	0.18	0.31	0.30	0.22	0.14	0.07
10.4	−0.24	−0.06	0.23	0.14	−0.15	−0.26	−0.10	0.14	0.29	0.31	0.24	0.15	0.08
10.6	−0.23	−0.10	0.21	0.18	−0.11	−0.26	−0.14	0.10	0.28	0.31	0.26	0.17	0.10
10.8	−0.20	−0.14	0.18	0.21	−0.06	−0.25	−0.17	0.06	0.25	0.31	0.27	0.19	0.11
11.0	−0.17	−0.18	0.14	0.23	−0.02	−0.24	−0.20	0.02	0.22	0.31	0.28	0.20	0.12
11.2	−0.13	−0.20	0.10	0.24	0.30	−0.22	−0.22	−0.02	0.19	0.30	0.29	0.22	0.14
11.4	−0.09	−0.22	0.05	0.24	0.08	−0.19	−0.24	−0.06	0.16	0.29	0.30	0.23	0.15
11.6	−0.04	−0.23	0	0.23	0.12	−0.15	−0.25	−0.10	0.12	0.27	0.30	0.25	0.17
11.8	0	−0.23	−0.04	0.22	0.15	−0.12	−0.25	−0.14	0.08	0.25	0.30	0.26	0.18
12.0	0.05	−0.22	−0.08	0.20	0.18	−0.07	−0.24	−0.17	0.05	0.23	0.30	0.27	0.20
12.2	0.09	−0.21	−0.12	0.17	0.21	−0.03	−0.23	−0.20	0.01	0.20	0.29	0.28	0.21
12.4	0.13	−0.18	−0.16	0.13	0.22	0.01	−0.21	−0.22	−0.03	0.17	0.29	0.29	0.22
12.6	0.16	−0.15	−0.19	0.09	0.23	0.06	−0.18	−0.23	−0.07	0.14	0.27	0.29	0.24
12.8	0.19	−0.11	−0.21	0.05	0.23	0.10	−0.15	−0.24	−0.11	0.10	0.25	0.29	0.25

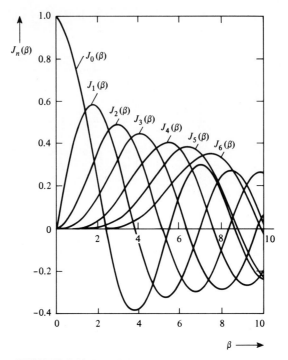

FIGURE 6-10 Bessel functions for $n = 0$ to $n = 6$.

Using this result in (6-49), we obtain the spectrum of the angle modulated signal. The magnitude spectrum for $f > 0$ is shown in Fig. 6-11 for the cases of $\beta = 0.2$, 1.0, 2.0, 5.0, and 8.0. It is noted that the discrete carrier term (at $f = f_c$) is proportional to $|J_0(\beta)|$; consequently, the level (magnitude) of the discrete carrier depends on the modulation index. It will be zero if $J_0(\beta) = 0$, which occurs if $\beta = 2.40$, 5.52, and so on, as shown in Table 6-4.

Figure 6-11 also shows that the bandwidth of the angle modulated signal depends on β and f_m. In fact, it can be shown that 98% of the total power is contained in the bandwidth

$$B_T = 2(\beta + 1)B \tag{6-61}$$

where β is either the phase modulating index or the frequency modulation index and B is the bandwidth of the modulating signal (which is f_m for sinusoidal modulation).[†] This

---

[†]For the case of FM (not PM) with $2 < B < 10$, Carson's rule, (6-61), actually underestimates B_T somewhat. In this case a better approximation is $B_T = 2(\beta + 2)B$. Also, if the modulation signal contains discontinuities, such as square-wave modulation, both formulas may not be too accurate and the B_T should be evaluated by examining the spectrum of the angle-modulated signal. However, to avoid confusion in computing B_T, we will assume that (6-61) is approximately correct for all cases.

TABLE 6-4 Zeros of Bessel Functions: Values for β When $J_n(\beta) = 0$

	Order of Bessel Function, n						
	0	1	2	3	4	5	6
β for 1st zero	2.40	3.83	5.14	6.38	7.59	8.77	9.93
β for 2nd zero	5.52	7.02	8.42	9.76	11.06	12.34	13.59
β for 3rd zero	8.65	10.17	11.62	13.02	14.37	15.70	17.00
β for 4th zero	11.79	13.32	14.80	16.22	17.62	18.98	20.32
β for 5th zero	14.93	16.47	17.96	19.41	20.83	22.21	23.59
β for 6th zero	18.07	19.61	21.12	22.58	24.02	25.43	26.82
β for 7th zero	21.21	22.76	24.27	25.75	27.20	28.63	30.03
β for 8th zero	24.35	25.90	27.42	28.91	30.37	31.81	33.23

formula gives a rule-of-thumb expression for evaluating the transmission bandwidth of PM and FM signals; it is called *Carson's rule*. B_T is shown in Fig. 6-11 for various values of β. Carson's rule, (6-61), is very important because it gives an easy way to compute the bandwidth of angle-modulated signals. Computation of the bandwidth using other definitions, such as 3-dB bandwidth, can be very difficult since the spectrum of the FM or PM signal must first be evaluated. This is a nontrivial task except for simple cases such as single-tone (sinusoidal) modulation or unless a digital computer is used to compute the approximate spectrum.

Since the exact spectrum of angle modulated signals is difficult to evaluate in general, formulas for the approximation of the spectra are extremely useful. Some relatively simple approximations may be obtained when the peak phase deviation is small and when the modulation index is large. These topics are discussed in the following sections on narrowband angle modulation and wideband FM.

Narrowband Angle Modulation

When $\theta(t)$ is restricted to a small value, say $|\theta(t)| < 0.2$ rad, the complex envelope $g(t) = A_c e^{j\theta}$ may be approximated by a Taylor's series where only the first two terms are used. Thus, since $e^x \approx 1 + x$ for $|x| \ll 1$,

$$g(t) \approx A_c[1 + j\theta(t)] \qquad (6\text{-}62)$$

Using this approximation in (5-9), we obtain the expression for a *narrowband angle-modulated signal*

$$s(t) = \underbrace{A_c \cos \omega_c t}_{\substack{\text{discrete} \\ \text{carrier term}}} - \underbrace{A_c \theta(t) \sin \omega_c t}_{\text{sideband term}} \qquad (6\text{-}63)$$

This result indicates that a narrowband angle modulated signal consists of two terms: a discrete carrier component (which does not change with modulating signal) and a sideband term. This is similar to AM-type signaling *except* that the sideband term is 90° out of

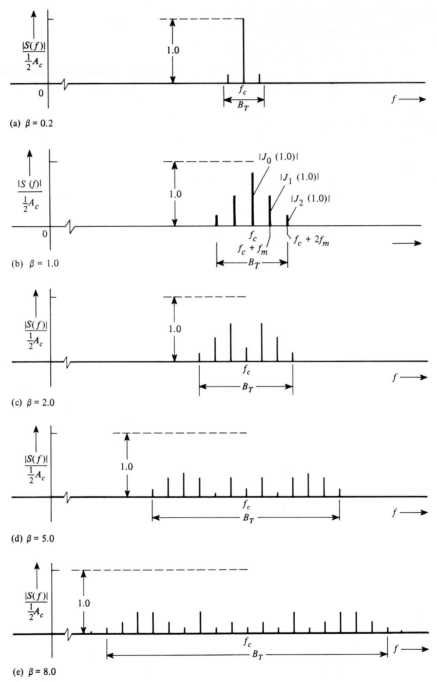

(a) $\beta = 0.2$

$|J_0 (1.0)|$
$|J_1 (1.0)|$
$|J_2 (1.0)|$

f_c
$f_c + f_m$
$f_c + 2f_m$

(b) $\beta = 1.0$

(c) $\beta = 2.0$

(d) $\beta = 5.0$

(e) $\beta = 8.0$

FIGURE 6-11 Magnitude spectra for FM or PM with sinusoidal modulation for various modulation indexes.

(a) Generation of NBFM Using a Balanced Modulator

(b) Generation of WBFM From a NBFM Signal

FIGURE 6-12 Indirect method of generating WBFM (Armstrong method).

phase with the discrete carrier term. The narrowband signal can be generated by using a balanced modulator (multiplier), as shown in Fig. 6-12a for the case of narrowband frequency modulation (NBFM). Furthermore, wideband frequency modulation (WBFM) may be generated from the NBFM signal by using frequency multiplication, as shown in Fig. 6-12b. Limiter circuits are needed to suppress the incidental AM [which is $\sqrt{1 + \theta^2(t)}$ as the result of the approximation (6-62)] that is present in the NBFM signal. This method of generating WBFM is called the *Armstrong method* or *indirect method*.

From (6-62) and (6-49), the spectrum of the narrowband angle-modulated signal is

$$S(f) = \frac{A_c}{2}\{[\delta(f - f_c) + \delta(f + f_c)] + j[\Theta(f - f_c) - \Theta(f + f_c)]\} \qquad (6\text{-}64)$$

where

$$\Theta(f) = \mathcal{F}[\theta(t)] = \begin{cases} D_p M(f), & \text{for PM signaling} \\[2mm] \dfrac{D_f}{j2\pi f} M(f), & \text{for FM signaling} \end{cases} \qquad (6\text{-}65)$$

Wideband Frequency Modulation

A *direct method* of generating wideband frequency modulation (WBFM) is to use a voltage-controlled oscillator (VCO), as illustrated in Fig. 6-8b. However, for VCOs that are designed for wide frequency deviation (ΔF large), the stability of the carrier frequency $f_c = f_0$ is not very good, so the VCO is incorporated into a PLL arrangement where the PLL is locked to a stable frequency source, such as a crystal oscillator (see Fig. 6-13). The frequency divider is needed to lower the modulation index of the WBFM signal to produce an NBFM signal ($\beta \approx 0.2$) so that a large discrete carrier term will always be present at

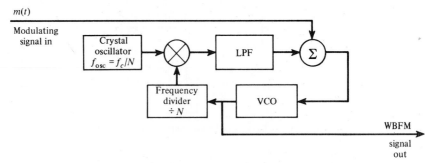

FIGURE 6-13 Direct method of generating WBFM.

frequency f_c/N to beat with the crystal oscillator signal and produce the dc control voltage [see Fig. 6-11a, (6-63), and (6-64)]. This dc control voltage holds the VCO on the assigned frequency with a tolerance determined by the crystal oscillator circuit.

The PSD of a WBFM signal may be *approximated* by using the probability density function (PDF) of the modulating signal. This is reasonable from an intuitive viewpoint, since the instantaneous frequency varies directly with the modulating signal voltage for the case of FM [$D_f/(2\pi)$ being the proportionality constant]. If the modulating signal spends more time at one voltage value than another, the instantaneous frequency will dwell at the corresponding frequency, and the power spectrum will have a peak at this frequency. A discussion of the approximation involved—called the *quasi-static approximation*—is well documented [Rowe, 1965]. This result is stated in the following theorem.

Theorem

For WBFM signaling, where

$$s(t) = A_c \cos\left[\omega_c t + D_f \int_{-\infty}^{t} m(\sigma)\,d\sigma\right]$$

$$\beta_f = \frac{D_f \max[m(t)]}{2\pi B} > 1$$

and B is the bandwidth of $m(t)$, the normalized PSD of the WBFM signal is approximated by

$$\mathcal{P}(f) = \frac{\pi A_c^2}{2D_f}\left[f_m\left(\frac{2\pi}{D_f}(f - f_c)\right) + f_m\left(\frac{2\pi}{D_f}(-f - f_c)\right)\right] \tag{6-66}$$

where $f_m(\cdot)$ is the PDF of the modulating signal.[†]

This theorem can be proved (see Prob. 6-44 of [Couch, 1993]).

[†] See Appendix B for the definition of probability density function (PDF) and examples of PDFs for various waveforms. This topic may be deleted if the reader is not sufficiently familiar with PDFs. Do not confuse the PDF of the modulation, $f_m(\cdot)$, with the frequency variable, f.

Example 6-3   Spectrum for WBFM with Triangular Modulation

The spectrum for a WBFM signal with a triangular modulating signal (Fig. 6-14a) will be evaluated. The associated PDF for triangular modulation is shown in Fig. 6-14b. The PDF is described by

$$f_m(m) = \begin{cases} \dfrac{1}{2V_p}, & |m| < V_p \\ 0, & m \text{ otherwise} \end{cases} \tag{6-67}$$

where V_p is the peak voltage of the triangular waveform. Substituting this equation into (6-66), we obtain

$$\mathcal{P}(f) = \frac{\pi A_c^2}{2D_f} \left[\begin{cases} \dfrac{1}{2V_p}, & \left| \dfrac{2\pi}{D_f}(f - f_c) \right| < V_p \\ 0, & f \text{ otherwise} \end{cases} \right.$$
$$\left. + \begin{cases} \dfrac{1}{2V_p}, & \left| \dfrac{2\pi}{D_f}(f + f_c) \right| < V_p \\ 0, & f \text{ otherwise} \end{cases} \right]$$

The PSD of the WBFM signal becomes

$$\mathcal{P}(f) = \begin{cases} \dfrac{A_c^2}{8\Delta F}, & (f_c - \Delta F) < f < (f_c + \Delta F) \\ 0, & f \text{ otherwise} \end{cases}$$
$$+ \begin{cases} \dfrac{A_c^2}{8\Delta F}, & (-f_c - \Delta F) < f < (-f_c + \Delta F) \\ 0, & f \text{ otherwise} \end{cases} \tag{6-68}$$

where the peak frequency deviation is

$$\Delta F = \frac{D_f V_p}{2\pi} \tag{6-69}$$

This PSD is plotted in Fig. 6-14c. It is recognized that this result is an *approximation* to the actual PSD. In this example the modulation is periodic with period T_m so that the actual spectrum is a line spectrum with the delta functions spaced $f_m = 1/T_m$ hertz apart from each other (like the spacing shown in Fig. 6-11 for the case of sinusoidal modulation). This approximation gives us the *approximate envelope* of the line spectrum. (If the modulation had been nonperiodic, the exact spectrum would be continuous and thus would not be a line spectrum.)

(a) Triangle Modulating Waveform   (b) PDF of Triangle Modulation

(c) PSD of WBFM Signal with Triangle Modulation, $\Delta F = D_f V_p / 2\pi$

FIGURE 6-14 Approximate spectrum of a WBFM signal with triangle modulation.

In the other example using sinusoidal (periodic) modulation, the exact PSD is known to contain line components with weights $[A_c J_n(\beta)]^2/2$ located at frequencies $f = f_c + nf_m$ (see Fig. 6-11). For the case of high index the envelope of these weights approximates the PDF of a sinusoid as given in Appendix B.

In summary, some important properties of angle modulated signals are

- It is a nonlinear function of the modulation, and, consequently, the bandwidth of the signal increases as the modulation index increases.
- The discrete carrier level changes, depending on the modulating signal, and is zero for certain types of modulating waveforms.
- The bandwidth of a narrowband angle modulated signal is twice the modulating signal bandwidth (same as that for AM signaling).
- The real envelope of an angle-modulated signal, $R(t) = A_c$, is constant and, consequently, does not depend on the modulating signal level.

Preemphasis and Deemphasis in Angle-Modulated Systems

In angle-modulated systems the signal-to-noise ratio at the output of the receiver can be improved if the level of the modulation (at the transmitter) is boosted at the top end of the (e.g., audio) spectrum—this is called *preemphasis*—and attenuated at high frequencies on

(a) Overall Block Diagram

$$H_p(f) = K \frac{1 + j(f/f_1)}{1 + j(f/f_2)} \quad \text{where } f_1 = \frac{1}{2\pi\tau_1} = \frac{1}{2\pi R_1 C}, f_2 = \frac{1}{2\pi\tau_2} = \frac{R_1 + R_2}{2\pi R_1 R_2 C}$$

(b) Preemphasis Filter   (c) Bode Plot of Preemphasis Frequency Response

$$H_d(f) = \frac{1}{1 + j(f/f_1)} \quad \text{where } f_1 = \frac{1}{2\pi\tau_1} = \frac{1}{2\pi R_1 C}$$

(d) Deemphasis Filter   (e) Bode Plot of Deemphasis Characteristic

FIGURE 6-15 Angle-modulated system with preemphasis and deemphasis.

the receiver output—this is called *deemphasis*. This gives an overall baseband frequency response that is flat while improving the signal-to-noise ratio at the receiver output (see Fig. 6-15). In the preemphasis characteristic the second corner frequency f_2 occurs much above the baseband spectrum of the modulating signal (say, 25 kHz for audio modulation). In FM broadcasting the time constant τ_1 is usually 75 μsec so that f_1 occurs at 2.12 kHz. The resulting overall system frequency response using preemphasis at the transmitter and deemphasis at the receiver is flat over the band of the modulating signal. It is interesting to note that in FM broadcasting with 75-μsec preemphasis, the signal transmitted is an FM signal for modulating frequencies up to 2.1 kHz but a *phase-modulated* signal for audio frequencies above 2.1 kHz since the preemphasis network acts as a differentiator for frequencies between f_1 and f_2. Hence, *preemphasized FM is actually a combination of FM and PM* and combines the advantages of both with respect to noise performance. Figure 6-18 demonstrates that preemphasis–deemphasis improves the signal-to-noise ratio at the receiver output.

6-7 Frequency-Division Multiplexing and FM Stereo

Frequency-division multiplexing (FDM) is a technique for transmitting multiple messages simultaneously over a wideband channel by first modulating the message signals onto several subcarriers and forming a composite baseband signal that consists of the sum of these modulated subcarriers. This composite signal may then be modulated onto the main carrier, as shown in Fig. 6-16. Any type of modulation, such as AM, DSB, SSB, PM, FM, and so on, could be used. The modulation types used on the subcarriers, as well as the type used on the main carrier, may be different. However, as shown in Fig. 6-16b, the composite signal spectrum must consist of modulated signals that do not have overlapping spectra; otherwise, crosstalk will occur between the message signals at the receiver output. The composite baseband signal then modulates a main transmitter to produce the FDM signal that is transmitted over the wideband channel.

The received FDM signal is first demodulated to reproduce the composite baseband signal that is passed through filters to separate the individual modulated subcarriers. The subcarriers are then demodulated to reproduce the message signals $m_1(t)$, $m_2(t)$, and so on.[†]

The FM stereo broadcasting system that has been adopted in the United States is an example of an FDM system. Furthermore, it is compatible with the monaural FM system that has existed since the 1940s. That is, a listener with a conventional monaural FM receiver will hear the monaural audio (which consists of the left- plus the right-channel audio), while the listener with a stereo receiver will receive the left-channel audio on the left speaker and the right-channel audio on the right speaker (see Fig. 6-17). To obtain the compatibility feature, the left- and right-channel audios are combined (summed) to produce the monaural signal, and the difference audio is used to modulate a 38-kHz DSB-SC signal. A 19-kHz pilot tone is added to the composite baseband signal $m_b(t)$ to provide a reference signal for coherent (product) subcarrier demodulation in the receiver. As seen from Fig. 6-17c, this system is compatible with existing FM monaural receivers. In Prob. 6-44 it will be found that a relatively simple switching (sampling) technique may be used to implement the demodulation of the subcarrier and the separation of the left and right signals in one operation.

[†] Figure 8-1 shows a typical FDM hierarchy used by the telephone industry.

(a) Transmitter

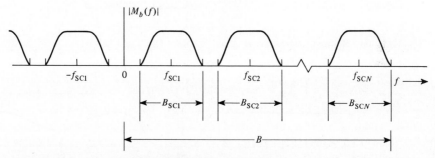

(b) Spectrum of Composite Baseband Signal

(c) Receiver

FIGURE 6-16 FDM system.

The FM station may also be given *subsidiary communications authorization* (SCA) by the FCC. This allows the station to add a FM subcarrier to permit the transmission of private background music to business subscribers for use in their store or office. The SCA FM subcarrier frequency is usually 67 kHz, although this frequency is not specified by FCC rules. Moreover, up to four SCA subcarriers are permitted by the FCC, and each may carry either data or audio material for private subscribers.

6-8 FM Broadcast Technical Standards

Table 6-5 gives some of the FCC technical standards that have been adopted for FM systems. In the United States, FM stations are classified into one of three major categories

(a) FM Stereo Transmitter

(b) Spectrum of Composite Baseband Signal

(c) FM Stereo Receiver

FIGURE 6-17 FM stereo system.

TABLE 6-5 FCC FM Standards

Class of Service	Item	FCC Standard
FM broadcasting	Assigned frequency, f_c	In 200-kHz increments from 88.1 MHz (FM Channel 201) to 107.9 MHz (FM Channel 300)
	Channel bandwidth	200 kHz
	Noncommercial stations	88.1 MHz (Channel 201) to 91.9 MHz (Channel 220)
	Commercial stations	92.1 MHz (Channel 221) to 107.9 MHz (Channel 300)
	Carrier frequency stability	± 2000 Hz of the assigned frequency
	100% modulation[a]	$\Delta F = 75$ kHz
	Audio frequency response[b]	50 Hz to 15 kHz following a 75-μsec preemphasis curve
	Modulation index	5 (for $\Delta F = 75$ kHz and $B = 15$ kHz)
	% harmonic distortion[b]	<3.5% (50–100 Hz) <2.5% (100–7500 Hz) <3.0% (7500–15,000 Hz)
	FM noise	At least 60 dB below 100% modulation at 400Hz
	AM noise	50 dB below the level corresponding to 100% AM in a band 50 Hz–15 kHz
	Maximum power licensed	100 kW in horizontal polarized plane plus 100 kW in vertical polarized plane
Two-way FM mobile radio	100% modulation	$\Delta F = 5$ kHz
	Modulation index	1 (for $\Delta F = 5$ kHz and $B = 5$ kHz)
	Carrier frequencies are within the frequency bands:	32–50 MHz (low VHF band) 144–148 MHz (2-m amateur band) 148–174 MHz (high VHF band)[c] 420–450 MHz ($\frac{3}{4}$-m amateur band) 450–470 MHz (UHF band) 470–512 MHz (UHF, T band) 806–928 MHz (900-MHz band)
TV aural (FM) signal	100% modulation	$\Delta F = 25$ kHz
	Modulation index	1.67 (for $\Delta F = 25$ kHz and $B = 15$ kHz)

[a]For stereo transmission the 19-kHz pilot tone may contribute as much as 10% of the total allowed 75-kHz peak deviation. If SCA is used, each SCA subcarrier may also contribute up to 10% and the total peak deviation may be 110% of 75 kHz provided that SCA subcarriers are present.

[b]Under the new FCC deregulation policy these requirements are deleted from the FCC rules, although broadcasters still use them as guidelines for minimum acceptable performance.

[c]Amplitude-compressed SSB is also permitted in the 150- to 170-MHz band in 5-kHz bandwidth channels.

that depend on their intended coverage area. Class A stations are local stations. They have a maximum effective radiated power (ERP) of 6 kW and a maximum antenna height of 300 ft above average terrain. The ERP is the average transmitter output power multiplied by the power gains of both the transmission line (a number less than 1) and the antenna (see Sec. 8-9 for some TV ERP calculations). Class B stations have a maximum ERP of 50 kW, with a maximum antenna height of 500 ft above average terrain. Class B stations are assigned to the northeastern part of the United States, southern California, Puerto Rico, and the Virgin Islands. Class C stations are assigned to the remainder of the United States. They have a maximum ERP of 100 kW and a maximum antenna height of 2000 ft above average terrain. As shown in Table 6-5, FM stations are further classified as commercial or noncommercial. Noncommercial stations operate in the 88.1 to 91.9 MHz segment of the FM band and provide educational programs with no commercials. Class D stations are limited to 10-W transmitter output and are for noncommercial service only. In the commercial segment of the FM band, 92.1 to 107.9 MHz, certain frequencies are reserved for Class A stations and the remainder are for Class B or Class C station assignment. A listing of these frequencies and the specific station assignments for each city is available [Broadcasting, 1991].

6-9 Noise Performance

The noise performance of the various types of bandpass systems is examined by evaluating the signal-to-noise power ratio at the receiver output, $(S/N)_{out}$, when a modulated signal plus noise is present at the receiver input. We would like to see if $(S/N)_{out}$ is larger for an AM system, a DSB-SC system, or an FM system. For comparison of these (S/N)'s, the power of the modulated signals at the inputs of these receivers is set to the same value and the PSD of the input noise is $N_0/2$. (That is, the input noise is white with a spectral level set to $N_0/2$.) This is equivalent to comparing the $(S/N)_{out}$ for the cases of AM, DSB-SC, and FM for a fixed value of

$$\left(\frac{S}{N}\right)_{baseband} = \frac{P_s}{N_0 B} \tag{6-70}$$

where P_s is the power of the AM, DSB-SC, or FM signal (at the AM, DSB-SC, or FM receiver input). B is chosen to be the bandwidth of the *baseband* (modulating) signal where the same baseband modulating signal is used for all cases so that the same basis of comparison will be realized. (If B were chosen to be the bandwidth of the input-modulated signal, B_T, the comparison would not be on an equal noise PSD basis of $N_0/2$ for a fixed value of $(S/N)_{baseband}$ because the B_T values for AM and FM signals are different.) The signal-to-noise ratio at the receiver input can also be obtained; it is

$$\left(\frac{S}{N}\right)_{in} = \frac{P_s}{N_0 B_T} = \left(\frac{S}{N}\right)_{baseband} \left(\frac{B}{B_T}\right) \tag{6-71}$$

where B_T is the bandwidth of the bandpass signal at the receiver input.

Shannon's Ideal System

It is interesting to ask the question: What is the best noise performance that is theoretically possible? Could a wide transmission-bandwidth be used to gain improved noise performance? The answer is given by Shannon's channel capacity theorem. The *ideal system* is defined as one that does not lose channel capacity in the detection process. Thus

$$C_{in} = C_{out} \qquad (6\text{-}72)$$

where C_{in} is the bandpass channel capacity and C_{out} is the channel capacity after detection. Using (1-10) in (6-72), we have

$$B_T \log_2[1 + (S/N)_{in}] = B \log_2[1 + (S/N)_{out}] \qquad (6\text{-}73)$$

where B_T is the transmission bandwidth of the bandpass signal at the receiver input and B is the bandwidth of the baseband signal at the receiver output. Solving for $(S/N)_{out}$, we have

$$\left(\frac{S}{N}\right)_{out} = \left[1 + \left(\frac{S}{N}\right)_{in}\right]^{B_T/B} - 1 \qquad (6\text{-}74)$$

using (6-71), this becomes

$$\left(\frac{S}{N}\right)_{out} = \left[1 + \left(\frac{B}{B_T}\right)\left(\frac{S}{N}\right)_{baseband}\right]^{B_T/B} - 1 \qquad (6\text{-}75)$$

Equation (6-75), which describes the ideal system performance, is plotted in Fig. 6-18 for the case of $B_T/B = 12$. As expected, none of the practical signaling systems equals the performance of the ideal system. However, some of the nonlinear systems (near threshold) approach the performance of the ideal system.

AM and FM Systems

The noise performance of AM, DSB-SC, SSB, FM, and PCM systems is shown in Fig. 6-18 using the formulas given in Table 6-6.[†] For the nonlinear systems a bandwidth spreading ratio of $B_T/B = 12$ is chosen for system comparisons. This corresponds to a $\beta_f = 5$ for the FM systems cited in the figure (which corresponds to commercial FM broadcasting). Results for other values of B_T/B can also be plotted by using the equations in Table 6-6.

Referring to Fig. 6-18, some of the curves terminate on the left with a large black dot. This dot indicates that the $(S/N)_{out}$ for these systems deteriorates very rapidly (i.e., becomes much smaller) as $(S/N)_{baseband}$ is reduced below the corresponding value indicated by the dot. The (S/N) values at the dot are called the *threshold* values. That is, when these systems are operated for $(S/N)_{baseband}$ below the threshold, the receiver output is so noisy that it is almost unusable. This threshold effect occurs because *nonlinear modulation* and/or *nonlinear detection* is being used.

Note that, except for the "wasted" carrier power in AM, all of the linear modulation

---

[†] Single-tone sinusoidal modulation is assumed with 100% modulation for AM signaling ($m_{rms} = 1/\sqrt{2}$) and $m_{rms} = V_p/\sqrt{2}$ for FM signaling.

FIGURE 6-18 Comparison of the noise performance of analog systems.
Source: [Couch, 1993]

methods have the same S/N performance as that for the baseband system. (SSB has the same performance as DSB because the coherence of the two sidebands in DSB compensates for the half noise power in SSB due to bandwidth reduction.) These comparisons are made on the basis of signals with equal *average* powers. If comparisons are made on equal *peak* powers (i.e., equal peak values for the signals), then SSB has a $(S/N)_{out}$ that is 3 dB better than DSB and 9 dB better than AM with 100% modulation. Of course, when operating above threshold, all of the nonlinear modulation systems have better S/N performance than linear modulation systems because the nonlinear systems have larger transmission bandwidths.

Dolby and DBX Noise Reduction Systems

As described previously, preemphasis and deemphasis are used in FM broadcasting for noise reduction. They are also used in audiotape recording for noise reduction. Other,

TABLE 6-6 Noise Performance of Modulation Systems[a]

Type	Linearity	Transmission Bandwidth Required[b]	$\dfrac{(S/N)_{out}}{(S/N)_{baseband}}$	Comments
AM	L[c]	$2B$	$\dfrac{m_{rms}^2}{1 + m_{rms}^2}$	Valid for all $(S/N)_{in}$ with coherent detection; valid above threshold for envelope detection and $\|m(t)\| \leq 1$
DSB-SC	L	$2B$	1	Coherent detection required
SSB	L	B	1	Coherent detection required; performance identical to baseboard system
PM	NL	$2(\beta_p + 1)B$	$\beta_p^2\left(\dfrac{m_{rms}}{V_p}\right)^2$	Coherent detection required; valid for $(S/N)_{in}$ above threshold
FM	NL	$2(\beta_f + 1)B$	$3\beta_f^2\left(\dfrac{m_{rms}}{V_p}\right)^2$	Valid for $(S/N)_{in}$ above threshold
FM with deemphasis	NL	$2(\beta_f + 1)B$	$\beta^2\left(\dfrac{B}{f_1}\right)^2\left(\dfrac{m_{rms}}{V_p}\right)^2$	Valid for $(S/N)_{in}$ above threshold
PCM	NL	[d]	$M^2/(S/N)_{baseband}$	Valid for $(S/N)_{in}$ above threshold (i.e., $P_e \to 0$)

[a] B, absolute bandwidth of the modulating signal; f_1, 3-dB bandwidth of the deemphasis signal; L, linear; m_{rms} is the rms value of the modulating signal $m(t)$; $M = 2^n$, number of quantizing steps, where n is the number of bits in the PCM word; NL, nonlinear; V_p, peak value of $m(t)$; β_p, PM index; β_f, FM index.

[b] Typical bandwidth specifications by the International Telecommunications Union (ITU) are larger than these minima [Jordan, 1985].

[c] In the strict sense, AM signaling is not linear because of the carrier term (see Table 5-1).

[d] The bandwidth depends on the type of digital modulation used (e.g., OOK, FSK).

SOURCE: L. W. Couch, *Digital and Analog Communication Systems,* 4th ed., Macmillan, New York, 1993.

more sophisticated noise reduction techniques have been developed in addition to companding (see Fig. 4-10). This section will describe some of these techniques.

In audiocassette tape recording, noise occurs predominantly at the higher frequencies and is commonly called *hiss*. These noise reduction techniques use a combination of preemphasis filtering and dynamic range compression at the encoder before recording. The playback decoder circuit uses a combination of deemphasis and dynamic range expansion. If done properly, a high-quality audio signal can be recovered with low noise. However, if the encoder and decoders are not "matched," a "breathing" or "pumping" effect can result that can be more disturbing than the hiss on an unprocessed signal. Another disadvantage of these techniques is that if a tape with a processed signal is played back on a regular amplifier system without decoding, the reproduction is poor, with excessive high-frequency response.

Dolby Laboratories has developed a number of noise reduction techniques designated as Dolby-A, Dolby-B, and Dolby-C. *Dolby-A* is designed for commercial use and, consequently, is a relatively expensive system. The Dolby-A processor divides the audio spectrum into four frequency bands: low-pass, below 80 Hz; bandpass, 80 Hz to 3 kHz; high-pass, above 3 kHz; and high-pass, above 9 kHz. At the encoder, the gain in each of these bands is adaptively increased as the signal level in the associated band becomes lower. This provides an overall compression characteristic for the encoder. A maximum boost of 10 to 15 dB is used in each of the bands if the signal level is 45 dB below the maximum recording level (0 dB). For playback the decoder provides the appropriate expansion of the signal in each of the bands so that the overall frequency response is flat and the dynamic range of the original audio signal is preserved. If the recording and playback levels are properly set, the Dolby-A system provides a 10- to 15-dB increase in the signal-to-noise ratio.

The *Dolby-B* and *Dolby-C* systems are designed for consumer audio cassette and reel-to-reel tape recording. They are relatively inexpensive to implement and use a two-band instead of a four-band system, as in Dolby-A. As shown in Fig. 6-19, the Dolby-B encoder preemphasizes the higher frequencies and provides up to a 10-dB boost when the level in the high-frequency band is 45 dB below the reference level. The Dolby-C encoder provides as much as a 20-dB boost for the high-frequency components when their level is low. The Dolby-C encoder uses two cascaded stages of compression, one activated at high signal levels and another at low signal levels. Overall, the Dolby-B system reduces the tape hiss by about 10 dB for frequencies above 4 kHz, and the Dolby-C system reduces the

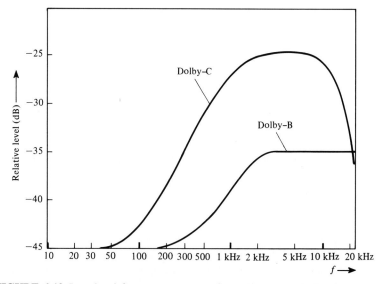

FIGURE 6-19 Low-level frequency response for Dolby-B and Dolby-C encoders.

hiss by about 20 dB for frequencies above 1 kHz. In FM broadcasting the Dolby-B system with a 6.6-kHz high-pass filter (25 μsec) is often used for additional signal-to-noise ratio improvement over the standard FM preemphasis–deemphasis system.

DBX, Inc. of Waltham, Massachusetts, has developed a noise reduction system that processes the whole audio signal in a single audio band. The *DBX system* uses voltage-controlled amplifiers with 130 dB of dynamic range at both the encoder and the decoder to provide the compression and expansion characteristics. The encoder also uses a 1.6-kHz preemphasis network that provides a 20-dB boost at the high end. The decoder has a matching deemphasis network. The DBX system provides a 20- to 30-dB signal-to-noise ratio improvement and can handle large signal overloads (above the 0-dB level) without distortion. This system has the disadvantage, however, of single band processing. That is, a large-level component located anywhere within the frequency band will control the compression level of the whole signal.

6-10 Summary

AM, PM, and FM signaling techniques were developed in detail. Single-sideband and vestigial sideband systems were also studied. The spectra of these bandpass signals were evaluated, and the transmission bandwidth was obtained. For example, in AM-type systems the transmission bandwidth is $B_T = 2B$, where B is the baseband bandwidth; and for FM-type systems, $B_T = 2(\Delta F + B)$, where ΔF is the peak frequency deviation of the carrier. Typical specifications for AM and FM broadcasting signals were also listed. Their noise performance was examined and compared with the performance of Shannon's ideal system.

In the next chapter we will use these tools to analyze a number of digital bandpass communication systems.

PROBLEMS

6-1 An AM broadcast transmitter is tested by feeding the RF output into a 50-Ω (dummy) load. Tone modulation is applied. The carrier frequency is 850 kHz and the FCC licensed power output is 5000 W. The sinusoidal tone of 1000 Hz is set for 90% modulation.

(a) Evaluate the FCC power in dBk (dB above 1 kW) units.

(b) Write an equation for the voltage that appears across the 50-Ω load, giving numerical values for all constants.

(c) Sketch the spectrum of this voltage as it would appear on a calibrated spectrum analyzer.

(d) What is the average power that is being dissipated in the dummy load?

(e) What is the peak envelope power?

6-2   An AM transmitter is modulated with an audio testing signal given by $m(t) = 0.2 \sin \omega_1 t + 0.5 \cos \omega_2 t$, where $f_1 = 500$ Hz, $f_2 = 500 \sqrt{2}$ Hz, and $A_c = 100$. Assume that the AM signal is fed into a 50-Ω load.
(a) Sketch the AM waveform.
(b) What is the modulation percentage?
(c) Evaluate and sketch the spectrum of the AM waveform.

6-3   For the AM signal given in Prob. 6-2:
(a) Evaluate the average power of the AM signal.
(b) Evaluate the PEP of the AM signal.

6-4   Assume that an AM transmitter is modulated with a video testing signal given by $m(t) = -0.2 + 0.6 \sin \omega_1 t$ where $f_1 = 3.57$ MHz. Let $A_c = 100$.
(a) Sketch the AM waveform.
(b) What is the percentage of positive and negative modulation?
(c) Evaluate and sketch the spectrum of the AM waveform about f_c.

6-5   A 50,000-W AM broadcast transmitter is being evaluated by means of a two-tone test. The transmitter is connected to a 50-Ω load and $m(t) = A_1 \cos \omega_1 t + A_1 \cos 2\omega_1 t$ where $f_1 = 500$ Hz. Assume that a perfect AM signal is generated.
(a) Evaluate the complex envelope for the AM signal in terms of A_1 and ω_1.
(b) Determine the value of A_1 for 90% modulation.
(c) Find the values for the peak current and average current into the 50-Ω load for the 90% modulation case.

6-6   An AM transmitter uses a two-quadrant multiplier so that the transmitted signal is described by (6-7). Assume that the transmitter is modulated by $m(t) = A_m \cos \omega_m t$, where A_m is adjusted so that 120% positive modulation is obtained. Evaluate the spectrum of this AM signal in terms of A_c, f_c, and f_m. Sketch your result.

6-7   A DSB-SC signal is modulated by $m(t) = \cos \omega_1 t + 2 \cos 2\omega_1 t$ where $\omega_1 = 2\pi f_1$, $f_1 = 500$ Hz, and $A_c = 1$.
(a) Write an expression for the DSB-SC signal and sketch a picture of this waveform.
(b) Evaluate and sketch the spectrum for this DSB-SC signal.
(c) Find the value of the average (normalized) power.
(d) Find the value of the PEP (normalized).

6-8   Assume that transmitting circuitry restricts the modulated output signal to a certain peak value, say A_P, because of power-supply voltages that are used and the peak voltage and current ratings of the components. If a DSB-SC signal with a peak value of A_P is generated by this circuit, show that the sideband power of this DSB-SC signal is four times the sideband power of a comparable AM signal having the same peak value, A_P, that could also be generated by this circuit.

6-9   A DSB-SC signal can be generated from two AM signals as shown in Fig. P6-9. Using mathematics to describe signals at each point on the figure, prove that the output is a DSB-SC signal.

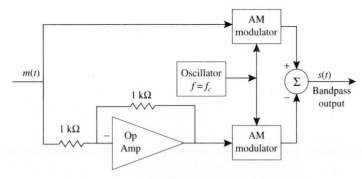

FIGURE P6-9

6-10 Show that the complex envelope $g(t) = m(t) - j\hat{m}(t)$ produces a lower SSB signal, provided that $m(t)$ is a real signal.

6-11 Show that the impulse response of a $-90°$ phase shift network (i.e., a Hilbert transformer) is $1/\pi t$. *Hint:*

$$H(f) = \lim_{\substack{\alpha \to 0 \\ \alpha > 0}} \begin{cases} -je^{-\alpha f}, & f > 0 \\ je^{\alpha f}, & f < 0 \end{cases}$$

6-12 SSB signals can be generated by the phasing method, Fig. 6-5a; the filter method, Fig. 6-5b; or by the use of Weaver's method as shown in Fig. P6-12. For Weaver's method (Fig. P6-12) where B is the bandwidth of $m(t)$:
   (a) Find a mathematical expression that describes the waveform out of each block on the block diagram.
   (b) Show that $s(t)$ is an SSB signal.

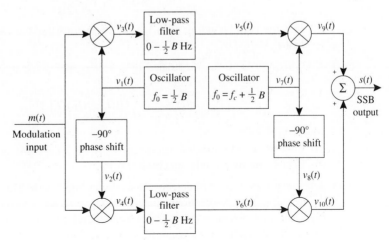

FIGURE P6-12 Weaver's method for generating SSB.

6-13 An SSB-AM transmitter is modulated with a sinusoid $m(t) = 5 \cos \omega_1 t$, where $\omega_1 = 2\pi f_1$, $f_1 = 500$ Hz, and $A_c = 1$.
(a) Evaluate $\hat{m}(t)$.
(b) Find the expression for a lower SSB signal.
(c) Find the rms value of the SSB signal.
(d) Find the peak value of the SSB signal.
(e) Find the normalized average power of the SSB signal.
(f) Find the normalized PEP of the SSB signal.

6-14 An SSB-AM transmitter is modulated by a rectangular pulse such that $m(t) = \Pi(t/T)$ and $A_c = 1$.
(a) Prove that

$$\hat{m}(t) = \frac{1}{\pi} \ln \left| \frac{2t + T}{2t - T} \right|$$

as given in Table A-7.
(b) Find an expression for the SSB-AM signal, $s(t)$, and sketch $s(t)$.
(c) Find the peak value of $s(t)$.

6-15 For Prob. 6-14:
(a) Find the expression for the spectrum of a USSB-AM signal.
(b) Sketch the magnitude spectrum, $|S(f)|$.

6-16 A USSB transmitter is modulated with the pulse

$$m(t) = \frac{\sin \pi a t}{\pi a t}$$

where the first zero crossing occurs at $1/a$ sec.
(a) Prove that

$$\hat{m}(t) = \frac{\sin^2[(\pi a/2)t]}{(\pi a/2)t}$$

(b) Plot the corresponding USSB signal waveform for the case of $A_c = 1$, $a = 2$, and $f_c = 20$ Hz.

6-17 A USSB-AM signal is modulated by a rectangular pulse train:

$$m(t) = \sum_{n=-\infty}^{\infty} \Pi[(t - nT_0)/T]$$

where $T_0 = 2T$.
(a) Find the expression for the spectrum of the SSB-AM signal.
(b) Sketch the magnitude spectrum, $|S(f)|$.

6-18 A phasing-type SSB-AM detector is shown in Fig. P6-18. This circuit is attached to the IF output of a conventional superheterodyne receiver to provide SSB reception.
(a) Determine whether this detector is sensitive to LSSB or USSB signals. How would the detector be changed to receive SSB signals with alternate (opposite type of) sidebands?

FIGURE P6-18

(b) Assume that the signal at point *A* is a USSB signal with $f_c = 455$ kHz. Find the mathematical expressions for the signals at points *B* through *I*.

(c) Repeat part (b) for the case of an LSSB-AM signal at point *A*.

(d) Discuss the IF and LP filter requirements if the SSB signal at point *A* has a 3-kHz bandwidth.

6-19 Can a Costas loop, as shown in Fig. 6-3, be used to demodulate an SSB-AM signal? Demonstrate that your answer is correct by using mathematics.

6-20 A modulated signal is described by the equation

$$s(t) = 10 \cos[(2\pi \times 10^8)\, t + 10 \cos(2\pi \times 10^3 t)]$$

Find each of the following.

(a) Percentage of AM.

(b) Normalized power of the modulated signal.

(c) Maximum phase deviation.

(d) Maximum frequency deviation.

6-21 A sinusoidal signal, $m(t) = \cos 2\pi f_m t$, is the input to an angle-modulated transmitter where the carrier frequency is $f_c = 1$ Hz and $f_m = f_c/4$.

(a) Plot $m(t)$ and the corresponding PM signal where $D_p = \pi$.

(b) Plot $m(t)$ and the corresponding FM signal where $D_f = \pi$.

6-22 A sinusoidal modulating waveform of amplitude 4 V and a frequency of 1 kHz is applied to an FM exciter that has a modulator gain of 50 Hz/V.

(a) What is the peak frequency deviation?

(b) What is the modulation index?

6-23 An FM signal has sinusoidal modulation with a frequency of $f_m = 15$ kHz and modulation index of $\beta = 2.0$.

(a) Find the transmission bandwidth using Carson's rule.

(b) What percentage of the total FM signal power lies within the Carson rule bandwidth?

6-24 An FM transmitter has a block diagram as shown in Fig. P6-24. The audio-frequency response is flat over the 20-Hz to 15-kHz audio band. The FM output signal is to have a carrier frequency of 103.7 MHz and a peak deviation of 75 kHz.
(a) Find the bandwidth and center frequency required for the bandpass filter.
(b) Calculate the frequency f_0 of the oscillator.
(c) What is the required peak deviation capability of the FM exciter?

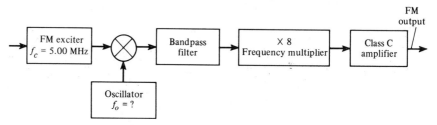

FIGURE P6-24

6-25 Analyze the performance of the FM circuit of Fig. 6-8b. Assume that the voltage appearing across the reversed-biased diodes, which provide the voltage variable capacitance, is $v(t) = 5 + 0.05m(t)$, where the modulating signal is a test tone, $m(t) = \cos \omega_1 t$, $\omega_1 = 2\pi f_1$, and $f_1 = 1$ kHz. The capacitance of each of the biased diodes is $C_d = 100/\sqrt{1 + 2v(t)}$ pF. Assume that $C_0 = 180$ pF and that L is chosen to resonate at 5 MHz.
(a) Find the value of L.
(b) Show that the resulting oscillator signal is an FM signal. For convenience, assume that the peak level of the oscillator signal is 10 V. Find the parameter D_f.

6-26 A modulated RF waveform is given by $500 \cos[\omega_c t + 20 \cos \omega_1 t]$, where $\omega_1 = 2\pi f_1$, $f_1 = 1$ kHz, and $f_c = 100$ MHz.
(a) If the phase deviation constant is 100 rad/V, find the mathematical expression for the corresponding phase modulation voltage $m(t)$. What is its peak value and its frequency?
(b) If the frequency deviation constant is 1×10^6 rad/V-sec, find the mathematical expression for the corresponding FM voltage, $m(t)$. What is its peak value and its frequency?
(c) If the RF waveform appears across a 50-Ω load, determine the average power and the PEP.

6-27 Given the FM signal $s(t) = 10 \cos [\omega_c t + 100 \int_{-\infty}^{t} m(\sigma) \, d\sigma]$, where $m(t)$ is a polar square-wave signal with a duty cycle of 50%, a period of 1 sec, and a peak value of 5 V.
(a) Sketch the instantaneous frequency waveform and the waveform of the corresponding FM signal (see Fig. 6-9).
(b) Plot the phase deviation $\theta(t)$ as a function of time.
(c) Evaluate the peak frequency deviation.

6-28 A carrier $s(t) = 100 \cos(2\pi \times 10^9 t)$ of an FM transmitter is modulated with a tone signal. For this transmitter a 1-V (rms) tone produces a deviation of 30 kHz. Determine the amplitude and frequency of all FM signal components (spectral lines) that are greater than 1% of the unmodulated carrier amplitude for the following modulating signals:
   (a) $m(t) = 2.5 \cos(3\pi \times 10^4 t)$.
   (b) $m(t) = 1 \cos(6\pi \times 10^4 t)$.

6-29 Referring to (6-58), show that

$$J_{-n}(\beta) = (-1)^n J_n(\beta)$$

6-30 Consider an FM exciter with the output $s(t) = 100 \cos[2\pi 1000t + \theta(t)]$. The modulation is $m(t) = 5 \cos(2\pi 8t)$ and the modulation gain of the exciter is 8 Hz/V. The FM output signal is passed through an ideal (brick-wall) bandpass filter which has a center frequency of 1000 Hz, a bandwidth of 56 Hz, and a gain of unity. Determine the normalized average power:
   (a) At the bandpass filter input.
   (b) At the bandpass filter output.

6-31 A 1-kHz sinusoidal signal phase modulates a carrier at 146.52 MHz with a peak phase deviation of 45°. Evaluate the exact magnitude spectra of the PM signal if $A_c = 1$. Sketch your result. Using Carson's rule, evaluate the approximate bandwidth of the PM signal and see if it is a reasonable number when compared with your spectral plot.

6-32 A 1-kHz sinusoidal signal frequency modulates a carrier at 146.52 MHz with a peak deviation of 5 kHz. Evaluate the exact magnitude spectra of the FM signal if $A_c = 1$. Sketch your result. Using Carson's rule, evaluate the approximate bandwidth of the FM signal and see if it is a reasonable number when compared with your spectral plot.

6-33 The calibration of a frequency deviation monitor is to be verified by using a Bessel function test. An FM test signal with a calculated frequency deviation is generated by frequency modulating a sine wave onto a carrier. Assume that the sine wave has a frequency of 2 kHz and that the amplitude of the sine wave is slowly increased from zero until the discrete carrier term (at f_c) of the FM signal reduces to zero, as observed on a spectrum analyzer. What is the peak frequency deviation of the FM test signal when the discrete carrier term is zero? Suppose that the amplitude of the sine wave is increased further until this discrete carrier term appears, reaches a maximum, and then disappears again. What is the peak frequency deviation of the FM test signal now?

6-34 A frequency modulator has a modulator gain of 10 Hz/V and the modulating waveform is

$$m(t) = \begin{cases} 0, & t < 0 \\ 5, & 0 < t < 1 \\ 15, & 1 < t < 3 \\ 7, & 3 < t < 4 \\ 0, & 4 < t \end{cases}$$

(a) Plot the frequency deviation in hertz over the time interval $0 < t < 5$.

(b) Plot the phase deviation in radians over the time interval $0 < t < 5$.

6-35 A square-wave (digital) test signal of 50% duty cycle phase modulates a transmitter where $s(t) = 10 \cos[\omega_c t + \theta(t)]$. The carrier frequency is 60 MHz and the peak phase deviation is 45°. Assume that the test signal is of the unipolar NRZ type with a period of 1 msec and that it is symmetrical about $t = 0$. Find the exact spectrum for $s(t)$.

6-36 Two sinusoids, $m(t) = A_1 \cos \omega_1 t + A_2 \cos \omega_2 t$, phase modulate a transmitter. Derive a formula that gives the exact spectrum for the resulting PM signal in terms of the signal parameters A_c, ω_c, D_p, A_1, A_2, ω_1, and ω_2. [*Hint:* Use $e^{ja(t)} = (e^{ja_1(t)})(e^{ja_2(t)})$, where $a(t) = a_1(t) + a_2(t)$.]

6-37 Plot the magnitude spectrum centered on $f = f_c$ for an FM signal where the modulating signal is

$$m(t) = A_1 \cos 2\pi f_1 t + A_2 \cos 2\pi f_2 t$$

Assume that $f_1 = 10$ Hz, $f_2 = 17$ Hz, and that A_1 and A_2 are adjusted so that each tone contributes a peak deviation of 20 Hz.

6-38 For small values of β, $J_n(\beta)$ can be approximated by $J_n(\beta) = \beta^n/(2^n n!)$. Show that for the case of FM with sinusoidal modulation, $\beta = 0.2$ is sufficiently small to give NBFM.

6-39 A polar square wave with a 50% duty cycle frequency modulates an NBFM transmitter such that the peak phase deviation is 10°. Assume that the square wave has a peak value of 5 V, a period of 10 msec, and a zero-crossing at $t = 0$ with a positive-going slope.

(a) Determine the peak frequency deviation of this NBFM signal.

(b) Evaluate and sketch the spectrum of this signal, using the narrowband analysis technique. Assume that the carrier frequency is 30 MHz.

6-40 Design a wideband FM transmitter that uses the indirect method for generating a WBFM signal. Assume that the carrier frequency of the WBFM signal is 96.9 MHz and that the transmitter is capable of producing a high-quality FM signal with a peak deviation of 75 kHz when modulated by a 1-V (rms) sinusoid of frequency 20 Hz. Show a complete block diagram of your design, indicating the frequencies and peak deviations of the signals at various points.

6-41 An FM signal, $100 \cos[\omega_c t + D_f \int_{-\infty}^{t} m(\sigma)\, d\sigma]$, is modulated by the waveform shown in Fig. P6-41. Let $f_c = 420$ MHz.

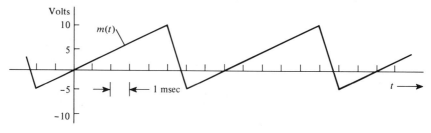

FIGURE P6-41

(a) Determine the value of D_f so that the peak-to-peak frequency deviation is 25 kHz.

(b) Evaluate and sketch the approximate PSD.

(c) Determine the bandwidth of this FM signal such that spectral components are down at least 40 dB from the unmodulated carrier level for frequencies outside this bandwidth.

6-42 A multilevel digital test signal as shown in Fig. P6-42 modulates a WBFM transmitter. Evaluate and sketch the approximate power spectrum of this WBFM signal if $A_c = 5$, $f_c = 2$ GHz, and $D_f = 10^5$.

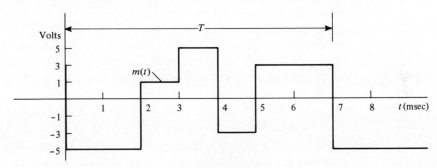

FIGURE P6-42

6-43 Refer to Fig. 6-15b, which displays the circuit diagram for a commonly used preemphasis filter network.

(a) Show that $f_1 = 1/(2\pi R_1 C)$.

(b) Show that $f_2 = (R_1 + R_2)/(2\pi R_1 R_2 C) \approx 1/(2\pi R_2 C)$.

(c) Evaluate K in terms of R_1, R_2, and C.

6-44 The composite baseband signal for FM stereo transmission is given by

$$m_b(t) = [m_L(t) + m_R(t)] + [m_L(t) - m_R(t)] \cos(\omega_{sc}t) + K \cos(\tfrac{1}{2}\omega_{sc}t)$$

A stereo FM receiver using a switching type of demultiplexer for recovery of $m_L(t)$ and $m_R(t)$ is shown in Fig. P6-44.

FIGURE P6-44

(a) Determine the switching waveforms at points C and D that activate the analog switches. Be sure to specify the correct phasing for each one. Sketch these waveforms.

(b) Draw a more detailed block diagram showing the blocks inside the PLL.

(c) Write equations for the waveforms at points A through F and explain how this circuit works by sketching typical waveforms at each of these points.

6-45 In a communication system two baseband signals (they may be analog or digital) are transmitted simultaneously by generating the RF signal

$$s(t) = m_1(t) \cos \omega_c t + m_2(t) \sin \omega_c t$$

The carrier frequency is 7.250 MHz. The bandwidth of $m_1(t)$ is 5 kHz and the bandwidth of $m_2(t)$ is 10 kHz.

(a) Evaluate the bandwidth of $s(t)$.

(b) Derive an equation for the spectrum of $s(t)$ in terms of $M_1(f)$ and $M_2(f)$.

(c) $m_1(t)$ and $m_2(t)$ can be recovered (i.e., detected) from $s(t)$ by using a superheterodyne receiver with two switching detectors. Draw a block diagram for the receiver and sketch the digital waveforms that are required to operate the samplers. Describe how they can be obtained. Show that the Nyquist sampling criterion is satisfied. (*Hint:* See Fig. P6-44.)

6-46 A FM broadcast receiver is designed to receive an FM signal with specifications as described in Table 6-5. If the output signal-to-noise ratio is to be 50 dB for the case of a sinusoidal test-tone modulating signal and the PSD of the input noise is $\mathcal{P}(f) = N_0/2 = 8 \times 10^{-21}$ W/Hz:

(a) Find the signal-to-noise ratio required at the receiver input.

(b) Find the FM signal voltage (in microvolts, rms) required at the 300-Ω antenna input of the receiver.

(*Note:* As developed in Chapter 8, the noise PSD of 8×10^{-21} W/Hz is used to simulate a receiver with an overall noise-figure specification of 6 dB as shown by the use of (8-15) with $T = 290$ K.)

6-47 Suppose that a low-level audio signal that has a flat spectrum from 30 Hz to 20 kHz is tape recorded using Dolby-B preemphasis.

(a) Sketch the spectrum of the Dolby-B preemphasized signal.

(b) If the recording is mistakenly played back on a machine using Dolby-C deemphasis, sketch the spectrum of the signal played back.

(*Hint:* Use Fig. 6-19.)

Bandpass Digital Signaling

Bandpass digital signaling consists of modulating a *baseband* digital signal onto a carrier using AM, PM, and FM as described in Chapter 6 (or some other type of modulation as described in Chapter 5). In particular, the bandpass signal can be described by

$$s(t) = \text{Re}\{g(t)e^{j\omega_c t}\} \tag{7-1}$$

where $\omega_c = 2\pi f_c$ and f_c is the carrier frequency. Using a selected modulation mapping function $g[m(t)]$, this bandpass signal will be a *digital* bandpass signal when the complex envelope, $g(t)$, of Chapters 5 and 6 is generated by using a *digital* baseband signal, $m(t)$, of Chapter 4. From (5-13), the resulting PSD for the digital bandpass signal is

$$\mathcal{P}_s(f) = \tfrac{1}{4}[\mathcal{P}_g(f - f_c) + \mathcal{P}_g(-f - f_c)] \tag{7-2}$$

where $\mathcal{P}_g$ is the PSD of the complex envelope.

The goals of this chapter are to:

- Study $g(t)$ and, consequently, $s(t)$, for various types of digital signaling.
- Evaluate $\mathcal{P}_s(f)$ for various types of digital signaling.
- Examine receiver structures for bandpass digital signals.
- Compare the spectral efficiency of several different bandpass digital systems.
- Compare the noise performance (probability of bit error) for many different bandpass digital systems.
- Learn about spread spectrum systems.

7-1 Binary Signaling

The most common binary bandpass signaling techniques are illustrated in Fig. 7-1. They are

- *On–off keying* (OOK), also called *amplitude shift keying* (ASK), which consists of keying (switching) a carrier sinusoid on and off with a unipolar binary signal. It is

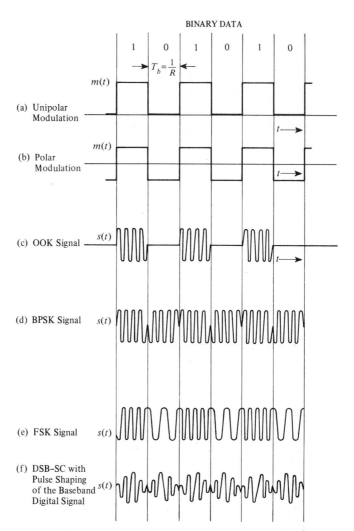

FIGURE 7-1 Bandpass digitally modulated signals.

identical to *unipolar* binary modulation on a DSB-SC signal, (6-13). Morse code radio transmission is an example of this technique. Consequently, OOK was one of the first modulation techniques to be used and precedes analog communication systems.

• *Binary-phase shift keying* (BPSK), which consists of shifting the phase of a sinusoidal carrier 0° or 180° with a unipolar binary signal. It is equivalent to PM signaling with a digital waveform and is also equivalent to modulating a DSB-SC signal with a polar digital waveform.

• *Frequency-shift keying* (FSK), which consists of shifting the frequency of a sinusoidal carrier from a mark frequency (corresponding, for example, to sending a binary 1) to a space frequency (corresponding to sending a binary 0) according to the baseband digital signal. It is identical to modulating a FM carrier with a binary digital signal.

As indicated in Sec. 4-5, usually the bandwidth of the digital signal needs to be minimized to achieve spectral conservation as one transmits information over a channel. This may be accomplished by using a premodulation raised cosine-rolloff filter to minimize the bandwidth of the digital signal and yet not introduce ISI. The shaping of the baseband digital signal produces an analog baseband waveform that modulates the transmitter. Figure 7-1f illustrates the resulting DSB-SC signal when a premodulation filter is used. Thus the BPSK signal of Fig. 7-1d becomes a DSB-SC signal (Fig. 7-1f) when premodulation filtering is used.

On–Off Keying (OOK)

The OOK signal is represented by

$$s(t) = A_c m(t) \cos \omega_c t \tag{7-3}$$

where $m(t)$ is a unipolar baseband data signal, as shown in Fig. 7-1a. Consequently, the complex envelope is simply

$$g(t) = A_c m(t) \qquad \text{for OOK} \tag{7-4}$$

and the PSD of this complex envelope is proportional to that for the unipolar signal. Using (4-35), we find that this PSD is

$$\mathscr{P}_g(f) = \frac{A_c^2}{2} \left[\delta(f) + T_b \left(\frac{\sin \pi f T_b}{\pi f T_b} \right)^2 \right] \qquad \text{for OOK} \tag{7-5}$$

where $m(t)$ has a peak value of $\sqrt{2}$ so that $s(t)$ has an average normalized power of $A_c^2/2$. The PSD for the corresponding OOK signal is then obtained by substituting (7-5) into (7-2). The result is shown for positive frequencies in Fig. 7-2a, where $R = 1/T_b$ is the bit rate. It is seen that the null-to-null bandwidth is $2R$. That is, the transmission bandwidth of the OOK signal is $B_T = 2B$ where B is the baseband bandwidth since OOK is AM-type signaling.

If raised cosine-rolloff filtering is used (to conserve bandwidth), the absolute bandwidth of the filtered binary signal is related to the bit rate R by (4-74), where $D = R$ for binary digital signaling. Thus

$$B = \tfrac{1}{2}(1 + r)R \tag{7-6}$$

where r is the rolloff factor of the filter. This gives an absolute transmission bandwidth of

$$B_T = (1 + r)R \tag{7-7}$$

for OOK signaling.

OOK may be detected using either an envelope detector (noncoherent detection) or a product detector (coherent detection) since it is a form of AM signaling. (In radio-frequency receiver applications where the input RF signal is very small, a superheterodyne receiver circuit of Fig. 5-28 is used where one of these detector circuits are placed after the IF output stage.) These detectors are shown in Figs. 7-3a and b. For product detection the

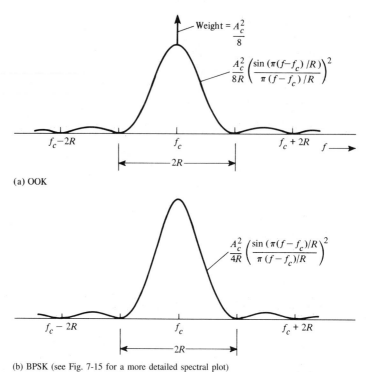

(a) OOK

(b) BPSK (see Fig. 7-15 for a more detailed spectral plot)

FIGURE 7-2 PSD of bandpass digital signals (positive frequencies shown).

carrier reference, $\cos \omega_c t$, must be provided. This is usually obtained from a phase-locked-loop (PLL) circuit (studied in Sec. 5-14) where the PLL is locked onto the discrete carrier term (see Fig. 7-2a) of the OOK signal.

For optimum detection of OOK—that is, to obtain the lowest probability of bit error when the input OOK signal is corrupted by additive white Gaussian noise (AWGN)—product detection with matched filter processing is required. This is shown in Fig. 7-3c, where waveforms at various points of the circuit are illustrated for the case of receiving an OOK signal that corresponds to the binary data stream 1101. This matched filter circuit is the implementation of (4-47) for the case of data with rectangular pulse shapes (as shown in Fig. 7-1a). Because of this circuit realization of (4-47), this matched filter is also called an *integrate-and-dump* filter. Note that the matched filter also requires a clocking signal that is used to reset the integrator at the beginning of each bit interval and to clock the sample-and-hold circuit at the end of each bit interval. This clock signal is provided by a bit synchronizer circuit (studied in Chapter 4).

Obviously, the optimum coherent OOK detector of Fig. 7-3c is more costly to implement than the noncoherent OOK detector of Fig. 7-3a. If the input noise is small, the noncoherent receiver may be the best solution considering both cost and noise performance. The trade-off in probability of bit error performance between optimum coherent and noncoherent detection will be studied in Sec. 7-4.

(a) Noncoherent Detection

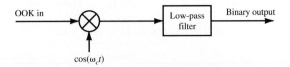

(b) Coherent Detection with Low-Pass Filter Processing

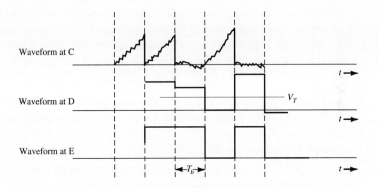

(c) Coherent Detection with Matched Filter Processing

FIGURE 7-3 Detection of OOK.

Binary-Phase Shift Keying (BPSK)

The BPSK signal is represented by

$$s(t) = A_c \cos[\omega_c t + D_p m(t)] \qquad (7\text{-}8a)$$

where $m(t)$ is a polar baseband data signal. For convenience, let $m(t)$ have peak values of ± 1 and a rectangle pulse shape.

It will now be shown that BPSK is also a form of AM-type signaling. Expanding (7-8a), we get

$$s(t) = A_c \cos(D_p m(t)) \cos \omega_c t - A_c \sin(D_p m(t)) \sin \omega_c t$$

Recalling that $m(t)$ has values of ± 1 and that $\cos(x)$ and $\sin(x)$ are even and odd functions of x, the representation of the BPSK signal reduces to

$$s(t) = \underbrace{(A_c \cos D_p) \cos \omega_c t}_{\text{pilot carrier term}} - \underbrace{(A_c \sin D_p) m(t) \sin \omega_c t}_{\text{data term}} \qquad (7\text{-}8\text{b})$$

The level of the pilot carrier term is set by the value chosen for the peak deviation, $\Delta\theta = D_p$.

For digital angle modulated signals, the *digital modulation index, h,* is defined by

$$h = \frac{2\Delta\theta}{\pi} \qquad (7\text{-}9)$$

where $2\Delta\theta$ is the maximum peak-to-peak phase deviation (radians) during the time required to send one symbol, T_s. For binary signaling, the symbol time is equal to the bit time, $T_s = T_b$.

The level of the pilot carrier term is set by the value of the peak deviation, which is $\Delta\theta = D_p$ for $m(t) = \pm 1$. If D_p is small, the pilot carrier term has a relatively large amplitude compared to the data term; consequently, there is very little power in the data term (which contains the source information). To maximize the signaling efficiency (low probability of error), the power in the data term needs to be maximized. This is accomplished by letting $\Delta\theta = D_p = 90° = \pi/2$ radians, which corresponds to a digital modulation index of $h = 1$. For this optimum case of $h = 1$, the BPSK signal becomes

$$s(t) = -A_c m(t) \sin \omega_c t \qquad (7\text{-}10)$$

and there is no pilot carrier term. Throughout this text, we will assume that $\Delta\theta = 90°$, $h = 1$, is used for BPSK signaling (unless otherwise stated). Equation (7-10) shows that BPSK is equivalent to DSB-SC signaling with a polar baseband data waveform. The complex envelope for this BPSK signal is

$$g(t) = jA_c m(t) \qquad \text{for BPSK} \qquad (7\text{-}11)$$

Using (4-37), we obtain the PSD for the complex envelope,

$$\mathcal{P}_g(f) = A_c^2 T_b \left(\frac{\sin \pi f T_b}{\pi f T_b} \right)^2 \qquad \text{for BPSK} \qquad (7\text{-}12)$$

where $m(t)$ has values of ± 1 so that $s(t)$ has an average normalized power of $A_c^2/2$. The PSD for the corresponding BPSK signal is readily evaluated by translating the baseband spectrum to the carrier frequency, as specified by substituting (7-12) into (7-2). The resulting BPSK spectrum is shown in Fig. 7-2b. The null-to-null bandwidth for BPSK is also $2R$, the same as that found for OOK.

To detect BPSK, synchronous detection must be used, as illustrated in Fig. 7-4a. Since there is no discrete carrier term in the BPSK signal, a PLL may be used to extract the carrier reference *only* if a low-level pilot carrier is transmitted together with this BPSK signal. Otherwise, a Costas loop or a squaring loop (Fig. 6-3) may be used to synthesize

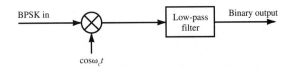

(a) Detection of BPSK (Coherent Detection)

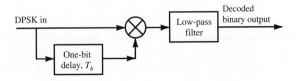

(b) Detection of DPSK (Partially Coherent Detection)

FIGURE 7-4 Detection of BPSK and DPSK.

the carrier reference from this DSB-SC (i.e., BPSK) signal and to provide coherent detection. However, the 180° phase ambiguity must be resolved as discussed in Sec. 6-4. This can be accomplished by using differential coding at the transmitter input and differential decoding at the receiver output, as illustrated previously in Fig. 4-13.

For optimum detection of BPSK (i.e., lowest probability of error for the case of AWGN) the low-pass filter in Fig. 7-4a is replaced by an integrate-and-dump matched filter processing that was illustrated in Fig. 7-3c, where V_T is set to zero volts for the case of BPSK. The resulting probability of bit error is given in Sec. 7-4.

Differential Phase-Shift Keying (DPSK)

Phase-shift-keyed signals cannot be detected incoherently. However, a partially coherent technique can be used whereby the phase reference for the present signaling interval is provided by a delayed version of the signal that occurred during the previous signaling interval. This is illustrated by the receiver shown in Fig. 7-4b, where differential decoding is provided by the (one-bit) delay and the multiplier. Consequently, if the data on a BPSK signal are differentially encoded (e.g., see the illustration in Table 4-3), the *decoded* data sequence will be recovered at the output of this receiver. This signaling technique consisting of transmitting a differentially encoded BPSK signal is known as *differential phase-shift keying* (DPSK).

For optimum detection of DPSK the low-pass filter of Fig. 7-4b is replaced by an integrate-and-dump matched filter and the DPSK input signal needs to be prefiltered by a bandpass filter that has an impulse response of $h(t) = \Pi[(t - 0.5T_b)/T_b]\cos\omega_c t$. For more details about this optimum receiver, see Chapters 7 and 8 of [Couch, 1993]. The resulting probability of bit error is given in Sec. 7-4.

In practice DPSK is often used instead of BPSK because the DPSK receiver does not require a carrier synchronizer circuit. An example is the Bell 212A modem (1200 bits/sec) that is described in Appendix C, Table C-13.

Frequency-Shift Keying (FSK)

The FSK signal can be characterized as one of two different types, depending on the method used to generate the FSK signal. One type is generated by switching the transmitter output line between two different oscillators, as shown in Fig. 7-5a. This type generates an output waveform that is discontinuous at the switching times. It is called *discontinuous-phase FSK* since $\theta(t)$ is discontinuous at the switching times. The discontinuous-phase FSK signal is represented by

$$s(t) = \begin{cases} A_c \cos(\omega_1 t + \theta_1), & \text{for } t \text{ in the time interval when a binary} \\ & \quad 1 \text{ is being sent} \\ A_c \cos(\omega_2 t + \theta_2), & \text{for } t \text{ in the time interval when a binary} \\ & \quad 0 \text{ is sent} \end{cases} \tag{7-13}$$

where f_1 is called the *mark* (binary 1) frequency and f_2 is called the *space* (binary 0) frequency. Since FSK transmitters are not usually built this way, we will turn to the second type, shown in Fig. 7-5b.

The *continuous-phase FSK* signal is generated by feeding the data signal into a frequency modulator, as shown in Fig. 7-5b. This FSK signal is represented by (referring to Sec. 6-6)

$$s(t) = A_c \cos\left[\omega_c t + D_f \int_{-\infty}^{t} m(\lambda)\, d\lambda \right]$$

or

$$s(t) = \text{Re}\{g(t)e^{j\omega_c t}\} \tag{7-14a}$$

(a) Discontinuous–Phase FSK

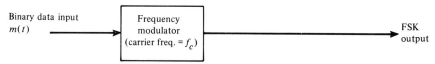

(b) Continous–Phase FSK

FIGURE 7-5 Generation of FSK.

where

$$g(t) = A_c e^{j\theta(t)} \tag{7-14b}$$

$$\theta(t) = D_f \int_{-\infty}^{t} m(\lambda)\, d\lambda \qquad \text{for FSK} \tag{7-14c}$$

and $m(t)$ is a baseband digital signal. Although $m(t)$ is discontinuous at the switching time, the phase function $\theta(t)$ is continuous because $\theta(t)$ is proportional to the integral of $m(t)$. If the serial data input waveform is binary, such as a polar baseband signal, the resulting FSK signal is called a *binary FSK* signal. Of course, a multilevel input signal would produce a multilevel FSK signal. We will assume that the input is a binary signal in this section and examine the properties of binary FSK signals.

In general, the spectra of FSK signals are difficult to evaluate since the complex envelope, $g(t)$, is a nonlinear function of $m(t)$. However, the techniques that were developed in Sec. 6-6 are applicable, as we show in the following example.

Example 7-1 Spectrum of the Bell-Type 103 FSK Modem

Keyboard-type computer terminals are often used for communication with a remote computer via analog dial-up telephone lines. *Dial-up* means that the computer terminal user calls the computer facility on a telephone and uses the telephone connection for data communication. To accomplish this, modems (i.e., a modulator and a demodulator) are connected to the phone line at each end, either by direct hardwire connection or by acoustical coupling with the telephone handset. This is illustrated in Fig. 7-6 with an FSK-type modem. (In Appendix C, specifications are also given for modems with other types of modulation.) The Bell Telephone System was the first to adopt this technique, with their Model 103 modem, which uses FSK with a signaling speed of 300 bits/sec. Each modem contains both an FSK transmitter and an FSK receiver so that the computer terminal can both "talk" and "listen." Two FSK frequency bands are used (one around 1 kHz and another around 2 kHz) so that it is possible to talk and listen simultaneously. This is called *full-duplex capability.* (In *half-duplex* one cannot listen while talking, and vice versa; in *simplex* one can only talk or only listen.) The standard mark and space frequencies for the

FIGURE 7-6 Computer communication using FSK signaling.

TABLE 7-1 Mark and Space Frequencies for the Bell-Type 103 Modem

	Originate Modem	Answer Modem
Transmit frequencies		
Mark (binary 1)	$f_1 = 1270$ Hz	$f_1 = 2225$ Hz
Space (binary 0)	$f_2 = 1070$ Hz	$f_2 = 2025$ Hz
Receive frequencies		
Mark (binary 1)	$f_1 = 2225$ Hz	$f_1 = 1270$ Hz
Space (binary 0)	$f_2 = 2025$ Hz	$f_2 = 1070$ Hz

two bands are shown in Table 7-1. From this table it is seen that the peak-to-peak deviation is $2\Delta F = 200$ Hz.

The spectrum for a Bell-type 103 modem will now be evaluated for the case of the widest-bandwidth FSK signal. It is obtained when the input data signal consists of a (periodic) square wave corresponding to an alternating data pattern (i.e., 10101010). This is illustrated in Fig. 7-7a, where T_b is the time interval for

(a) Baseband Modulating Signal

(b) Corresponding Phase Function

FIGURE 7-7 Input data signal and FSK signal phase function.

one bit and $T_0 = 2T_b$ is the period of the data modulation. The spectrum is obtained by using the Fourier series technique developed in Sec. 6-6 and Example 6-2. Since the modulation is periodic, we would expect the FSK spectrum to be a line spectrum (i.e., delta functions). Using (7-14c) and (6-42), we find that the peak frequency deviation is $\Delta F = D_f/(2\pi)$ for $m(t)$ having values of ± 1. This results in the triangular phase function shown in Fig. 7-7b. From this figure the digital modulation index is

$$h = \frac{2\Delta\theta}{\pi} = \Delta F T_0 = \frac{2\Delta F}{R} \qquad (7\text{-}15)$$

where the bit rate is $R = 1/T_b = 2/T_0$. In this application, note that the digital modulation index as given by (7-15) is identical to the FM modulation index as defined by (6-48) since

$$h = \frac{\Delta F}{1/T_0} = \frac{\Delta F}{B} = \beta_f$$

provided that the bandwidth of $m(t)$ is defined as $B = 1/T_0$.

The Fourier series for the complex envelope is

$$g(t) = \sum_{-\infty}^{\infty} c_n e^{jn\omega_0 t} \qquad (7\text{-}16)$$

where

$$\begin{aligned} c_n &= \frac{A_c}{T_0} \int_{-T_0/2}^{T_0/2} e^{j\theta(t)} e^{-jn\omega_0 t}\, dt \\ &= \frac{A_c}{T_0} \left[\int_{-T_0/4}^{T_0/4} e^{j\Delta\omega t - jn\omega_0 t}\, dt + \int_{T_0/4}^{3T_0/4} e^{-j\Delta\omega(t-(T_0/2))} e^{-jn\omega_0 t}\, dt \right] \end{aligned} \qquad (7\text{-}17)$$

and $\Delta\omega = 2\pi\Delta F = 2\pi h/T_0$. This reduces to

$$c_n = \frac{A_c}{2} \left[\left(\frac{\sin[(\pi/2)(h-n)]}{(\pi/2)(h-n)} \right) + (-1)^n \left(\frac{\sin[(\pi/2)(h+n)]}{(\pi/2)(h+n)} \right) \right] \qquad (7\text{-}18)$$

where the digital modulation index is $h = 2\Delta F/R$. $2\Delta F$ is the peak-to-peak frequency shift and R is the bit rate. Using (6-49) and (6-59), we see that the spectrum of this FSK signal with alternating data is

$$S(f) = \tfrac{1}{2} \left[G(f - f_c) + G^*(-f - f_c) \right] \qquad (7\text{-}19a)$$

where

$$G(f) = \sum_{-\infty}^{\infty} c_n\, \delta(f - nf_0) = \sum_{-\infty}^{\infty} c_n\, \delta\!\left(f - \frac{nR}{2} \right) \qquad (7\text{-}19b)$$

and c_n is given by (7-18).

TABLE 7-2 BASIC Program for FSK Spectrum with 10101010 Data

```
10  PRINT:PRINT
20  PRINT "** SPECTRUM FOR A FSK SIGNAL WITH 10101010 DATA ****"
30  PRINT "L. W. COUCH
40  PRINT:PRINT
50  CLEAR
60  INPUT "THE BIT RATE (in bits/sec) IS";R
70  INPUT "THE FREQUENCY OF THE LOW FSK TONE IS";FL
80  INPUT "THE FREQUENCY SHIFT (between Mark and Space) IS";S
90  INPUT "DO YOU WANT A PRINT LISTING (Y or N)";PRT$
100 PI2=3.1415926#/2
110 DEF FNSA(X)=(SIN(PI2*X))/(PI2*X)
120 PRINT "N","FREQ","SPECTRUM","DB SPECTRUM"
130 IF PRT$="Y" THEN LPRINT "BIT RATE=";R,"LOW FREQ=";FL,"FREQ
    SHIFT=";S:LPRINT:LPRINT: LPRINT "N";TAB(6);"FREQ","SPECTRUM",
    "DB SPECTRUM","|-120 dB",TAB(61);"|-60";TAB(80);"0"
140 FOR I=1 TO 21
150 N=I-11
160 F=FL+(S/2)+(N*R/2)
170 X=(S/R)-N
180 Y=(S/R)+N
190 IF ABS(X)<1E-08 THEN XX=1 ELSE XX=FNSA(X)
200 IF ABS(Y)<1E-08 THEN YY=1 ELSE YY=FNSA(Y)
210 SPEC=(ABS(XX+((-1)^N)*YY))/2
220 IF SPEC<.000001 THEN SPEC=.000001
230 DB=20*(LOG(SPEC))/LOG(10)
240 PRINT N,F,SPEC,DB
250 TT=(120+DB)/3.1579
260 IF TT>=37 THEN GOTO 320
270 STAB$=STRING$(TT,42)
280 IF PRT$="Y" THEN LPRINT N;TAB(6);F,SPEC,DB,STAB$;TAB(80);"|"
290 NEXT I
300 IF PRT$="Y" THEN LPRINT:LPRINT:LPRINT
310 END
320 STAB$=STRING$(38,42)
330 IF PRT$="Y" THEN LPRINT N;TAB(6);F,SPEC,DB,STAB$
340 GOTO 290
```

FSK spectra can be evaluated easily for cases of different frequency shifts ΔF and bit rates R if a personal computer is used. A BASIC program that evaluates (7-18) and (7-19) is shown in Table 7-2. The resulting spectral values for the case of Bell 103 modem parameters are shown in Table 7-3. A summary of three computer runs using different sets of parameters is shown in Fig. 7-8. Figure 7-8a gives the FSK spectrum for the Bell 103. For this case, where the Bell 103 parameters are used, the digital modulation index is $h = 0.67$. Note that for this Bell 103 case there are no spectral lines at the mark and space frequencies, f_1 and f_2. Figures 7-8b and 7-8c give the FSK spectra for $h = 1.82$

TABLE 7-3 Spectrum for Bell 103 FSK Modem: Originate Mode, $f_2 = 1070$ Hz, $f_1 = 1270$ Hz, $2\Delta F = 200$ Hz for $h = 0.67$

N	FREQ	SPECTRUM	DB SPECTRUM
-10	-330	3.691949E-03	-48.65489
-9	-180	2.634233E-03	-51.58692
-8	-30	5.783178E-03	-44.75667
-7	120	4.370366E-03	-47.18965
-6	270	1.033743E-02	-39.71175
-5	420	8.641859E-03	-41.26786
-4	570	2.362843E-02	-32.5313
-3	720	2.480333E-02	-32.1098
-2	870	.1033742	-19.71175
-1	1020	.3819719	-8.359373
0	1170	.8269934	-1.64996
1	1320	.3819719	-8.359373
2	1470	.1033742	-19.71175
3	1620	2.480333E-02	-32.1098
4	1770	2.362843E-02	-32.5313
5	1920	8.641859E-03	-41.26786
6	2070	1.033743E-02	-39.71175
7	2220	4.370366E-03	-47.18965
8	2370	5.783178E-03	-44.75667
9	2520	2.634233E-03	-51.58692
10	2670	3.691949E-03	-48.65489

and $h = 3.33$. Note that as the modulation index is increased, the spectrum concentrates about f_1 and f_2. This is the same result predicted by the PSD theorem for wideband FM (6-66) studied in Chapter 6, since the PDF of the binary modulation consists of two delta functions (one for $+1$ and one for -1 of Fig. 7-7a).

The approximate transmission bandwidth B_T for the FSK signal is given by Carson's rule: $B_T = 2(\beta + 1)B$, where $\beta = \Delta F/B$. This is equivalent to

$$B_T = 2\Delta F + 2B \tag{7-20}$$

B is the bandwidth of the digital (e.g., square-wave) modulation waveform. For our example of an alternating binary 1 and 0 test pattern waveform, the bandwidth of this square-wave modulating waveform (assuming that the first null type of bandwidth is used) is $B = R$ and, using (7-20), the FSK transmission bandwidth becomes

$$B_T = 2(\Delta F + R) \tag{7-21}$$

(a) FSK Spectrum with $f_2 = 1070$ Hz, $f_1 = 1270$ Hz, and $R = 300$ bits/sec
(Bell 103 Parameters, Originate mode) for $h = 0.67$

(b) FSK Spectrum with $f_2 = 1070$ Hz, $f_1 = 1270$ Hz, and $R = 110$ bits/sec
for $h = 1.82$

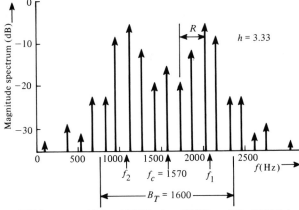

(c) FSK Spectrum with $f_2 = 1070$ Hz, $f_1 = 2070$ Hz, and $R = 300$ bits/sec
for $h = 3.33$

FIGURE 7-8 FSK spectra for alternating data modulation (positive frequencies shown with one-sided magnitude values).

This result is illustrated in Fig. 7-8. If a raised cosine-rolloff premodulation filter is used, the transmission bandwidth of the FSK signal becomes

$$B_T = 2\Delta F + (1 + r)R \tag{7-22}$$

For wideband FSK, where $\beta \gg 1$, ΔF dominates in these equations and we have $B_T = 2\Delta F$. For narrowband FSK the transmission bandwidth is $B_T = 2B$.

The exact PSD for continuous-phase FSK signals is difficult to evaluate for the case of random data modulation. However, it can be done by using some elegant statistical techniques [Anderson and Salz, 1965; Bennett and Rice, 1963; Proakis, 1983, pp. 130–135]. The resulting PSD for the complex envelope of the FSK signal is[†]

$$\mathcal{P}_g(f) = \frac{A_c^2 T_b}{2}$$
$$\times \left(A_1^2(f)[1 + B_{11}(f)] + A_2^2(f)[1 + B_{22}(f)] + 2B_{12}(f)A_1(f)A_2(f)\right) \tag{7-23a}$$

where

$$A_n(f) = \frac{\sin[\pi T_b(f - \Delta F(2n - 3))]}{\pi T_b(f - \Delta F(2n - 3))} \tag{7-23b}$$

and

$$B_{nm}(f) = \frac{\cos[2\pi f T_b - 2\pi\Delta F T_b(n + m - 3)] - \cos(2\pi\Delta F T_b)\cos[2\pi\Delta F T_b(n + m - 3)]}{1 + \cos^2(2\pi\Delta F T_b) - 2\cos(2\pi\Delta F T_b)\cos(2\pi f T_b)} \tag{7-23c}$$

where ΔF is the peak frequency deviation, $R = 1/T_b$ is the bit rate, and the digital modulation index is $h = 2\Delta F/R$. The PSD is plotted in Fig. 7-9 for several values of the digital modulation index. The curves in this figure were obtained by using the MathCAD computation shown in Appendix D.

FSK can be detected by using either a frequency (noncoherent) detector or two product detectors (coherent detection), as shown in Fig. 7-10. For optimum detection—that is, to obtain the lowest probability of bit error when the received FSK signal is corrupted by AWGN— coherent detection with matched filter processing is required [Couch, 1993]. The probability of bit error for noncoherent detection and optimum coherent detection of FSK is given in Sec. 7-4.

7-2 Multilevel Signaling

With multilevel signaling, digital inputs with more than two modulation levels are allowed on the transmitter input. This is illustrated in Fig. 7-11, which shows how multilevel signals can be generated from a serial binary input stream using a digital-to-analog converter (DAC). For example, suppose that an $\ell = 2$-bit DAC is used. Then the number of

---

[†] This result assumes that the carrier oscillator phase is not synchronized to any external source and that $h \neq 0, 1,$ 2, ... When $h = 0, 1, 2, . . .$, there are also discrete terms (delta functions) in the spectrum.

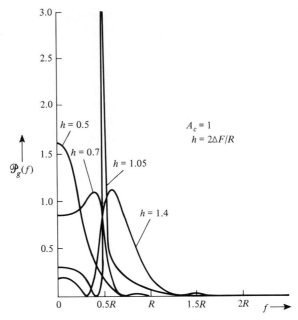

FIGURE 7-9 PSD for the complex envelope of FSK (positive frequencies shown).

levels (symbols) in the multilevel signal is $M = 2^\ell = 2^2 = 4$. The symbol rate (baud) of the multilevel signal is $D = R/\ell = \frac{1}{2}R$, where the bit rate is $R = 1/T_b$ bits/sec.

Quadrature Phase-Shift Keying (QPSK) and *M*-ary Phase-Shift Keying (MPSK)

If the transmitter is a PM transmitter with an $M = 4$ level digital modulation signal, *M-ary phase-shift keying* (MPSK) is generated at the transmitter output. A plot of the permitted

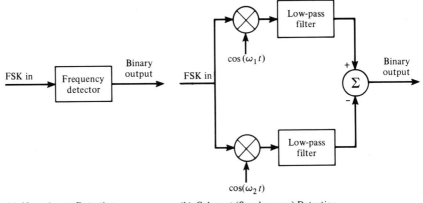

(a) Noncoherent Detection   (b) Coherent (Synchronous) Detection

FIGURE 7-10 Detection of FSK.

FIGURE 7-11 Multilevel digital transmission system.

values of the complex envelope, $g(t) = A_c e^{j\theta(t)}$, would contain four points, one value of g (a complex number in general) for each of the four multilevel values, corresponding to the four phases that θ is permitted to have. A plot of two possible sets of $g(t)$ is shown in Fig. 7-12. For instance, suppose that the permitted multilevel values at the DAC are -3, -1, $+1$, and $+3$ V; then in Fig. 7-12a these multilevel values might correspond to PSK phases of 0, 90, 180, and 270°, respectively. In Fig. 7-12b these levels would correspond to carrier phases of 45, 135, 225, and 315°, respectively. These two signal constellations are essentially the same except for a shift in the carrier-phase reference.[†] This example of *M*-ary PSK where $M = 4$ is called *quadrature-phase-shift-keyed* (QPSK) signaling.

MPSK can also be generated by using two quadrature carriers modulated by the x and y components of the complex envelope (instead of using a phase modulator)

$$g(t) = A_c e^{j\theta(t)} = x(t) + jy(t) \tag{7-24}$$

where the permitted values of x and y are

$$x_i = A_c \cos \theta_i \tag{7-25}$$

$$y_i = A_c \sin \theta_i \tag{7-26}$$

for the permitted phase angles θ_i, $i = 1, 2, \ldots , M$, of the MPSK signal. This is illustrated by Fig. 7-13, where the signal processing circuit implements (7-25) and (7-26). Figure

[†] A constellation is an *N*-dimensional plot of the possible signal vectors corresponding to the possible digital signals (see Sec. 3-6).

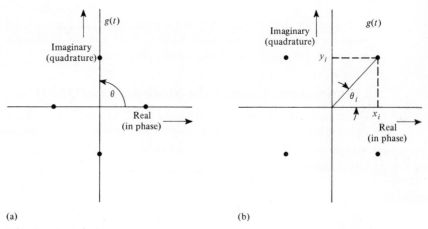

(a)   (b)

FIGURE 7-12 QPSK signal constellations (permitted values of the complex envelope).

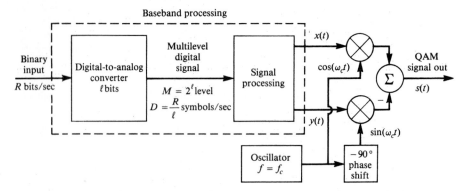

(a) Modulator for Generalized Signal Constellation

$$g(t) = x(t) + jy(t)$$
$$M = 2^\ell \text{ point constellation}$$
$$D = R/\ell \text{ symbols/sec}$$

(b) Modulator for Rectangular Signal Constellation

FIGURE 7-13 Generation of QAM signals.

7-12 gives the relationship between the permitted phase angles θ_i and the (x_i, y_i) components for two QPSK signal constellations. Note that this is identical to the quadrature method of generating modulated signals presented in Fig. 5-27.

Quadrature Amplitude Modulation (QAM)

Quadrature carrier signaling, as shown in Fig. 7-13, is called *quadrature amplitude modulation* (QAM). In general, QAM signal constellations are not restricted to having permitted signaling points only on a circle (of radius A_c, as was the case for MPSK). The general QAM signal is

$$s(t) = x(t) \cos \omega_c t - y(t) \sin \omega_c t \tag{7-27}$$

where

$$g(t) = x(t) + jy(t) = R(t)e^{j\theta(t)} \tag{7-28}$$

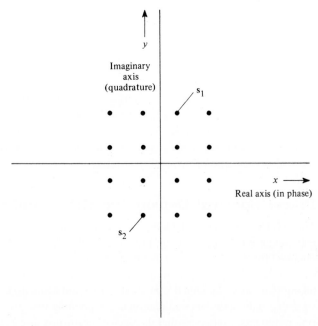

FIGURE 7-14 16-symbol QAM constellation (four levels per dimension).

For example, a popular 16-symbol ($M = 16$ levels) QAM constellation is shown in Fig. 7-14, where the relationship between (R_i, θ_i) and (x_i, y_i) can readily be evaluated for each of the 16 signal values permitted. This type of signaling is used by 2400 bit/sec V.22 bis computer modems (see Table C-13). Here x_i and y_i are each permitted to have four levels per dimension. This 16-symbol QAM signal may be generated by using two ($\ell/2 = 2$)-bit digital-to-analog converters and quadrature balanced modulators as shown in Fig. 7-13b. The waveforms of x and y are represented by

$$x(t) = \sum_n x_n h_1\left(t - \frac{n}{D}\right) \tag{7-29}$$

and

$$y(t) = \sum_n y_n h_1\left(t - \frac{n}{D}\right) \tag{7-30}$$

where $D = R/\ell$ and (x_n, y_n) denotes one of the permitted (x_i, y_i) values during the symbol time that is centered on $t = nT = n/D$ seconds. (It takes T seconds to send each symbol.) $h_1(t)$ is the pulse shape that is used for each symbol. If the bandwidth of the QAM signal is not to be restricted, the pulse shape will be rectangular of T-second duration. In some applications the timing between the $x(t)$ and $y(t)$ components is offset by $T/2 = 1/(2D)$

seconds. That is, $x(t)$ would be described by (7-29), and the offset $y(t)$ would be described by

$$y(t) = \sum_n y_n h_1\left(t - \frac{n}{D} - \frac{1}{2D}\right) \qquad (7\text{-}31)$$

One popular type of offset signaling is *offset QPSK (OQPSK)*, which is offset QAM when $M = 4$. A special case of OQPSK when $h_1(t)$ has a sinusoidal type of pulse shape is called *minimum-shift keying* (MSK). This type will be studied immediately after the next section. Furthermore, a QPSK signal is said to be *unbalanced* if the $x(t)$ and $y(t)$ components have unequal powers and/or unequal data rates.

Power Spectral Density for MPSK and QAM

The PSD for MPSK and QAM signals is relatively easy to evaluate for the case of rectangular bit shape signaling. In this case, the PSD has the same spectral shape that was obtained for BPSK, *provided* that proper frequency scaling is used. For example, take the case of $M = 16$ QAM signaling illustrated in Fig. 7-14. The PSD can be evaluated by taking two *antipodal* signal vectors at a time and evaluating the PSD for the condition of signaling only with data modulation corresponding to those signal vectors. That is, referring to the figure, suppose that the vectors corresponding to the points s_1 and s_2 are used. This is equivalent to BPSK signaling. When we use (7-12), the *conditional* PSD of the complex envelope is of the form

$$\mathcal{P}_g(f|s_1 \text{ or } s_2) = A_1\left(\frac{\sin \pi fT}{\pi fT}\right)^2 \qquad (7\text{-}32)$$

where the time that it takes to send one symbol is T and $T = 1/D = \ell/R = \ell T_b$. The resulting PSD, considering all possible antipodal signal pairs, is (using the probability theory of Appendix B)

$$\mathcal{P}_g(f) = \sum_{\substack{i=1 \\ i=\text{odd}}}^{M} \mathcal{P}(f|s_i \text{ or } s_{i+1})P(s_i \text{ or } s_{i+1}) \qquad (7\text{-}33)$$

where $i = 1, 3, 5, \ldots$ and $P(s_i \text{ or } s_{i+1})$ is the probability of sending the s_i or s_{i+1} antipodal vector pair. For equally likely random data (i.e., the usual situation), $P(s_i \text{ or } s_{i+1}) = 1/(M/2)$, so (7-33) becomes

$$\mathcal{P}_g(f) = \frac{2}{M}\sum_{\substack{i=1 \\ i=\text{odd}}}^{M} A_i\left(\frac{\sin \pi fT}{\pi fT}\right)^2 = \frac{2}{M}\left(\frac{\sin \pi fT}{\pi fT}\right)^2 \sum_{\substack{i=1 \\ i=\text{odd}}}^{M} A_i \qquad (7\text{-}34)$$

But ΣA_i is just a constant. Thus the PSD for the complex envelope of MPSK or QAM signals with data modulation of rectangular bit shape is

$$\mathcal{P}_g(f) = K\left(\frac{\sin \pi f\ell T_b}{\pi f\ell T_b}\right)^2 \qquad \text{for MPSK and QAM} \qquad (7\text{-}35)$$

where $M = 2^\ell$ is the number of points in the signal constellation and the bit rate is $R = 1/T_b$. For a total transmitted power of P watts the value of K is $K = 2P\ell T_b$ since

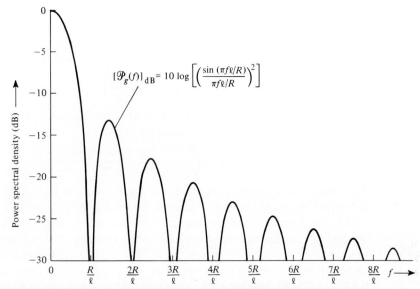

FIGURE 7-15 PSD for the complex envelope of MPSK and QAM where $M = 2^\ell$, R is bit rate, and $R/\ell = D$ is baud rate (positive frequencies shown).

$\int_{-\infty}^{\infty} \mathscr{P}_s(f)\, df = P$. This PSD for the complex envelope is plotted in Fig. 7-15. The PSD of the MPSK or QAM signal is obtained by simply translating the PSD of Fig. 7-15 to the carrier frequency, as described by (7-2). Of course, for $\ell = 1$, the figure gives the PSD for BPSK (i.e., compare Fig. 7-15, $\ell = 1$, with Fig. 7-2b).

From Fig. 7-15 we see that the null-to-null transmission bandwidth of MPSK or QAM is

$$B_T = 2R/\ell \qquad (7\text{-}36)$$

when we use (4-55), the spectral efficiency of MPSK or QAM signaling with rectangular data pulses is

$$\eta = \frac{R}{B_T} = \frac{\ell}{2} \quad \frac{\text{bits/sec}}{\text{Hz}} \qquad (7\text{-}37)$$

where $M = 2^\ell$ is the number of points in the signal constellation. For example, for the $M = 16$ QAM signal, the bandwidth efficiency is $\eta = 2$ bits/sec per hertz of bandwidth. For a 2400-bit/sec V.22bis modem ($M = 16$, QAM; see Table C-12), the null-to-null transmission bandwidth is $B_T = 1200$ Hz.

When QAM (or the QAM equivalent of MPSK) with a pulse shape of $h_1(t)$—see (7-29) and (7-30)—is transmitted over a bandlimited channel, the overall filter characteristic needs to be selected so that the intersymbol interference is negligible. $h_1(t) = h(t) * h_T(t)$ corresponds to the transmitter pulse shape, as described in Sec. 4-5. If the overall pulse shape satisfies the raised cosine-rolloff filter characteristic, then, by use of (4-74), the absolute bandwidth of the M-level modulating signal is

$$B = \tfrac{1}{2}(1 + r)D \qquad (7\text{-}38)$$

where $D = R/\ell$ from Fig. 7-13 and r is the rolloff factor of the filter characteristic. Furthermore, from our study of AM (and DSB-SC to be specific) we know that the transmission bandwidth is related to the modulation bandwidth by $B_T = 2B$, so that the overall absolute transmission bandwidth of the QAM signal is

$$B_T = \left(\frac{1+r}{\ell}\right) R \tag{7-39}$$

Since $M = 2^\ell$, which implies that $\ell = \log_2 M = (\ln M)/(\ln 2)$, the spectral efficiency of QAM-type signaling with raised cosine filtering is

$$\eta = \frac{R}{B_T} = \frac{\ln M}{(1+r)\ln 2} \quad \frac{\text{bits/sec}}{\text{Hz}} \tag{7-40}$$

This result is an extremely important one since it tells us how fast we can signal for a prescribed bandwidth. Of course, this result holds for MPSK since this is a special case of QAM. This formula is used to generate Table 7-4, which illustrates the allowable bit rate per hertz of transmission bandwidth for QAM signaling. For example, suppose that we want to signal over a telephone line that has an available bandwidth of 2.4 kHz. If we used BPSK ($M = 2$) with a 50% rolloff factor, we could signal at a rate of $B_T \times \eta = 2.4 \times 0.677 = 1.60$ kbits/sec; but if we used QPSK ($M = 4$) with a 25% rolloff factor, we could signal at a rate of $2.4 \times 1.6 = 3.84$ kbits/sec.

In order to conserve bandwidth, the number of levels M in (7-40) cannot be increased too much since, for a given peak envelope power (PEP), the spacing between the signal points in the signal constellation will decrease and noise on the received signal will cause errors (since the noise moves the received signal vector to a new location that might correspond to a different signal level). However, we know that R certainly has to be less than C, the channel capacity (Sec. 1-9) if the errors are to be kept small. Consequently, using (4-56), we require

$$\eta < \eta_{\text{max}} \tag{7-41a}$$

where

$$\eta_{\text{max}} = \log_2\left(1 + \frac{S}{N}\right) \tag{7-41b}$$

TABLE 7-4 Spectral Efficiency for QAM Signaling with Raised Cosine-Rolloff Pulse Shaping

Number of Levels, M (symbols)	Size of DAC, ℓ (bits)	$\eta = \dfrac{R}{B_T}\left(\dfrac{\text{bits/sec}}{\text{Hz}}\right)$					
		$r = 0.0$	$r = 0.1$	$r = 0.25$	$r = 0.5$	$r = 0.75$	$r = 1.0$
2	1	1.00	0.909	0.800	0.667	0.571	0.500
4	2	2.00	1.82	1.60	1.33	1.14	1.00
8	3	3.00	2.73	2.40	2.00	1.71	1.50
16	4	4.00	3.64	3.20	2.67	2.29	2.00
32	5	5.00	4.55	4.0	3.33	2.86	2.50

7-3 Minimum-Shift Keying (MSK)

Minimum-shift keying is another bandwidth conservation technique that has been developed. It has the advantage of being a constant-amplitude signal and, consequently, can be amplified with Class C amplifiers without distortion. As we will see, MSK is equivalent to OQPSK with sinusoidal pulse shaping [for $h_i(t)$].

> **DEFINITION:** *Minimum-shift keying* (MSK) is continuous-phase FSK with a minimum modulation index ($h = 0.5$) that will produce orthogonal signaling.

First, let us show that $h = 0.5$ is the minimum index allowed for orthogonal continuous-phase FSK. For a binary 1 to be transmitted over the bit interval $0 < t < T_b$, the FSK signal would be $s_1(t) = A_c \cos(\omega_1 t + \theta_1)$, and for a binary 0 to be transmitted, the FSK signal would be $s_2(t) = A_c \cos(\omega_2 t + \theta_2)$, where $\theta_1 = \theta_2$ for the continuous-phase condition at the switching time $t = 0$. For orthogonal signaling, from (2-74), we require the integral of the product of the two signals over the bit interval to be zero. Thus we require that

$$\int_0^{T_b} s_1(t)s_2(t)\, dt = \int_0^{T_b} A_c^2 \cos(\omega_1 t + \theta_1) \cos(\omega_2 t + \theta_2)\, dt = 0 \qquad (7\text{-}42a)$$

This reduces to the requirement

$$\frac{A_c^2}{2}\left[\frac{\sin[(\omega_1 - \omega_2)T_b + (\theta_1 - \theta_2)] - \sin(\theta_1 - \theta_2)}{\omega_1 - \omega_2}\right]$$

$$+ \frac{A_c^2}{2}\left[\frac{\sin[(\omega_1 + \omega_2)T_b + (\theta_1 + \theta_2)] - \sin(\theta_1 + \theta_2)}{\omega_1 + \omega_2}\right] = 0 \quad (7\text{-}42b)$$

The second term is negligible because $\omega_1 + \omega_2$ is large,[†] so the requirement is that

$$\frac{\sin[2\pi h + (\theta_1 - \theta_2)] - \sin(\theta_1 - \theta_2)}{2\pi h} = 0 \qquad (7\text{-}43)$$

where $(\omega_1 - \omega_2)T_b = 2\pi(2\Delta F)T_b$ and, from (7-15), $h = 2\Delta F T_b$. For the *continuous-phase* case $\theta_1 = \theta_2$, and (7-43) is satisfied for a minimum value of $h = 0.5$ or a peak frequency deviation of

$$\Delta F = \frac{1}{4T_b} = \frac{1}{4}R \qquad \text{for MSK} \qquad (7\text{-}44)$$

Note that for *discontinuous-phase* FSK $\theta_1 \neq \theta_2$ and the minimum value for orthogonality for that case is $h = 1.0$.

Now we will demonstrate that the MSK signal (which is $h = 0.5$ continuous-phase FSK) is a form of OQPSK signaling with sinusoidal pulse shaping. First, consider the FSK signal over the signaling interval $(0, T_b)$. When we use (7-14), the complex envelope is

$$g(t) = A_c e^{j\theta(t)} = A_c e^{j2\pi\Delta F \int_0^t m(\lambda)\, d\lambda}$$

[†] If $\omega_1 + \omega_2$ is not sufficiently large to make the second term negligible, choose $f_c = \frac{1}{2}m/T_b = \frac{1}{2}mR$ where m is a positive integer. This will make the second term zero ($f_1 = f_c - \Delta F$ and $f_2 = f_c + \Delta F$).

where $m(t) = \pm 1$, $0 < t < T_b$. Using (7-44), we find that the complex envelope becomes

$$g(t) = A_c e^{\pm j\pi t/(2T_b)} = x(t) + jy(t), \qquad 0 < t < T_b$$

where the $\pm$ signs denote the possible data during the $(0, T_b)$ interval. Thus

$$x(t) = A_c \cos\left(\pm 1 \frac{\pi t}{2T_b}\right), \qquad 0 < t < T_b \tag{7-45a}$$

$$y(t) = A_c \sin\left(\pm 1 \frac{\pi t}{2T_b}\right), \qquad 0 < t < T_b \tag{7-45b}$$

and the MSK signal is

$$s(t) = x(t) \cos \omega_c t - y(t) \sin \omega_c t \tag{7-45c}$$

A typical input data waveform, $m(t)$, and the resulting $x(t)$ and $y(t)$ quadrature modulation waveforms, are shown in Fig. 7-16. From (7-45a) and (7-45b), and realizing that $\cos[\pm \pi t/(2T_b)] = \cos[\pi t/(2T_b)]$ and $\sin[\pm \pi t/(2T_b)] = \pm\sin[\pi t/(2T_b)]$, we see that the ± 1 sign of $m(t)$ during the $(0,T_b)$ interval affects only $y(t)$ and not $x(t)$ over the signaling interval of $(0,2T_b)$. We also realize that the $\sin[\pi t/(2T_b)]$ pulse of $y(t)$ is $2T_b$ sec wide. Similarly, it can be seen that the ± 1 sign of $m(t)$ over the $(T_b,2T_b)$ interval affects only $x(t)$ and not $y(t)$ over the interval $(T_b,3T_b)$. In other words, the binary data of $m(t)$ *alternately* modulates the $x(t)$ and $y(t)$ components, and the pulse shape for the $x(t)$ and $y(t)$ symbols (which are $2T_b$ wide instead of T_b) is a sinusoid, as shown in the figure. Thus MSK is equivalent to OQPSK with sinusoidal pulse shaping.

The $x(t)$ and $y(t)$ waveforms as shown in Fig. 7-16 illustrate the so-called Type II MSK [Bhargava, Haccoun, Matyas, and Nuspl, 1981], where the basic pulse shape is always a positive half-cosinusoid. For Type I MSK, the pulse shape [for both $x(t)$ and $y(t)$] alternates between a positive and a negative half-cosinusoid. For both Type I and Type II MSK, it can be shown that there is *not* a one-to-one relationship between the input data $m(t)$ and the resulting mark and space frequencies, f_1 and f_2, in the MSK signal. This can be demonstrated by evaluating the instantaneous frequency, f_i, as a function of the data presented by $m(t)$ during the different bit intervals. The instantaneous frequency is $f_i = f_c + (1/2\pi)[d\theta(t)/dt] = f_c \pm \Delta F$, where $\theta(t) = \tan^{-1}[y(t)/x(t)]$. The $\pm$ sign is determined by the encoding technique (Type I or II) that is used to obtain the $x(t)$ and $y(t)$ waveforms in each bit interval, T_b, as well as the sign of the data on $m(t)$. To get a one-to-one frequency relationship between a Type I MSK signal and the corresponding $h = 0.5$ FSK signal, called a *fast frequency-shift keyed* (FFSK) signal, the data input to the Type I FSK modulator is first differentially encoded. Examples of the waveforms for MSK, Type I and II, and for FFSK can be found in the MathCAD solutions for Probs. 7-24, 7-25, and 7-26. Regardless of the differences noted, FFSK, MSK Type I, and MSK Type II are all constant-amplitude, continuous-phase FSK signals with a modulation index of $h = 0.5$.

The PSD for MSK (Type I and Type II) can be evaluated as follows. Since $x(t)$ and $y(t)$ have independent data and their dc value is zero, and since $g(t) = x(t) + jy(t)$, the PSD for the complex envelope is

$$\mathcal{P}_g(f) = \mathcal{P}_x(f) + \mathcal{P}_y(f) = 2\mathcal{P}_x(f)$$

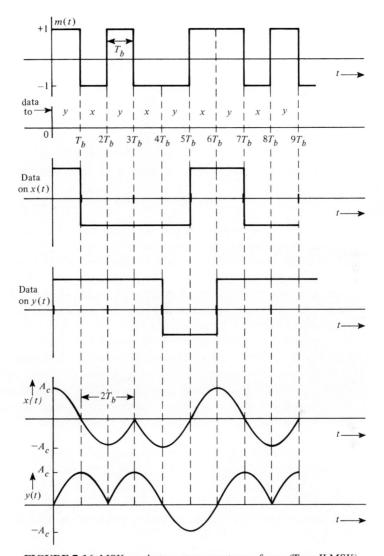

FIGURE 7-16 MSK quadrature component waveforms (Type II MSK).

where $\mathscr{P}_x(x) = \mathscr{P}_y(f)$ because $x(t)$ and $y(t)$ have the same type of pulse shape. When we use (4-36) in (4-28) with a pulse width of $2T_b$, this PSD becomes

$$\mathscr{P}_g(f) = \frac{2}{2T_b} |F(f)|^2 \qquad (7\text{-}46)$$

where $F(f) = \mathscr{F}[f(t)]$ and $f(t)$ is the pulse shape. For the MSK half-cosinusoidal pulse

shape, we have

$$
f(t) = \begin{cases} A_c \cos\left(\dfrac{\pi t}{2T_b}\right), & |t| < T_b \\[2ex] 0, & t \text{ elsewhere} \end{cases} \tag{7-47a}
$$

and the Fourier transform is

$$
F(f) = \frac{4A_c T_b \cos 2\pi T_b f}{\pi[1 - (4T_b f)^2]} \tag{7-47b}
$$

Thus, the PSD for the complex envelope of an MSK signal is

$$
\mathcal{P}_g(f) = \frac{16A_c^2 T_b}{\pi^2}\left(\frac{\cos^2 2\pi T_b f}{[1 - (4T_b f)^2]^2}\right) \tag{7-48}
$$

where the normalized power in the MSK signal is $A_c^2/2$. The PSD for MSK is readily obtained by translating this spectrum up to the carrier frequency, as described by (7-2). This complex envelope PSD for MSK is shown by the solid-line curve in Fig. 7-17. For comparison purposes, the corresponding PSD for OQPSK and (QPSK) complex envelopes is shown by the dashed-line curve. It is also known that there are other digital modulation techniques, such as *tamed frequency modulation* (TFM), that have even better spectral characteristics than MSK [DeJager and Dekker, 1978; Pettit, 1982; Taub and Schilling, 1986], and the optimum pulse shape for minimum spectral occupancy of FSK-type signals has been found [Campanella, LoFaso, and Mamola, 1984].

MSK signals can be generated by using any one of several methods, as illustrated in Fig. 7-18. Figure 7-18a shows the generation of FFSK (which is equivalent to Type I MSK with differential encoding of the input data). Here a simple FM-type modulator having a peak deviation of $\Delta F = 1/(4T_b) = (1/4)R$ is used. Figure 7-18b shows an MSK Type I modulator that is a realization of (7-45). This is called the *parallel* method of generating MSK since parallel in-phase (I) and quadrature-phase (Q) channels are used. Figure 7-18c shows the *serial* method of generating MSK. In this approach, BPSK is first generated at a carrier frequency of $f_2 = f_c - \Delta F$ and the bandpass filtered about $f_1 = f_c + \Delta F$ to produce an MSK signal with a carrier frequency of f_c. (See Prob. 7-27 to demonstrate that this technique is correct.) For more interesting properties of MSK the reader is referred to a recent paper [Leib and Pasupathy, 1993].

7-4 Comparison of Bandpass Digital Signaling Systems

As seen in previous sections, there are many types of digital modulated signals, such as OOK, BPSK, DPSK, FSK, MPSK, QAM, and MSK. Then the question arises: Which is the best one to use? There is no universal answer to this question. Each digital modulation technique has advantages and disadvantages. In this section we compare these modulation techniques based on (1) their bandwidth requirements via their spectral efficiency,

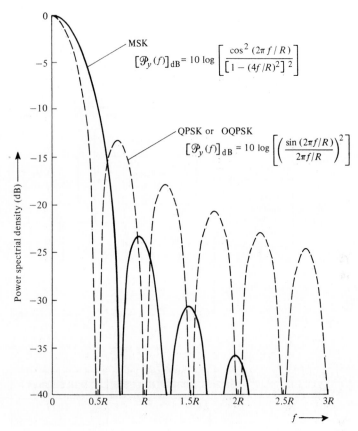

FIGURE 7-17 PSD for complex envelope of MSK, QPSK, and OQPSK where R is the bit rate (positive frequencies shown).

(2) their noise performance via their detected probability of error, and (3) their synchronization requirements. Ultimately, one usually selects the lowest-cost system that will give acceptable performance in a particular application.

Special Efficiency

The spectral efficiency for digital signals, $\eta = R/B_T$, was first defined in Chapter 4—see (4-55)—and has a maximum usable value that depends on Shannon's channel capacity—see (7-41). Table 7-5 gives a comparison of the spectral efficiency for several bandpass digital signals using two different bandwidth criteria—the null-to-null bandwidth and the 30-dB bandwidth. Of course, a larger value of η indicates better spectral efficiency. It is seen that MSK ranks better or worse than QPSK and 64 QAM depending on the bandwidth criteria used.

(a) Generation of Fast Frequency-Shift Keying (FFSK)

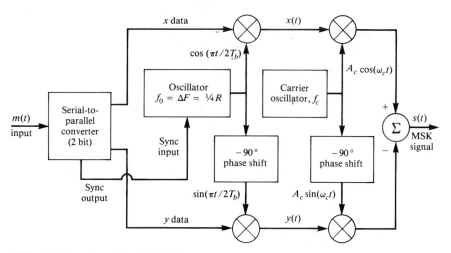

(b) Parallel Generation of Type I MSK (This will generate FFSK if a differential encoder is inserted at the input.)

(c) Serial Generation of MSK

FIGURE 7-18 Generation of MSK signals.

Probability of Bit Error, P_e

The probability of bit error, P_e, for many types of digital signals and receivers is given in Table 7-6. The probability of bit error is also called *bit error rate* (BER) by many practicing engineers. In all cases the input to the receiver is the designated digital signal plus additive white Gaussian noise (AWGN). Using the results in this table, P_e is plotted as a function of E_b/N_0 in Fig. 7-19. E_b/N_0 is proportional to the signal-to-noise ratio (S/N) at the receiver input. In particular, E_b is the energy in the signal (at the receiver input) over a

TABLE 7-5 Spectral Efficiency of Digital Signals

Type of Signal	Spectral Efficiency, $\eta = \dfrac{R}{B_T} \left(\dfrac{\text{bits/sec}}{\text{Hz}} \right)$	
	Null-to-Null Bandwidth	30-dB Bandwidth
OOK and BPSK	0.500	0.052
QPSK and OQPSK	1.00	0.104
MSK	0.667	0.438
16 QAM	2.00	0.208
64 QAM	3.00	0.313

one-bit interval and N_0 is related to the PSD of the noise (at the receiver input), $\mathcal{P}_n(f)$, by $\mathcal{P}_n(f) = N_0/2$. E_b/N_0 is related to the S/N at the receiver input by

$$\left(\frac{S}{N} \right)_{in} = \frac{P_s}{(N_0/2)(2B_T)} = \frac{E_b/T_b}{N_0 B_T} = \frac{E_b}{N_0} \left(\frac{R}{B_T} \right) \tag{7-49}$$

where B_T is the transmission bandwidth of the digital bandpass signal and $R = 1/T_b$ is the bit rate.

Except for the noncoherent detection cases, all of these results in Table 7-6 and Fig. 7-19 assume that the optimum filter—the matched filter—is used in the receiver. In practice, simpler filters work almost as well as the matched filter. For example, in a computer simulation of a BPSK system with a three-pole Butterworth receiving filter having a bandwidth equal to the bit rate, the E_b/N_0 needs to be increased no more than 0.4 dB to obtain the same BER as that obtained when a matched filter is used (for error rates above 10^{-12}).

Comparing the various bandpass signaling techniques, we see that QPSK and MSK give the best overall performance in terms of the minimum bandwidth required for a given signaling rate and one of the smallest P_e for a given E_b/N_0. However, QPSK is relatively expensive to implement since it requires coherent detection. Figure 7-19 shows that for the same P_e, DPSK (using a noncoherent receiver) requires only about 1 dB more E_b/N_0 than that for QPSK or BPSK, for error rates of 10^{-4} or less. Since DPSK is much easier to receive than BPSK, it is often used in practice in preference to BPSK. Similarly, the BER performance of a noncoherent FSK receiver is very close to that of a coherent FSK receiver. Since noncoherent FSK receivers are simpler than coherent FSK receivers, they are often used in practice. In some applications there are multiple paths of different lengths between the transmitter and receiver (e.g., caused by reflection). This causes fading and noncoherence in the received signal (phase). In this case, it is very difficult to implement coherent detection, regardless of the complexity of the receiver, and one resorts to the use of noncoherent detection techniques.

Channel coding can be used to reduce the P_e below the values given in Fig. 7-19. This concept was developed in Chapter 1. By using Shannon's channel capacity formula, it was found that theoretically the BER would approach zero as long as E_b/N_0 was above

TABLE 7-6 Probability of Bit Error, P_e, of Digital Systems[a]

Type of Digital Signaling	Probability of Bit Error, P_e	
Baseband signaling		
Unipolar	$Q\left[\sqrt{\dfrac{E_b}{N_0}}\right]$	
Polar	$Q\left[\sqrt{2\left(\dfrac{E_b}{N_0}\right)}\right]$	
Bipolar	$\dfrac{3}{2}Q\left[\sqrt{\dfrac{E_b}{N_0}}\right]$	
Bandpass signaling	*Coherent detection*	*Noncoherent detection*
OOK	$Q\left[\sqrt{\dfrac{E_b}{N_0}}\right]$	$\frac{1}{2}e^{-(1/2)(E_b/N_0)}$, $E_b/N_0 > \frac{1}{4}$
BPSK	$Q\left[\sqrt{2\left(\dfrac{E_b}{N_0}\right)}\right]$	Requires coherent detection
FSK	$Q\left[\sqrt{\dfrac{E_b}{N_0}}\right]$	$\frac{1}{2}e^{-(1/2)(E_b/N_0)}$
DPSK	Not used in practice	$\frac{1}{2}e^{-(E_b/N_0)}$
QPSK	$Q\left[\sqrt{2\left(\dfrac{E_b}{N_0}\right)}\right]$	Requires coherent detection
MSK	$Q\left[\sqrt{2\left(\dfrac{E_b}{N_0}\right)}\right]$	$\frac{1}{2}e^{-(1/2)(E_b/N_0)}$

SOURCE: L. W. Couch, *Digital and Analog Communication Systems,* 4th ed., Macmillan, New York, 1993.

[a] $Q(z)$ is the Q function as defined in (A-112) and plotted in Fig. B-7.

-1.59 dB when optimum (unknown) coding was used on an infinite bandwidth channel. With practical coding it was found that coding gains as large as 9 dB could be achieved on BPSK and QPSK systems. That is, for a given BER the E_b/N_0 requirements in Fig. 7-19 could be reduced by as much as 9 dB when coding was used.

Synchronization

As we have seen, three levels of synchronization are needed in digital communication systems.

1. Bit synchronization.
2. Frame or word synchronization.

FIGURE 7-19 Comparison of the probability of bit error for several digital signaling schemes.

3. Carrier synchronization.

Bit and frame synchronizations were discussed in Chapter 4.

Carrier synchronization is required in receivers that use coherent detection. If the spectrum of the digital signal has a discrete line at the carrier frequency, such as in equally likely OOK signaling, a PLL can be used to recover the carrier reference from the received signal. In BPSK signaling there is no discrete carrier term, but the spectrum is symmetrical about the carrier frequency. Consequently, a Costas loop or a squaring loop may be used for carrier sync recovery. These loops were illustrated in Figs. 6-3 and P7-6. As indicated in Sec. 6-4, these loops may lock up with a 180° phase error, which must be resolved to ensure that the recovered data will not be complemented. For QPSK signals, the carrier reference may be obtained by a more generalized Costas loop or, equivalently, by a fourth-power loop [Spilker, 1977]. These loops have a four-phase ambiguity of 0, ±90, or 180°, which must also be resolved to obtain correctly demodulated data. These facts illustrate once again why noncoherent reception techniques (which can be used for OOK, FSK, and DPSK) are so popular.

Bit synchronizers are needed at the receiver to provide the bit sync signal for clocking the sample-and-hold circuit and, if used, the matched filter circuit. The bit synchronizer was illustrated in Figs. 4-17 and 4-18.

All the BER formulas that we have obtained assume that noise-free bit sync and carrier sync (for coherent detection) are available at the receiver. Of course, if these sync signals are obtained from noisy signals that are present at the receiver input, the reference signals are also noisy. Consequently, the P_e will be larger than that given for the ideal case when noise-free sync is assumed.

The third type of synchronization that is required by most digital systems is frame sync or word sync. In some systems this sync is used simply to demark the serial data into digital words or *bytes*. In other systems, block coding or convolutional coding is used at the transmitter so that some of the bit errors at the output of the threshold device of the receiver can be detected and corrected by using decoding circuits. In these systems word sync is needed to clock the receiver decoding circuits. In addition, frame sync is required in time-division multiplex (TDM) systems. This was described in Fig. 4-34. Higher levels of synchronization, such as network synchronization, may be required when data are received from several sources. For example, multiple-access satellite communication systems require network synchronization.

For further reading on the interesting topic of synchronization, the reader is referred to a special issue of the *IEEE Transactions on Communications,* which presents tutorial as well as in-depth papers on the different aspects of synchronization problems [Gardner and Lindsey, 1980].

7-5 Spread Spectrum Systems

Thus far in our study of communication systems, we have been primarily concerned with the performance of communication systems in terms of bandwidth efficiency and energy efficiency (i.e., detected S/N or probability of bit error) with respect to natural noise. However, in some applications, we also need to consider multiple-access capability, anti-jam capability, interference rejection, and covert operation, or low probability of intercept (LPI) capability. (The latter considerations are especially important to military applications.) These performance objectives can be optimized by using spread spectrum techniques.

Multiple-access capability is needed in cellular telephone and personal communication applications where a large number of users share a band of frequencies, because there is not enough available bandwidth to assign a permanent frequency channel to each user. As we shall see, spread spectrum techniques can be used to provide simultaneous use of a wide-frequency band by a large number of users via *code-division multiple-access* (CDMA) techniques. This is an alternative approach to band sharing. Two other approaches, time-division multiple access (TDMA) and frequency-division multiple access (FDMA), have already been studied in Chapters 4 and 6, respectively.

There are many types of *spread spectrum* (SS) systems. To be considered an SS system, a system must satisfy two criteria.

1. The bandwidth of the transmitted signal, $s(t)$, needs to be much greater than that of the message, $m(t)$.
2. The relatively wide bandwidth of $s(t)$ must be caused by an independent modulating

waveform, $c(t)$, called the *spreading signal,* and this signal must be known by the receiver in order for the message signal, $m(t)$, to be detected.

Consequently, the SS signal is

$$s(t) = \text{Re}\{g(t)e^{j\omega_c t}\} \tag{7-50a}$$

where the complex envelope of the SS signal is a function of both $m(t)$ and $c(t)$. In most cases, a product function is used, so that

$$g(t) = g_m(t)g_c(t) \tag{7-50b}$$

where $g_m(t)$ and $g_c(t)$ are the usual types of modulation complex envelope functions that generate AM, PM, FM, and so on, as given in Table 5-1. The SS signals are classified by the type of mapping functions that are used for $g_c(t)$.

Some of the most common types of SS signals are:

- *Direct Sequence* (DS). Here a DSB-SC type of spreading modulation is used [i.e., $g_c(t) = c(t)$] and $c(t)$ is a polar waveform.
- *Frequency Hopping* (FH). Here $g_c(t)$ is of the FM type where there are $M = 2^k$ hop frequencies determined by the k-bit words obtained from the spreading code waveform, $c(t)$.
- *Hybrid* techniques that include both DS and FH.

We will illustrate exactly how DS and FH systems work in the following sections.

Direct Sequence

Assume that the information waveform, $m(t)$, comes from a digital source and that $m(t)$ is a polar waveform having values of ± 1. Furthermore, let us examine the case of BPSK modulation where $g_m(t) = A_c m(t)$. Thus, for DS where $g_c(t) = c(t)$ is used in (7-50b), the complex envelope for the SS signal becomes

$$g(t) = A_c m(t)c(t) \tag{7-51}$$

The resulting $s(t) = \text{Re}\{g(t)e^{j\omega_c t}\}$ is called a *binary-phase-shift keyed data, direct sequence spreading, spread spectrum signal* (BPSK-DS-SS) and $c(t)$ is a polar spreading signal. Furthermore, let this spreading waveform be generated by using a *pseudonoise* (PN) code generator, as shown in Fig. 7-20b, where the values of $c(t)$ are ± 1. The pulse width of $c(t)$ is denoted by T_c and is called a *chip* interval (as compared to a bit interval). The code generator uses a modulo 2 adder and r shift register stages that are clocked every T_c sec. It can be shown that $c(t)$ is periodic. Furthermore, feedback taps from the stage of the shift registers and modulo 2 adders are arranged so that the $c(t)$ waveform has a maximum period of N chips where $N = 2^r - 1$ [Ziemer and Peterson, 1985]. This type of PN code generator is said to generate a *maximum-length sequence* or *m-sequence* waveform.

Properties of Maximum-Length Sequences   Some properties of m-sequences are [Ziemer and Peterson, 1985]:

   Property 1. In one period the number of 1s is always one more than the number of 0s.
   Property 2. The modulo 2 sum of any m-sequence when summed chip by chip with a

(a) BPSK-DS-SS Transmitter

(b) Spreading Code Generator

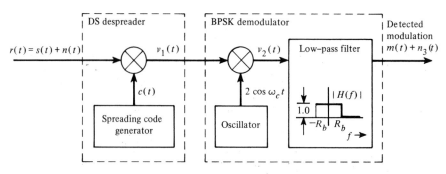

(c) BPSK-DS-SS Receiver

FIGURE 7-20 Direct sequence spread spectrum system (DS-SS).

shifted version of the same sequence produces another shifted version of the same sequence.

Property 3. If a window of width r (where r is the number of stages in the shift register) is slid along the sequence for N shifts, then all possible r-bit words will appear exactly once, except for the all 0 r-bit word.

Property 4. If the 0s and 1s are represented by -1 volt and $+1$ volt, the autocorrelation of the *sequence*, denoted by $R_c(k)$, is

$$R_c(k) = \begin{cases} 1, & k = \ell N \\ -\dfrac{1}{N}, & k \neq \ell N \end{cases} \qquad (7\text{-}52)$$

where $R_c(k) \triangleq (1/N) \sum_{n=0}^{N-1} c_n c_{n+k}$ and $c_n = \pm 1$.

The autocorrelation of the *waveform*, $c(t)$, denoted by $R_c(\tau)$, is

$$R_c(\tau) = \left(1 - \frac{\tau_\epsilon}{T_c}\right) R_c(k) + \frac{\tau_\epsilon}{T_c} R_c(k+1) \qquad (7\text{-}53)$$

where $R_c(\tau) = \langle c(t)c(t+\tau)\rangle$ and τ_ϵ is defined by

$$\tau = kT_c + \tau_\epsilon \qquad \text{and} \qquad 0 \leq \tau_\epsilon < T_c \qquad (7\text{-}54)$$

Equation (7-53) reduces to

$$R_c(\tau) = \left[\sum_{\ell=-\infty}^{\ell=\infty} \left(1 + \frac{1}{N}\right) \Lambda\left(\frac{\tau - \ell N T_c}{T_c}\right)\right] - \frac{1}{N} \qquad (7\text{-}55)$$

This is plotted in Fig. 7-21a, where it is apparent that the autocorrelation function for the PN waveform is periodic with triangular pulses of width $2T_c$ repeated every NT_c seconds and that a correlation level of $-1/N$ occurs between these triangular pulses. Furthermore, since the autocorrelation function is periodic, the associated PSD is a line spectrum. That is, the autocorrelation is expressed as a Fourier series

$$R_c(\tau) = \sum_{n=-\infty}^{\infty} r_n e^{j2\pi n f_0 t} \qquad (7\text{-}56)$$

where $f_0 = 1/(NT_c)$ and $\{r_n\}$ is the set of Fourier series coefficients. Thus, using (2-103) yields

$$\mathcal{P}_c(f) = \mathcal{F}[R_c(\tau)] = \sum_{n=-\infty}^{\infty} r_n \delta(f - n f_0) \qquad (7\text{-}57)$$

where the Fourier series coefficients are evaluated and found to be

$$r_n = \begin{cases} \dfrac{1}{N^2}, & n = 0 \\[2mm] \left(\dfrac{N+1}{N^2}\right)\left(\dfrac{\sin(\pi n/N)}{\pi n/N}\right)^2, & n \neq 0 \end{cases} \qquad (7\text{-}58)$$

This PSD is plotted in Fig. 7-21b.

(a) Autocorrelation Function

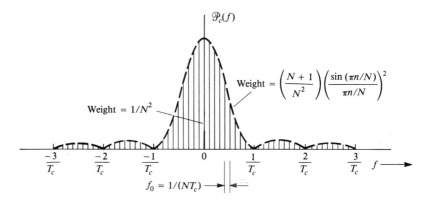

(b) Power Spectral Density (PSD)

FIGURE 7-21 Autocorrelation and PSD for an m-sequence PN waveform.

Now let us demonstrate that the bandwidth of the SS signal is relatively large compared to the data rate, R_b, and is determined primarily by the spreading waveform, $c(t)$, and not by the data modulation, $m(t)$. Referring to Fig. 7-20, we see that the PSDs of both $m(t)$ and $c(t)$ are of the $[(\sin x)/x]^2$ type, where the bandwidth of $c(t)$ is much larger than that of $m(t)$ because it is assumed that the chip rate, $R_c = 1/T_c$ is much larger than the data rate, $R_b = 1/T_b$. That is, $R_c \gg R_b$. To simplify the mathematics, approximate these PSDs by rectangular spectra, as shown in Fig. 7-22a and b, where the heights of the PSD are selected so that the areas under the curves are unity because the powers of $m(t)$ and $c(t)$ are unity. (They both have only ± 1 values.) From (7-51), $g(t)$ is obtained by multiplying $m(t)$ and $c(t)$ in the time domain, and $m(t)$ and $c(t)$ are independent. Thus the PSD for the complex envelope of the BPSK–DS–SS signal is obtained by a convolution operation in the frequency domain.

$$\mathcal{P}_g(f) = A_c^2 \, \mathcal{P}_m(f) * \mathcal{P}_c(f) \tag{7-59}$$

This result is shown in Fig. 7-22c for the approximate PSDs of $m(t)$ and $c(t)$. The bandwidth of the BPSK–DS–SS signal is determined essentially by the chip rate, R_c, since $R_c \gg R_b$. For example, let $R_b = 9.6$ kbits/sec and $R_c = 9.6$ Mchips/sec. Then the bandwidth of the SS signal is $B_T \approx 2R_c = 19.2$ MHz.

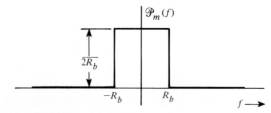

(a) Approximate PSD for $m(t)$

(b) Approximate PSD for $c(t)$

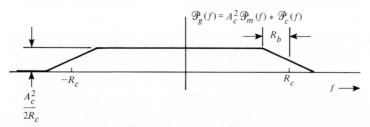

(c) Approximate PSD for Complex Envelope of the SS Signal

FIGURE 7-22 Approximate PSD of the BPSK–DS–SS signal.

From Fig. 7-22 we can also demonstrate that the spreading has made the signal less susceptible to detection by an eavesdropper. That is, this signal has LPI. Without spreading [i.e., if $c(t)$ was unity], the level of the in-band PSD would be proportional to $A_c^2/(2R_b)$, as seen in Fig. 7-22a, but with spreading the in-band spectral level drops to $A_c^2/(2R_c)$, as seen in Fig. 7-22c. This is a reduction of R_c/R_b. For example, for the values of R_b and R_c just cited, the reduction factor would be (9.6 Mchips/sec)/(9.6 kbits/sec) = 1000 or 30 dB. Often the eavesdropper detects the presence of a signal by using a spectrum analyzer, but when SS is used, this level will drop by 30 dB. This is often below the noise floor of the potential eavesdropper, and thus the SS signal will escape detection by the eavesdropper.

Figure 7-20c shows a receiver that recovers the modulation on the SS signal. The receiver has a despreading circuit that is driven by a PN code generator in synchronism with the transmitter spreading code. Assume that the input to the receiver consists of the SS signal plus a narrowband (sine wave) jammer signal. Then,

$$r(t) = s(t) + n(t) = A_c m(t)c(t) \cos \omega_c t + n_J(t) \tag{7-60}$$

where the jamming signal is

$$n_J(t) = A_J \cos \omega_c t \tag{7-61}$$

Here it is assumed that the jamming power is $A_J^2/2$ relative to the signal power of $A_c^2/2$ and that the jamming frequency is set to f_c for the worst-case jamming effect. Referring to Fig. 7-20c, we find that the output of the despreader is

$$v_1(t) = A_c m(t) \cos \omega_c t + A_J c(t) \cos \omega_c t \qquad (7\text{-}62)$$

since $c^2(t) = (\pm 1)^2 = 1$. The BPSK–DS–SS signal has become simply a BPSK signal at the output of the despreader. That is, at the receiver input the SS signal has a bandwidth of $2R_c$, but at the despreader output the bandwidth of the resulting BPSK signal is $2R_b$, a 1000:1 reduction for the figures previously cited. The data on the BPSK despread signal are recovered by using a BPSK detector circuit as shown.

Now it will be shown that this SS receiver provides an antijam capability of 30 dB for the case of $R_b = 9.6$ kbits/sec and $R_c = 9.6$ Mchips/sec. From (7-62) it is seen that the narrowband jammer signal that was present at the receiver input has been *spread* by the despreader since it has been multiplied by $c(t)$. It is this spreading effect on the jamming signal that produces the antijam capability. Using (7-62) and referring to Fig. 7-20c, we obtain an input to the LPF of

$$v_2(t) = A_c m(t) + n_2(t) \qquad (7\text{-}63)$$

where

$$n_2(t) = A_J c(t) \qquad (7\text{-}64)$$

and the terms about $f = 2f_c$ have been neglected since they do not pass through the LPF. Referring to Fig. 7-20c, we note that the jammer power at the receiver output is

$$P_{n_3} = \int_{-R_b}^{R_b} \mathcal{P}_{n_2}(f)\, df = \int_{-R_b}^{R_b} A_J^2 \frac{1}{2R_c}\, df = \frac{A_J^2}{R_c/R_b} \qquad (7\text{-}65)$$

and the jammer power at the input to the LPF is A_J^2. $[\mathcal{P}_{n_2}(f) = A_J^2/(2R_c)$ as seen from Fig. 7-22b and (7-64).] For a conventional BPSK system (i.e., no spread spectrum), $c(t)$ would be unity and (7-64) would become $n_2(t) = A_J$, so the jamming power out of the LPF would be A_J^2 instead of $A_J^2/(R_c/R_b)$ for the case of an SS system. [The output signal should be $A_c m(t)$ for both cases.] Thus, the SS receiver has reduced the effect of narrowband jamming by the factor of R_c/R_b. This factor, R_c/R_b, is called the *processing gain* of the SS receiver.[†] For our example of $R_c = 9.6$ Mchips/sec and $R_b = 9.6$ kbits/sec, the processing gain is 30 dB. This means that the narrowband jammer would have to have 30 dB more power to have the same jamming effect on this SS system, as compared to the conventional BPSK system (no SS). Thus this SS technique provides 30 dB of antijam capability for the R_c/R_b ratio cited in the example.

SS techniques can also be used to provide multiple access. This is called *code division multiple access* (CDMA). Here each user is assigned a spreading code such that the signals are orthogonal. Thus multiple SS signals can be transmitted simultaneously in the same frequency band, and yet the data on a particular SS signal can be decoded by a receiver, *provided* that this receiver uses a PN code that is identical to that used on the

---

[†]The processing gain is defined as the ratio to the noise power out without SS divided by the noise power out with SS. This is equivalent to the ratio $(S/N)_{out}/(S/N)_{in}$ when $(S/N)_{in}$ is the signal-to-noise power into the receiver and $(S/N)_{out}$ is the signal-to-noise power out of the LPF.

particular SS signal that is to be decoded. Although CDMA provides a neat solution for the multiple access problem in an interference environment, it can be shown that TDMA and FDMA are more bandwidth efficient [Viterbi, 1985].

To accommodate more users in frequency bands that are now saturated with conventional narrowband users (such as the two-way radio bands), it is possible to assign in addition new SS stations. This is called *spread spectrum overlay.* The SS stations would operate with such a wide bandwidth that their PSD would appear to be negligible to narrowband receivers located sufficiently distant from the SS transmitters. On the other hand, to the SS receiver, the narrowband signals would have a minimal jamming effect because of the large coding gain of the SS receiver.

Frequency Hopping

As indicated previously, a frequency-hopped (FH) SS signal uses a $g_c(t)$ that is of the FM type where there are $M = 2^k$ hop frequencies controlled by the spreading code where k chip words are taken to determine each hop frequency. An FH-SS transmitter is shown in Fig. 7-23a. The source information is modulated onto a carrier using conventional FSK or BPSK techniques to produce an FSK or a BPSK signal. The frequency hopping is accomplished by using a mixer circuit where the LO signal is provided by the output of a frequency synthesizer that is hopped by the PN spreading code. The serial-to-parallel converter reads k serial chips of the spreading code and outputs a k chip parallel word to the programmable dividers in the frequency synthesizer. (See Fig. 5-25 and the related discussion of frequency synthesizers.) The k chip word specifies one of the possible $M = 2^k$ hop frequencies, ω_1, ω_2, . . ., ω_M.

The FH signal is decoded as shown in Fig. 7-23b. Here the receiver has the knowledge of the transmitter, $c(t)$, so that the frequency synthesizer in the receiver can be hopped in synchronism with that at the transmitter. This despreads the FH signal, and the source information is recovered from the dehopped signal by use of a conventional FSK or BPSK demodulator, as appropriate.

In 1985 the FCC opened up three shared frequency bands—902 to 928 MHz, 2400 to 2483.5 MHz, and 5725 to 5850 MHz—for commercial SS use with unlicensed 1-W transmitters. This has led to the production and use of SS equipment for telemetry systems, personal communication networks (PCNs), wireless local area networks for personal computers, and wireless fire and security systems [Schilling, Pickholtz, and Milstein, 1990]. Also, commercial SS applications have been proposed that have advantages over present systems. For example, a digital SS cellular telephone system (i.e., CDMA) appears to be able to accommodate about 1000 users per cell as compared to the U.S. analog cellular system, which accommodates 55 users per cell [Schilling, Pickholtz, and Milstein, 1990]. In another application, digital stereo broadcasting using SS techniques appears to accommodate up to 75 stations in a region using the U.S. FM band, 88 to 108 MHz [Schilling et al., 1991]. This is a larger number of stations than found with present analog FM stereo assignments; moreover, digital stereo SS broadcasting will provide a much larger audio signal-to-noise ratio for the listener.

Limited space does not permit further discussion of SS systems. For further study on

(a) Transmitter

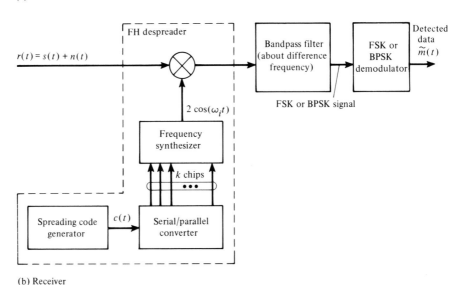

(b) Receiver

FIGURE 7-23 Frequency-hopped spread spectrum system (FH–SS).

this interesting topic, the reader is referred to books that have been written on this subject [Cooper and McGillem, 1986; Dixon, 1984; Ziemer and Peterson, 1985].

7-6 Summary

In this chapter, a wide range of digital modulation systems were presented based on the theory developed in Chapters 1 through 6.

Basic bandpass digital signaling techniques such as OOK, BPSK, and FSK were developed from classical AM, PM, and FM theory. The spectra of these digital signals were evaluated in terms of the bit rate of the digital information source. Multilevel digital signaling techniques such as QPSK, MPSK, QAM, and MSK were also studied, and their spectra were evaluated. Receiver structures and their probability of bit error were studied.

Spread spectrum signaling was examined since it has multiple-access capability, anti-jam capability, interference rejection, and low probability of intercept that are applicable to personal communication systems and military systems. This study included the calculation of the spectrum for a spread spectrum signal and the examination of transmitter and receiver block diagrams for both direct sequence and frequency hopped spread spectrum systems.

PROBLEMS

7-1 A digital baseband signal consisting of rectangular binary pulses occurring at a rate of 2400 bits/sec is to be transmitted over a bandpass channel.
(a) Evaluate the magnitude spectrum for OOK signaling that is keyed by a baseband digital test pattern consisting of alternating 1's and 0's.
(b) Sketch the magnitude spectrum and indicate the value of the first null-to-null bandwidth. Assume a carrier frequency of 50 kHz.
(c) For a random data pattern, find the PSD and plot the result. Compare this result with that obtained in parts (a) and (b) for alternating data.

7-2 Repeat Prob. 7-1 for the case of BPSK signaling.

7-3 A carrier is angle modulated with a polar baseband data signal to produce a BPSK signal, $s(t) = 10 \cos[\omega_c t + D_p m(t)]$, where $m(t) = \pm 1$ corresponds to the binary data $\{10010110\}$. $T_b = 0.0025$ sec and $\omega_c = 1000\pi$. Using MathCAD or MATLAB, plot the BPSK signal waveform and its corresponding FFT spectrum for the following digital modulation indices:
(a) $h = 0.2$.
(b) $h = 0.5$.
(c) $h = 1.0$.

7-4 Evaluate the magnitude spectrum for an FSK signal with alternating 1 and 0 data. Assume that the mark frequency is 50 kHz, the space frequency is 55 kHz, and the bit rate is 2400 bits/sec. Find the first null-to-null bandwidth.

7-5 Assume that 4800-bit/sec random data are sent over a bandpass channel by BPSK signaling. Find the transmission bandwidth B_T such that the spectral envelope is down at least 35 dB outside this band.

7-6 As indicated in Sec. 7-1, a BPSK signal can be demodulated by using a synchronous detector where the carrier reference is provided by a Costas loop for the case of $h = 1.0$. Alternatively, the carrier reference can be provided by a squaring loop that uses a $\times 2$ frequency multiplier. A block diagram for a squaring loop is shown in Fig. P7-6.

FIGURE P7-6

(a) Draw an overall block diagram for a BPSK receiver using the squaring loop.
(b) By using mathematics to represent the waveforms, show how the squaring loop recovers the carrier reference.
(c) Demonstrate that the squaring loop does or does not have a 180° phase ambiguity problem.

7-7   A binary data signal is differentially encoded and modulates a PM transmitter to produce a differentially encoded phase-shift-keyed signal (DPSK). The peak-to-peak phase deviation is 180° and f_c is harmonically related to the bit rate R.
(a) Draw a block diagram for the transmitter, including the differential encoder.
(b) Show typical waveforms at various points on the block diagram if the input data sequence is 01011000101.
(c) Assume that the receiver consists of a superheterodyne circuit. The detector that is used is shown in Fig. P7-7, where $T = 1/R$. If the DPSK IF signal $v_1(t)$ has a peak value of A_c volts, determine the appropriate value for the threshold voltage setting V_T.
(d) Sketch the waveforms that appear at various points of this detector circuit for the data sequence in part (b).

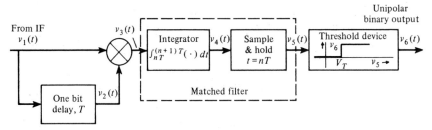

FIGURE P7-7

7-8   A binary baseband signal is passed through a raised cosine-rolloff filter with a 50% rolloff factor and is then modulated onto a carrier. The data rate is 2400 bits/sec. Evaluate:
(a) The absolute bandwidth of a resulting OOK signal.

(b) The approximate bandwidth of a resulting FSK signal when the mark frequency is 50 kHz and the space frequency is 55 kHz.

(*Note:* It is interesting to compare these bandwidths with those obtained in Probs. 7-1 and 7-4.)

7-9 Evaluate the exact magnitude spectrum of the FSK signal that is emitted by a Bell-type 103 modem operating in the answer mode at 300 bits/sec. Assume that the data are alternating 1's and 0's.

7-10 Repeat Prob. 7-9 if the data have the periodic pattern 111000111000.

7-11 Starting with (7-17), work out all of the mathematical steps to derive the result given in (7-18).

7-12 When FSK signals are detected using coherent detection as shown in Fig. 7-10b, it is assumed that $\cos \omega_1 t$ and $\cos \omega_2 t$ are orthogonal functions. This is approximately true if $f_1 - f_2 = 2 \Delta F$ is sufficiently large. Find the *exact* condition required for the mark and space FSK signals to be orthogonal. (*Hint:* The answer relates f_1, f_2, and R.)

7-13 Show that the approximate transmission bandwidth for FSK is given by $B_T = 2R(1 + h/2)$, where h is the digital modulation index and R is the bit rate.

7-14 Assume that a QPSK modem is used to send data at a rate of 3.6 kbits/sec over a twisted pair telephone line. The line has a bandwidth of 2.4 kHz.
   (a) If the line is equalized to have an equivalent raised cosine filter characteristic, what is the rolloff factor, r, required?
   (b) Could a rolloff factor, r, be found so that a 4.8-kbit/sec data rate could be supported?

7-15 Show that two BPSK systems can operate simultaneously over the same channel by using quadrature (sine and cosine) carriers. Give a block diagram for the transmitters and receivers. What is the overall aggregate data rate, R, for this quadrature carrier multiplex system as a function of the channel null bandwidth, B_T? How does the aggregate data rate of this system compare to the data rate for a system that first time-division-multiplexes the two sources and transmits the TDM data via a QPSK carrier?

7-16 Assume that a telephone line channel is equalized to allow bandpass data transmission over a frequency range of 600 to 3000 Hz with raised cosine-rolloff filtering. The available channel bandwidth is 2400 Hz with a midchannel frequency of 1800 Hz.
   (a) Design a 2400-bit/sec QPSK transmission system with $f_c = 1800$ Hz. Show that the spectrum of this signal will fit into the channel when $r = 1$. Find the absolute and 6-dB bandwidths.
   (b) Repeat part (a) for the case of 4800-bit/sec eight-phase PSK signaling.

7-17 Assume that a telephone line channel is equalized to allow bandpass data transmission over a frequency range of 400 to 3100 Hz so that the available channel bandwidth is 2700 Hz and the midchannel frequency is 1750 Hz. Design a 16-symbol QAM signaling scheme that will allow a data rate of 9600 bits/sec to be transferred over the channel. In your design, choose an appropriate rolloff factor r and indicate the absolute and 6-dB QAM signal bandwidth. Discuss why you selected the particular value of r that you used.

7-18 Assume that $R = 9600$ bits/sec. Calculate the *second* null-to-null bandwidth of BPSK, QPSK, MSK, 64PSK, and 64QAM. Discuss the advantages and disadvantages of using each of these signaling methods.

7-19 Referring to Fig. 7-13b, sketch the waveforms that appear at the output of each block assuming that the input is a TTL level signal with data 110100101 and $\ell = 4$. Explain how this QAM transmitter works.

7-20 Design a receiver (i.e., determine the block diagram) that will detect the data on a QAM waveform having an $M = 16$ point signal constellation as shown in Fig. 7-14. Explain how your receiver works. (*Hint:* Study Fig. 7-13b.)

7-21 Using MathCAD or MATLAB, plot the QPSK and OQPSK in-phase and quadrature modulation waveforms for the data stream

$$\{-1, -1, -1, +1, +1, +1, -1, -1, -1, +1, -1, -1, +1, -1, -1\}$$

Use a rectangular pulse shape. For convenience let $T_b = 1$.

7-22 Calculate and plot the PSD for a CCITT V.22bis 2400-bit/sec computer modem operating in the originate mode and sending random data. See Table C-12 for the modem specifications.

7-23 (a) Fig. 7-16 shows the $x(t)$ and $y(t)$ waveforms for Type II MSK. Redraw these waveforms for the case of Type I MSK.
      (b) Show that (7-47b) is the Fourier transform of (7-47a).

7-24 Using MathCAD or MATLAB, plot the MSK Type I modulation waveforms $x(t)$, $y(t)$, and the MSK signal $s(t)$. Assume that the input data stream is

$$\{+1, -1, -1, +1, -1, -1, +1, -1, -1, +1, +1, -1, +1, +1, -1\}$$

Assume that $T_b = 1$ and that f_c has a value such that a good plot of $s(t)$ is obtained for a reasonable amount of computer time.

7-25 Repeat Prob. 7-24 but use the data stream

$$\{-1, -1, -1, +1, +1, +1, -1, -1, -1, +1, -1, -1, +1, -1, -1\}$$

This data stream is the differentially encoded version of the data stream in Prob. 7-24. The generation of FFSK is equivalent to Type I MSK with differential encoding of the data input. FFSK has a one-to-one relationship between the input data and the mark and space frequencies.

7-26 Using MathCAD or MATLAB, plot the MSK Type II modulation waveforms $x(t)$, $y(t)$, and the MSK signal $s(t)$. Assume that the input data stream is

$$\{-1, -1, -1, +1, +1, +1, -1, -1, -1, +1, -1, -1, +1, -1, -1\}$$

Assume that $T_b = 1$ and f_c has a value such that a good plot of $s(t)$ is obtained for a reasonable amount of computer time.

7-27 Show that MSK can be generated by the serial method of Fig. 7-18c. That is, show that the PSD for the signal at the output of the MSK bandpass filter is the MSK spectrum as described by (7-48) and (7-2).

7-28 Recompute the spectral efficiencies for all of the signals shown in Table 7-5 using a 40-dB bandwidth criterion.

7-29 In most applications, communication systems are designed to have a BER of 10^{-5} or less. Find the minimum E_b/N_0 decibels required to achieve an error rate of 10^{-5} for the following types of signaling.
   (a) Polar baseband.
   (b) OOK.
   (c) BPSK.
   (d) FSK.
   (e) DPSK.

7-30 A BER of 10^{-5} or less is desired for an OOK communication system where the bit rate is $R = 2400$ bits/sec. The input to the receiver consists of the OOK signal plus white Gaussian noise.
   (a) Find the minimum transmission bandwidth required.
   (b) Find the minimum E_b/N_0 required at the receiver input for coherent matched-filter detection.
   (c) Rework part (b) for the case of noncoherent detection.

7-31 Rework Prob. 7-30 for the case when FSK signaling is used where $2\Delta F = f_2 - f_1 = 1.5R$.

7-32 Digital data are to be transmitted over a twisted-pair wire telephone system using BPSK. Regenerative repeaters are spaced 50 miles apart along the system. The total length of the system is 600 miles. The telephone lines between the repeater sites are equalized over a 300- to 2700-Hz band and provide an E_b/N_0 (Gaussian noise) of 15 dB to the repeater input.
   (a) Find the largest bit rate R that can be accommodated with no ISI.
   (b) Find the overall P_e for the system. (Be sure to include the receiver at the end of the system.)

7-33 A BER of 10^{-5} is desired for a FSK communication system that uses noncoherent detection where the bit rate is $R = 2400$ bits/sec and $\Delta F = 100$ Hz. The input to the recceiver consists of the FSK signal plus AWGN.
   (a) Find the minimum E_b/N_0 in dB units that is required at the receiver input.
   (b) Find the bandwidth of the FSK signal.
   (b) Find the minimum S/N ratio in dB units that is required at the receiver input.

7-34 Prove that (7-53)—the autocorrelation for an m-sequence PN code—is correct. *Hint:* Use the definition for the autocorrelation function, $R_c(\tau) = \langle c(t)c(t + \tau)\rangle$ and (7-52) where

$$c(t) = \sum_{-\infty}^{\infty} c_n p(t - nT_c)$$

and

$$p(t) = \begin{cases} 1, & 0 < t < T_c \\ 0, & t \text{ elsewhere} \end{cases}$$

7-35 Find an expression for the power spectral density (PSD) of an m-sequence PN code when the chip rate is 10 MHz and there are eight stages in the shift register. Sketch your result.

7-36 Referring to Fig. 6-16a, show that the complex Fourier series coefficients for the autocorrelation of an m-sequence PN waveform are given by (7-58).

7-37 Assume that the modulator and demodulator for the FH–SS system of Fig. 7-23 are of the FSK type.
(a) Find a mathematical expression for the FSK–FH–SS signal, $s(t)$, at the transmitter output.
(b) Using your result for $s(t)$ from part (a) as the receiver input in Fig. 7-23b [i.e., $r(t) = s(t)$], show that the output of the receiver bandpass filter is an FSK signal.

Case Studies of Communication Systems

The goal of this chapter is to examine the design of some practical communication systems. These systems are based on the communication principles that have been developed in previous chapters. Also, we see how modern designs are influenced by industry standards and how some sophisticated systems are the evolution of historical systems. This should be a "fun" chapter.

Case studies are presented for wire-line telephone systems, satellite systems, link budget system analysis, fiber optic systems, cellular telephone systems, and television systems. Link budget analysis is concerned with the design of a system to meet a required performance specification as a function of trade-off in the transmitted power, antenna gain, and noise figure of the receiving systems. This performance specification is the maximum allowed probability of error for digital systems, and the minimum allowed output S/N ratio for analog systems.

8-1 Telecommunication Systems

Telecommunication systems are designed to transmit voice, data, or visual information over some distance. (The prefix *tele* is derived from a Greek word meaning distance.) Modern telecommunication systems have evolved from the telegraph and telephone systems of the 1800s. Telecommunication companies that provide services for a large number of users over their *public switched telephone networks* (PSTN) on a for-hire basis are known as *common carriers*. The term is applied to widely diverse businesses such as mail, airline, trucking, telephone, and data services. The common carriers are usually regulated by the government for the general welfare of the public, and, in some countries, certain common carrier services are provided by the government. The information from multiple users is transmitted over these systems primarily by using time-division multiplexing (TDM) and frequency-division multiplexing (FDM).

Time-Division Multiplexing

In Chapter 3, TDM techniques were first introduced. Examples of common carrier TDM techniques using digital signaling of the types DS-O, DS-1, DS-2, DS-3, DS-4, and DS-5 were studied. For a review of these techniques, the reader is referred to Sec. 4-8, specifically Figs. 4-36 and 4-37 and Tables 4-8 and 4-9. These figures and tables give the TDM standards that have been developed by the common carriers. For bandpass transmission, such as over microwave radio relay, fiber optic, or satellite systems, these TDM baseband signals are digitally modulated onto RF carriers using the OOK, QPSK, MPSK, or QAM techniques that were studied in Secs. 7-1 and 7-2. Fiber optic systems with OOK are described in Sec. 8-7.

TDM techniques are generally preferred to FDM techniques because of the ease of transmission of error-free data and voice information.

Frequency-Division Multiplexing

FDM techniques were introduced in Chapter 6 (Fig. 6-16). This was followed by a discussion of the FDM technique used in FM stereo broadcasting, where the left and right audio signals are multiplexed onto one radio-frequency carrier. In toll telephone service, voice signals are transmitted over high-capacity channels using either TDM or FDM. The FDM technique was used historically; now TDM has become dominant and FDM is being phased out.

The telephone FDM technique is illustrated by the American Telephone and Telegraph Company (AT&T) FDM hierarchy, which is given in Fig. 8-1. Here, 12 analog (0- to 4-kHz voice frequency) telephone signals are frequency-division-multiplexed using lower SSB modulators to form one *group* signal. Five group signals are frequency-division-multiplexed to form one *supergroup* signal. The supergroup signal contains the information of 60 voice-frequency (VF) telephone signals. The bandwidth of the group signal is 48 kHz, and any 48-kHz signal (analog or digital) with spectrum centered in the group passband may replace a group input in the FDM hierarchy. Similarly, a supergroup signal may be replaced by any 240-kHz bandwidth signal when needed. Ten supergroup signals are frequency-division-multiplexed to form one *mastergroup* signal, which contains 600 VF signals. In Fig. 8-1 the carrier frequencies are given for the AT&T Type U600 mastergroup [Bell Telephone Laboratories, 1970]. Six mastergroup signals may be frequency-division-multiplexed to form a *jumbo-group* containing the information of 3600-VF signals.

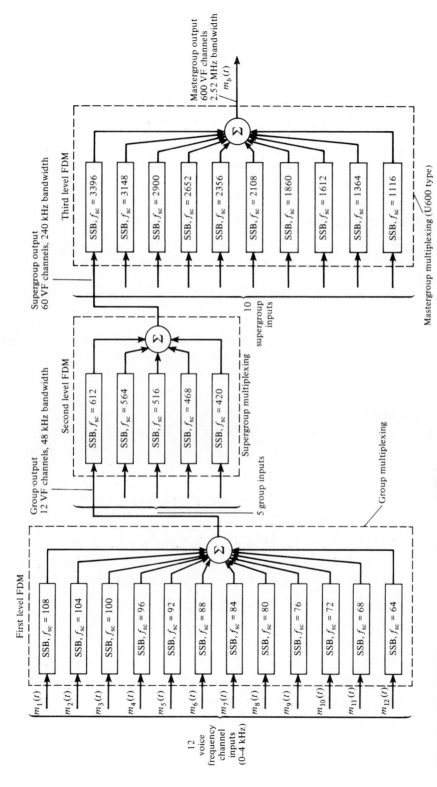

FIGURE 8-1 AT&T FDM hierarchy (f_{sc} given in kilohertz).

8-2 Telephone Systems

Historically, telephone systems were designed only to reproduce voice signals that originated from a distant location. Today, modern telephone systems can be very sophisticated. They use large digital computers at the central office (CO) to switch calls and to monitor the performance of the telephone system. The modern CO routes time-division-multiplexed (TDM) PCM voice data, video data, and computer data to remote terminals and to other central offices.

Historical Basis

As we shall see, modern telephone systems have evolved from the relatively simple analog circuit that was invented by Alexander Graham Bell in 1876. This circuit is shown in Fig. 8-2, where two telephone handsets are connected together by a twisted-pair (i.e., two-wire) telephone line and the telephone handsets are powered by a battery located at the CO. (Historically, the telephone-wire connection between the two parties was made by a telephone switchboard operator.) The battery produces a dc current around the telephone-wire loop. A carbon microphone element is used in each telephone handset. It consists of loosely packed carbon granules in a box that has one flexible side—the diaphragm. As sound pressure waves strike the diaphragm, the carbon granules are compressed and decompressed. This creates a variable resistance that causes the dc loop current to be modulated. Thus an ac audio current signal is produced, as shown in the

FIGURE 8-2 Historical telephone system.

figure. The handset earphone consists of an electromagnet with a paramagnetic diaphragm placed within the magnetic field. The ac current passing through the electromagnet causes the earphone diaphragm to vibrate and sound is reproduced.

The simple two-wire telephone system of Fig. 8-2 has three important advantages: (1) it is inexpensive; (2) the telephone sets are powered from the CO via the telephone line, so no power supply is required at the user's location; and (3) the circuit is full duplex.[†] The two-wire system has one main disadvantage—amplifiers cannot be used since they amplify the signal in only one direction. Consequently, for distant telephone connections, a more advanced technique—called a four-wire circuit—is required, as will be discussed subsequently. In summary, telephone circuits may be divided into two main categories:

• Two-wire or local loop circuits.
• Four-wire circuits.

Modern Telephone Systems and Remote Terminals

A simplified diagram for a local loop system that is used today is shown in Fig. 8-3. The local switching office connects the two parties by making a hardwire connection between the two appropriate local loops. This is essentially a series connection, with the earphone and carbon microphone of each telephone handset wired in a series with a battery (located at the telephone plant). Figure 8-3 illustrates this analog local-loop system, which is said to supply *plain old telephone service* (POTS). The wire with positive voltage from the *central office* (CO) is called the *tip* lead and it is color coded *green.* The wire with negative voltage is called the *ring* lead and is color coded *red.* The terms *tip* and *ring* are derived from the era when a plug switchboard was used at the CO and these leads were connected to a plug with tip and ring contacts. This jack is similar to a stereo headphone jack that has tip, ring, and sleeve contacts. The Earth ground lead was connected to the sleeve contact.

The sequence of events that occur when placing a local phone call will now be described with the aid of Fig. 8-3 and Table 8-1. The calling party—the upper telephone set in Fig. 8-3—removes the telephone handset; this action closes the switchhook contact (off-hook) so that dc current flows through the caller's telephone line. The current, about 40 mA, is sensed at the CO and causes the CO to place a dial-tone signal (approximately 400 Hz) on the calling party's line. The calling party dials the number by using either pulse or touch-tone dialing. If pulse dialing is used, the dc line current is interrupted for the number of times equal to the digit dialed (at a rate of 10 pulses/sec). For example, there are five interruptions of the line current when the number 5 is dialed. Upon reception of the complete number sequence for the called party, the CO places the ringing generator (90 V, 20 Hz, on 2 sec, off 4 sec) on the line corresponding to the number dialed. This rings the phone. When the called party answers, dc current flows in that line to signal the CO to disconnect the ringing generator and to connect the two parties together via the CO circuit switch. Direct current is now flowing in the lines of both the called and the calling

---

[†] With full-duplex circuits each person can talk and listen simultaneously to the other person.

FIGURE 8-3 Local telephone system (simplified).

party, and there is a connection between the two parties via transformer coupling[†] as shown in Fig. 8-3. When either person speaks, the sound vibrations cause the resistance of the carbon microphone element to change in synchronization with the vibrations so that the dc line current is modulated (varied). This produces the ac audio signal that is coupled

---

[†]The transformers are called ''repeat coils'' in telephone parlance.

TABLE 8-1 Telephone Standards for the Subscriber Loop

Item	Standard
On-hook (idle status)	Line open circuit, minimum dc resistance 30 kΩ
Off-hook (busy status)	Line closed circuit, maximum dc resistance 200 Ω
Battery voltage	48 V
Operating current	20–80 mA, 40 mA typical
Subscriber-loop resistance	0–1300 Ω, 3600 Ω (max)
Loop loss	8 dB (typical), 17 dB (max)
Ringing voltage	90 V rms, 20 Hz (typical) (usually pulsed on 2 sec, off 4 sec)
Ringer equivalence number (REN)[a]	0.2 REN (minimum), 5.0 REN (maximum)
Pulse dialing	Momentary open-circuit loop
Pulsing rate	10 pulses/sec ±10%
Duty cycle	58–64% break (open)
Time between digits	600 msec minimum
Pulse code	1 pulse = 1, 2 pulses = 2, . . . , 10 pulses = 0
Touch-tone[b] dialing	Uses two tones, a low-frequency tone and a high-frequency tone, to specify each digit:

	High Tone (Hz)		
Low Tone	1209	1336	1477
697 Hz	1	2	3
770	4	5	6
852	7	8	9
941	*	0	#

Level each tone	−6 to −4 dBm
Maximum difference in levels	4 dB
Maximum level (pair)	+2 dBm
Frequency tolerance	±1.5%
Pulse width	50 msec
Time between digits	45 msec minimum
Dial tone	350 plus 440 Hz
Busy signal	480 plus 620 Hz, with 60 interruptions per minute
Ringing signal tone	440 plus 480 Hz, 2 sec on, 4 sec off
Caller ID[c]	1.2-kbit/sec FSK signal between first and second rings (Bell 202 modem standard; see Table C-13)[d]

[a] Indicates the impedance loading caused by the telephone ringer. An REN of 1.0 equals about 8 kΩ, 0.2 REN is 40 kΩ, and 5.0 REN is 1.6 kΩ.

[b] Touch-tone was a registered trademark of AT&T. It is also known as *dual-tone multiple frequency* (DTMF) signaling.

[c] Other display services are also proposed [Schwartz, 1993].

[d] [Lancaster, 1991].

to the headphone of the other party's telephone. Note that both parties may speak and hear each other simultaneously. This is full-duplex operation.

In most modern telephone sets, the carbon microphone element is replaced with an electret or dynamic microphone element and an associated IC amplifier that is powered by the battery voltage from the CO, but the principle of operation is the same as previously described.

The telephone system of Fig. 8-3 is satisfactory as long as the resistance of the twisted-pair loops is 1300 Ω or less. This limits the distance that telephones can be placed from this type of CO to about 15,000 ft for 26-gauge wire, 24,000 ft for 24-gauge, and 38,000 ft or about 7 miles if 22-gauge twisted-pair wire is used. Sometimes 19-gauge wire is used in rural areas so that phones may be located up to 20 miles from the CO.

Supplying a dedicated wire pair from each subscriber all the way to the CO is expensive. In applications where a large number of subscribers are clustered some distance from the CO, costs can be substantially reduced by using *remote terminals* (RT) (see Fig. 8-4). Remote terminals also allow telephones to be placed at any distance from the CO, as we will describe subsequently.

The circuit for a typical RT is illustrated in Fig. 8-5. The RT supplies battery voltage and ringing current to the subscriber's telephone. The *two-wire circuit* that carries the duplex VF signals to and from the subscriber is converted into a *four-wire circuit* that carries two one-way (simplex) transmit and receive signals by the use of a *hybrid* circuit. The hybrid is a balanced transformer circuit (or its equivalent electronic circuit) that

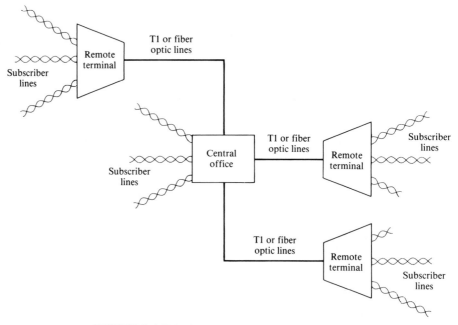

FIGURE 8-4 Telephone system with remote terminals.

FIGURE 8-5 Remote terminal (RT).

provides isolation for the transmit and receive signals, so that self-oscillation will not occur if the amplified transmitted signal is fed back via the receive line. As shown in the figure, the transmit VF signal is converted to a DS-0 PCM signal, which is time-division-multiplexed with the PCM signals from other subscribers attached to the RT. The TDM signal is sent over a DS-1 trunk to the CO. Similarly, the received DS-1 signal from the CO is demultiplexed and decoded to obtain the received VF audio for the subscriber. In a popular RT system manufactured by AT&T called SLC-96, 96 VF subscriber lines are digitized and multiplexed onto four T1 lines, and one additional T1 line is on standby in case one of the other T1 lines fails [Chapman, 1984]. From Chapter 4 it is recalled that a T1 line requires two twisted pairs (one for the transmit data and one for the receive data) and that each T1 line (1.544 Mbits/sec) carries the equivalent of 24 VF signals.

Let us now compare the twisted-pair requirements for systems with and without RTs. If no RT is used, 96 pairs will be required to the CO for 96 subscribers, but if a SLC-96 RT is used, only 10 pairs (5 T1 lines) are needed to the CO. This provides a pair savings (also called pair gain) of 9.6 to 1. Furthermore, the RT may be located at any distance from the CO (there is no 1300-Ω limit) since the pairs are used for DS-1 signaling with repeaters spaced about every mile. Of course, fiber optic lines can also be used to connect the RT to the CO. For example, if two 560-Mbit/sec fiber optic lines are used (one for data sent in each direction), this has a capacity of 8064 VF channels for DS-5 signaling (see Table 4-8 and Fig. 4-37). Thus an RT with a 560-Mbit/sec fiber optic link to the CO could serve 8064 subscribers. Furthermore, in Sec. 8-7 we see that no optical repeaters will be required if the RT is located within 25 miles (typically) of the CO.

Telephone companies are replacing their analog switches at the CO with digital switches. Historically, at the CO a circuit switch was used to connect the calling and the called party (as shown in Fig. 8-3). These switches were controlled by hardwired relay logic. Now, modern telephone offices use *electronic switching* systems (ESS). With ESS, a digital computer controls the switching operation as directed by software called *stored program control*. Moreover, the latest ESS switches use *digital switching* instead of *analog switching*. Examples are AT&T's No. 5 ESS (electronic switching system), and Northern Telcom's DMS-100 switches. In a digitally switched CO, the customer's VF signal is converted to PCM and time-division-multiplexed with other PCM signals onto a high-speed digital line. (When RTs are used, the conversion of the VF signal to PCM is carried out at the RT.) The digital CO switches a call by placing the PCM data of the calling party into the TDM time slot that has been assigned for the destination (called) party. This is called *time-slot interchange* (TSI). The digital switch is less expensive on a per customer basis than the analog switch (for a large number of customers), and it allows switching of data and digitized video as well as PCM audio. However, many analog switch COs remain since it is not cost effective to scrap existing analog facilities, and, of course, analog VF signals must be converted to TDM PCM signaling before a digital switch can be used. On the other hand, there is the incentive to upgrade analog telephone systems to digital switching with remote terminals since this allows the ISDN service, as introduced in Chapter 4 and described in more detail in the next section. That is, the use of RTs permits the subscriber line to be short (about 1 mile). With short subscriber lines, ISDN service, and, if needed, DS-1 (1.544-Mbits/sec) service, can be provided directly over the existing twisted-pair lines that are already in place to the customer's premises.

For toll calls, the local CO switches the call to trunk lines that connect the local CO to a distant CO. The trunk lines usually carry either TDM or FDM signals, with TDM being the preferred technique. If the local CO uses analog switches, the two-wire circuit must be converted to a four-wire circuit (using a hybrid as described in Fig. 8-5) since unidirectional repeaters are used on the long-distance trunk lines. If the local CO uses a digital switch, it acts much like an RT with respect to the distant CO, and the two COs are connected by high-speed TDM digital trunk lines. Interestingly, long-distance lines are less than 5% of the total cost of the telephone network; most of the cost is in the switching equipment.

In summary, the analog telephone subscriber is connected to a CO or a RT via a two-wire twisted-pair subscriber line. The CO or RT as a terminator of this subscriber loop provides the following functions for POTS:

1. Terminates the line with a 900-Ω ac load (balanced with respect to ground).
2. Supplies dc loop current from its battery through balanced 200-Ω resistors (for a total driven-point dc impedance of 400 Ω).
3. Monitors loop current to determine on-hook and off-hook conditions.
4. Receives dialing information from the subscriber via touch-tone or dial pulse.
5. Applies ringing voltage and call progress signaling (i.e., dial tone, busy signal, ringing tone, etc.).
6. Converts the two-wire line to a four-wire line (transmit and receive path) for use by digital COs and RTs or for use on toll calls. Two-wire to four-wire conversion is usually not required for analog COs that switch local calls.
7. Provides analog-to-digital (i.e., PCM) and digital-to-analog conversion for digital systems.
8. Tests subscriber line and line termination (i.e., telephone loads connected to other end of the line).
9. Provide protective isolation of CO/RT equipment from unwanted line potentials such as lighting or cross connection to some ac power source.

8-3 Integrated Service Digital Network (ISDN)

As indicated previously, the telephone industry is evolving from an analog network to a digital network. Presently, the trend is to provide a digital CO and a digital network out to the RT; the "last mile" from the RT to the subscriber is usually analog. A new approach called the *integrated service digital network* (ISDN) converts the "last mile" analog subscriber line (ASL) to a *digital subscriber line* (DSL) so that digital data can be delivered directly to the subscriber's premises. The ISDN subscriber can demultiplex the data to provide any one or all of the following applications simultaneously: (1) decode data to produce VF signals for telephone handsets, (2) decode data for a video display, or (3) process data for telemetry and/or PC applications.

As indicated in Chapter 4, there are two categories of ISDN: (1) *narrowband* or *"basic rate"* ISDN, denoted by N-ISDN, and (2) *broadband* or *"primary rate"* ISDN, denoted by B-ISDN. B-ISDN is in the process of being developed; consequently, there are many proposed protocols and data rates. One proposal has an aggregate data rate of 1.536 Mbits/sec (approximately the same rate as for T1 lines) consisting of 23 B channels (64 kbits/sec each) and one D channel (64 kbits/sec). The B channels carry user (or bearer) data which may be PCM for encoded video or audio. The D channel is used for signaling to set up calls, disconnect calls, and/or route data for the 23 B channels.

Since B-ISDN standards are not yet fully developed, B-ISDN will be discussed only briefly. It is clear that twisted-pair copper lines must be used (presently) to provide B-ISDN for the "last mile" to the subscriber since it is not financially feasible to replace all copper lines already installed (about a $100 billion investment for U.S. copper line facilities) with fiber. Of course, fiber might be the economical solution for new installations. Furthermore, since 24-gauge copper lines have an attenuation of about 35 dB/mile at 1 MHz, the "last mile" copper line length from the RT to the subscriber will have to be limited to a mile or two, assuming that no repeaters are used. As discussed in Sec. 4-8, twisted-pair copper lines with repeaters spaced every mile can support a 1.5-Mbit/sec data rate (T1 line, which has a bipolar line code), or 6.4-Mbit/sec data rate (T1G line, which has a quarternary line code). Fiber optic (or coaxial) lines will be required for data rates on the order of 10 Mbits/sec or larger. For further reading on the developing B-ISDN technology, the reader is referred to the literature [Hsing, Chen, Bellisio, 1993; Saltzberg et al., 1991].

The standard implementation of N-ISDN is shown in Fig. 8-6. The N-ISDN subscriber is connected to the RT of the telephone company by a two-wire twisted pair (unloaded) telephone line. This allows existing copper pairs to be used for either POTS or N-ISDN simply by connecting the ends of the pairs to the appropriate terminating equipment. For

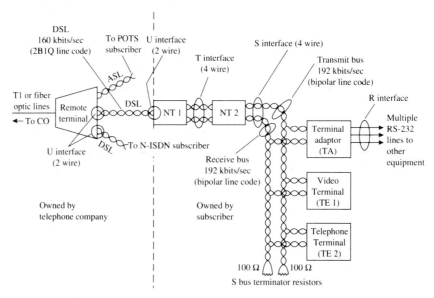

FIGURE 8-6 N-ISDN system with subscriber equipment attached.

N-ISDN service the line must be no longer than 18 kft (3.4 miles) for the 160-kbit/sec N-ISDN aggregate data rate. (If the subscriber is located within 18 kft of the CO, an RT is not necessary.) The data rate available to the N-ISDN subscriber is 144 kbits/sec, consisting of data partitioned into two B channels of 64 kbits/sec each and one D channel of 16 kbits/sec. In addition to the 2B + D data, the telephone company adds 12 kbits/sec for framing/timing plus 4 kbits/sec for overhead to support network operations. This gives an overall data rate of 160 kbits/sec on the DSL in both the transmit and receive directions (simultaneously) for full-duplex operation. The DSL is terminated on the subscriber's end at the U interface as shown on Fig. 8-6. The NT1 (network termination) incorporates a hybrid circuit to convert the two-wire U interface to a four-wire T interface which has two two-wire buses, one for the transmit and one for the receive data signals. The NT1 is a slave transceiver that derives its clocking signals from the DSL signal that is transmitted from the RT. The NT1 passes the 2B + D data between the U and T interfaces and also processes additional bits that appear on the transmit and receive lines at the T interface. The additional bits are needed for addressing, control, and supervision of terminal equipment. The data rate on each transmit and receive T line is 192 kbits/sec. The NT2 may or may not be needed. When used, it provides the appropriate higher-level protocols for a terminal cluster controller or for a local area network (LAN) access node. If not used, the NT1 four-wire interface becomes the S/T interface. The S and T interfaces are electrically identical and use a RJ45 8-pin modular connector. The S/T interface bus provided the connection medium for ISDN terminals (video, audio, and/or data) and/or a terminal adapter (TA). Up to eight terminals may be bridged onto the S/T bus. The TA allows non-ISDN terminals with RS-232 ports to be used on the ISDN network. For example, a personal computer (PC) can be connected to the N-ISDN network via its serial port and the R interface of the TA. Also, using an alternative approach, a PC adapter card with a built-in NT1 and a telephone codec can be used. That is, the DSL U interface modular connector is plugged directly into this adapter card on the PC. The PC then acts as an ISDN video terminal with a built-in telephone. For details on the protocols used at the U, S, and T interfaces, the reader is referred to application notes for ISDN chips such as Motorola's MC 145472 U interface transceiver, MC 145474 S/T interface, and MC 145554 telephone codec.

N-ISDN service to the subscriber via two-wire twisted-pair DSL up to 18 kft from a RT is made possible by the use of multilevel signaling. Referring to Fig. 7-15 with R = 160 bits/sec, a four-level (i.e., $\ell = 2$ bit) 80-kbaud line code has a null bandwidth of only 80 kHz instead of the 160-kHz null bandwidth for a binary ($\ell = 1$) line code. The 80-kHz bandwidth is supported by 26-gauge twisted-pair cable if it is less than about 18 kft in length. The particular four-level signal used is the 2B1Q line code (for two binary digits encoded into one quadrenary symbol) as shown in Fig. 8-7. Note that the 2B1Q line code is a differential symbol code. Thus if (due to wiring error) the twisted pair is "turned over" so that the tip wire is connected to the ring terminal and the ring to the tip so that the 2B1Q signal polarity is inverted, the decoded binary data will still have the correct polarity (i.e., not complemented).

The primary advantage of ISDN is obvious—it provides TDM data channels directly to the subscriber. It also has disadvantages. For example, since the ISDN subscriber equip-

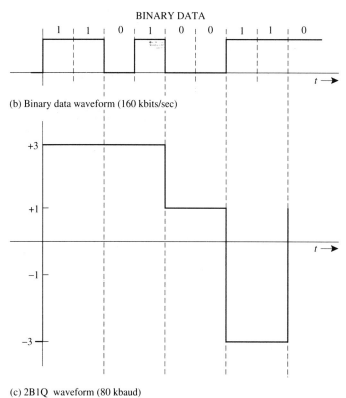

Previous 2B1Q level	Current binary word	Present 2B1Q level
+1 or +3	00	+1
	01	+3
	10	−1
	11	−3
−1 or −3	00	−1
	01	−3
	10	+1
	11	+3

(a) 2B1Q differential code table

BINARY DATA

1 1 0 1 0 0 1 1 0

(b) Binary data waveform (160 kbits/sec)

(c) 2B1Q waveform (80 kbaud)

FIGURE 8-7 2B1Q Line code.

ment is not powered by the DSL, it will not function when local ac power fails unless a backup power supply is provided by the subscriber. If only POTS is required, the conventional analog telephone is usually much cheaper and more reliable.

For study of additional N-ISDN topics, such as frame structure, timing recovery, synchronization, and echo cancellation, the reader is referred to a tutorial paper by [Huang and Valenti, 1991] and a book [Stallings, 1992]. For additional study of telephone systems in general, the interested reader is urged to look at some of the numerous publications that are available [Briley, 1983; Chorafas, 1984; Fike and Friend, 1984; Jordan, 1985].

8-4 Capacities of Public Switched Telephone Networks (PSTN)

In FDM and TDM signaling, the wideband channels used to connect the toll offices consist of three predominant types: fiber optic cable, microwave radio relay systems, and (buried) coaxial cable systems. Table 8-2 lists some of the wideband systems that are used, or have been used in the past, and indicates the capacity of these systems in terms of the number of VF channels they can handle and their bit rate.

In 1980 the AR6A microwave relay system was introduced into service [Markle, 1978, 1983]. Until this time FDM/FM was the modulation method used on microwave links because the intermodulation distortion on klystron microwave power amplifiers was too large for SSB techniques to be used. The development of a low-distortion TWT (traveling-wave tube) amplifier has made FDM/SSB possible in the AR6A. The VF capacity of the AR6A is *three times* that of microwave systems using the FDM/FM technique, so that it will handle 10 mastergroups of 600 VF channels each. The performance of digital microwave systems is also shown.

Referring again to Table 8-2, we realize that almost all of the open-wire pairs have been replaced by twisted-pair cable, but occasionally some can still be seen along railroad tracks. Fiber cable with TDM/OOK signaling is now rapidly overtaking twisted-pair and coaxial cable.

Tropospheric scatter radio is the transmission of UHF signals "over the horizon" by reflecting and refracting the signals in the troposphere. A ground range of 400 miles can be obtained by using high-power and large parabolic antennas. In most applications "tropo" systems are being replaced by satellite systems.

The capacity of satellite communication also depends on the type of modulation used. With FDM/FM the *Intelsat IV* and *V* series satellites can handle 300 VF channels on each 36-MHz bandwidth transponder (receiver–transmitter relay system). If quadrature phase-shift-keyed/single VF channel per carrier (QPSK/SCPC) is used, 800 VF channels can be accommodated. This subject is discussed in more detail in the following section, which describes satellite communication systems.

8-5 Satellite Communication Systems

The number of satellite communication systems has increased tremendously over the last few years. Satellite communications now relay the bulk of transoceanic telephone traffic, having greatly surpassed that sent by submarine cable. In addition, satellites have made transoceanic relaying of television signals possible. Satellite communications thus provide

TABLE 8-2 Capacity of Public Switched Telephone Networks

Transmission Medium	Name	Developer	Year in Service	Number of Voice-Frequency Channels	Bit Rate (Mbits/sec)	Repeater Spacing (miles)	Operating Frequency (MHz)	Modulation[a] D/A	Modulation[a] Method
Open-wire pair	A	Bell	1918	4			0.005–0.025	A	SSB
	C	Bell	1924	3		150	0.005–0.030	A	SSB
		CCITT		12		50	0.036–0.140	A	SSB
	J	Bell	1938	12		50	0.036–0.143	A	SSB
		CCITT		28			0.003–0.300	A	SSB
Twisted-pair cable	K	Bell	1938	12		17	0.012–0.060	A	SSB
		CCITT		12		19	0.012–0.060	A	SSB
	N1	Bell	1950	12			0.044–0.260	A	SSB
	N3	Bell	1964	24			0.172–0.268	A	SSB
	T1[b]	Bell	1962	24	1.544 (DS-1)	1		D	Bipolar
	T1G[b]	AT&T	1985	96	6.312 (DS-2)			D	Four-level
	T2[b]	Bell		96	6.312 (DS-2)	2.3		D	B6ZS
Coaxial cable	L1	Bell	1941	600		8	0.006–2.79	A	SSB
	L3	Bell	1953	1,860		4	0.312–8.28	A	SSB
	L4	Bell	1967	3,600		2	0.564–17.55	A	SSB
	L5	Bell	1974	10,800		1	3.12–60.5	A	SSB
	T4[b]	Bell		4,032	274.176 (DS-4)	1		D	Polar
	T5[b]	Bell		8,064	560.16 (DS-5)	1		D	Polar
Fiber optic	FT3	Bell	1981	672	44.763 (DS-3)	4.4	0.82 μm	D	TDM/OOK
		Brit. Telcom	1984		140	6	1.3 μm	D	TDM/OOK
		Sask. Telcom	1985		45	6–18	0.84 and 1.3 μm	D	TDM/OOK
	F-400M	Nippon	1985		400	12	1.3 μm	D	TDM/OOK
	FT3C-90	AT&T	1985	1,344	90.254 (DS-3C)	16	1.3 μm	D	TDM/OOK
	FT4E-432	AT&T	1986	6,048	432 (DS-432)	16	1.3 μm	D	TDM/OOK
	LaserNet[d]	Microtel	1985	6,048	417.79 (9DS-3)	25	1.3 μm	D	TDM/OOK
	FTG1.7	AT&T	1987	24,192	1.668 (36DS-3)	29	1.3 μm	D	TDM/OOK

									[a]	
Transoceanic	TAT-1 (SB)	Bell	1956	48			20	0.024–0.168	A	SSB
	TAT-3 (SD)	Bell	1963	138			11	0.108–1.05	A	SSB
	TAT-5 (SF)	Bell	1970	845			6	0.564–5.88	A	SSB
	TAT-6 (SG)	Bell	1976	4,200			3	0.5–30	A	SSB
	TAT-8 (3 fibers)		1988	8,000		280		1.3 μm	D	TDM/OOK
	TAT-9 (3 fibers)		1991	16,000		565		1.55 μm	D	TDM/OOK
	TAT-10 (6 fibers)		1992	80,000[e]		565		1.55 μm	D	TDM/OOK
	TAT-12 (6 fibers)	Alcatel	1995	200,000		5,000	30	1.48 μm	D	TDM/OOK
Troposphere scatter radio	DMEW		1961	240				UHF	A	FDM/FM
Microwave relay	TD-2	Bell	1948	600	(1954)	plus 1.544[c]	30	3700–4200	A	FDM/FM
	TH-1	Bell	1961	2,400	(1979)	plus 1.544[c]	30	5925–6245	A	FDM/FM
	TD-3	Bell	1967	1,800	(1979)	plus 1.544[c]	30	3700–4200	A	FDM/FM
	TN-1	Bell	1974	1,800		plus 1.544[c]	30	K band, 18 GHz	A	FDM/FM
	AR6A	Bell	1980	6,000			30	5925–6425	A	FDM/SSB
	18G274	NEC	1974	4,032		274.176 (DS-4)	7	18 GHz	D	4 PSK
	6G90	NEC	1979	1,344		90 (2DS-3)	30	6 GHz	D	16 QAM
	11G135	NEC	1980	2,016		135 (3 DS-3)	30	11 GHz	D	16 QAM
	6G135	NEC	1983	2,016		135 (3 DS-3)	30	6 GHz	D	64 QAM
	MDR-2306	Collins	1983	2,016		135 (3 DS-3)	30	6 GHz	D	64 QAM
	RD-6A	Northern Tel.	1984	2,016		135 (3 DS-3)	30	6 GHz	D	64 QAM
Communication satellite	Intelsat IV	COMSAT	1970	8,000			22,300	6 GHz up/4 GHz down	A/D	FDM/FM, QPSK/ SCPC
	Intelsat V	COMSAT	1980	25,000			22,300	6/4 and 14/11 GHz	A/D	FDM/FM, QPSK/ SCPC
	Intelsat VI	COMSAT	1986	80,000			22,300	6/4 and 14/11 GHz	A/D	FDM/FM, QPSK/ SCPC

[a] A-analog; D-digital plus modulation type.   [b] See Table 4-9 for more details on the T-carrier system.
[c] Since 1974 data under voice were added to give a 1.544-Mbit/sec (DS-1) data channel in addition to the stated VF FDM capacity.
[d] See Example 8-5 in Sec. 8-7.   [e] VF capacity with statistical multiplexing.

the relaying of data, telephone, and television signals, and it is now feasible to provide national direct-into-the-home television transmission via satellite.

Most communication satellites are placed in *geosynchronous* orbit. This is a circular orbit in Earth's equatorial plane. The orbit is located 22,300 miles above the equator so that the orbital period is the same as that of the Earth. Consequently, from Earth these satellites appear to be located at an approximately fixed point in the sky, as shown in Fig. 8-8. This enables the Earth station antennas to be simplified since they are pointed in a fixed direction and do not have to track a moving object. (For communication to the polar regions of the Earth, satellites in polar orbits are used, which require Earth stations with tracking antennas.) To prevent the satellite from tumbling, one of two spin stabilization techniques—spin stabilization or three-axis stabilization—is used. For spin stabilization, the outside cylinder of the satellite is spun to create a gyroscopic effect that stabilizes the satellite. For three-axis stabilization, internal gyroscopes are used to sense satellite movement and the satellite is stabilized by firing appropriate thruster jets.

The most desired frequency band for satellite communication systems is 6 GHz on the uplink (Earth-to-satellite transmission) and 4 GHz on the downlink (satellite-to-Earth transmission). In this frequency range the equipment is relatively inexpensive, the cosmic noise is small, and the frequency is low enough so that rainfall does not appreciably attenuate the signals. Other losses, such as ionospheric scintillation and atmospheric absorption, are small at these frequencies [Spilker, 1977]. (Absorption occurs in specific frequency bands and is caused by the signal exciting atmospheric gases and water vapor.) However, existing terrestrial microwave radio relay links are already assigned to operate within the 6- and 4-GHz bands (see Table 8-2), so the FCC limits the power density on Earth from the satellite transmitters. One also has to be careful in locating the Earth station satellite receiving antennas so that they do not receive interfering signals from the terrestrial microwave radio links that are using the same frequency assignment. In the 6/4-GHz band, synchronous satellites are assigned an orbital spacing of 2° (U.S. standard).

Newer satellites have to operate in higher-frequency bands because there are so few vacant spectral assignments in the 6/4-GHz band (C band). The Ku band satellites use

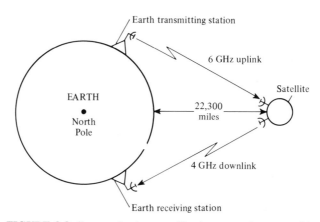

FIGURE 8-8 Communications satellite in geosynchronous orbit.

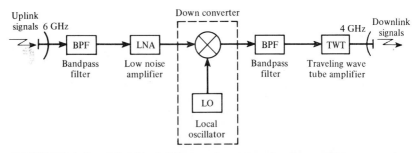

FIGURE 8-9 Simplified block diagram of a communications satellite transponder.

14 GHz on the uplink and 12 GHz on the downlink with an orbital spacing of 3 degrees. Some new Ku-band satellites have high-power amplifiers that feed 60 to 120 watts into their transmitting antenna, as compared with 20 to 40 watts for low- or medium-power satellites. In several European countries, high-power satellites—called direct broadcast satellites (DBS)—provide TV service directly to the homeowner that has a small receiving antenna (2 ft or less in diameter).

Each satellite has a number of *transponders* (receiver-to-transmitter) aboard to amplify the received signal from the uplink and to down-convert the signal for transmission on the downlink (see Fig. 8-9). This figure shows a "bent pipe transponder" that does not demodulate the received signal and perform signal processing but acts as a high-power-gain down converter. Most transponders are designed for a bandwidth of 36, 54, or 72 MHz, with 36 MHz being the standard used for C-band (6/4 GHz) television relay service. As technology permits, processing transponders will come into use since an improvement in error performance (for digital signaling) can be realized.

Each satellite is assigned a synchronous orbit position and a frequency band in which to operate. In the 6/4-GHz band, each satellite is permitted to use a 500-MHz-wide spectral assignment, and a typical satellite has 24 transponders aboard, with each transponder using 36 MHz of the 500-MHz bandwidth assignment. The satellites reuse the same frequency band by having 12 transponders operating with vertically polarized radiated signals and 12 transponders with horizontally polarized signals.[†] A typical 6/4-GHz frequency assignment for satellites is shown in Fig. 8-10. The transponders are denoted by C1 for channel 1, C2 for channel 2, and so on. These satellites are used mainly to relay signals for cable antenna television (CATV) systems.

Figure 8-11 shows an example of a 6/4-GHz satellite. This is the *Galaxy* series of satellites manufactured by the Hughes Aircraft Company, a member of their HS 376 family of spin-stabilized satellites. The satellite is approximately 21 ft 8 in. high after deployment and has a diameter of 7 ft 1 in. The *Galaxy* mission's lifetime is 9 years and is limited by the amount of propellant stored onboard for firing thrusters that keep the satellite to within 0.1° of its assigned position (in both the north–south and east–west

---

[†] A vertically polarized satellite signal has an E field that is oriented vertically (parallel with the axis of rotation of the Earth). With horizontal polarization the E field is horizontal.

(a) Horizontal Polarization[a]

(b) Vertical Polarization[a]

[a]These are the polarizations used for the Galaxy Satellites. Some of the other satellites use opposite polarization assignments.

FIGURE 8-10 6/4-GHz satellite transponder frequency plan for the downlink channels. (For the uplink frequency plan, add 2225 MHz to the numbers given above.)

directions). The body of the satellite is spun at a rate of 50 rpm to provide gyroscopic stability. The solar cell/battery system supplies a dc power of at least 741 W to operate the electronics.

Television Signal Transmission

Broadcast-quality TV signals are relayed via satellite by using a single transponder (36-MHz bandwidth) for each TV signal. This is accomplished by modulating the composite 4.5-MHz bandwidth visual signal onto a 6-GHz FM carrier, as shown in Fig. 8-12. The composite visual signal consists of the black-and-white video signal, the color subcarrier signals, and the synchronizing pulse signal, as discussed in Sec. 8-9. The aural signal is also relayed over the same transponder by frequency modulating it onto a 6.8-MHz subcarrier that is frequency-division-multiplexed with the composite video signal. The resulting wideband signal frequency modulates the transmitter.

The bandwidth of the 6-GHz FM signal may be evaluated by using Carson's rule. The peak deviation of the composite video is 10.5 MHz and the peak deviation of the subcarrier is 2 MHz, giving an overall peak deviation of $\Delta F = 12.5$ MHz. The baseband bandwidth is approximately 6.8 MHz. The transmission bandwidth is

$$B_T = 2(\Delta F + B) = 2(12.5 + 6.8) = 38.6 \text{ MHz} \tag{8-1}$$

which is accepted by the 36-MHz transponder.

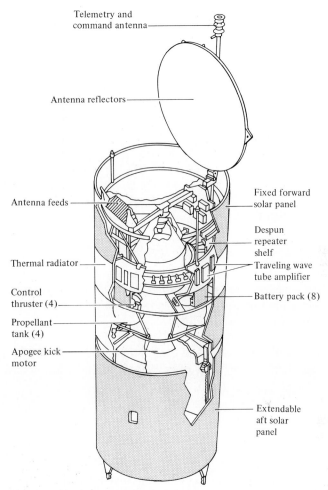

FIGURE 8-11 *Galaxy* satellite. [Courtesy of Hughes Communications, Inc., a wholly owned subsidiary of Hughes Aircraft Company.]

This FDM/FM technique is also used by telephone companies for terrestrial relay of TV signals over microwave radio links that were characterized in Table 8-2 (except for the AR6A system, which cannot be used for TV relay). Each microwave link has the capacity for one TV channel (or for the number of VF channels, as indicated in the table). When video signals are relayed, wideband aural signals (0- to 15-kHz) can also be relayed by using FM subcarriers. Some typical subcarrier frequencies that are used are 5.58, 5.76, 6.2, 6.3, 6.48, 6.8, 7.38, and 7.56 MHz.

Data and Telephone Signal Multiple Access

Satellite relays provide a channel for data and VF (telephone) signaling similar to conventional terrestrial microwave radio links. That is, data may be time-division-multiplexed

FIGURE 8-12 Transmission of broadcast-quality TV signals from a ground station.

into DS-1, DS-2, and so on, types of signals and (digitally) modulated onto a carrier for transmission via a satellite. The data may also be frequency-division-multiplexed. In this case, modems are used to convert the data into signals that are compatible with VF group, supergroup, or mastergroup bandwidths, which are (analog) modulated onto the carrier for transmission to the satellite.

Satellite communication systems do differ from terrestrial microwave links in the techniques used for *multiple access* of a single transponder by multiple uplink and multiple downlink stations. Four main methods are used for multiple access.

1. *Frequency-division multiple access* (FDMA), which is similar to FDM.
2. *Time-division multiple access* (TDMA), which is similar to TDM.[†]
3. *Code-division multiple access* (CDMA) or *spread-spectrum multiple access* (SSMA).
4. *Space-division multiple access* (SDMA) where narrow-beam antenna patterns are switched from one direction to another.[†]

In addition, either of the following may be used:

1. A *fixed assigned multiple access* (FAMA) mode using either FDMA, TDMA, or CDMA techniques.
2. A *demand assigned multiple access* (DAMA) mode using either FDMA, TDMA, or CDMA.

In the FAMA mode the FDMA, TDMA, or CDMA format does not change, even though the traffic load of various Earth stations changes. For example, there is more telephone traffic between Earth stations during daylight hours (local time) than between these stations in the hours after midnight. In the FAMA mode a large number of satellite

---

[†] *Satellite-switched time-division multiple access* (SS-TDMA) can also be used. With SS-TDMA satellites, different narrow-beam antennas are switched in at the appropriate time in the TDMA frame period to direct the transmit and receive beams to the desired direction. Thus, with multiple SS-TDMA beams the same transmit and receive frequencies may be reused simultaneously so that the capacity of the SS-TDMA satellite is much larger than that of a TDMA satellite. The *Intelsat VI* is a SS-TDMA satellite.

channels would be idle during the early morning hours since they are fixed assigned. In the DAMA mode, the FDMA or TDMA formats are changed as needed depending on the traffic demand of the Earth stations involved. Consequently, the DAMA mode uses the satellite capacity more efficiently, but it usually costs more to implement and maintain.

In CDMA the different users share the same frequency band simultaneously in time, as opposed to FDMA and TDMA, where users are assigned different frequency slots or time slots. With CDMA each user is assigned a particular digitally encoded waveform $\varphi_j(t)$ that is (nearly) orthogonal to the waveforms used by the others (see Secs. 2-4 and 7-5). Data may be modulated onto this waveform, transmitted over the communication system, and recovered. For example, if one bit of data, m_j, is modulated onto the waveform, the transmitted signal from the jth user might be $m_j\varphi_j(t)$ and the composite CDMA signal from all users would be $w(t) = \Sigma_j m_j\varphi_j(t)$. The data from the jth user could be recovered from the CDMA waveform by evaluating $\int_0^t w(t)\varphi_j(t)\, dt = m_j$, where T is the length of encoded waveform $\varphi_j(t)$. Gold codes are often used to obtain the encoded waveforms.

Example 8-1   Fixed Assigned Multiple Access Mode Using an FDMA Format

A good example of the fixed assigned multiple access technique is the FDM/FM format used with the *Intelsat IV* and *V* series satellites. Suppose that ground station A is sharing one 36-MHz transponder in the FDM mode with stations B, C, D, E, F, and G, which are all transmitting simultaneously through the transponder, as shown by their frequency assignments in Fig. 8-13a. Station A has an assigned band of 6237.5 to 6242.5 MHz in which it can transmit 60 VF channels using FDM/FM. This is the capacity of one supergroup. Suppose that station A has traffic as follows: 24 VF channels for station B, 24 VF channels for station D, and 12 VF channels for station E; then the equipment configuration would be as shown in Fig. 8-13b. In a similar way, the remaining spectrum of the 36-MHz transponder is divided among the other Earth stations according to their traffic needs on a fixed assignment basis.

Example 8-2   Spade System

The *Intelsat IV* and *V* series satellites may also be operated in a DAMA mode using an FDMA format consisting of a single QPSK carrier for each telephone (VF) channel. This type of signaling is called *single channel per carrier* (SCPC), in which 800 QPSK signals may be accommodated in the 36-MHz bandwidth of the transponder, as shown in Fig. 8-14a. Thus 800 VF messages may be transmitted simultaneously through one satellite transponder, where each QPSK signal is modulated by a 64-kbit/sec PCM (digitized) voice signal (studied earlier in Example 4-1 and used as inputs to the North American

(a) Transponder Frequency Allocation

(b) Station A Ground Transmitting Equipment

FIGURE 8-13 Fixed assigned FDMA format for satellite communications.

digital hierarchy shown in Fig. 4-42). This SCPC-DAMA technique, illustrated in Fig. 8-14, is called the *SPADE system,* which is an acronym for *s*ingle channel per carrier, *p*ulse code modulation, multiple *a*ccess, *d*emand assignment *e*quipment [Edelson and Werth, 1972]!

The demand assignment of the carrier frequency for the QPSK signal to a particular Earth station uplink is carried out by TDM signaling in the *common signaling channel* (CSC) (see Fig. 8-14a). The CSC consists of a 128-kbit/sec PSK signal that is time shared among the Earth stations by using a TDMA format, as shown in Fig. 8-14c. PA denotes the synchronizing preamble that occurs at the beginning of each frame, and A, B, C, and so on denote the 1-msec time slots that are reserved for transmission by Earth stations A, B, C, and so on. In this way 49 different Earth stations may be accommodated in the

(a) Transponder Frequency Allocation

(b) Possible QPSK SCPC Transmitter Configuration

(c) TDMA CSC Signaling Format

FIGURE 8-14 SPADE satellite communication system for telephone VF message transmission.

50-msec frame. For example, if Earth station B wishes to initiate a call to Earth station D, station B selects a QPSK carrier frequency randomly from among the idle channels that are available and transmits this frequency information along the address of station D (the call destination) in the station B TDMA time slot. If it is assumed that the frequency has not been selected by another station for another call, station D will acknowledge the request in its TDMA time slot. This acknowledgment would be heard by station B about 600 msec after its TDMA signaling request since the round-trip time delay to the satellite is

240 msec, plus equipment delays and the delay to the exact time slot assigned to station D with respect to that of station B. If another station, say station C, had selected the same frequency during the request period, a busy signal would be received at station B, and station B would randomly select another available frequency and try again. When the call is over, disconnect signals are transmitted in the TDMA time slot and that carrier frequency is returned for reuse. Since the CSC signaling rate is 128 kbits/sec and each time slot is 1 msec in duration, 128 bits are available for each accessing station to use for transmitting address information, frequency request information, and disconnect signaling.

In practice, since only 49 time slots are available for the TDMA mode, a number of the SCPC frequencies are assigned on a fixed basis.

In FDMA, such as the SPADE system, when the carriers are turned on and off on demand, there is amplitude modulation on the composite 36-MHz-wide signal that is being amplified by the transponder TWT. Consequently, the drive level of the TWT has to be "backed off" so that the amplifier is not saturated and will be sufficiently linear. Then the intermodulation products will be sufficiently low. On the other hand, if a single constant-amplitude signal (such as a single-wideband FM signal used in relaying television signals), had been used, IM products would not be a consideration and the amplifier could be driven harder to provide the full saturated power output level.

As indicated earlier, TDMA is similar to TDM, where the different Earth stations send up bursts of RF energy that contain packets of information. During the time slot designated for a particular Earth station, that station's signal uses the bandwidth of the whole transponder (see Fig. 8-15). Since the Earth stations use a constant envelope modulation technique, such as QPSK, and only one high-rate modulated signal is being passed through the transponder during any time interval, no inband IM products are generated (as in the FDMA technique described earlier). Thus the final TWT amplifier in the satellite may be driven into saturation for more power output. This advantage of TDMA over FDMA may be compared with the main disadvantage of the TDMA technique. The disadvantage of TDMA is that strict burst timing is required at the Earth station in order to prevent collision of the bursts at the satellite. In other words, the burst from a particular Earth station has to arrive at the satellite in the exact time slot designated for that station, so that its signal will not interfere with the bursts that are arriving from other Earth stations that are assigned adjacent time slots. Since the ground stations are located at different distances from the satellite and may use different equipment configurations, the time delay from each Earth station to the satellite will be different, and this must be taken into account when the transmission time for each Earth station is computed. In addition the satellite may be moving with respect to the Earth station, which means that the time delay is actually changing with time. Another disadvantage of TDMA is that the Earth stations are probably transmitting data that have arrived from synchronous terrestrial lines; consequently, the Earth station equipment must contain a large memory in which to buffer the

FIGURE 8-15 Interleaving of bursts in a TDMA satellite.

data, which are read out at high speed when the packet of information is sent to the satellite.

A typical TDMA frame format for the data being relayed through a satellite is shown in Fig. 8-16. In this example, station B is sending data to stations A, E, G, and H. One frame consists of data arriving from each Earth station. At any time, only one Earth station provides the time reference signal for the other Earth stations to use for computation of their transmitting time for their data bursts (frame synchronization). The burst lengths from the various stations could be different depending on the traffic volume. The second part of the figure shows an exploded view of a typical burst format that is transmitted from station B. This consists of two main parts, the preamble and data that are being sent to other Earth stations from station B. The preamble includes a guard time before transmission is begun. Then a string of synchronization characters is transmitted that give the carrier sync recovery loops and bit timing recovery loops (in the ground station receivers) time to lock onto this burst from station B. The end of the preamble usually contains a unique word that identifies the burst as coming from station B and might indicate the addresses (stations) for which the data are intended.

Another multiple access method which is similar to TDMA is the *ALOHA* technique [Lam, 1979]. Here the multiple users send bursts of data, called *packets,* whenever they wish. If two or more of the bursts overlap in time, called a *collision,* the users involved retransmit their packets after a random time delay. It is hoped that a second collision will not occur. If it does, the retransmission process is repeated until each party is successful. This technique has the advantage of being relatively inexpensive to implement, but it will

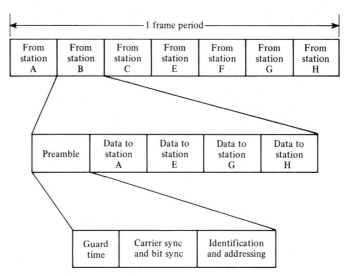

FIGURE 8-16 Typical TDMA frame format.

not work if there is heavy traffic loading on the satellite. Then the satellite becomes saturated with colliding packets, and the collisions can be avoided only by stopping all new transmissions and increasing the random delay required before retransmission. A more elaborate technique is called *slotted ALOHA*. Here the packets are transmitted at random, but only in certain time slots. This avoids collisions due to partial packet overlap.

Very small aperture terminals (VSAT) have become popular with the availability of Ku-band satellites and with the recent advances that have made low-cost terminals possible. "Very small aperture" implies that these systems use Earth-terminal antennas that are relatively small, about 1 or 2 meters in diameter. Solid-state power amplifiers (1 to 2 W), low-cost frequency converters, digital processing, and VLSI circuits have made VSATs feasible. The objective of VSAT systems is to provide low-cost data and voice transmission directly to users such as auto dealerships, banks (automatic teller machines), brokerage firms, pipeline companies (monitor and control), hotels and airlines (reservations), retail stores (data networks), and corporations (point-to-multipoint transmission). Typically, VSATs offer high-quality transmission (bit error rates of less than 10^{-7} for 99.5% of the time) at data rates from 100 bits/sec to 9.6 kbits/sec [Chakraborty, 1988]. Many users share a single satellite transponder via SCPC, TDMA, or CDMA so that the user's cost can be substantially less than that for the same type of service provided by the long-distance public telephone network [Dorf, 1993, p. 2201; Rana, McCoskey, and Check, 1990].

Satellite systems are now being developed for communication directly to *personal communication system* (PCS) devices, such as hand-held portable telephones and mobile data terminals. In general, these PCS devices use small nondirectional antennas that have very little gain. Consequently, the signal from the satellite needs to be relatively strong at the user's location. Strong user signals can be achieved if the distance to the satellite is relatively small—around 400 to 1200 miles. Thus *low-Earth-orbit* (LEO) satellites, which are not geosynchronous, provide a solution to this problem. Motorola has proposed to use as many as 77 satellites in LEO [Foley, 1991; Grubb, 1991]. These satellites are to be distributed around the globe in polar orbits (cross the north and south pole) so that a worldwide communication service will be provided. Motorola calls this the Iridium system, named after the chemical element that has 77 electrons circling its nucleus. Cellular technology (see Sec. 8-8) will be used so that the service can be provided to a very large number of users—that is, a worldwide cellular telephone service. Competitive LEO satellite systems have been proposed by Qualcomm (their Globestar system) and by TRW (their Odyssey system).

More details about satellite systems can be obtained from books devoted specifically to that subject [Ha, 1986; Ha, 1989; Pratt and Bostian, 1986; Spilker, 1977].

In the next section, a procedure is developed for calculating the signal strength of a received satellite signal and for evaluating the amount of noise that is present in a receiving system. This will be used to evaluate the BER at the output of the digital receivers and the S/N at the output of analog receivers.

8-6 Link Budget Analysis

In this section, formulas will be developed for the signal-to-noise ratio at the detector input as a function of the transmitted *effective isotropic radiated power* (EIRP), the free-space loss, the receiver antenna gain, and the receiver system noise figure. These results will allow us to evaluate the quality of the receiver output (as measured by the probability of bit error for digital systems and output signal-to-noise ratio for analog systems), provided that the noise characteristics of the receiver detector circuit are known.

Signal Power Received

In communication systems the received signal power (as opposed to the voltage or current level) is the important quantity since it is the output signal power that ultimately drives the display device, which, for example, may be a loudspeaker or a cathode ray tube (CRT). Consequently, it is the *power* of the received signal that is of prime importance while trying to *minimize* the effect of *noise sources* that feed into the system and get amplified. The voltage gain, current gain, and impedance levels have to be such that the required power gain is achieved. In FET circuits it is accomplished by using relatively large voltage levels and small currents (high-impedance circuitry). With bipolar transistors power gain is achieved with relatively small voltages and large currents (low-impedance circuitry).

A block diagram of a communication system with a free-space transmission channel is shown in Fig. 8-17. The overall power gain (or power transfer function) of the channel is

$$\frac{P_{Rx}}{P_{Tx}} = G_{AT}G_{FS}G_{AR} \qquad (8\text{-}2)$$

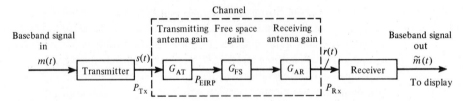

FIGURE 8-17 Block diagram of a communication system with a free-space transmission channel.

where P_{Tx} is the signal power into the transmitting antenna, G_{AT} is the transmitting antenna power gain, G_{FS} is the free-space power gain[†] (which is orders of magnitude less than one in typical communication systems), G_{AR} is the receiving antenna power gain, and P_{Rx} is the signal power into the receiver.

In order to use this relationship, these gains should be expressed in terms of useful antenna and free-space parameters [Kraus, 1986]. Here G_{AT} and G_{AR} are taken to be the power gains with respect to an isotropic antenna.[‡] The EIRP is

$$P_{\text{EIRP}} = G_{\text{AT}} P_{\text{Tx}} \tag{8-3}$$

The antenna power gain is defined as

$$G_A = \frac{\begin{array}{c}\text{radiation power density of the actual antenna} \\ \text{in the direction of maximum radiation}\end{array}}{\begin{array}{c}\text{radiation power density of an isotropic antenna} \\ \text{with the same power input}\end{array}}$$

where the power density (W/m^2) is evaluated at the same distance, d, for both antennas. The gain for some practical antennas is given in Table 8-3.

The power density (W/m^2) of an isotropic antenna at a distance d from the antenna is

$$\text{power density at } d = \frac{\text{transmitted power}}{\text{area of a sphere with radius } d} = \frac{P_{\text{EIRP}}}{4\pi d^2} \tag{8-4}$$

The FCC and others often specify the strength of an electromagnetic field by the field intensity, $\mathscr{E}$ (V/m), instead of power density (W/m^2). The two are related by

$$\text{power density} = \frac{\mathscr{E}^2}{377} \tag{8-5}$$

where the power density and the field strength are evaluated at the same point in space and 377 Ω is the *free-space intrinsic impedance*. If the receiving antenna is placed at d meters from the transmitting antenna, it will act like a "catcher's mitt" and intercept the power in an effective area of $(A_e)_{\text{Rx}}$ (meters²), so that the received power will be

$$P_{\text{Rx}} = G_{\text{AT}} \left(\frac{P_{\text{Tx}}}{4\pi d^2} \right) (A_e)_{\text{Rx}} \tag{8-6}$$

[†] A gain transfer function is the output quantity divided by the input quantity, whereas a loss transfer function is the input quantity divided by the output quantity.

[‡] An isotropic antenna is a nonrealizable theoretical antenna that radiates equally well in all directions and is a useful reference for comparing practical antennas.

TABLE 8-3 Antenna Gains and Effective Areas

Type of Antenna	Power Gain, G_A (absolute units)	Effective Area, A_e (meters^2)
Isotropic	1	$\lambda^2/4\pi$
Infinitesimal dipole or loop	1.5	$1.5\lambda^2/4\pi$
Half-wave dipole	1.64	$1.64\lambda^2/4\pi$
Horn (optimized), mouth area, A	$10A/\lambda^2$	$0.81A$
Parabola or "dish" with face area, A	$7.0A/\lambda^2$	$0.56A$
Turnstile (two crossed dipoles fed 90° out of phase)	1.15	$1.15\lambda^2/4\pi$

where the gain of the transmitting antenna (with respect to an isotropic antenna), G_{AT}, has been included. Table 8-3 also gives the effective area for several types of antennas. The gain and the effective area of an antenna are related by

$$G_A = \frac{4\pi A_e}{\lambda^2} \tag{8-7}$$

where $\lambda = c/f$ is the wavelength, c being the speed of light (3×10^8 m/sec) and f the operating frequency (hertz). An antenna is a *reciprocal element*. That is, it has the same gain properties whether it is transmitting or receiving. Substituting (8-7) into (8-6), we obtain

$$\frac{P_{Rx}}{P_{Tx}} = G_{AT}\left(\frac{\lambda}{4\pi d}\right)^2 G_{AR} \tag{8-8}$$

where the free-space gain is

$$G_{FS} = \left(\frac{\lambda}{4\pi d}\right)^2 = \frac{1}{L_{FS}} \tag{8-9}$$

and L_{FS} is the free-space path loss (absolute units). The channel gain, expressed in decibel units, is obtained from (8-2):

$$(G_{channel})_{dB} = (G_{AT})_{dB} - (L_{FS})_{dB} + (G_{AR})_{dB} \tag{8-10}$$

where the free-space loss is

$$(L_{FS})_{dB} = 20 \log\left(\frac{4\pi d}{\lambda}\right) \quad dB \tag{8-11}$$

For example, the free-space loss at 4 GHz for the shortest path to a synchronous satellite from Earth (22,300 miles) is 195.6 dB.

Thermal Noise Sources

The noise power generated by a thermal noise source will be studied since the receiver noise is evaluated in terms of this phenomenon. A conductive element with two terminals may be characterized by its resistance, R ohms. This resistive or lossy element contains

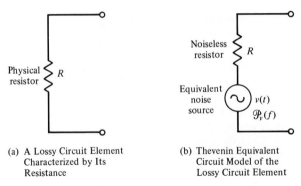

(a) A Lossy Circuit Element
    Characterized by Its
    Resistance

(b) Thevenin Equivalent
    Circuit Model of the
    Lossy Circuit Element

FIGURE 8-18 Thermal noise source.

free electrons that have some random motion if the resistor has a temperature above absolute zero. This random motion causes a noise voltage to be generated at the terminals of the resistor. Although the noise is small, when the noise is amplified by a high-gain receiver it can become a problem. (If no noise were present, we could communicate to the edge of the universe with infinitely small power since the signal could always be amplified without having noise introduced.)

This physical lossy element, or physical resistor, can be modeled by an equivalent circuit that consists of a noiseless resistor in series with a noise voltage source (see Fig. 8-18). From quantum mechanics, it can be shown that the (normalized) power spectrum corresponding to the voltage source is [Van der Ziel, 1986]

$$\mathcal{P}_v(f) = 2R\left[\frac{h|f|}{2} + \frac{h|f|}{e^{h|f|/(kT)} - 1}\right] \tag{8-12}$$

where R = value of the physical resistor (ohms)
$\quad h = 6.2 \times 10^{-34}$ J-sec is Planck's constant
$\quad k = 1.38 \times 10^{-23}$ J/K is Boltzmann's constant, where K is kelvin
$\quad T = (273 + C)$ is the absolute temperature of the resistor (kelvin)

At room temperature for frequencies below 1000 GHz, $[h|f|/(kT)] < 1/5$, so that $e^x = 1 + x$ is a good approximation. Then (8-12) reduces to

$$\mathcal{P}_v(f) = 2RkT \tag{8-13}$$

This equation will be used to develop other formulas in this text since the RF frequencies of interest are usually well below 1000 GHz and we are not dealing with temperatures near absolute zero.

If the open-circuit noise voltage that appears across a physical resistor is read by a true rms voltmeter that has a bandwidth of B hertz, then, using (2-67), the reading would be

$$V_{\text{rms}} = \sqrt{\langle v^2 \rangle} = \sqrt{2\int_0^B \mathcal{P}_v(f)\, df} = \sqrt{4kTBR} \tag{8-14}$$

Characterization of Noise Sources

Noise sources may be characterized by the maximum amount of noise power or PSD that can be passed to a load.

DEFINITION: The *available noise power* is the *maximum*[†] actual (i.e., not normalized) power that can be drawn from a source. The *available PSD* is the *maximum* actual (i.e., not normalized) PSD that can be obtained from a source.

For example, the available PSD for a thermal noise source is easily evaluated using Fig. 8-19 and (3-13).

$$\mathscr{P}_a(f) = \frac{\mathscr{P}_v(f)|H(f)|^2}{R} = \tfrac{1}{2}kT \quad \text{W/Hz} \tag{8-15}$$

where $H(f) = \tfrac{1}{2}$ for the resistor divider network. The available power from a thermal source in a bandwidth of B hertz is

$$P_a = \int_{-B}^{B} \mathscr{P}_a(f)\, df = \int_{-B}^{B} \frac{1}{2} kT\, df$$

or

$$P_a = kTB \tag{8-16}$$

This equation indicates that the available noise power from a thermal source does *not* depend on the value of R, even though the open-circuit rms voltage does.

The available noise power from a source (it does not have to be a thermal source) can be specified by a number called the noise temperature.

DEFINITION: The *noise temperature* of a source is given by

$$T = \frac{P_a}{kB} \tag{8-17}$$

where P_a is the available power from the source in a bandwidth of B hertz.

In using this definition, it is noted that if the source happens to be of thermal origin, T will be the temperature of the device in kelvin, but if the source is not of thermal origin,

---

[†] The maximum power or maximum PSD is obtained when $Z_L(f) = Z_s^*(f)$, where $Z_L(f)$ is the load impedance and $Z_s^*(f)$ is the conjugate of the source impedance.

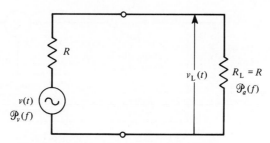

FIGURE 8-19 Thermal source with a matched load.

the number obtained for T may have nothing to do with the physical temperature of the device.

Noise Characterization of Linear Devices

A linear device with internal noise generators may be modeled as shown in Fig. 8-20. Any device that can be built will have some internal noise sources. As shown in the figure, the device could be modeled as a noise-free device having a power gain $G_a(f)$ and an excess noise source at the output to account for the internal noise of the actual device. Some examples of linear devices that have to be characterized in receiving systems are lossy transmission lines, RF amplifiers, down converters, and IF amplifiers.

The power gain of the devices is the available power gain.

DEFINITION: The *available power gain* of a linear device is

$$G_a(f) = \frac{\text{available PSD out of the device}}{\text{available PSD out of the source}} = \frac{\mathcal{P}_{ao}(f)}{\mathcal{P}_{as}(f)} \tag{8-18}$$

When $\mathcal{P}_{ao}(f)$ is measured to obtain $G_a(f)$, the source noise power is made large enough so that the amplified *source* noise that appears at the output dominates any other noise. In addition, note that $G_a(f)$ is defined in terms of actual (i.e., not normalized) PSD. In general, $G_a(f)$ will depend on the driving source impedance as well as on elements within the device itself, but it does *not* depend on the load impedance. If the source impedance and the output impedance of the device are equal, $G_a(f) = |H(f)|^2$, where $H(f)$ is the voltage or current transfer function of the linear device.

To characterize the goodness of a device, a figure of merit is needed that compares the actual (noisy) device with an ideal device (i.e., no internal noise sources). Two figures of merit, both of which tell us the same thing—namely, how bad the noise performance of the actual device is—are universally used. They are noise figure and effective input-noise temperature.

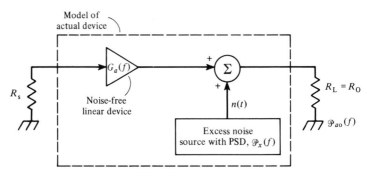

FIGURE 8-20 Noise model for an actual device.

DEFINITION: The *spot noise figure* of a linear device is obtained by terminating the device with a thermal noise source of temperature T_0 on the input and a matched load on the output as indicated in Fig. 8-20. The spot noise figure is

$$F_s(f) = \frac{\text{measured available PSD}}{\text{available PSD out of an ideal device}}$$
$$\frac{\text{out of the actual device}}{\text{with the same available gain}}$$

or

$$F_s(f) = \frac{\mathcal{P}_{ao}(f)}{(kT_0/2)G_a(f)} = \frac{(kT_0/2)G_a(f) + \mathcal{P}_x(f)}{(kT_0/2)G_a(f)} > 1 \qquad (8\text{-}19)$$

The value of R_s is the same as the source resistance that was used when $G_a(f)$ was evaluated. A standard temperature of $T_0 = 290$ K is used as adopted by the IEEE [Haus, 1963].

$F_s(f)$ is called the *spot noise figure* since it refers to the noise characterization at a particular "spot" or frequency in the spectrum. Note that $F_s(f)$ is always greater than unity for an actual device, but it is nearly unity if the device is almost an ideal device. $F_s(f)$ is a function of the source temperature, T_0. Consequently, when the noise figure is evaluated, a standard temperature of $T_0 = 290$ K is used. This corresponds to a room temperature of 62.3°F.

Often an average noise figure instead of a spot noise figure is desired. The average is measured over some bandwidth B.

DEFINITION: The *average noise figure* is

$$F = \frac{P_{ao}}{kT_0 \int_{f_0 - B/2}^{f_0 + B/2} G_a(f)\, df} \qquad (8\text{-}20)$$

where

$$P_{ao} = 2 \int_{f_0 - B/2}^{f_0 + B/2} \mathcal{P}_{ao}(f)\, df$$

is the measured available output in a bandwidth B hertz wide centered on a frequency of f_0 and $T_0 = 290$ K.

If the available gain is constant over the band so that $G_a(f) = G_a$ over the frequency interval $(f_0 - B/2) \le f \le (f_0 + B/2)$, the noise figure becomes

$$F = \frac{P_{ao}}{kT_0 B G_a} \qquad (8\text{-}21a)$$

The noise figure is often measured by using the Y-factor method. This technique is illustrated by Prob. 8-15. The Hewlett-Packard HP8970B noise figure meter uses the Y-factor method for measuring the noise figure of devices.

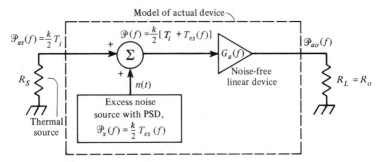

FIGURE 8-21 Another noise model for an actual device.

The noise figure can also be specified in decibel units,[†]

$$F_{dB} = 10 \log(F) = 10 \log\left(\frac{P_{ao}}{kT_0 BG_a}\right) \tag{8-21b}$$

For example, suppose that the manufacturer of an RF preamplifier specifies that an RF preamp has a 2-dB noise figure. This means that the actual noise power at the output is 1.58 times the power that would occur because of amplification of noise from the input. The other figure of merit for evaluating the noise performance of a linear device is the effective input-noise temperature, which is illustrated in Fig. 8-21.

DEFINITION: The *spot effective input-noise temperature, $T_{es}(f)$*, of a linear device is the *additional* temperature required for an input source, which is driving an ideal (noise-free) device, to produce the same available PSD at the ideal device output as is obtained from the actual device when it is driven by the input source of temperature T_i kelvin. That is, $T_{es}(f)$ is defined by

$$\mathcal{P}_{ao}(f) = G_a(f)\, \frac{k}{2}\, [T_i + T_{es}(f)] \tag{8-22}$$

where $\mathcal{P}_{ao}(f)$ is the available PSD out of the actual device when driven by an input source of temperature T_i, and $T_{es}(f)$ is the spot effective input-noise temperature.

The *average effective input-noise temperature, T_e*, is defined by the equation

$$P_{ao} = k(T_i + T_e) \int_{f_0 - B/2}^{f_0 + B/2} G_a(f)\, df \tag{8-23}$$

where the measured available noise power out of the device in a band B hertz wide is

$$P_{ao} = 2 \int_{f_0 - B/2}^{f_0 + B/2} \mathcal{P}_{ao}(f)\, df \tag{8-24}$$

Since $G_a(f)$ depends on the source impedance as well as on the device parameters, $T_e(f)$ will depend on the source impedance used as well as on the characteristics of the device

---

[†] Some authors call F the *noise factor* and F_{dB} the *noise figure*.

itself, but it is independent of the value of T_i used. In the definition of T_e, note that the IEEE standards do not specify that $T_i = T_0$ since the value of T_e obtained does not depend on the value of T_i that is used. However, $T_i = T_0 = 290$ may be used for convenience. The effective input-noise temperature can also be evaluated by the Y-factor method, as illustrated by Prob. 8-15.

When the gain is flat (constant) over the frequency band, $G_a(f) = G_a$, the effective input-noise temperature is simply

$$T_e = \frac{P_{ao} - kT_i G_a B}{kG_a B} \tag{8-25}$$

Note that $T_{es}(f)$ and T_e are greater than zero for an actual device, but if the device is nearly ideal (small internal noise sources), they will be very close to zero.

When T_e was evaluated by use of (8-23), an input source was used with some convenient value for T_i. However, when the device is used in a system, the available noise power from the source will be different if T_i is different. For example, suppose that the device is an RF preamplifier and the source is an antenna. The available power out of the amplifier when it is connected to the antenna is now[†]

$$P_{ao} = 2 \int_{f_0 - B/2}^{f_0 + B/2} \mathscr{P}_{as}(f) G_a(f) \, df + kT_e \int_{f_0 - B/2}^{f_0 + B/2} G_a(f) \, df \tag{8-26}$$

where $\mathscr{P}_{as}(f)$ is the available PSD out of the source (antenna). T_e is the average effective input temperature of the amplifier that was evaluated by using the input source T_i. If the gain of the amplifier is approximately constant over the band, this reduces to

$$P_{ao} = G_a P_{as} + kT_e B G_a \tag{8-27}$$

where the available power from the source (antenna) is

$$P_{as} = 2 \int_{f_0 - B/2}^{f_0 + B/2} \mathscr{P}_{as}(f) \, df \tag{8-28}$$

Furthermore, the available power from the source might be characterized by its noise temperature, T_s, so that, using (8-17),

$$P_{as} = kT_s B \tag{8-29}$$

In satellite Earth station receiving applications, the antenna (source) noise temperature might be $T_s = 32$ K at 4 GHz for a parabolic antenna with a diameter of 5 m, where the noise from the antenna is due to cosmic radiation and to energy received from the ground as the result of the sidelobe beam pattern of the antenna. (The Earth acts as a blackbody noise source with $T = 280$ K.) Note that the $T_s = 32$ K of the antenna is "caused" by *radiation* resistance, which is not the same as a loss resistance ($I^2 R$ losses) associated with a thermal source and T_s has no relation to the physical temperature of the antenna.

In summary, two figures of merit have been defined: noise figure and effective input-noise temperature. By combining (8-19) and (8-22) where $T_i = T_0$, a relationship between these two figures of merit for the spot measures is obtained:

$$T_{es}(f) = T_0[F_s(f) - 1] \tag{8-30a}$$

[†]The value of P_{ao} in (8-26) and (8-27) is different from that in (8-23), (8-24), and (8-25).

Here $T_i = T_0$ is required because $T_i = T_0$ is used in the definition for the noise figure that precedes (8-19).

Using (8-21a) and (8-25) where $T_i = T_0$, we obtain the same relationship for the average measures:

$$T_e = T_0(F - 1) \qquad (8\text{-}30b)$$

Example 8-3 T_e and F for a Transmission Line

The effective input-noise temperature, T_e, and the noise figure, F, for a lossy transmission line (a linear device) will now be evaluated.[†] This can be accomplished by terminating the transmission line with a source and a load resistance (all having the same physical temperature) that are both equal to the characteristic impedance of the line, as shown in Fig. 8-22. The gain of the transmission line is $G_a = 1/L$, where L is the transmission line loss (power in divided by power out) in absolute units (i.e., not dB units). Looking into the output port of the transmission line, one sees an equivalent circuit that is resistive (thermal source) with a value of R_0 ohms since the input of the line is terminated by a resistor of R_0 ohms (the characteristic impedance). Assume that the physical temperature of the transmission line is T_L, as measured on the Kelvin scale. Since the line acts as a thermal source, the available noise power at its output is $P_{ao} = kT_L B$. Using (8-25) where the source is at the same physical temperature, $T_i = T_L$, we get

$$T_e = \frac{kT_L B - kT_L G_a B}{kG_a B} = T_L\left(\frac{1}{G_a} - 1\right)$$

Thus the effective input-noise temperature for the transmission line is

$$T_e = T_L(L - 1) \qquad (8\text{-}31a)$$

where T_L is the physical temperature (Kelvin) of the line and L is the line loss. If the physical temperature of the line happens to be T_0, this becomes

$$T_e = T_0(L - 1) \qquad (8\text{-}31b)$$

The noise figure for the transmission line is obtained by using (8-30b) to convert T_e to F. Thus, substituting (8-31a) into (8-30b), we get

$$T_L(L - 1) = T_0(F - 1)$$

[†] These results also hold for the T_e and F of (impedance) matched attenuators.

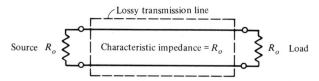

FIGURE 8-22 Noise figure measurement of a lossy transmission line.

Solving for F, we obtain the noise figure for the transmission line

$$F = 1 + \frac{T_L}{T_0}(L - 1) \tag{8-32a}$$

where T_L is the physical temperature (Kelvin) of the line, $T_0 = 290$, and L is the line loss. If the physical temperature of the line is 290 K (63°F), (8-32a) reduces to

$$F = \frac{1}{G_a} = L \tag{8-32b}$$

In decibel measure, this is $F_{dB} = L_{dB}$. In other words, if a transmission line has a 3-dB loss, it has a noise figure of 3 dB provided that it has a physical temperature of 63°F. If the temperature is 32°F (273 K), the noise figure, using (8-32a), will be 2.87 dB. Thus F_{dB} is approximately L_{dB}, if the transmission line is located in an environment (temperature range) that is inhabitable by humans.

Noise Characterization of Cascaded Linear Devices

In a communication system several linear devices, supplied by different vendors, are often cascaded together to form an overall system, as indicated in Fig. 8-23. In a receiving system these devices might be an RF preamplifier connected to a transmission line that feeds a down converter and an IF amplifier. (As discussed in Sec. 5-11, the down converter is a linear device and may be characterized by its conversion power gain and its noise figure.) For system performance calculations, we need to evaluate the overall power gain, G_a, and the overall noise characterization (which is given by the overall noise figure or the overall effective input-noise temperature) from the specifications for the individual devices provided by the vendors.

The overall available power gain is

$$G_a(f) = G_{a1}(f)G_{a2}(f)G_{a3}(f)G_{a4}(f)\cdots \tag{8-33}$$

since, for example, for a four-stage system,

$$G_a(f) = \frac{\mathscr{P}_{ao4}}{\mathscr{P}_{as}} = \left(\frac{\mathscr{P}_{ao1}}{\mathscr{P}_{as}}\right)\left(\frac{\mathscr{P}_{ao2}}{\mathscr{P}_{ao1}}\right)\left(\frac{\mathscr{P}_{ao3}}{\mathscr{P}_{ao2}}\right)\left(\frac{\mathscr{P}_{ao4}}{\mathscr{P}_{ao3}}\right)$$

Theorem

The overall noise figure for cascaded linear devices is[†]

$$F = F_1 + \frac{F_2 - 1}{G_{a1}} + \frac{F_3 - 1}{G_{a1}G_{a2}} + \frac{F_4 - 1}{G_{a1}G_{a2}G_{a3}} + \cdots \tag{8-34}$$

as shown in Fig. 8-23 (for a four-stage system).

[†]This is known as Friis's noise formula.

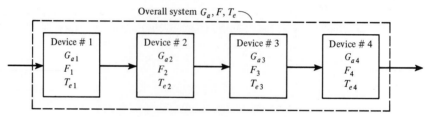

FIGURE 8-23 Cascade of four devices.

PROOF. This result may be obtained by using an excess-noise model of Fig. 8-20 for each stage. We will prove the result for a two-stage system as modeled in Fig. 8-24. The overall noise figure is

$$F = \frac{P_{ao2}}{(P_{ao2})_{ideal}} = \frac{P_{x2} + P_{ao1}G_{a2}}{G_{a1}G_{a2}P_{as}}$$

which becomes

$$F = \frac{P_{x2} + G_{a2}(P_{x1} + G_{a1}P_{as})}{G_{a1}G_{a2}P_{as}} \tag{8-35}$$

where $P_{as} = kT_0B$ is the available power from the thermal source. P_{x1} and P_{x2} can be obtained from the noise figures of the individual devices by using Fig. 8-20, so that for the ith device

$$F_i = \frac{P_{aoi}}{G_{ai}P_{as}} = \frac{P_{xi} + G_{ai}P_{as}}{G_{ai}P_{as}}$$

or

$$P_{xi} = G_{ai}P_{as}(F_i - 1) \tag{8-36}$$

Substituting this equation into (8-35) for P_{x1} and P_{x2}, we obtain

$$F = F_1 + \frac{F_2 - 1}{G_{a1}}$$

which is identical to (8-34) for the case of two cascaded stages. In a similar way (8-34) can be shown to be true for any number of stages. ∎

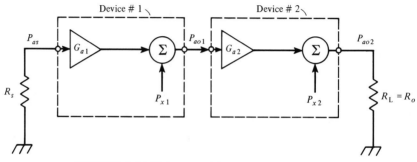

FIGURE 8-24 Noise model for two cascaded devices.

Looking at (8-34), we see that if the terms G_{a1}, $G_{a1}G_{a2}$, $G_{a1}G_{a2}G_{a3}$, and so on, are relatively large, F_1 will dominate the overall noise figure. Thus, in receiving system design, it is important that the first stage have a low noise figure and a large available gain so that the noise figure of the overall system will be as small as possible.

The overall effective input-noise temperature of several cascaded stages can also be evaluated.

Theorem

The **overall effective input-noise temperature** for cascaded linear devices is

$$T_e = T_{e1} + \frac{T_{e2}}{G_{a1}} + \frac{T_{e3}}{G_{a1}G_{a2}} + \frac{T_{e4}}{G_{a1}G_{a2}G_{a3}} + \cdots \tag{8-37}$$

as shown in Fig. 8-23.

A proof of this result is left for the reader as an exercise.

For further study concerning the topics of effective input-noise temperature and noise figure, the reader is referred to an authoritative monograph [Mumford and Scheibe, 1968].

Link Budget Evaluation

The performance of a communication system depends on how large the signal-to-noise (S/N) ratio is at the detector input in the receiver. It is engineering custom to call the signal-to-noise ratio before detection the *carrier-to-noise* ratio (C/N). Thus, in this section, we will use C/N to denote the signal-to-noise ratio before detection (bandpass case) and S/N to denote the signal-to-noise ratio after detection (baseband case). Here we are interested in evaluating the detector input C/N as a function of the communication link parameters, such as transmitted EIRP, space loss, receiver antenna gain, and the effective input-noise temperature of the receiving system. The formula that relates these system link parameters to the C/N at the detector input is called the *link budget*.

The communication system may be described by the block diagram shown in Fig. 8-25. In this model, the receiving system from the receiving-antenna output to the detector input is modeled by one linear block that represents the cascaded stages in the receiving system, such as a transmission line, a low-noise amplifier (LNA), a down converter, and an IF amplifier. This linear block describes the overall available power gain and effective input-noise temperature of these cascaded devices, as described in the preceding section and modeled in Fig. 8-22.

As shown in Fig. 8-25, the C/N at the ideal amplifier input (with gain G_a) is identical to that at the detector input since the ideal amplifier adds no excess noise and it amplifies the signal and noise equally well in a bandwidth of B hertz (the IF bandwidth). Thus, denoting this simply by C/N,

$$\left(\frac{C}{N}\right) \triangleq \left(\frac{C}{N}\right)_{Rx} = \left(\frac{C}{N}\right)_{det} \tag{8-38}$$

where these carrier-to-noise power ratios are indicated on the figure.

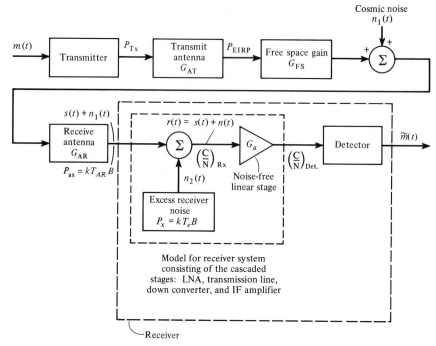

FIGURE 8-25 Communication system model for link budget evaluation.

Using (8-2) and (8-3), we obtain the received signal power

$$C_{\text{Rx}} = (P_{\text{EIRP}})G_{\text{FS}}G_{\text{AR}} \qquad (8\text{-}39)$$

where P_{EIRP} is the EIRP from the transmitter, G_{FS} is the free-space gain, and G_{AR} is the receiving antenna power gain.

When we use (8-17), the available noise power at the input to the ideal amplifier in the model (Fig. 8-25) is

$$N = kT_{\text{syst}}B \qquad (8\text{-}40)$$

where B is the IF bandwidth. The receiving system noise temperature is

$$T_{\text{syst}} = T_{\text{AR}} + T_e \qquad (8\text{-}41)$$

where T_{AR} is the noise temperature of the antenna (due to received cosmic noise and Earth blackbody radiation) and T_e is the effective input-noise temperature of the overall receiving system.

When (8-39) and (8-40) are combined, the carrier-to-noise ratio at the detector input is

$$\frac{C}{N} = \frac{P_{\text{EIRP}}G_{\text{FS}}G_{\text{AR}}}{kT_{\text{syst}}B} \qquad (8\text{-}42)$$

For engineering applications, this formula is converted to decibel units. Using (8-9) in (8-42), the received carrier-to-noise ratio at the detector input in decibels is

$$\left(\frac{C}{N}\right)_{\text{db}} = (P_{\text{EIRP}})_{\text{dBw}} - (L_{\text{FS}})_{\text{dB}} + \left(\frac{G_{\text{AR}}}{T_{\text{syst}}}\right)_{\text{dB}} - k_{\text{dB}} - B_{\text{dB}} \qquad (8\text{-}43)$$

where $(P_{EIRP})_{dBw} = 10 \log(P_{EIRP})$ is the EIRP of the transmitter in dB above
1 W

$(L_{FS})_{dB} = 20 \log[(4\pi d)/\lambda]$ is the path loss

$k_{dB} = 10 \log(1.38 \times 10^{-23}) = -228.6$

$B_{dB} = 10 \log(B)$ (B is the IF bandwidth in hertz)

For analog communication systems, the S/N at the detector output can be related to the C/N at the detector input. The exact relationship depends on the type of detector as well as the modulation used. This is shown by Table 6-6 and Fig. 6-18 with the use of (6-71), where C/N = $(S/N)_{in}$. Example 8-4 uses (8-43) to evaluate the performance of a CATV satellite receiving system.

E_b/N_0 Link Budget for Digital Systems

In digital communication systems the probability of bit error P_e for the digital signal at the detector output describes the quality of the recovered data. The P_e is a function of the ratio of the energy per bit to the noise PSD (E_b/N_0) as measured at the detector input. The exact relationship between P_e and E_b/N_0 depends on the type of digital signaling used, as shown in Table 7-6 and Fig. 7-19. In this section we evaluate the E_b/N_0 obtained at the detector input as a function of the communication link parameters.

The energy per bit is given by $E_b = CT_b$, where C is the signal power and T_b is the time required to send one bit. Using (8-17), we see that the noise PSD (one-sided) is $N_0 = kT_{syst}$. Thus

$$\frac{C}{N} = \frac{E_b/T_b}{N_0 B} = \frac{E_b R}{N_0 B} \qquad (8\text{-}44)$$

where $R = 1/T_b$ is the data rate (bits/sec). Using (8-44) in (8-42), we have

$$\frac{E_b}{N_0} = \frac{P_{EIRP} G_{FS} G_{AR}}{kT_{syst} R} \qquad (8\text{-}45)$$

In decibel units, the E_b/N_0 received at the detector input in a digital communications receiver is related to the link parameters by

$$\left(\frac{E_b}{N_0}\right)_{dB} = (P_{EIRP})_{dBw} - (L_{FS})_{dB} + \left(\frac{G_{AR}}{T_{syst}}\right)_{dB} - k_{dB} - R_{dB} \qquad (8\text{-}46)$$

where $(R)_{dB} = 10 \log(R)$ and R is the data rate (bits/second).

For example, suppose that we have BPSK signaling and an optimum detector is used in the receiver; then $(E_b/N_0)_{dB} = 8.4$ dB is required for $P_e = 10^{-4}$ (see Fig. 7-19).[†] Using (8-46), the communication link parameters may be selected to give the required $(E_b/N_0)_{dB}$ of 8.4 dB. Note that as the bit rate is increased, the transmitted power has to be increased or the receiving system performance—denoted by $(G_{AR}/T_{syst})_{dB}$—has to be improved to maintain the required $(E_b/N_0)_{dB}$ of 8.4 dB.

[†]If, in addition, coding were used with a coding gain of 3 dB (see Sec. 1-10), an E_b/N_0 of 5.4 dB would be required for $P_e = 10^{-4}$.

Example 8-4   Link Budget Evaluation for a Television
Receive-Only Terminal for Satellite Signals

The link budget for a television receive-only (TVRO) terminal used for
reception of TV signals from a satellite will be evaluated. It is assumed that this
receiving terminal is located at Washington, D.C., and is receiving signals from
a Hughes *Galaxy* satellite that is in a geostationary orbit at 134° W longitude
above the equator. The specifications on the proposed receiving equipment are
given in Table 8-4 together with the receiving site coordinates and satellite
parameters. This TVRO terminal is typical of those used at the head end of
CATV systems for reception of TV signals that are relayed via satellite. As
discussed in Sec. 8-5, the composite NTSC baseband video signal is relayed via
satellite by frequency-modulating this signal on a 6-GHz carrier that is radiated
to the satellite. The satellite down-converts the FM signal to 4 GHz and
retransmits this FM signal to the TVRO terminal.

The transmit antenna EIRP footprint for the *Galaxy I* satellite is shown in
Fig. 8-26. From this figure it is seen that the EIRP directed toward Washington,
D.C., is approximately 36 dBW, as obtained for inclusion in Table 8-4.

TABLE 8-4 Typical Satellite Television Relay Parameters

Item	Parameter Value
Hughes *Galaxy I* satellite	
Orbit	Geostationary
Location (above equator)	134° W longitude
Uplink frequency band	6 GHz
Downlink frequency band	4 GHz
$(P_{\text{EIRP}})_{\text{dBw}}$	36 dBw
TVRO terminal	
Site location	Washington, D.C., 38.8° N latitude, 77° W longitude
Antenna	
Antenna type	10 ft diameter parabola
Noise temperature	32 K (at feed output) for 16.8° elevation
Feedline gain	0.98
Low-noise amplifier	
Noise temperature	40 K
Gain	50 dB
Receiver	
Manufacturer	Microdyne Corp., Model 1100-TVR (×24)
Noise temperature	2610 K
IF bandwidth	30 MHz
FM threshold	8 dB C/N

Vertical transmit

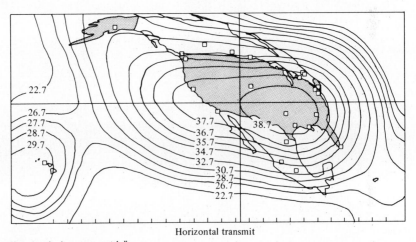

Horizontal transmit

Note: Actual values may vary ± 1 db.

FIGURE 8-26 *Galaxy I* (134° W longitude) antenna pattern EIRP footprint (contours given in dBw units). [Courtesy of Hughes Communications, Inc., a wholly owned subsidiary of Hughes Aircraft Company.]

It can be shown that the *look angles* of the TVRO antenna can be evaluated using the following formulas [Davidoff, 1984, Chap. 9]. The elevation of the TVRO antenna is

$$E = \tan^{-1}\left[\frac{1}{\tan \beta} - \frac{R}{(R + h)\sin \beta}\right] \qquad (8\text{-}47)$$

where

$$\beta = \cos^{-1}[\cos \phi \cos \lambda] \qquad (8\text{-}48)$$

and λ is the difference between the longitude of the TVRO site and the longitude of the *substation point* (i.e., the point directly below the geostationary satellite along the equator). ϕ is the latitude of the TVRO site, $R = 3963$ statute miles is the Earth radius, and $h = 22{,}242$ statute miles is the altitude of the synchronous satellite. The distance between the TVRO site and the satellite, called the *slant range,* is given by the cosine law:

$$d = \sqrt{(R + h)^2 + R^2 - 2R(R + h) \cos \beta} \qquad (8\text{-}49)$$

The azimuth of the TVRO antenna is

$$A = \cos^{-1}\left(-\frac{\tan \phi}{\tan \beta}\right) \qquad (8\text{-}50)$$

where the true azimuth as measured clockwise from the north is given by either A or $360° - A$, as appropriate, since a calculator gives a value between 0 and $180°$ for $\cos^{-1}(x)$. Using these formulas for the Washington, D.C., TVRO site,[†] we get $\lambda = 134 - 77 = 57°$ and

$$\beta = \cos^{-1}[\cos(38.8)\ \cos(57)] = 64.9° \qquad (8\text{-}51)$$

The slant range is

$$d = \sqrt{(26{,}205)^2 + (3963)^2 - 2(3963)(26{,}205)\ \cos(64.9)}$$
$$= 24{,}784 \quad \text{miles} \qquad (8\text{-}52)$$

The elevation angle of the TVRO antenna is

$$E = \tan^{-1}\left[\frac{1}{\tan(64.9)} - \frac{3963}{(26{,}205)\ \sin(64.9)}\right] = 16.8° \qquad (8\text{-}53)$$

The azimuth angle of the TVRO antenna is

$$A = \cos^{-1}\left[\frac{-\tan(38.8)}{\tan(64.9)}\right] = 247.9° \qquad (8\text{-}54)$$

Thus, the look angles of the TVRO antenna at Washington, D.C., to the *Galaxy I* satellite are $E = 16.8°$ and $A = 247.9°$.

A block diagram describing the receiving system is shown in Fig. 8-27. Using (8-43), the carrier-to-noise ratio at the detector input of the receiver is

$$\left(\frac{C}{N}\right)_{dB} = (P_{EIRP})_{dBw} - (L_{FS})_{dB} + \left(\frac{G_{AR}}{T_{syst}}\right)_{dB} - k_{dB} - B_{dB} \qquad (8\text{-}55)$$

The corresponding path loss for $d = 24{,}784$ mi at a frequency of 4 GHz is

$$(L_{FS})_{dB} = 20\ \log\left(\frac{4\pi d}{\lambda}\right) = 196.5 \text{ dB}$$

[†] Here for convenience and for ease in interpretation of answers, the calculator is set to evaluate all trigonometric functions in degrees (not radians).

FIGURE 8-27 TVRO terminal.

For a 10-ft (3.05-m) parabola, using Table 8-3, the receiving antenna gain is

$$(G_{AR})_{dB} = 10 \ log \left[\frac{7\pi(3.05/2)^2}{\lambda^2} \right] = 10 \ log(9085) = 39.6 \ dB$$

Using (8-41) and (8-37), we obtain the system noise temperature

$$T_{syst} = T_{AR} + T_{feed} + \frac{T_{LNA}}{G_{feed}} + \frac{T_{receiver}}{G_{feed}G_{LNA}} \qquad (8\text{-}56)$$

where the specified antenna noise temperature, including the feed, is $T_A = (T_{AR} + T_{feed}) = 32$ K.

The T_{AR} is *not* the ambient temperature of the antenna (which is about 290 K) because the effective resistance of the antenna does not consist of a thermal resistor but of a radiation resistor. That is, if RF power is fed into the antenna, it will not be dissipated in the antenna but instead will be radiated into space. Consequently, T_{AR} is called the *sky noise temperature* and is a measure of the amount of cosmic noise power that is received from outer space and noise caused by atmospheric attenuation, where this power is $P_{AR} = kT_{AR}B$. Graphs giving the measured sky noise temperature as a function of the RF frequency and the elevation angle of the antenna are available [Jordan, 1985, Chap. 27; Pratt and Bostian, 1986].

Substituting the receive system parameters into (8-55), we have

$$T_{syst} = 32 + \frac{40}{0.98} + \frac{2610}{(0.98)(100,000)} = 72.8 \ K$$

Thus[†]

$$\left(\frac{G_{AR}}{T_{syst}} \right)_{dB} = 10 \ log \left(\frac{9,085}{72.8} \right) = 21.0 \ dB/K$$

Also,

$$(B)_{dB} = 10 \ log(30 \times 10^6) = 74.8$$

Substituting these results into (8-55) yields

$$\left(\frac{C}{N} \right)_{dB} = 36 - 196.5 + 21.0 - (-228.6) - 74.8$$

[†]Engineers specify dB/K as the units for $(G/T)_{dB}$, although it is a misnomer.

Thus the carrier-to-noise ratio at the detector input (inside the FM receiver) is

$$\left(\frac{C}{N}\right)_{dB} = 14.3 \text{ dB} \qquad (8\text{-}57)$$

A C/N of 14.3 dB does not seem to be a very good signal-to-noise ratio, does it? Actually, the question is: Does a C/N of 14.3 dB at the detector input give a high-quality video signal at the detector output? This question can be answered easily if we have some detector performance curves as shown in Fig. 8-28. Two curves are plotted in this figure. One is for the output of a receiver that uses an FM discriminator for the FM detector, and the other is for a receiver (Microdyne 1100TVR) that uses a PLL FM detector to provide threshold extension.[†] For a C/N of 14.3 dB on the input, both receivers will give a 51-dB

[†]The threshold point is the point where the knee occurs in the $(S/N)_{out}$ versus $(C/N)_{in}$ characteristic. In the characteristic for threshold extension receivers, this knee is extended to the left (improved performance) when compared to the knee for the corresponding receiver that uses a discriminator as a detector.

FIGURE 8-28 Output S/N as a function of FM detector input C/N. [Curve for the Microdyne receiver, Model 1100TVR, courtesy of the Microdyne Corporation, Ocala, FL, 1981.]

output S/N, which corresponds to a high-quality picture. However, if the receive signal from the satellite fades because of atmospheric conditions, and so on, by, say, 6 dB, the output S/N of the receiver with an FM discriminator will be only about 36 dB, whereas the receiver with threshold extension detection will have an output S/N of about 45 dB.

8-7 Fiber Optic Systems

Since 1980 fiber optic cable transmission systems have become commercially viable. This is indicated in Table 8-2, which shows that common carriers have installed extensive fiber optic systems in the United States, Japan, Britain, and Canada. Fiber optic cable is the preferred underground transmission medium and is superseding twisted-pair cable and coaxial cable. Also, as shown in Table 8-2, transoceanic fiber optic cable systems are becoming popular. Digital fiber optic systems use simple OOK modulation of an optical source to produce a modulated light beam. The optical source has a wavelength in the range of 0.85 to 1.6 μm, which is about 77,000 GHz. (Analog AM fiber optic systems can also be built.)

The optical sources can be classified into two categories: (1) light-emitting diodes (LED) that produce noncoherent light and (2) solid-state lasers that produce coherent (single-carrier-frequency) light. The LED source is popular because it is rugged and inexpensive. It has a relatively low power output, about -15 dBm (including coupling loss), and a small modulation bandwidth of about 50 MHz. The laser diode has a relatively high power output, about $+5$ dBm (including coupling loss), and a large modulation bandwidth of about 1 GHz. The laser diode is preferred over the LED since it produces coherent light and has high output power, but it is high in cost and has a short lifetime. OOK modulation is obtained simply by switching the bias current on and off.

The light source is coupled into the fiber optic cable, and this cable is the channel transmission medium. Fiber cables can be classified into two categories: (1) multimodal and (2) single-mode. Multimodal fiber has a core diameter of 50 μm and a cladding diameter of 125 μm. The light is reflected off the core–cladding boundary as it propagates down the fiber to produce multiple paths of different lengths. This causes pulse dispersion of the OOK signal at the receiving end and thus severely limits the transmission bit rate that can be accommodated. The single-mode fiber has a core diameter of approximately 8 μm and propagates a single wave. Consequently, there is little dispersion of the received pulses of light. Because of its superior performance, single-mode fiber is preferred.

At the receiving end of the fiber, the receiver consists of a PIN diode, an avalanche photodiode (APD), or a GaAsMESFES transistor used as an optical detector. In 0.85-μm systems any of these devices may be used as a detector. In 1.3- and 1.55-μm systems the APD is usually used. The PIN diode is low in cost and reliable but is used only in 0.85-μm systems. These detectors act like a simple envelope detector. As shown in Fig. 7-19, better performance (lower probability of bit error) could be obtained by using a coherent detection system that has a product detector. This requires a coherent light source at the receiver that is mixed with the received OOK signal via the nonlinear action of the photodetector. Of course, it is possible to have coherent PSK and FSK systems [Basch and Brown, 1985], but they are usually not cost-effective.

Example 8-5   Link Budget for a Fiber Optic System

Tables 8-5 through 8-7 show the performance characteristics of a fiber optic common-carrier cable system that has been installed and operated by Microtel, Inc. in Florida [Siperko, 1985]. Called LaserNet, this system has been installed along the east coast between Jacksonville and Miami, with a connecting link from Cocoa to Tampa via Orlando and a link from Tampa down to Naples on the west coast. From Table 8-10 it is seen that the average transmitted power is -3.5 dBm and the receiver sensitivity is -36.0 dBm. The link budget analysis shows that repeaters (demodulators and remodulators) are required every 40 km (or 25 miles). The bit rate is 417.792 Mbits/sec, as shown in Table 8-7, so that nine DS-3 signals can be accommodated on the TDM OOK light-wave signal. This is equivalent to a VF capacity of 6048 channels (see Table 4-8). In 1985, 480 miles of this system was constructed at a cost of $3.50 per foot or $6.98 per VF channel mile. These figures are impressive. However, with newly developed optical termination equipment, the capacity can be increased to 1.3 Gbits/sec or 28 DS-3 channels, for a VF capacity of 18,816 channels when needed.

TABLE 8-5 Link Budget Analysis for LaserNet Operating at 1.3 μm

Description	Value
Average effective transmitter power	-3.5 dBm
Receiver sensitivity	-36.0 dBm
Available margin	32.5 dB
Losses in a fiber optic link	
Chromatic dispersion/reflection noise (40-km span)	1.5 dB
Fiber attenuation (40 km $\times$ 0.5 dB/km)	20.0 dB
15 splices at 0.1 dB/splice	1.5 dB
Connector losses	3.0 dB
Design margin	5.0 dB
Excess margin	1.5 dB
Total loss	32.5 dB

SOURCE: Siperko [1985].

TABLE 8-6 Single-Mode Optical Fiber Specifications

Core diameter	$8.7 \pm 1.3 \ \mu$m
Reference surface diameter	$125.0 \pm 3 \ \mu$m
Reference surface noncircularity	$\leq 2.0\%$
Coating diameter	$250.0 \pm 15 \ \mu$m
Spot size	$5.0 \pm 0.5 \ \mu$m
Core/cladding concentricity (offset)	$\leq 1.0 \ \mu$m
Effective mode cutoff wavelength	1130–1270 nm
Refractive index difference	$0.3 \pm 0.5\%$
Zero dispersion wavelength	1310 nm nominal
Maximum dispersion at 1310 nm $\pm$ 20 nm	3.5 ps/nm-km
Dispersion at 1550 nm	17.0 ± 2.0 psec/nm-km
Mode field diameter	$9.8 \pm 1.0 \ \mu$m
Attenuation at 1310 nm	0.5 dB/km maximum
Attenuation at 1550 nm[a]	0.4 dB/km maximum

SOURCE: Charles M. Siperko, "LaserNet—a fiber optic intrastate network," *IEEE Communications Magazine*, May 1985, p. 41. © 1985 IEEE.

[a] Attenuation at 1550 nm typically 0.1 dB lower than attenuation at 1310 nm.

TABLE 8-7 Interface Specifications for an Optical Light Multiplexer

Line rate	417.792 Mbits/sec $\pm$ 15 ppm
Line code	Scrambled binary code, RZ
Wavelength	1310 nm $\pm$ 0.03 nm
Optical source	Indium gallium arsenide phosphide—ILD (InGaAsP)
Optical detector	Germanium, avalanche photodiode—APD
Optical fiber	8.7/125-μm single-mode step index
Transmitter power	Peak: $+2$ dBm $\pm$ 0.5 dB
	Average: -3.5 dBm $\pm$ 0.5 dB
Receiver sensitivity	Average: -36 dBm
Bit error rate (BER)	$\leq 10^{-11}$ for average -36 dBm receiver input

SOURCE: Charles M. Siperko, "LaserNet—a fiber optic intrastate network," *IEEE Communications Magazine*, May 1985, p. 43. © 1985 IEEE.

8-8 Cellular Telephone Systems

Since the invention of radio systems, the goal of telephone engineers has been to provide personal telephone service to individuals by using radio systems to link phone lines with persons in their cars or on foot. In the past this type of personal telephone service was not possible because limited spectrum space did not permit the assignment of a "private-line" radio channel for each subscriber. In addition, the existing radio equipment was bulky and

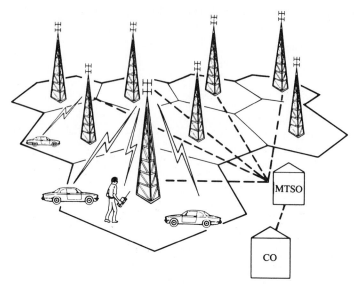

FIGURE 8-29 Cellular telephone system.

expensive. However, with the development of the integrated circuit technology, radio equipment can now be miniaturized, and relatively sophisticated operations can be implemented at low cost. This development allows the sharing of a number of radio channels on demand (FDMA) where a particular channel is assigned to a specific user only when a telephone call is in progress. An example is *trunked mobile radio systems* in which a number of radio channels are shared with different groups of users (i.e., statistical multiplexing on a FDMA basis). In these trunked systems, relatively high-power transmitters are used so that each radio channel covers a whole city or county. Consequently, when a channel is being used by anyone in that area, it is not available for use by others. Many more users can be accommodated simultaneously if the coverage of each transmitter is reduced to some small geographical area (a cell) so that the same radio frequency channel can be reused by another individual a few miles away in a distant cell.

This *cellular radio* concept is illustrated in Fig. 8-29. Each user communicates via radio from a cellular telephone set to the cell-site base station. This base station is connected via telephone lines to the *mobile telephone switching office* (MTSO). The MTSO connects the user to the called party. If the called party is land based, the connection is via the central office (CO) to the terrestrial telephone network. If the called party is mobile, the connection is made to the cell site that covers the area in which the called party is located, using an available radio channel in the cell associated with the called party. Theoretically, this cellular concept allows any number of mobile users to be accommodated for a given set of radio channels. That is, if more channels are needed, the existing cell sizes are decreased and additional small cells are inserted so that the existing channels can be reused more efficiently. The critical consideration is to design the cells for acceptable levels of cochannel interference [Lee, 1986]. As the mobile user travels from one cell to another, the

MTSO automatically switches the user to an available channel in the new cell and the telephone conversation continues uninterrupted.

The cellular concept has the following advantages.

• Large subscriber capacity.
• Efficient use of the radio spectrum.
• Nationwide compatibility.
• Service to hand-held portables as well as vehicles.
• High-quality telephone and data service to the mobile user at relatively low cost.

Unfortunately, there are many cellular standards used throughout the world [Okumura and Shinji, 1986]. For example, as many as 15 different types of cellular phones are needed to remain in communication as one travels around Europe. Table 8-8 shows three major analog standards that are used around the world. Moreover, since cellular telephones are so popular, it is clear that these wideband FM analog systems do not have the capacity to accommodate the expected new subscribers. Consequently, narrowband FM analog systems with higher capacity, as shown in Table 8-9, are replacing wideband systems on a channel-by-channel basis as needed. For example, one wideband 30-kHz AMPS channel can be replaced by three narrowband 10-kHz NAMPS channels to triple the capacity. For larger capacity, new digital cellular systems, as shown in Table 8-10, will be used. The GSM digital system is being placed into service in Europe to provide one uniform standard that replaces the numerous analog systems that are being phased out. By 1996 it is estimated that the number of GSM subscribers will equal or surpass the number of European analog subscribers.

As shown in Table 8-8, the present cellular system used in the United States is the Advanced Mobile Phone System (AMPS), which was developed by AT&T and Motorola. To implement this cellular concept in the United States, the FCC had to find spectral space for assignment. It did so by using the 806- to 890-MHz band that was once assigned to TV channels 70 to 83 (see Table 8-12) but discontinued in 1974. Part of this band was assigned for cellular service as shown in Table 8-8. Furthermore, the FCC decided to license two competing call systems in each geographical area—one licensed to a conventional telephone company and another to a nontelephone company common carrier. The nontelephone system is called the *A service* or *nonwireline service,* and the telephone company system is called the *B service* or *wireline service.* Thus cell system subscribers have the option of renting service from the wireline company or the nonwireline company, or from both. In addition, as shown in the table, the standards provide for full duplex service. That is, one carrier frequency is used for mobile to cell base-station transmission, and another carrier frequency is used for base-station to mobile transmission. The telephone VF signals are frequency modulated onto the carriers, and control is provided by FSK signaling. Of the 416 channels that may be used by a cellular service licensee, 21 are used for paging and control with FSK signaling. FSK signaling is also used at the beginning and end of each call on a VF channel. When a cellular telephone is turned on, its receiver scans the paging channels looking for the strongest cell-site signal and then locks onto it. The cell site transmits FSK data continuously on a paging channel, and, in particular, it sends control information addressed to a particular cellular phone when a call comes

TABLE 8-8 Major Analog Cellular Telephone Systems

	System Name[a] and Where Used			
	AMPS North America		ETACS United Kingdom	JTACS Japan
Item	A Service (Nonwire Line)	B Service (Wire Line)		
Base cell station Transmit bands (MHz)	869–880, 890–891.5	880–890, 891.5–894	872–905	860–870
Mobile station Transmit bands (MHz)	824–835, 845–846.5	835–845, 846.5–849	917–950	915–925
Maximum power (watts)	3	3	3	2.8
Cell size, radius (km)	2–20	2–20	2–20	2–20
Number of duplex channels	416[b]	416[b]	1320	399
Channel bandwidth (kHz)	30	30	25	25
Modulation Voice	FM 12-kHz peak deviation	FM 12-kHz peak deviation	FM 9.5-kHz peak deviation	FM 9.5-kHz peak deviation
Control signal (Voice and paging channels)	FSK 8-kHz peak deviation 10 kbits/sec Manchester line code	FSK 8-kHz peak deviation 10 kbits/sec Manchester line code	FSK 6.4-kHz peak deviation 8 kbits/sec Manchester line code	FSK 6.4-kHz peak deviation 8 kbits/sec Manchester line code

SOURCE: Most of the data in this table were assembled by Jim Worsham, Matsushita Communication Industrial Corporation of America/Panasonic, Alpharetta, Georgia.

[a] AMPS, advanced mobile phone system; ETACS, extended total access communication system; JTACS, Japan total access communication system.
[b] 21 of the 416 channels are used exclusively for paging.

TABLE 8-9 Narrowband Analog Cellular Telephone Systems

Item	System Name[a] and Where Used:	
	NAMPS North America	NTACS Japan
Base cell station		
Transmit band (MHz)	869–894	843–870
Mobile station		
Transmit band (MHz)	824–849	898–925
Maximum power (watts)	3	2.8
Number of duplex channels	2496	2160
Channel bandwidth		
Voice (kHz)	10	12.5
Paging (kHz)	30	25
Modulation		
Voice	FM 5-kHz peak deviation	FM 5-kHz peak deviation
Signaling (voice channel)	FSK 0.7-kHz peak deviation 100 bits/sec, Manchester	FSK 0.7-kHz peak deviation 100 bits/sec, Manchester
Signaling (paging channel)	FSK 8-kHz peak deviation 10 kbits/sec, Manchester	FSK 6.4-kHz peak deviation 8 kbits/sec, Manchester

SOURCE: Most of the data in this table were assembled by Jim Worsham, Matsushita Communication Industrial Corporation of America/Panasonic, Alpharetta, Georgia.

[a]NAMPS, narrowband advanced mobile phone system; NTACS, narrowband total access communication system.

in for it. That is, the FSK control signal tells the phone which voice-frequency (VF) channel to use for a call.

Each cellular telephone contains a PROM (programmable read-only memory) or EPROM (erasable programmable read-only memory)—called a *numeric assignment module* (NAM)—that is programmed to contain

- The telephone number—also called the *electronic service number* (ESN)—of the phone.
- The serial number of the phone as assigned by the manufacturer.
- Personal codes that can be used to prevent unauthorized use of the phone.

When the phone is ''on-the-air'' it automatically transmits its serial number to the MTSO. The serial number is used by the MTSO to lock out phone service to any phone that has been stolen. This feature, of course, discourages theft of the units. The MTSO uses the telephone number of the unit to provide billing information. When the phone is used in a

TABLE 8-10 Major Digital Cellular Telephone Systems

Item	System Name[a] and Where Used		
	GSM Europe	NADC North America	JDC Japan
Base cell station			
Transmit bands (MHz)	935–960	869–894	810–826, 1477–1489, 1501–1513
Mobile station			
Transmit bands (MHz)	890–915	824–849	940–956, 1429–1441, 1453–1465
Maximum power (watts)	20	3	
Number of duplex channels	125	832	1600
Channel bandwidth (kHz)	200	30	25
Channel access method	TDMA	TDMA	TDMA
Users per channel	8	3	3
Modulation[b]			
Type	GMSK	$\pi/4$ DQPSK	$\pi/4$ DQPSK
Data rate	270.833 kbits/sec	48.6 kbits/sec	42 kbits/sec
Filter	0.3R Gaussian[c]	$r = 0.35$ raised cosine[d]	$r = 0.5$ raised cosine[d]
Speech coding[e]	RPE-LTP 13 kbits/sec	VSELF 8 kbits/sec	VSELF 8 kbits/sec

SOURCE: Most of the data in this table were assembled by Jim Worsham, Matsushita Communication Industrial Corporation of America/Panasonic, Alpharetta, Georgia.

[a] GSM, group special mobile; NADC, North American digital cellular; JDC, Japan digital cellular.
[b] GMSK, Gaussian MSK (i.e., $h = 0.5$ FSK, also called FFSK, with Gaussian premodulation filter; see Sec. 7-3 and footnote c below); $\pi/4$ DQPSK, differential QPSK with $\pi/4$ rotation of reference phase for each symbol transmitted.
[c] Baseband Gaussian filter with 3 dB bandwidth equal to 0.3 of the bit rate.
[d] Square root of raised cosine characteristic at transmitter and receiver.
[e] RPE-LTP, regular pulse excitation—long-term prediction; VSELF, vector sum excited linear prediction filter.

remote city, it can be placed in the *roam* mode so that calls can be initiated or received and yet the service will be billed via the caller's "hometown" company.

To place a call the following sequence of events occurs.

1. The cellular subscriber initiates a call by keying in the telephone number of the called party and then presses the *send* key.
2. The MTSO verifies that the telephone number is valid and that the user is authorized to place a call.
3. The MTSO issues instructions to the user's cellular phone indicating which radio channel to use.
4. The MTSO sends out a signal to the called party to ring his or her phone. All of these operations occur within 10 sec of initiating the call.
5. When the called party answers, the MTSO connects the trunk lines for the two parties and initiates billing information.
6. When one party hangs up, the MTSO frees the radio channel and completes the billing information.

While a call is in progress, the cellular subscriber may be moving from one cell area to another, so the MTSO:

- Monitors the signal strength from the cellular telephone as received at the cell base station. If the signal drops below some designated level, the MTSO initiates a "hand-off" sequence.
- For "hand-off," the MTSO inquires about the signal strength as received at adjacent cell sites.
- When the signal level becomes sufficiently large at an adjacent cell site, the MTSO instructs the cellular radio to switch over to an appropriate channel for communication with that new cell site. This switching process takes less than 250 msec and usually is unnoticed by the subscriber.

As indicated by the tables, cellular systems and the standards for these systems are in a process of evolution throughout the world. The first commercial cellular service was implemented in the United States in 1983. There is a strong push for development of all digital cellular systems that have large user capacity, as illustrated by the proposed NADC and JDC systems listed in Table 8-10. For bandwidth conservation, these systems use low-bit-rate encoding of the VF signal. For example, the vector sum excited linear prediction filter (VSELF) encoder proposed for the NADC and JDC systems is a modified version of the codebook excited linear prediction (CELP) technique developed by B. Atal at the AT&T Bell Laboratories [Gerson and Jasiuk, 1990]. This technique mimics the two main parts of the human speech system, the vocal cords and the vocal tract. The vocal tract is simulated by a time-varying linear prediction filter, and the vocal cord sounds used for the filter excitation are simulated with a database (i.e., a codebook) of possible excitations. The VSELF encoder (at the transmitter) partitions the talker's VF signal into 20-msec segments. The encoder sequences through the possible codebook excitation patterns and the possible values for the filter parameters to find the synthesized speech segment that gives the best match to the VF segment. The encoder parameters that specify this best match are then transmitted via digital data to the receiver, where the received data establish the parameters for the receiver speech synthesizer so that the VF signal may be reproduced for the listener.

The new digital cellular telephones need to be relatively inexpensive and compact in size. This, of course, requires the use of advanced integrated-circuit technology. For more details about cellular systems, the reader is referred to the technical literature, such as the *IEEE Transactions on Vehicular Technology* [Rhee and Lee, 1991], the *IEEE Communications Magazine* [Goodman, 1991] and a book [Lee, 1989].

8-9 Television

Television (TV) is a method of reproducing fixed or moving visual images by the use of electronic signals. There are numerous kinds of TV systems and different standards have been adopted around the world. Moreover, as discussed subsequently, TV standards are in a state of flux since there is a worldwide push to adopt a new *high-definition television* (HDTV) standard. First we will concentrate on black-and-white broadcast TV as it has developed in the United States since the 1930s and then color television and HDTV will be examined.

Black-and-White Television

The black-and-white image of a scene is essentially the intensity of the light as a function of the x and y coordinates of the scene and of time. However, an electrical waveform is only a function of time, so that some means of encoding the x and y coordinates associated with the intensity of light from a single point in the scene must be used. In broadcast TV this is accomplished by using *raster scanning,* as shown in Fig. 8-30. It is assumed that the whole scene is scanned before any object in the scene has moved appreciably. Thus moving images can be transmitted by sending a series of still images, just as in motion pictures. As the scene is scanned, its intensity is signified by the amplitude of the video signal. A synchronizing pulse is inserted at the end of each scan line by the electronic switch, as shown in Fig. 8-30, to tell the TV receiver to start another scan line. For illustrative purposes, a black triangle is located in the upper left portion of the scene. In Figs. 8-30b and 8-30c, numbers are used to indicate the corresponding times on the video waveform, with the location of the point being scanned in the scene at that instant. The composite video signal is actually a hybrid signal that consists of a digital waveform during the synchronizing interval and an analog waveform during the video interval. Operating personnel monitor the quality of the video by looking at a *waveform monitor,* which displays the composite video waveform as shown in Fig. 8-30c.

The picture (as viewed) is generated by scanning left to right to create a line, and the lines move from the top to the bottom of the screen. During retrace, indicated by the dashed lines from right to left, the CRT is turned off by the video level that is "blacker than black" during the sync pulse interval.[†] The scene is actually covered by scanning

---

[†] In addition, most TV sets switch off the electron beam during retrace by using the sync pulse obtained from the horizontal output (flyback) transformer.

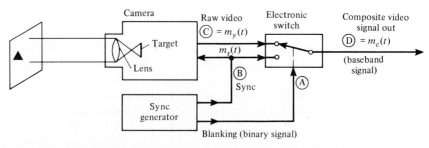

(a) Block Diagram of Camera System

(b) TV Raster Scan

(c) TV Waveforms

FIGURE 8-30 Generation of a composite black-and-white video signal.

alternate lines from the top to the bottom (one field) and returning to the top to scan the missed lines (the next field). This technique is called *interlacing* and reduces the flicker effect on moving pictures, giving two fields (passes down the screen) for every frame. In the United States there are approximately 30 frames/sec transmitted, which is equivalent to 60 fields/sec for the 2:1 interlacing that is used. When the scan reaches the bottom of a field, the sync pulse is widened out to cover the whole video interval plus sync interval. This occurs for 21 lines, and, consequently, a black bar is seen across the screen if the picture is "rolled up" by misadjusting the vertical hold control. In the receiver, the vertical sync (wide pulse) can be separated from the horizontal sync (narrow pulse) by using a differentiator circuit to recover the horizontal sync and an integrator to recover the vertical sync. The vertical interval is also used to send special signals, such as testing signals that can be used by TV engineers to test the frequency response and linearity of the equipment on-line [Solomon, 1979]. In addition, some TV programs have closed-caption information that can be decoded on special TV sets used by deaf viewers. These sets insert subtitles across the bottom of the screen. As shown in Table 8-11, this closed-captioning information is transmitted during line 21 of the vertical interval by inserting a 16-bit code word. Details of the exact sync structure are rigorously specified by the FCC (see Fig. 8-37).

The composite baseband signal consisting of the *luminance* (intensity) video signal $m_y(t)$ and the *synchronizing* signal $m_s(t)$ is described by

$$m_c(t) = \begin{cases} m_s(t) & \text{during the sync interval} \\ m_y(t) & \text{during the video interval} \end{cases} \tag{8-58}$$

The spectrum of $m_c(t)$ is very wide since $m_c(t)$ contains rectangular synchronizing pulses. In fact, the bandwidth would be infinite if the pulses had perfect rectangular shapes. In order to reduce the bandwidth, the pulses are rounded as specified by FCC standards (see Fig. 8-37). This allows $m_c(t)$ to be filtered to a bandwidth of $B = 4.2$ MHz (U.S. standard). For a still picture, the exact spectrum can be calculated using Fourier series analysis (as shown in Sec. 2-5). For a typical picture all fields are similar, thus $m_c(t)$ would be periodic with a period of approximately $T_0 = 1/60$ sec corresponding to the field rate of 60 fields/sec (see Table 8-11 for exact values). Thus, for a still picture, the spectrum would consist of lines spaced at 60-Hz intervals. However, from Fig. 8-30, we can observe that there are dominant intervals of width T_h corresponding to scanned lines of the frame. Furthermore, the adjacent lines usually have similar waveshapes. Consequently, $m_c(t)$ is quasiperiodic with period T_h, and the spectrum consists of clusters of spectral lines that are centered on harmonics of the scanning frequency, $nf_h = n/T_h$ where the spacing of the lines within these clumps is 60 Hz. For moving pictures, the line structure of the spectrum "fuzzes out" to a continuous spectrum with spectral clusters centered about nf_h. Furthermore, between these clusters the spectrum is nearly empty. As we will see, these "vacant" intervals in the spectrum are used to transmit the color information for a color TV signal. This, of course, is a form of frequency-division multiplexing.

The resolution of TV pictures is often specified in terms of lines of resolution. The number of horizontal lines that can be distinguished from the top to the bottom of a TV screen for a horizontal line test pattern is called the *vertical line resolution*. The maximum number of distinguishable horizontal lines (vertical line resolution) is the total number of scanning lines in the raster less those not used for the image. That is, the vertical resolution is

$$n_v = (N_f - N_v) \quad \text{lines} \tag{8-59a}$$

where N_f is the total number of scanning lines per frame and N_v is the number of lines in the vertical interval (not image lines) for each frame. For U.S. standards (Table 8-11), the

TABLE 8-11 U.S. Television Broadcasting Standards

Item	FCC Standard
Channel bandwidth	6 MHz
Visual carrier frequency	1.25 MHz $\pm$ 1000 Hz above the lower boundary of the channel
Aural carrier frequency	4.5 MHz $\pm$ 1000 Hz above the visual carrier frequency
Chrominance subcarrier frequency	3.579545 MHz $\pm$ 10 Hz
Aspect (width-to-height) ratio	Four units horizontally for every three units vertically
Modulation-type visual carrier	AM with negative polarity (i.e., a decrease in light level causes an increased real envelope level)
Aural carrier	FM with 100% modulation being $\Delta F = 25$ kHz with a frequency response of 50 to 15,000 Hz using 75-μsec preemphasis
Visual modulation levels	
Blanking level	75% $\pm$ 2.5% of peak real envelope level (sync tip level)
Reference black level	7.5% $\pm$ 2.5% (of the video range between blanking and reference white level) below blanking level; this is called the *setup* level by TV engineers[a]
Reference white level	12.5% $\pm$ 2.5% of sync tip level[a]
Scanning	
Number of lines	525 lines/frame, interlaced 2:1
Scanning sequence	Horizontally: left to right; vertically: top to bottom
Horizontal scanning frequency, f_h	15,734.264 $\pm$ 0.044 Hz (2/455 of chrominance frequency); 15,750 Hz may be used during monochrome transmissions
Vertical scanning frequency, f_v	59.94 Hz (2/525 of horizontal scanning frequency); 60 Hz may be used during monochrome transmissions; 21 equivalent horizontal lines occur during the vertical sync interval of each field
Vertical interval signaling	Lines 13, 14, 15, 16. Teletext
	Lines 17, 18. Vertical interval test signals (VITS)
	Line 19. Vertical interval reference (VIR)
	Line 20, Field 1. Station identification
	Line 21, Field 1. Captioning data
	Line 21, Field 2. Captioning framing code ($\frac{1}{2}$ line)

[a] See Fig. 8-31b.

maximum vertical resolution is

$$n_v = 525 - 42 = 483 \quad \text{lines} \tag{8-59b}$$

The resolution in the horizontal direction is limited by the frequency response allowed for $m_c(t)$. For example, if a sine-wave test signal is used during the video interval, the highest sine-wave frequency that can be transmitted through the system will be $B =$

4.2 MHz (U.S. standard) where B is the system video bandwidth. For each peak of the sine wave a dot will appear along the horizontal direction as the CRT beam sweeps from left to right. Thus the horizontal resolution for 2:1 interlacing is

$$n_h = 2B(T_h - T_b) \quad \text{lines} \tag{8-60a}$$

where B is the video bandwidth, T_h is the horizontal interval, and T_b is the blanking interval (see Fig. 8-30). For U.S. standards, $B = 4.2$ MHz, $T_h = 63.5 \ \mu s$, and $T_b = 10.5 \ \mu s$ so that the horizontal resolution is

$$n_h = 445 \quad \text{lines} \tag{8-60d}$$

Furthermore, because of poor video bandwidth and the poor interlacing characteristics of consumer TV sets, this horizontal resolution of 445 is usually not obtained in practice.[†] At best, the U.S. standard of 445 × 483 does not provide very good resolution, and this poor resolution is especially noticeable on large-screen TV sets. [For comparison the super VGA computer monitor standard provides a resolution as large as 1024 × 768.]

For broadcast TV transmission (U.S. standard), the composite video signal of (8-58) is inverted and amplitude modulated onto an RF carrier so that the AM signal is

$$s_v(t) = A_c[1 - 0.875m_c(t)] \cos \omega_c t \tag{8-61}$$

This is shown in Fig. 8-31. The lower sideband of this signal is attenuated so that the spectrum will fit into the 6-MHz TV channel bandwidth. This attenuation can be achieved by using a vestigial sideband filter, which is a bandpass filter that attenuates most of the lower sideband. The resulting filtered signal is called a *vestigial sideband* (VSB) signal, $s_{v_0}(t)$ as described in Sec. 6-5. The discrete carrier term in the VSB signal changes when the picture is switched from one scene to another because the composite baseband signal has a nonzero dc level that depends on the particular scene being televised. The audio signal for the TV program is transmitted via a separate FM carrier located exactly 4.5 MHz above the visual carrier frequency.

The rated power of a TV visual signal is the effective isotropic radiated peak envelope power (EIRP, i.e., effective sync tip average power), and is usually called simply the *effective radiated power* (ERP). The EIRP is the power that would be required to be fed into an isotropic antenna to get the same field strength as that obtained from an antenna that is actually used as measured in the direction of its maximum radiation. The antenna pattern of an omnidirectional TV station is shaped like a doughnut with the tower passing through the hole. (The antenna structure is located at the top of the tower for maximum line-of-sight coverage.) The ERP of the TV station (visual or aural) signal is

$$P_{\text{ERP}} = P_{\text{PEP}}G_A G_L \tag{8-62}$$

where P_{PEP} = peak envelope power out of the transmitter
$\quad G_A$ = power gain of the antenna (absolute units as opposed to decibel units) with respect to an isotropic antenna
$\quad G_L$ = total gain of the transmission line system from the transmitter output to the antenna (including the duplexer gain)

[†]Typically, a horizontal resolution of about 300 lines is obtained.

(a) Equipment Block Diagram

(b) AM Visual Carrier Waveform, $s_v(t)$
(Typical Video Modulation Illustrated)

(c) Magnitude Spectrum of RF Output
(Frequency Response Characteristic)

FIGURE 8-31 TV transmission system.

For a VHF TV station operating on channel 5, some typical values are $G_A = 5.7$, $G_L = 0.873$ (850 ft of transmission line plus duplexer), and a visual PEP of 20.1 kW. This gives an overall ERP of 100 kW, which is the maximum power licensed by the FCC for channels 2 to 6 (low-VHF band). For a UHF station operating on channel 20, some typical values are $P_{PEP} = 21.7$ kW, $G_A = 27$, $G_L = 0.854$ (850 ft of transmission line), which gives an ERP of 500 kW.

A simplified block diagram of a black-and-white TV receiver is shown in Fig. 8-32. The composite video, $m_c(t)$, as described earlier, plus a 4.5-MHz FM carrier containing the audio modulation, appears at the output of the envelope detector. The 4.5-MHz FM carrier is present because of the nonlinearity of the envelope detector and because the detector input (IF signal) contains, among other terms, the FM aural carrier plus a discrete (i.e., sinusoidal) term, which is the video carrier, located 4.5 MHz away from the FM carrier signal. The intermodulation product of these two signals produces the 4.5-MHz FM signal, which is called the *intercarrier signal*, and contains the aural modulation. Of course, if either of these two input signal components disappears, the 4.5-MHz output signal will also disappear. This will occur if the white level of the picture is allowed to go below, say, 10% of the peak envelope level (sync tip level) of the AM visual signal. This is why the

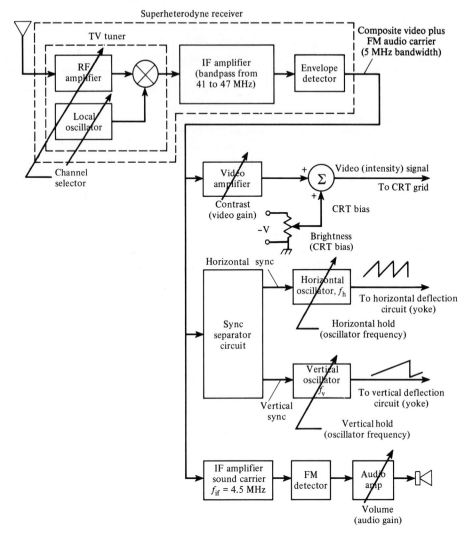

FIGURE 8-32 Black-and-white TV receiver.

FCC specifies that the white level cannot be lower than $(12.5 \pm 2.5)\%$ of the peak envelope level (see Table 8-11). When this occurs, a buzz will be heard in the sound signal since the 4.5-MHz FM carrier is disappearing at a 60-Hz (field) rate during the white portion of the TV scene. The sync separator circuit consists of a lossy integrator to recover the (wide) vertical sync pulses and a lossy differentiator to recover the (narrow) horizontal pulses. The remainder of the block diagram is self-explanatory. The user-available adjustments for a black-and-white TV are also shown.

MTS Stereo Sound

Stereo audio, also known as *multichannel television sound* (MTS), is also available and is accomplished using the FDM technique shown in Fig. 8-33. This FDM technique is similar to that used in standard FM broadcasting, studied in Sec. 6-7 and illustrated by Fig. 6-17. For compatibility with monaural audio television receivers, the left plus right audio, $m_L(t) + m_R(t)$, is frequency modulated directly onto the aural carrier of the television station. Stereo capability is obtained by using a DSB-SC subcarrier with $m_L(t) - m_R(t)$ modulation. The subcarrier frequency is $2f_h$, where $f_h = 15.734$ kHz is the horizontal sync frequency for the video (see Table 8-11). Capability is also provided for a *second audio program* (SAP), such as audio in a second language. This is accomplished by using an FM subcarrier of frequency $5f_h$. DBX audio noise reduction processing is used on the audio on both the DSB-SC stereo subcarrier and the SAP subcarrier that is frequency modulated by the second audio signal. (See Sec. 6-9 for a discussion of the DBX noise reduction technique.) Furthermore, a *professional channel* subcarrier at $6.5f_h$ is allowed for transmission of voice or data on a subscription service basis to paying customers. For further details on the FDM aural standards that have been adopted by television broadcasters and for other possible FDM formats, see a paper by Eilers [1985].

Color Television

Color television pictures are synthesized by combining red, green, and blue light in the proper proportion to produce the desired color. This is done by using a color CRT that has three types of phosphors—one type that emits red light, one that emits green, and a third type that emits blue light when they are struck by electrons. Therefore, three electronic video signals—$m_R(t)$, $m_G(t)$, and $m_B(t)$—are needed to drive the circuits that create the

FIGURE 8-33 Spectrum of composite FDM baseband modulation on the FM aural carrier of U.S. TV stations.

red, green, and blue light. Furthermore, a compatible color TV transmission system is needed such that black-and-white TV sets will receive the luminance video signal, $m_y(t)$, which corresponds to the gray scale of the scene. This compatibility between color and black-and-white transmission is accomplished by using a multiplexing technique analogous to that of FM stereo, except that three signals are involved in the problem instead of two.

The National Television System Committee (NTSC) compatible color TV system that was developed in the United States and adopted for U.S. transmissions in 1954 will be discussed. This technique is illustrated in Fig. 8-34. For compatible transmission, the waveforms that correspond to the intensity of the red, green, and blue components of the scene—$m_R(t)$, $m_G(t)$, and $m_B(t)$—are linearly combined to synthesize the equivalent black-and-white signal, $m_y(t)$, and two other independent video signals, called the *in-phase* and *quadrature* components, $m_i(t)$ and $m_q(t)$. (The names of these components arise from the quadrature modulation technique that is used to modulate them onto a subcar-

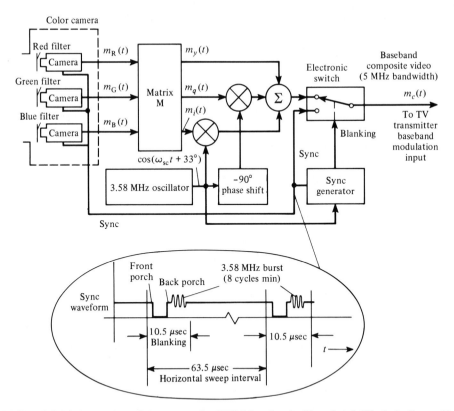

FIGURE 8-34 Generation of the composite NTSC baseband video signal. [Technically, $m_q(t)$ is low-pass filtered to an 0.5-MHz bandwidth and $m_i(t)$ is low-pass filtered to a 1.5-MHz bandwidth.]

rier.) The exact equations used for these signals can be expressed in matrix form:

$$\begin{bmatrix} m_y(t) \\ m_i(t) \\ m_q(t) \end{bmatrix} = \underbrace{\begin{bmatrix} 0.3 & 0.59 & 0.11 \\ 0.6 & -0.28 & -0.32 \\ 0.21 & -0.52 & 0.31 \end{bmatrix}}_{M} \begin{bmatrix} m_R(t) \\ m_G(t) \\ m_B(t) \end{bmatrix} \qquad (8\text{-}63)$$

where M is a 3×3 matrix that translates the red, green, and blue signals to the brightness, in-phase, and quadrature phase video (baseband) signals. For example, from (8-63), the equation for the *luminance* (black and white) signal is

$$m_y(t) = 0.3m_R(t) + 0.59m_G(t) + 0.11m_B(t) \qquad (8\text{-}64)$$

Similarly, the equations for $m_i(t)$ and $m_q(t)$, which are called the *chrominance* signals, are easy to obtain. In addition, note that *if* $m_R(t) = m_G(t) = m_B(t) = 1$, which corresponds to maximum red, green, and blue, then $m_y(t) = 1$, which corresponds to the white level in the black-and-white picture.

The chrominance components are two other linearly independent components, and if they are transmitted to the color TV receiver together with the luminance signal, these three signals can be used to recover the red, green, and blue signals using an inverse matrix operation. The bandwidth of the luminance signal needs to be maintained at 4.2 MHz to preserve sharp (high-frequency) transition in the intensity of the light that occurs along edges of objects in the scene. However, the bandwidth of the chrominance signals does not need to be this large since the eye is not as sensitive to color transitions in a scene. In NTSC standards the bandwidth of the $m_i(t)$ signal is 1.5 MHz and the bandwidth of $m_q(t)$ is 0.5 MHz. When they are quadrature-modulated onto a subcarrier, the resulting composite baseband signal will then have a bandwidth of 4.2 MHz. (The upper sideband of the in-phase subcarrier signal is attenuated to keep a 4.2-MHz bandwidth.)

The composite NTSC baseband video signal is

$$m_c(t) = \begin{cases} m_s(t) & \text{during the sync interval} \\ m_y(t) + \text{Re}\{g_{sc}(t)e^{j\omega_{sc}t}\} & \text{during the video interval} \end{cases} \qquad (8\text{-}65)$$

where

$$g_{sc}(t) = [m_i(t) - jm_q(t)]e^{j33°} \qquad (8\text{-}66)$$

Equation (8-66) indicates that the chrominance information is quadrature modulated onto a subcarrier (as described in Table 5-1). $m_s(t)$ is the sync signal, $m_y(t)$ is the luminance signal, and $g_{sc}(t)$ is the complex envelope of the subcarrier signal. The subcarrier frequency is $f_{sc} = 3.579545$ MHz $\pm$ 10 Hz, which, as we will see later, is chosen so that the subcarrier signal will not interfere with the luminance signal even though both signals fall within the 4.2-MHz passband.

In broadcast TV, this composite NTSC baseband color signal is amplitude-modulated onto the visual carrier as described by (8-61) and shown in Fig. 8-31. In microwave relay applications and satellite relay applications, this NTSC baseband signal is frequency-modulated onto a carrier, as described in Sec. 8-5. These color baseband signals can be transmitted over communication systems that are used for black-and-white TV, although the frequency response and linearity tolerances that are specified are tighter for color TV transmission.

As indicated before, the complex envelope for the subcarrier, as described by (8-66), contains the color information. The magnitude of the complex envelope, $|g_{sc}(t)|$, is the *saturation* or amount of color in the scene as it is scanned with time. The angle of the complex envelope, $\underline{/g_{sc}(t)}$, indicates hue or tint as a function of time. Thus $g_{sc}(t)$ is a vector that moves about in the complex plane as a function of time as the lines of the picture are scanned. This vector may be viewed on an instrument called a *vectorscope,* which has a CRT that displays the vector $g_{sc}(t)$, as shown in Fig. 8-35. The vectorscope is a common piece of test equipment that is used to calibrate color TV equipment and to provide an on-line measure of the quality of the color signal being transmitted. The usual vectorscope presentation has the x axis located in the vertical direction, as indicated on the figure. Using (8-66), the positive axis directions for the $m_i(t)$ and $m_q(t)$ signals are also indicated on the vectorscope presentation, together with the vectors for the saturated red, green, and blue colors. For example, if saturated red is present, then $m_R = 1$ and $m_G = m_B = 0$.

FIGURE 8-35 Vectorscope presentation of the complex envelope for the 3.58-MHz chrominance subcarrier.

Using (8-63), we get $m_i = 0.6$ and $m_q = 0.21$. Thus, from (8-66), the saturated red vector is

$$(g_{sc})_{red} = (0.60 - j0.21)e^{j33°} = 0.64 \underline{/13.7°}$$

Similarly, the saturated green vector is $(g_{sc})_{green} = 0.59 \underline{/151°}$, and the saturated blue vector is $(g_{sc})_{blue} = 0.45 \underline{/257°}$. These vectors are shown in Fig. 8-35. It is interesting to note that the complementary colors have the opposite polarity on the vectorscope, where cyan is the complement of red, magenta is the complement of green, and yellow is the complement of blue.

For color subcarrier demodulation at the receiver, a phase reference is needed. This is provided by keying in an eight-cycle (or more) burst of the 3.58-MHz subcarrier sinusoid on the "back porch" of the horizontal sync pulse, as shown in Fig. 8-34. The phase of the reference sinusoid is $+90°$ with respect to the x axis, as indicated on the vectorscope display (Fig. 8-35).

A color receiver is similar to a black-and-white TV receiver except that it has color demodulator circuits and a color CRT. This is shown in Fig. 8-36, where the color demod-

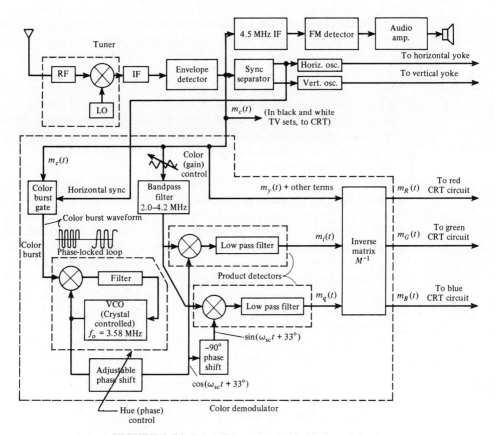

FIGURE 8-36 Color TV receiver with IQ demodulators.

ulator circuitry is indicated. The in-phase and quadrature signals, $m_i(t)$ and $m_q(t)$, are recovered (demodulated) by using product detectors where the phase reference signal is obtained from a PLL circuit that is locked onto the color burst (which was transmitted on the back porch of the sync pulse). M^{-1} is the inverse matrix of that given in (8-63) so that the three video waveforms corresponding to the red, green, and blue intensity signals are recovered. It is realized that the hue control on the TV set adjusts the phase of the reference that sets the tint of the picture on the TV set. The color control sets the gain of the chrominance subcarrier signal. If the gain is reduced to zero, no subcarrier will be present at the input to the product detectors. Consequently, a black-and-white picture will be reproduced on the color TV CRT.

Of course, it is also possible to use different reference phases on the balanced detector inputs *provided* that the decoding matrix is changed to produce m_R, m_G, and m_B at its output. For example, one popular technique uses the R-Y and B-Y phases on the input to the balanced modulators [Grob, 1975]. Here the reference phase out of the hue control circuit is 0° instead of 33°, as shown in Fig. 8-36. This corresponds to detecting the subcarrier along the R-Y and B-Y axes, as indicated on the vectorscope presentation (Fig. 8-35). In this case $m_R(t) - m_Y(t)$ is obtained at the output of the upper product detector, and if a gain of two is used on the lower product detector, $m_B(t) - m_Y(t)$ is obtained at its output. These two outputs may be added in the proper proportions to obtain $m_G(t) - m_Y(t)$. These three signals, $m_R(t) - m_Y(t)$, $m_G(t) - m_Y(t)$, and $m_B(t) - m_Y(t)$, may be applied to the three control grids of a three-gun color CRT (one gun activating the red phosphor, one gun for the green, and one for the red). The $-m_Y(t)$ signal is applied to the common cathode of the three guns so that the effective signals on the guns are $m_R(t)$, $m_G(t)$, and $m_B(t)$, respectively, which are the desired control signals. Furthermore, for black-and-white operation, it is only necessary to remove the three signals from the control grid since the luminance drive signal is applied at the cathode.

As stated earlier, both the luminance and chrominance subcarrier signals are contained in the 4.2-MHz composite NTSC baseband signal. This gives rise to interfering signals in the receiver video circuits. For example, in Fig. 8-36 there is an interfering signal on the input to the inverse matrix circuit. Here $m_Y(t)$ plus interference is averaged out on a line-by-line scanning basis by the viewer's vision if the chrominance subcarrier frequency is an odd multiple of half of the horizontal scanning frequency. For example, from Table 8-11, $f_{sc} = 3,579,545$ Hz and $f_h = 15,734$ Hz. Consequently, there are 227.5 cycles of the 3.58-MHz chrominance interference across one scanned line of the picture. Since there is a half cycle left over, the interference on the *next* scanned line will be *180° out of phase* with that of the present line and the interference will be *canceled out* by the eye when one views the picture.

As we have seen, the NTSC color system is a very ingenious application of basic engineering principles, and this ingenuity is certainly not appreciated by the average color TV viewer.

Standards for TV and CATV Systems

A summary of some of the U.S. TV transmission standards as adopted by the FCC is shown in Table 8-11, and details of the synchronizing waveform are given in Fig. 8-37. A listing of the frequencies for the TV channels is given in Table 8-12. In addition, a comparison of some broadcast TV standards that are used by various countries is shown in Table 8-13. The CCIR system B standard, which is a 625-lines/frame, 25-frames/sec, negative modulation system is the dominant European TV standard [Dhake, 1980]. In addition to these standards for conventional TV as shown in this table, there are U.S. standards for HDTV as will be discussed in the next section. When TV signals are relayed from one country to another via satellite, the standards of the originating country are used, and, if needed, the signal is converted to the standards of the receiving country at the receiving ground station using Digital Intercontinental Conversion Equipment (DICE).

U.S. CATV channel standards are presented in Table 8-14. CATV systems use coaxial cable with amplifiers to distribute TV and other signals from the "head end" to the subscriber. Since the cable signals are not radiated, the frequencies that are normally

TABLE 8-12 U.S. Television Channel Frequency Assignments

	Channel Number	Band (MHz)	UHF Channel Number	Band	UHF Channel Number	Band
Radio astronomy	2	54–60	29	560–566	57	728–734
Aeronautical	3	60–66	30	566–572	58	734–740
Two-way radio	4	66–72	31	572–578	59	740–746
	5	76–82	32	578–584	60	746–752
FM broadcasting	6	82–88	33	584–590	61	752–758
Aeronautical	7	174–180	34	590–596	62	758–764
Two-way radio	8	180–186	35	596–602	63	764–770
	9	186–192	36	602–608	64	770–776
	10	192–198	37	608–614	65	776–782
	11	198–204	38	614–620	66	782–788
VHF	12	204–210	39	620–626	67	788–794
channels	13	210–216	40	626–632	68	794–800
			41	632–638	69	800–806
UHF channels	14	470–476	42	638–644	70[a]	806–812
	15	476–482	43	644–650	71[a]	812–818
	16	482–488	44	650–656	72[a]	818–824
	17	488–494	45	656–662	73[a]	824–830
	18	494–500	46	662–668	74[a]	830–836
	19	500–506	47	668–674	75[a]	836–842
	20	506–512	48	674–680	76[a]	842–848
	21	512–518	49	680–686	77[a]	848–854
	22	518–524	50	686–692	78[a]	854–860
	23	524–530	51	692–698	79[a]	860–866
	24	530–536	52	698–704	80[a]	866–872
	25	536–542	53	704–710	81[a]	872–878
	26	542–548	54	710–716	82[a]	878–884
	27	548–554	55	716–722	83[a]	884–890
	28	554–560	56	722–728		

[a]These frequencies are now allocated to two-way radio and cellular telephone service but were once allocated to UHF TV broadcasting.

FIGURE 8-37 U.S. television synchronizing waveform standards for color transmission. (From Part 73 of FCC Rules and Regulations.)

assigned to two-way radio and other on-the-air services can be used for additional TV channels on the cable. Consequently, the CATV channel assignments have been standardized as shown in this table. To receive these added channels, the subscriber has to have a TV set with CATV channel capability or use a down converter to convert the CATV channel to a standard channel such as channel 3 or channel 4. CATV systems can also be *bidirectional*, allowing some subscribers to transmit signals to the head end. In low-band split systems, frequencies below 50 MHz (T-band channels) are used for transmission to the head end. In mid-band, split system frequencies below 150 MHz are used for transmission to the head end.

Premium TV programs are often available to subscribers for an additional cost. The premium channels are usually scrambled by modifying the video sync or possibly by using digital encryption techniques. Subscribers to the premium services are provided with appropriate decoders that, in some systems, are addressable and remotely programmable by the CATV company. More details about TV standards and engineering practice can be found in the *Television Engineering Handbook* [Benson and Whitaker, 1992].

NOTES TO FIGURE 8-37

1 H = time from start of one line to start of next line = $1/f_h$ (see Table 8-11).

2 V = time from start of one field to start of next field = $1/f_v$ (see Table 8-11).

3 Leading and trailing edges of vertical blanking should be complete in less than 0.1 H.

4 Leading and trailing slopes of horizontal blanking must be steep enough to preserve minimum and maximum values of $(x + y)$ and (z) under all conditions of picture content.

*5 Dimensions marked with asterisk indicate that tolerances given are permitted only for long-time variations and not for successive cycles.

6 Equalizing pulse area shall be between 0.45 and 0.5 of area of a horizontal sync pulse.

7 Color burst follows each horizontal pulse, but is omitted following the equalizing pulses and during the broad vertical pulses.

8 Color bursts to be omitted during monochrome transmission.

9 The burst frequency shall be 3.579545 MHz. The tolerance on the frequency shall be ±10 Hz with a maximum rate of change of frequency not to exceed 1/10 Hz/sec.

10 The horizontal scanning frequency shall be 2/455 times the burst frequency.

11 The dimensions specified for the burst determine the times of starting and stopping the burst but not its phase. The color burst consists of amplitude modulation of a continuous sine wave.

12 Dimension P represents the peak excursion of the luminance signal from blanking level, but does not include the chrominance signal. Dimension S is the sync amplitude above blanking level. Dimension C is the peak carrier amplitude.

13 Start of field 1 is defined by a whole line between first equalizing pulse and preceding H sync pulses.

14 Start of field 2 is defined by a half line between first equalizing pulse and preceding H sync pulses.

15 Field 1 line numbers start with first equalizing pulse in field 1.

16 Field 2 line numbers start with second equalizing pulse in field 2.

17 Refer to Table 8-11 for further explanations and tolerances.

TABLE 8-13 Comparison of Some Broadcast Television Standards

Item	North America, South America, Japan	Spain, Italy, England, Germany, CCIR System B[a]	France		USSR
			Where Used		
Lines/frame	525	625	625	819	625
Lines/second	15,750	15,625	15,625	20,475	15,625
Frames/second	30	25	25	25	25
Baseband video bandwidth (MHz)	4.2	5	6	10	6
Channel bandwidth (MHz)	6	7	8	14	8
Polarity of AM video modulation	Negative	Negative	Positive	Positive	Negative
Type of aural carrier	FM	FM	AM	AM	FM
Color system	NTSC[b]	PAL[c]	SECAM[d]	SECAM[d]	SECAM[d]
Color subcarrier frequency (MHz)	3.58	4.43	4.43	4.43	4.43

[a]The 625-line/frame, 25-frame/sec system is the CCIR (International Radio Consultative Committee) system B standard and is the dominant TV standard used on the European continent.
[b]NTSC, National Television System Committee (United States).
[c]PAL, Phase Alternation Line (Europe).
[d]SECAM, Sequential Couleur à Mémoire (French).

HDTV

There is a great incentive to adopt a *high-definition television* (HDTV) standard in which the resolution is at least twice that of the present TV standard so that it approaches the quality of 35mm film and which has an aspect ratio of horizontal picture width to vertical width of 16:9 instead of the present 4:3 ratio. In the recent past more than 20 methods have been proposed for implementing HDTV in the United States, with some using analog and some using digital techniques [Jurgen, 1988; Jurgen, 1991]. The number of competing systems has been reduced to four and they are all digital video-encoded systems that use data compression to reduce the overall transmission data rate [Harris, 1993; Zou, 1991]. These four digital HDTV systems are described in Table 8-15. During 1993 all four of these systems were field tested for the FCC, but no one system had a clear advantage over the others. In February 1994, the FCC adopted a Zenith VSB digital HDTV standard that is a compromise of these. It is expected that this standard will be tested and refined by the end of 1994 or early 1995 and that HDTV broadcasting will begin in 1996 or 1997.

TABLE 8-14 CATV Channel Frequencies

CATV Channel Number	Band (MHz)	Letter Channel Designator	CATV Channel Number	UHF Band (MHz)
Sub-VHF			37	300–306
	5.75–11.75	T-7	38	306–312
	11.75–17.75	T-8	39	312–318
	17.75–23.75	T-9	40	318–324
	23.75–29.75	T-10	41	324–330
	29.75–35.75	T-11	42	330–336
	35.75–41.75	T-12	43	336–342
	41.75–47.55	T-13	44	342–348
Low-VHF			45	348–354
2	54–60		46	354–360
3	60–66		47	360–366
4	66–72		48	366–372
5	76–82		49	372–378
6	82–88		50	378–384
FM Broadcasting	88–108		51	384–390
High-VHF			52	390–396
7	174–180		53	396–402
8	180–186		54	402–408
9	186–192		55	408–414
10	192–198		56	414–420
11	198–204		57	420–426
12	204–210		58	426–432
13	210–216		59	432–438
Midband			60	438–444
14	120–126	A	61	444–450
15	126–132	B	·	
16	132–138	C	·	
17	138–144	D	·	
18	144–150	E	89	612–618
19	150–156	F	90	618–624
20	156–162	G	91	624–630
21	162–168	H	92	630–636
22	168–174	I	93	636–642
Superband			94	642–648
23	216–222	J	95	90–96
24	222–228	K	96	96–102
25	228–234	L	97	102–108
26	234–240	M	98	108–114
27	240–246	N	99	114–120
28	246–252	O		
29	252–258	P		
30	258–264	Q		
31	264–270	R		
32	270–276	S		
33	276–282	T		
34	282–288	U		
35	288–294	V		
36	294–300	W		

TABLE 8-15 Proposed HDTV Systems

			System		
Item	DigiCipher	Digital Spectrum Compatible (DSC)	Advanced Digital Television (ADTV)	Channel-Compatible DigiCipher (CCDC)	
Developer	American TV Alliance (ATVA) General Instrument Mass. Institute of Technology	Zenith/AT&T Zenith Electronics Corp, AT&T Scientific–Atlanta	Advanced TV Research Consortium (ATRC) Thomson Consumer Electronics Phillips, NBC, Sarnoff Research	American TV Alliance (ATVA) General Instrument Mass. Institute of Technology	
Lines per frame	1050	787.5	1050	787.5	
Frames per second	29.97	59.94	29.97	59.94	
Interlace	2:1	None, progressive scan	2:1	None, progressive scan	
Horizontal scan frequency	31.469 kHz	47.203 kHz	31.469 kHz	47.203 kHz	
Aspect ratio	16:9	16:9	16:9	16:9	
Number of pixels					
Horiz. (luminance)	1408	1280	1440	1280	
Vert. (luminance)	960	720	960	720	
Horiz. (chrominance)	352	640	720	640	
Vert. (chrominance)	480	360	480	360	
Bandwidth					
Luminance	21.5 MHz	34 MHz	23.6 MHz	34 MHz	
Chrominance	5.4 MHz	17 MHz	11.8 MHz	17 MHz	
Video					
Motion-compensation	Yes	Yes	Yes	Yes	
Compression algorithm[a]	DCT	DCT and VQ	DCT (MPEG-based)	Transform/suband	
Block size	8 × 8	8 × 8	8 × 8	8 × 8	
Sampling frequency	53.65 MHz	75.3 MHz	56.64 MHz	75.5 MHz	
Data rate (option 1 or 2)	17.47 or 12.59 Mbits/sec	17.1 or 8.6 Mbits/sec	17.73 Mbits/sec	18.88 or 13.6 Mbits/sec	
Audio					
Bandwidth	20 kHz	20 kHz	20 kHz	20 kHz	
Sampling frequency	48 kHz	47.203 kHz	48 kHz	48 kHz	
Data rate	503 kbits/sec	500 kbits/sec	512 kbits/sec	755 kbits/sec	
Dynamic range	85 dB	96 dB	96 dB	94 dB	
Data rate					
Error correction overhead	6.17 Mbits/sec	1.3 or 2.4 Mbits/sec	5.64 Mbits/sec	6.54 Mbits/sec	
Overall (option 1 or 2)	24.39 or 19.51 Mbits/sec	21.0 or 11.1 Mbits/sec	24.0 or 4.8 Mbits/sec	26.43 or 21.15 Mbits/sec	

SOURCE: [Harris, 1993; Zou, 1991].

[a]DCT, two-dimensional (horizontal and vertical) Discrete Cosine Transform is taken over a block of pixels. The insignificant DCT values are ignored to provide data compression; MPEG, Moving Picture Experts Group of the ISO; VQ, Vector Quantization.

A digital HDTV standard has been adopted because digital TV has the following advantages:

- Use of digital signal processing (DSP) circuits.
- Error-free regeneration of relayed and recorded TV pictures since binary data represent the picture.
- Multiple sound channels (four to six) of CD quality for stereo multilingual capability via TDM of PCM signals.
- Data may be multiplexed for text captioning screen graphics and for control of TV recording and other equipment.
- Multipath (ghost) images and ignition noise can be canceled using DSP circuits.
- Lower TV transmitter power will be required because digital modulation is used.
- Co-channel digital HDTV signals will interfere less with each other than co-channel NTSC analog signals.

The FCC plans to implement the new HDTV system by assigning a new UHF TV channel (for HDTV transmission) for each existing NTSC TV station. Thus each station will simultaneously broadcast a NTSC signal on their existing channel and a HDTV signal on their new UHF channel. By the year 2008, the FCC expects everyone to be using HDTV receivers, so the NTSC TV stations will cease transmission. This will free the VHF TV frequencies (channels 2 to 13) for assignment to other uses. Since the present UHF TV channels will be assigned for HDTV, the HDTV signal will be restricted to a 6-MHz bandwidth. Consequently, to achieve a 6-MHz bandwidth, multilevel modulation techniques—such as QAM—will be used since the proposed overall data rate might be as large as 26.4 Mb/sec (Table 8-15).

It will be interesting to see how this HDTV plan works out. It will require broadcasters to purchase expensive HDTV studio and transmission equipment. Initially, HDTV sets will cost much more than NTSC TV sets. Obviously, the economics of the marketplace will dictate how fast (or if) this transition to HDTV will occur.

8-10 Summary

Case studies for a wide range of practical communication systems have been presented. Modern telephone systems that have large computer-controlled central offices and remote terminals have been studied. ISDN service was described. Specifications of PSTN systems were given for voice and data transmission via fiber-optic cable, twisted-pair wire, satellite and microwave radio relay. Satellite systems for TV signal relay and data transmission with FDMA and TDMA were described. Noise figure and effective input-noise temperature of receiving systems were defined. Case studies of link budgets were presented. U.S. and worldwide standards for cellular telephone systems, both present and proposed, were examined. Finally, a case study of the U.S. NTSC TV system was presented with standards given for the United States, other countries, and for U.S. CATV channels. In addition, proposed digital HDTV systems were discussed.

PROBLEMS

8-1 A distant telephone subscriber is served by a twisted-pair line that is connected directly to the central office as shown in Fig. 8-3. The long telephone line has such a high resistance that the audio signals are weak. Suggest a way to modify the CO equipment so that the audio signal levels will be increased. (This modification is called a line extender and does not use a remote terminal.)

8-2 A 50-pair line provides telephone service to 50 subscribers in a rural subdivision via local loops to the CO. How many subscribers can be served if the 50 pairs are converted to T1 lines and a remote terminal is installed in the subdivision?

8-3 Assume that a telephone company has remote terminals connected to its CO via T1 lines. Draw a block diagram that illustrates how the T1 lines are interfaced with the CO switch if the CO uses:
(a) An analog switch.
(b) An integrated digital switch.

8-4 Indicate whether a conference-call connection may be better or may be worse if a digital switch is used (at the CO) instead of an analog switch. Explain your answer.

8-5 Full-duplex data of 1200 bits/sec in each direction from a personal computer is sent via a twisted-pair telephone line having a bandpass from 300 to 2700 Hz. Explain why modems are needed at each end of the line.

8-6 A satellite with twelve 36-MHz bandwidth transponders operates in the 6/4-GHz bands with 500 MHz bandwidth and 4-MHz guardbands on the 4-GHz downlink, as shown in Fig. 8-10. Calculate the percentage bandwidth that is used for the guardbands.

8-7 An Earth station uses a 3-m-diameter parabolic antenna to receive a 4-GHz signal from a geosynchronous satellite. If the satellite transmitter delivers 10 W into a 3-m-diameter transmitting antenna and the satellite is located 36,000 km from the receiver, what is the power received?

8-8 Figure 8-13b shows an FDM/FM ground station for a satellite communication system. Find the peak frequency deviation needed to achieve the allocated spectral bandwidth for the 6240-MHz signal.

8-9 A microwave transmitter has an output of 0.1 W at 2 GHz. Assume that this transmitter is used in a microwave communication system where the transmitting and receiving antennas are parabolas, each 4 ft in diameter.
(a) Evaluate the gain of the antennas.
(b) Calculate the EIRP of the transmitted signal.
(c) If the receiving antenna is located 15 miles from the transmitting antenna over a free-space path, find the available signal power out of the receiving antenna in dBm units.

8-10 Using MathCAD or MATLAB, plot the PSD for a thermal noise source with a resistance of 10 kΩ over a frequency range of 10 to 100,000 GHz where $T = 300$ K.

8-11 Given the RC circuit of Fig. P8-11, where R is a physical resistor at temperature T, find the rms value of the noise voltage that appears at the output in terms of k, T, R, and C.

FIGURE P8-11

8-12 A receiver is connected to an antenna system that has a noise temperature of 100 K. Find the noise power that is available from the source over a 20-MHz band.

8-13 A bipolar transistor amplifier is modeled as shown in Fig. P8-13. Find a formula for the available power gain in terms of the appropriate parameters.

FIGURE P8-13

8-14 Using the definition for the available power gain, $G_a(f)$, as given by (8-18), show that $G_a(f)$ depends on the driving source impedance as well as the elements of the device and that $G_a(f)$ does not depend on the load impedance. [*Hint:* Calculate $G_a(f)$ for a simple resistive network.]

8-15 Show that the effective input-noise temperature and the noise figure can be evaluated from measurements that use the Y-factor method. With this method the device under test (DUT) is first connected to a noise source that has a relatively large output denoted by its source temperature, T_h, where the subscript h denotes "hot," and then the available noise power at the output of the DUT, P_{aoh} is measured with a power meter. Next, the DUT is connected to a source that has relatively low source temperature, T_c, where the subscript c denotes "cold," and noise power at the output of the DUT is measured, P_{aoc}. Show that

(a) The effective input noise temperature of the DUT is

$$T_e = \frac{T_h - YT_c}{Y - 1}$$

where $Y = P_{aoh}/P_{aoc}$ is obtained from the measurements.

(b) The noise figure of the DUT is

$$F = \frac{[(T_h/T_0) - 1] - Y[(T_c/T_0) - 1]}{Y - 1}$$

where $T_0 = 290$ K.

8-16 If a signal plus noise is fed into a linear device, show that the noise figure of that device is given by $F = (S/N)_{in}/(S/N)_{out}$. (*Hint:* Start with the basic definition of noise figure that is given in this chapter.)

8-17 An antenna is pointed in a direction such that it has a noise temperature of 30 K. It is connected to a preamplifier that has a noise figure of 1.6 dB and an available gain of 30 dB over an effective bandwidth of 10 MHz.

(a) Find the effective input noise temperature for the preamplifier.

(b) Find the available noise power out of the preamplifier.

8-18 A 10-MHz SSB-AM signal, which is modulated by an audio signal that is bandlimited to 5 kHz, is being detected by a receiver that has a noise figure of 10 dB. The signal power at the receiver input is 10^{-10} mW and the PSD of the input noise, $\mathcal{P}(f) = kT/2$, is 2×10^{-21}. Evaluate:

(a) The IF bandwidth needed.

(b) The signal-to-noise ratio at the receiver input.

(c) The signal-to-noise ratio at the receiver output, assuming that a product detector is used.

8-19 An FSK signal with $R = 110$ bits/sec is transmitted over an RF channel that has white Gaussian noise. The receiver uses a noncoherent detector and has a noise figure of 6 dB. The impedance of the antenna input of the receiver is 50 Ω. The signal level at the receiver input is 0.05 μV, and the noise level is $N_0 = kT_0$, where $T_0 = 290$ K and k is Boltzmann's constant. Find the P_e for the digital signal at the output of the receiver.

8-20 Work Prob. 8-19 for the case of DPSK signaling.

8-21 Prove that the overall effective input-noise temperature for cascaded linear devices is given by (8-37).

8-22 A TV set is connected to an antenna system as shown in Fig. P8-22. Evaluate:

(a) The overall noise figure.

(b) The overall noise figure if a 20-dB RF preamp with a 3-dB noise figure is inserted at point B.

(c) The overall noise figure if the preamp is inserted at point A.

FIGURE P8-22

8-23 An Earth station receiving system consists of a 20-dB gain antenna with $T_{AR} = 80$ K, an RF amplifier with $G_a = 40$ dB and $T_e = 200$ K, and a down converter with $T_e = 15,000$ K. What is the overall effective input-noise temperature of this receiving system?

8-24 A low-noise amplifier (LNA), a down converter, and an IF amplifier are connected in cascade. The LNA has a gain of 40 dB and a T_e of 100 K. The down converter has a noise figure of 8 dB and a conversion gain of 6 dB. The IF amplifier has a gain of 60 dB and a noise figure of 14 dB. Evaluate the overall effective input-noise temperature for this system.

8-25 A geosynchronous satellite transmits 13.5 dBw EIRP on a 4-GHz downlink to an Earth station. The receiving system has a gain of 60 dB, an effective input-noise temperature of 80 K, an antenna source noise temperature of 60 K, and an IF bandwidth of 36 MHz. If the satellite is located 24,500 miles from the receiver, what is the $(C/N)_{dB}$ at the input of the receiver detector circuit?

8-26 An antenna with $T_{AR} = 160$ K is connected to a receiver by means of a waveguide that has a physical temperature of 290 K and a loss of 2 dB. The receiver has a noise bandwidth of 1 MHz, an effective input-noise temperature of 800 K, and a gain of 120 dB from its antenna input to its IF output. Using MathCAD or MATLAB, find:
(a) The system noise temperature at the input of the receiver.
(b) The overall noise figure.
(c) The available noise power at the IF output.

8-27 The *Intelsat IV* satellite uses 36-MHz transponders with downlinks operating in the 4-GHz band. Each satellite transponder has a power output of 3.5 W and may be used with a 17° global coverage antenna that has a gain of 20 dB.
(a) For users located at the subsatellite point (i.e., directly below the satellite), show that $(C/N)_{dB} = (G_{AR}/T_{syst})_{dB} - 17.1$, where $(G_{AR}/T_{syst})_{dB}$ is the Earth receiving station figure of merit.
(b) Design a ground receiving station (block diagram) showing reasonable specifications for each block so that the IF output C/N will be 12 dB. Discuss the trade-offs that are involved.

8-28 The efficiency of a parabolic antenna is determined by the accuracy of the parabolic reflecting surface and other factors. The gain is $G_A = 4\pi\eta A/\lambda^2$, where η is the antenna efficiency. In Table 8-3 an efficiency of 56% was used to obtain the formula $G_A = 7A/\lambda^2$. In a ground receiving system for the *Intelsat IV* satellite, assume that a (G_{AR}/T_{syst}) of 40 dB is needed. Using a 30-m antenna, give the required antenna efficiency if the system noise temperature is 85 K. How does the required antenna efficiency change if a 28-m antenna is used?

8-29 Evaluate the performance of a TVRO system. Assume that the TVRO terminal is located in Miami, Florida (26.8° N latitude, 80.2° W longitude). A 10-ft-diameter parabolic receiving antenna is used and is pointed toward the *Galaxy I* satellite. Other TVRO parameters are given in Table 8-4, Fig. 8-26, and Fig. 8-28.
(a) Find the TVRO antenna look angles to the satellite and find the slant range.
(b) Find the overall receiver system temperature.
(c) Find the $(C/N)_{dB}$ into the receiver detector.
(d) Find the $(S/N)_{dB}$ out of the receiver.

8-30 Repeat Prob. 8-29 if the TVRO terminal is located at Anchorage, Alaska (61.2° N latitude, 149.8° W longitude), and a 8-m-diameter parabolic antenna is used.

8-31 A TVRO receive system consists of an 8-ft-diameter parabolic antenna that feeds a 50-dB, 85 K LNA. The sky noise temperature (with feed) is 32 K. The system is designed to receive signals from the *Galaxy I* satellite. The LNA has a post-mixer circuit that down-converts the satellite signal to 70 MHz. The 70-MHz signal is fed to the TVRO receiver via a 120-ft length of 75-Ω coaxial cable. The cable has a loss of 3 dB/100 ft. The receiver has a bandwidth of 36 MHz and a noise temperature of 3800 K. Assume that the TVRO site is located in Los Angeles, California (34° N latitude, 118.3° W longitude) and vertical polarization is of interest.
(a) Find the TVRO antenna look angles to the satellite and find the slant range.
(b) Find the overall system temperature.
(c) Find the $(C/N)_{dB}$ into the receiver detector.

8-32 An Earth station receiving system operates at 11.95 GHz and consists of a 20-m antenna with a gain of 65.53 dB and $T_{AR} = 60$ K, a waveguide with a loss of 1.28 dB and a physical temperature of 290 K, a LNA with $T_e = 150$ K and 60 dB gain, and a down converter with $T_e = 11,000$ K. Using MathCAD or MATLAB, find $(G/T)_{dB}$ for the receiving system evaluated at:
(a) The input to the LNA.
(b) The input to the waveguide.
(c) The input to the down converter.

8-33 Rework Example 8-4 for the case of reception of TV signals from a direct broadcast satellite (DBS). Assume that the system parameters are similar to those given in Table 8-4, except that the satellite power is 316 kW EIRP radiated in the 12-GHz band. Furthermore, assume that a 1-m parabolic receiving antenna is used and the LNA has a 240-K noise temperature.

8-34 The most distant planet from our sun is Pluto, which is located at a (greatest) distance from the Earth of 7.5×10^9 km. Assume that an unmanned spacecraft with a 2-GHz, 10-W transponder is in the vicinity of Pluto. A receiving Earth station with a 64-m antenna is available that has a system noise temperature of 16 K at 2 GHz. Calculate the size of a spacecraft antenna that is required for a 300-bit/sec BPSK data link to Earth that has a 10^{-3} bit error rate (corresponding to E_b/N_0 of 9.88 dB). Allow 2 dB for incidental losses.

8-35 Using MathCAD, MATLAB, or some spreadsheet program that will run on a personal computer (PC), design a spreadsheet that will solve Prob. 8-31. Run the spreadsheet on your PC and verify that it gives the correct answers. Print out your results. Also try other parameters, such as those appropriate for your location, and print out the results.

8-36 Assume that you want to analyze the overall performance of a satellite relay system that uses a "bent-pipe" transponder. Let $(C/N)_{up}$ denote the carrier-to-noise ratio for the transponder as evaluated in the IF band of the satellite transponder. Let $(C/N)_{dn}$ denote the IF carrier-to-noise ratio at the downlink receiving ground station when the satellite is sending a perfect (noise-free) signal. Show that the overall operating carrier-to-noise ratio at the IF of the receiving ground station, $(C/N)_{ov}$, is given by

$$\frac{1}{(C/N)_{ov}} = \frac{1}{(C/N)_{up}} + \frac{1}{(C/N)_{dn}}$$

8-37 Referring to Table 8-13, evaluate the maximum horizontal and vertical resolution (lines) for the CCIR System B TV standard. Assume that the horizontal blanking time is 10 μsec.

8-38 A VSB signal may be analyzed by using

$$g(t) = [m_1(t) + m_2(t)] + j[\hat{m}_2(t)]$$

as a model for the complex envelope. Explain how this model may be used to represent U.S. TV signals.

8-39 A low-power TV station is licensed to operate on TV Channel 35 with an effective radiated visual power of 1000 W. The tower height is 400 ft and the transmission line is 450 ft long. Assume that a $1\frac{5}{8}$-in.-diameter semirigid 50-Ω coaxial transmission line will be used that has a loss of 0.6 dB/100 ft (at the operating frequency). The antenna has a gain of 5.6 dB and the duplexer loss is negligible. Find the PEP required at the visual transmitter output.

8-40 A TV visual transmitter is tested by modulating it with a periodic test signal. The envelope of the transmitter output is viewed on an oscilloscope as shown in Fig. P8-40, where K is an unknown constant. The output of the transmitter is connected to a 50-Ω dummy load that has a calibrated average reading wattmeter. The wattmeter reads 6.9 kW. Find the PEP of the transmitter output.

FIGURE P8-40

8-41 Specifications for the MTS stereo audio system for TV are given in Fig. 8-33. Using this figure:

(a) Design a block diagram for TV receiver circuitry that will detect the stereo audio signals and the second audio program (SAP) signal.

(b) Describe how the circuit works. That is, give mathematical expressions for the signal at each point on your block diagram and explain in words. Be sure to specify all filter transfer functions, VCO center frequencies, and so on.

8-42 A TV broadcaster wants to send digital data to subscribers concerning the stock market using the professional aural subcarrier. Propose two digital signaling techniques that will satisfy the spectral requirements of Fig. 8-33 where the available bandwidth is $0.5f_h$. Specifically, design and draw block diagrams of transmit and receive modems and give the specifications for transmitting data at a rate of **(a)** 1200 bits/sec and **(b)** 9600 bits/sec. Discuss why you think you have a good design.

8-43 In the R-Y, B-Y color TV subcarrier demodulation system, the G-Y signal is obtained from the R-Y and B-Y signals. That is,

$$[m_G(t) - m_Y(t)] = K_1[m_R(t) - m_Y(t)] + K_2[m_B(t) - m_Y(t)]$$

(a) Find the values for K_1 and K_2 that are required.

(b) Draw a possible block diagram for a R-Y, B-Y system and explain how it works.

Mathematical Techniques, Identities, and Tables

A-1 Trigonometry

Definitions

$$\sin x = \frac{e^{jx} - e^{-jx}}{2j} \tag{A-1}$$

$$\cos x = \frac{e^{jx} + e^{-jx}}{2} \tag{A-2}$$

$$\tan x = \frac{\sin x}{\cos x} = \frac{e^{jx} - e^{-jx}}{j(e^{jx} + e^{-jx})} \tag{A-3}$$

Trigonometric Identities

$$e^{\pm jx} = \cos x \pm j \sin x \quad \text{(Euler's theorem)} \tag{A-4}$$
$$\cos(x \pm y) = \cos x \cos y \mp \sin x \sin y \tag{A-5}$$
$$\sin(x \pm y) = \sin x \cos y \pm \cos x \sin y \tag{A-6}$$
$$\cos\left(x \pm \frac{\pi}{2}\right) = \mp \sin x \tag{A-7}$$
$$\sin\left(x \pm \frac{\pi}{2}\right) = \pm \cos x \tag{A-8}$$
$$\cos 2x = \cos^2 x - \sin^2 x \tag{A-9}$$
$$\sin 2x = 2 \sin x \cos x \tag{A-10}$$
$$2 \cos x \cos y = \cos(x - y) + \cos(x + y) \tag{A-11}$$

$$2 \sin x \sin y = \cos(x - y) - \cos(x + y) \tag{A-12}$$
$$2 \sin x \cos y = \sin(x - y) + \sin(x + y) \tag{A-13}$$
$$2 \cos^2 x = 1 + \cos 2x \tag{A-14}$$
$$2 \sin^2 x = 1 - \cos 2x \tag{A-15}$$
$$4 \cos^3 x = 3 \cos x + \cos 3x \tag{A-16}$$
$$4 \sin^3 x = 3 \sin x - \sin 3x \tag{A-17}$$
$$8 \cos^4 x = 3 + 4 \cos 2x + \cos 4x \tag{A-18}$$
$$8 \sin^4 x = 3 - 4 \cos 2x + \cos 4x \tag{A-19}$$
$$A \cos x - B \sin x = R \cos(x + \theta) \tag{A-20a}$$
$$\text{where } R = \sqrt{A^2 + B^2} \tag{A-20b}$$
$$\theta = \tan^{-1}(B/A) \tag{A-20c}$$
$$A = R \cos \theta \tag{A-20d}$$
$$B = R \sin \theta \tag{A-20e}$$

A-2 Differential Calculus

Definition

$$\frac{df(x)}{dx} = \lim_{\Delta x \to 0} \frac{f(x + (\Delta x/2)) - f(x - (\Delta x/2))}{\Delta x} \tag{A-21}$$

Differentiation Rules

$$\frac{du(x)v(x)}{dx} = u(x)\frac{dv(x)}{dx} + v(x)\frac{du(x)}{dx} \quad \text{(products)} \tag{A-22}$$

$$\frac{d\left(\frac{u(x)}{v(x)}\right)}{dx} = \frac{v(x)\frac{du(x)}{dx} - u(x)\frac{dv(x)}{dx}}{v^2(x)} \quad \text{(quotient)} \tag{A-23}$$

$$\frac{du[v(x)]}{dx} = \frac{du}{dv}\frac{dv}{dx} \quad \text{(chain rule)} \tag{A-24}$$

Derivative Table

$$\frac{d[x^n]}{dx} = nx^{n-1} \tag{A-25}$$

$$\frac{d \sin ax}{dx} = a \cos ax \tag{A-26}$$

$$\frac{d \cos ax}{dx} = -a \sin ax \tag{A-27}$$

$$\frac{d \tan ax}{dx} = \frac{a}{\cos^2 ax} \tag{A-28}$$

$$\frac{d \sin^{-1} ax}{dx} = \frac{a}{\sqrt{1 - (ax)^2}} \tag{A-29}$$

$$\frac{d \cos^{-1} ax}{dx} = -\frac{a}{\sqrt{1 - (ax)^2}} \tag{A-30}$$

$$\frac{d \tan^{-1} ax}{dx} = \frac{a}{1 + (ax)^2} \tag{A-31}$$

$$\frac{d[e^{ax}]}{dx} = ae^{ax} \tag{A-32}$$

$$\frac{d[a^x]}{dx} = a^x \ln a \tag{A-33}$$

$$\frac{d(\ln x)}{dx} = \frac{1}{x} \tag{A-34}$$

$$\frac{d(\log_a x)}{dx} = \frac{1}{x} \log_a e \tag{A-35}$$

$$\frac{d\left[\int_{a(x)}^{b(x)} f(\lambda, x) \, d\lambda\right]}{dx} = f(b(x), x) \frac{db(x)}{dx} - f(a(x), x) \frac{da(x)}{dx}$$

$$+ \int_{a(x)}^{b(x)} \frac{\partial f(\lambda, x)}{\partial x} \, d\lambda \quad \text{(Leibniz's rule)} \tag{A-36}$$

A-3 Indeterminate Forms

If $\lim_{x \to a} f(x)$ is of the form

$$\frac{0}{0}, \quad \frac{\infty}{\infty}, \quad 0 \cdot \infty, \quad \infty - \infty, \quad 0^0, \quad \infty^0, \quad 1^\infty$$

then

$$\lim_{x \to a} f(x) = \lim_{x \to a} \left[\frac{N(x)}{D(x)}\right] = \lim_{x \to a} \left[\frac{(dN(x)/dx)}{(dD(x)/dx)}\right] \quad \text{(l'Hospital's rule)} \tag{A-37}$$

where $N(x)$ is the numerator of $f(x)$, $D(x)$ is the denominator of $f(x)$, $N(a) = 0$, and $D(a) = 0$.

A-4 Integral Calculus

Definition

$$\int f(x) \, dx = \lim_{\Delta x \to 0} \left\{\sum_n [f(n \, \Delta x)] \, \Delta x\right\} \tag{A-38}$$

Integration Techniques

1. Change in variable. Let $v = u(x)$:

$$\int_a^b f(x)\,dx = \int_{u(a)}^{u(b)} \left(\frac{f(x)}{dv/dx} \bigg|_{x=u^{-1}(v)} \right) dv \qquad \text{(A-39)}$$

2. Integration by parts

$$\int u\,dv = uv - \int v\,du \qquad \text{(A-40)}$$

3. Integral tables
4. Complex variable techniques
5. Numerical methods

A-5 Integral Tables

Indefinite Integrals

$$\int (a + bx)^n\,dx = \frac{(a + bx)^{n+1}}{b(n + 1)}, \qquad 0 < n \qquad \text{(A-41)}$$

$$\int \frac{dx}{a + bx} = \frac{1}{b}\,\ln|a + bx| \qquad \text{(A-42)}$$

$$\int \frac{dx}{(a + bx)^n} = \frac{-1}{(n - 1)b(a + bx)^{n-1}}, \qquad 1 < n \qquad \text{(A-43)}$$

$$\int \frac{dx}{c + bx + ax^2} = \begin{cases} \dfrac{2}{\sqrt{4ac - b^2}}\,\tan^{-1}\!\left(\dfrac{2ax + b}{\sqrt{4ac - b^2}} \right), & b^2 < 4ac \\[2ex] \dfrac{1}{\sqrt{b^2 - 4ac}}\,\ln\left| \dfrac{2ax + b - \sqrt{b^2 - 4ac}}{2ax + b + \sqrt{b^2 - 4ac}} \right|, & b^2 > 4ac \\[2ex] \dfrac{-2}{2ax + b}, & b^2 = 4ac \end{cases} \qquad \text{(A-44)}$$

$$\int \frac{x\,dx}{c + bx + ax^2} = \frac{1}{2a}\,\ln|ax^2 + bx + c| - \frac{b}{2a}\int \frac{dx}{c + bx + ax^2} \qquad \text{(A-45)}$$

$$\int \frac{dx}{a^2 + b^2 x^2} = \frac{1}{ab}\,\tan^{-1}\!\left(\frac{bx}{a} \right) \qquad \text{(A-46)}$$

$$\int \frac{x\,dx}{a^2 + x^2} = \frac{1}{2}\,\ln(a^2 + x^2) \qquad \text{(A-47)}$$

$$\int \frac{x^2\,dx}{a^2 + x^2} = x - a\,\tan^{-1}\!\left(\frac{x}{a} \right) \qquad \text{(A-48)}$$

$$\int \frac{dx}{(a^2 + x^2)^2} = \frac{x}{2a^2(a^2 + x^2)} + \frac{1}{2a^3} \tan^{-1}\left(\frac{x}{a}\right) \tag{A-49}$$

$$\int \frac{x\,dx}{(a^2 + x^2)^2} = \frac{-1}{2(a^2 + x^2)} \tag{A-50}$$

$$\int \frac{x^2\,dx}{(a^2 + x^2)^2} = \frac{-x}{2(a^2 + x^2)} + \frac{1}{2a} \tan^{-1}\left(\frac{x}{a}\right) \tag{A-51}$$

$$\int \frac{dx}{(a^2 + x^2)^3} = \frac{x}{4a^2(a^2 + x^2)^2} + \frac{3x}{8a^4(a^2 + x^2)} + \frac{3}{8a^5} \tan^{-1}\left(\frac{x}{a}\right) \tag{A-52}$$

$$\int \frac{x^2\,dx}{(a^2 + x^2)^3} = \frac{-x}{4(a^2 + x^2)^2} + \frac{x}{8a^2(a^2 + x^2)} + \frac{1}{8a^3} \tan^{-1}\left(\frac{x}{a}\right) \tag{A-53}$$

$$\int \frac{x^4\,dx}{(a^2 + x^2)^3} = \frac{a^2 x}{4(a^2 + x^2)^2} - \frac{5x}{8(a^2 + x^2)} + \frac{3}{8a} \tan^{-1}\left(\frac{x}{a}\right) \tag{A-54}$$

$$\int \frac{dx}{(a^2 + x^2)^4} = \frac{x}{6a^2(a^2 + x^2)^3} + \frac{5x}{24a^4(a^2 + x^2)^2}$$
$$+ \frac{5x}{16a^6(a^2 + x^2)} + \frac{5}{16a^7} \tan^{-1}\left(\frac{x}{a}\right) \tag{A-55}$$

$$\int \frac{x^2\,dx}{(a^2 + x^2)^4} = \frac{-x}{6(a^2 + x^2)^3} + \frac{x}{24a^2(a^2 + x^2)^2}$$
$$+ \frac{x}{16a^4(a^2 + x^2)} + \frac{1}{16a^5} \tan^{-1}\left(\frac{x}{a}\right) \tag{A-56}$$

$$\int \frac{x^4\,dx}{(a^2 + x^2)^4} = \frac{a^2 x}{6(a^2 + x^2)^3} - \frac{7x}{24(a^2 + x^2)^2} + \frac{x}{16a^2(a^2 + x^2)}$$
$$+ \frac{1}{16a^3} \tan^{-1}\left(\frac{x}{a}\right) \tag{A-57}$$

$$\int \frac{dx}{a^4 + x} = \frac{1}{4a^3\sqrt{2}} \ln\left(\frac{x^2 + ax\sqrt{2} + a^2}{x^2 - ax\sqrt{2} + a^2}\right)$$
$$+ \frac{1}{2a^3\sqrt{2}} \tan^{-1}\left(\frac{ax\sqrt{2}}{a^2 - x^2}\right) \tag{A-58}$$

$$\int \frac{x^2\,dx}{a^4 + x^4} = -\frac{1}{4a\sqrt{2}} \ln\left(\frac{x^2 + ax\sqrt{2} + a^2}{x^2 - ax\sqrt{2} + a^2}\right)$$
$$+ \frac{1}{2a\sqrt{2}} \tan^{-1}\left(\frac{ax\sqrt{2}}{a^2 - x^2}\right) \tag{A-59}$$

$$\int \cos x\,dx = \sin x \tag{A-60}$$

$$\int x \cos x\,dx = \cos x + x \sin x \tag{A-61}$$

$$\int x^2 \cos x\,dx = 2x \cos x + (x^2 - 2) \sin x \tag{A-62}$$

$$\int \sin x \, dx = -\cos x \tag{A-63}$$

$$\int x \sin x \, dx = \sin x - x \cos x \tag{A-64}$$

$$\int x^2 \sin x \, dx = 2x \sin x - (x^2 - 2) \cos x \tag{A-65}$$

$$\int e^{ax} \, dx = \frac{e^{ax}}{a}, \qquad a \text{ real or complex} \tag{A-66}$$

$$\int x e^{ax} \, dx = e^{ax}\left(\frac{x}{a} - \frac{1}{a^2}\right), \qquad a \text{ real or complex} \tag{A-67}$$

$$\int x^2 e^{ax} \, dx = e^{ax}\left(\frac{x^2}{a} - \frac{2x}{a^2} + \frac{2}{a^3}\right), \qquad a \text{ real or complex} \tag{A-68}$$

$$\int x^3 e^{ax} \, dx = e^{ax}\left(\frac{x^3}{a} - \frac{3x^2}{a^2} + \frac{6x}{a^3} - \frac{6}{a^4}\right), \qquad a \text{ real or complex} \tag{A-69}$$

$$\int e^{ax} \sin x \, dx = \frac{e^{ax}}{a^2 + 1}(a \sin x - \cos x) \tag{A-70}$$

$$\int e^{ax} \cos x \, dx = \frac{e^{ax}}{a^2 + 1}(a \cos x + \sin x) \tag{A-71}$$

Definite Integrals

$$\int_0^\infty \frac{x^{m-1}}{1 + x^n} \, dx = \frac{\pi/n}{\sin(m\pi/n)}, \qquad n > m > 0 \tag{A-72}$$

$$\int_0^\infty x^{\alpha-1} e^{-x} \, dx = \Gamma(\alpha), \qquad \alpha > 0 \tag{A-73a}$$

where

$$\Gamma(\alpha + 1) = \alpha \Gamma(\alpha) \tag{A-73b}$$

$$\Gamma(1) = 1; \ \Gamma(\tfrac{1}{2}) = \sqrt{\pi} \tag{A-73c}$$

$$\Gamma(n) = (n - 1)! \qquad \text{if } n \text{ is a positive integer} \tag{A-73d}$$

$$\int_0^\infty x^{2n} e^{-ax^2} \, dx = \frac{1 \cdot 3 \cdot 5 \cdots (2n - 1)}{2^{n+1} a^n} \sqrt{\frac{\pi}{a}} \tag{A-74}$$

$$\int_{-\infty}^\infty e^{-a^2 x^2 + bx} \, dx = \frac{\sqrt{\pi}}{a} e^{b^2/(4a^2)}, \qquad a > 0 \tag{A-75}$$

$$\int_0^\infty e^{-ax} \cos bx \, dx = \frac{a}{a^2 + b^2}, \qquad a > 0 \tag{A-76}$$

$$\int_0^\infty e^{-ax} \sin bx \, dx = \frac{b}{a^2 + b^2}, \qquad a > 0 \tag{A-77}$$

$$\int_0^\infty e^{-a^2 x^2} \cos bx \, dx = \frac{\sqrt{\pi} e^{-b^2/4a^2}}{2a}, \qquad a > 0 \tag{A-78}$$

$$\int_0^\infty x^{\alpha-1} \cos bx \, dx = \frac{\Gamma(\alpha)}{b^\alpha} \cos \tfrac{1}{2}\pi\alpha, \qquad 0 < \alpha < 1, \, b > 0 \tag{A-79}$$

$$\int_0^\infty x^{\alpha-1} \sin bx \, dx = \frac{\Gamma(\alpha)}{b^\alpha} \sin \tfrac{1}{2}\pi\alpha, \qquad 0 < |\alpha| < 1, \, b > 0 \tag{A-80}$$

$$\int_0^\infty xe^{-ax^2} I_k(bx) \, dx = \frac{1}{2a} e^{b^2/4a} \tag{A-81a}$$

where

$$I_k(bx) = \frac{1}{\pi} \int_0^\pi e^{bx\cos\theta} \cos k\theta \, d\theta \tag{A-81b}$$

$$\int_0^\infty \frac{\sin x}{x} \, dx = \int_0^\infty \mathrm{Sa}(x) \, dx = \frac{\pi}{2} \tag{A-82}$$

$$\int_0^\infty \left(\frac{\sin x}{x}\right)^2 dx = \int_0^\infty \mathrm{Sa}^2(x) \, dx = \frac{\pi}{2} \tag{A-83}$$

$$\int_0^\infty \frac{\cos ax}{b^2 + x^2} \, dx = \frac{\pi}{2b} e^{-ab}, \qquad a > 0, \, b > 0 \tag{A-84}$$

$$\int_0^\infty \frac{x \sin ax}{b^2 + x^2} \, dx = \frac{\pi}{2} e^{-ab}, \qquad a > 0, \, b > 0 \tag{A-85}$$

$$\int_{-\infty}^\infty e^{\pm j2\pi yx} \, dx = \delta(y) \tag{A-86}$$

A-6 Series Expansions

Finite Series

$$\sum_{n=1}^N n = \frac{N(N+1)}{2} \tag{A-87}$$

$$\sum_{n=1}^N n^2 = \frac{N(N+1)(2N+1)}{6} \tag{A-88}$$

$$\sum_{n=1}^N n^3 = \frac{N^2(N+1)^2}{4} \tag{A-89}$$

$$\sum_{n=0}^N a^n = \frac{a^{N+1} - 1}{a - 1} \tag{A-90}$$

$$\sum_{n=0}^N \frac{N!}{n!\,(N-n)!} x^n y^{N-n} = (x + y)^N \tag{A-91}$$

$$\sum_{n=0}^{N} e^{j(\theta + n\phi)} = \frac{\sin[(N + 1)\phi/2]}{\sin(\phi/2)} e^{j[\theta + (N\phi/2)]} \tag{A-92}$$

$$\sum_{k=0}^{N} \binom{N}{k} a^{N-k} b^k = (a + b)^N \tag{A-93a}$$

where

$$\binom{N}{k} = \frac{N!}{(N - k)! \, k!} \tag{A-93b}$$

Infinite Series

$$f(x) = \sum_{n=0}^{\infty} \left(\frac{f^{(n)}(a)}{n!} \right) (x - a)^n \qquad \text{(Taylor's series)} \tag{A-94}$$

$$f(x) = \sum_{n=-\infty}^{\infty} c_n e^{jn\omega_0 x} \qquad \text{for } a \le x \le a + T \qquad \text{(Fourier series)} \tag{A-95a}$$

where

$$c_n = \frac{1}{T} \int_{a}^{a+T} f(x) e^{-jn\omega_0 x} \, dx \tag{A-95b}$$

and

$$\omega_0 = \frac{2\pi}{T} \tag{A-95c}$$

$$e^x = \sum_{n=0}^{\infty} \frac{x^n}{n!} \tag{A-96}$$

$$\sin x = \sum_{n=0}^{\infty} \frac{(-1)^n x^{2n+1}}{(2n + 1)!} \tag{A-97}$$

$$\cos x = \sum_{n=0}^{\infty} \frac{(-1)^n x^{2n}}{(2n)!} \tag{A-98}$$

A-7 Hilbert Transform Pairs[†]

$$\hat{x}(t) \triangleq x(t) * \frac{1}{\pi t} = \frac{1}{\pi} \int_{-\infty}^{\infty} \frac{x(\lambda)}{t - \lambda} \, d\lambda \tag{A-99}$$

[†]Fourier transform theorems are given in Table 2-1, and Fourier transform pairs are given in Table 2-2.

Function	Hilbert Transform
1. $x(at + b)$	$\hat{x}(at + b)$
2. $x(t) + y(t)$	$\hat{x}(t) + \hat{y}(t)$
3. $\dfrac{d^n x(t)}{dt^n}$	$\dfrac{d^n}{dt^n} \hat{x}(t)$
4. A constant	0
5. $\dfrac{1}{t}$	$-\pi\delta(t)$
6. $\sin(\omega_0 t + \theta)$	$-\cos(\omega_0 t + \theta)$
7. $\dfrac{\sin at}{at} = \text{Sa}(at)$	$-\dfrac{1}{2\pi} at\, \text{Sa}^2(at)$
8. $e^{\pm j\omega_0 t}$	$\mp je^{\pm j\omega_0 t}$
9. $\delta(t)$	$\dfrac{1}{\pi t}$
10. $\dfrac{a}{\pi(t^2 + a^2)}$	$\dfrac{t}{\pi(t^2 + a^2)}$
11. $\Pi\left(\dfrac{t}{T}\right) \triangleq \begin{cases} 1, & \lvert t \rvert \le T/2 \\ 0, & t \text{ elsewhere} \end{cases}$	$\dfrac{1}{\pi} \ln\left\lvert \dfrac{2t + T}{2t - T} \right\rvert$

A-8 The Dirac Delta Function

DEFINITION: The *Dirac delta function* $\delta(x)$, also called the *unit impulse function,* satisfies *both* of the following conditions:

$$\int_{-\infty}^{\infty} \delta(x)\, dx = 1 \qquad\qquad \text{(A-100)}$$

$$\delta(x) = \begin{cases} \infty, & x = 0 \\ 0, & x \ne 0 \end{cases} \qquad\qquad \text{(A-101)}$$

Consequently, $\delta(x)$ is a "singular" function.[†]

[†]The Dirac delta function is not an ordinary function since it is really undefined at $x = 0$. However, it is described by the mathematical theory of distributions [Bremermann, 1965].

Properties of Dirac Delta Functions

1. $\delta(x)$ can be expressed in terms of the limit of some ordinary functions such that (in the limit of some parameter) the ordinary function satisfies the definition for $\delta(x)$. For example,

$$\delta(x) = \lim_{\sigma \to 0} \left(\frac{1}{\sqrt{2\pi}\sigma} e^{-x^2/(2\sigma^2)} \right) \tag{A-102}$$

$$= \lim_{a \to \infty} \left[\frac{a}{\pi} \left(\frac{\sin ax}{ax} \right) \right] \tag{A-103}$$

For these two examples, $\delta(-x) = \delta(x)$, so for *these* cases $\delta(x)$ is said to be an *even-sided delta function*. The even-sided delta function is used throughout this text except when specifying the PDF of a discrete random variable.

$$\delta(x) = \begin{cases} \lim_{a \to \infty} (ae^{ax}), & x \le 0 \\ \\ 0, & x > 0 \end{cases} \tag{A-104}$$

This is an example of a single-sided delta function; in particular, this is a *left-sided delta function*. This type of delta function is used to specify the PDF of a discrete point of a random variable (see Appendix B).

2. Sifting property:

$$\int_{-\infty}^{\infty} w(x)\, \delta(x - x_0)\, dx = w(x_0) \tag{A-105}$$

3. For *even-sided* delta functions

$$\int_{a}^{b} w(x)\delta(x - x_0)\, dx = \begin{cases} 0, & x_0 < a \\ \frac{1}{2}w(a), & x_0 = a \\ w(x_0), & a < x_0 < b \\ \frac{1}{2}w(b), & x_0 = b \\ 0, & x_0 > b \end{cases} \tag{A-106}$$

where $b > a$.

4. For *left-sided* delta functions

$$\int_{a}^{b} w(x)\, \delta(x - x_0)\, dx = \begin{cases} 0, & x_0 \le a \\ w(x_0), & a < x_0 \le b \\ 0, & x_0 > b \end{cases} \tag{A-107}$$

where $b > a$.

5. $\displaystyle\int_{-\infty}^{\infty} w(x)\, \delta^{(n)}(x - x_0)\, dx = (-1)^n\, w^{(n)}(x_0)$ \hfill (A-108)

where the superscript (n) denotes the nth derivative with respect to x.

6. The Fourier transform of $\delta(x)$ is unity. That is,

$$\mathscr{F}[\delta(x)] = 1 \qquad\qquad \text{(A-109a)}$$

Conversely,

$$\delta(x) = \mathscr{F}^{-1}[1] \qquad\qquad \text{(A-109b)}$$

7. Scaling property:

$$\delta(ax) = \frac{1}{|a|}\,\delta(x) \qquad\qquad \text{(A-110)}$$

8. For *even-sided* delta functions,

$$\delta(x) = \int_{-\infty}^{\infty} e^{\pm j2\pi xy}\,dy \qquad\qquad \text{(A-111)}$$

A-9 Tabulation of Sa(x) = (sin x)/x

x	Sa(x)	Sa^2(x)	x	Sa(x)	Sa^2(x)
0.0	1.0000	1.0000	5.2	−0.1699	0.0289
0.2	0.9933	0.9867	5.4	−0.1431	0.0205
0.4	0.9735	0.9478	5.6	−0.1127	0.0127
0.6	0.9411	0.8856	5.8	−0.0801	0.0064
0.8	0.8967	0.8041	6.0	−0.0466	0.0022
1.0	0.8415	0.7081	6.2	−0.0134	0.0002
1.2	0.7767	0.6033	2π	0.0000	0.0000
1.4	0.7039	0.4955	6.4	0.0182	0.0003
1.6	0.6247	0.3903	6.6	0.0472	0.0022
1.8	0.5410	0.2927	6.8	0.0727	0.0053
2.0	0.4546	0.2067	7.0	0.0939	0.0088
2.2	0.3675	0.1351	7.2	0.1102	0.0122
2.4	0.2814	0.0792	7.4	0.1214	0.0147
2.6	0.1983	0.0393	7.6	0.1274	0.0162
2.8	0.1196	0.0143	7.8	0.1280	0.0164
3.0	0.0470	0.0022	8.0	0.1237	0.0153
π	0.0000	0.0000	8.2	0.1147	0.0132
3.2	−0.0182	0.0003	8.4	0.1017	0.0104
3.4	−0.0752	0.0056	8.6	0.0854	0.0073
3.6	−0.1229	0.0151	8.8	0.0665	0.0044
3.8	−0.1610	0.0259	9.0	0.0458	0.0021
4.0	−0.1892	0.0358	9.2	0.0242	0.0006
4.2	−0.2075	0.0431	9.4	0.0026	0.0000
4.4	−0.2163	0.0468	3π	0.0000	0.0000
4.6	−0.2160	0.0467	9.6	−0.0182	0.0003
4.8	−0.2075	0.0431	9.8	−0.0374	0.0014
5.0	−0.1918	0.0368	10.0	−0.0544	0.0030

A-10 Tabulation of $Q(z)$

$$Q(z) \triangleq \frac{1}{\sqrt{2\pi}} \int_z^\infty e^{-\lambda^2/2} \, d\lambda \qquad\qquad \text{(A-112)}$$

For $z \geq 3$:

$$Q(z) \approx \frac{1}{\sqrt{2\pi}\, z} e^{-z^2/2} \qquad \text{(see Fig. B-7)} \qquad\qquad \text{(A-113)}$$

Also,

$$Q(-z) = 1 - Q(z) \qquad\qquad \text{(A-114)}$$

$$Q(z) = \tfrac{1}{2}\text{erfc}\left(\frac{z}{\sqrt{2}}\right) = \tfrac{1}{2}\left[1 - \text{erf}\left(\frac{z}{\sqrt{2}}\right)\right] \qquad\qquad \text{(A-115a)}$$

where

$$\text{erfc}(x) \triangleq \frac{2}{\sqrt{\pi}} \int_x^\infty e^{-\lambda^2} \, d\lambda \qquad\qquad \text{(A-115b)}$$

$$\text{erf}(x) = \frac{2}{\sqrt{\pi}} \int_0^x e^{-\lambda^2} \, d\lambda \qquad\qquad \text{(A-115c)}$$

For $z \geq 0$, a rational function approximation is [Ziemer and Tranter, 1990]

$$Q(z) = \frac{e^{-z^2/2}}{\sqrt{2\pi}}(b_1 t + b_2 t^2 + b_3 t^3 + b_4 t^4 + b_5 t^5) \qquad\qquad \text{(A-116)}$$

where $t = 1/(1 + pz)$, with $p = 0.2316419$, and

$$b_1 = 0.31981530$$
$$b_2 = -0.356563782$$
$$b_3 = 1.781477937$$
$$b_4 = -1.821255978$$
$$b_5 = 1.330274429$$

Another approximation for $Q(z)$ for $z \geq 0$ is [Börjesson and Sunberg, 1979; Peebles, 1993]

$$Q(z) = \left[\frac{1}{(1 - 0.339)z + 0.339\sqrt{z^2 + 5.510}}\right] \frac{e^{-z^2/2}}{\sqrt{2\pi}} \qquad\qquad \text{(A-117)}$$

This approximation has a maximum absolute error of 0.27% for $z \geq 0$.

z	$Q(z)$	z	$Q(z)$
0.0	0.50000	2.0	0.02275
0.1	0.46017	2.1	0.01786
0.2	0.42074	2.2	0.01390
0.3	0.38209	2.3	0.01072
0.4	0.34458	2.4	0.00820
0.5	0.30854	2.5	0.00621
0.6	0.27425	2.6	0.00466
0.7	0.24196	2.7	0.00347
0.8	0.21186	2.8	0.00256
0.9	0.18406	2.9	0.00187
1.0	0.15866	3.0	0.00135
1.1	0.13567	3.1	0.00097
1.2	0.11507	3.2	0.00069
1.3	0.09680	3.3	0.00048
1.4	0.08076	3.4	0.00034
1.5	0.06681	3.5	0.00023
1.6	0.05480	3.6	0.00016
1.7	0.04457	3.7	0.00011
1.8	0.03593	3.8	0.00007
1.9	0.02872	3.9	0.00005
		4.0	0.00003

Also see Fig. B-7 for a plot of $Q(z)$.

B

Probability and Random Variables

B-1 Introduction

The need for probability theory arises in every scientific discipline since it is impossible to be exactly sure of values that are obtained by measurement. For example, we might say that we are 90% sure that a voltage is within ± 0.1 V of a 5-V level. This is a statistical description of the voltage parameter as opposed to a deterministic description whereby we might define the voltage as being exactly 5 V.

This appendix is intended to be a short course in probability and random variables. Numerous excellent books cover this topic in more detail [Davenport and Root, 1958; Papoulis, 1984, 1991; Peebles, 1987, 1993; Shanmugan and Breipohl, 1988]. However, this appendix will provide a good introduction to the topic for the new student or a quick review for the student who is already knowledgeable in this area.

If probability and random variables are new topics for you, you will soon realize that to understand them, you will need to master many new definitions that seem to be introduced all at once. It is important to memorize these definitions in order to have a vocabulary that can be used when conversing with others about statistical results. In addition, you must develop a feeling for the engineering application of these definitions and theorems. If you accomplish this at the beginning, you can grasp more complicated statistical ideas easily.

B-2 Sets

DEFINITION: A *set* is a collection (or class) of objects.

The largest set or the all-embracing set of objects under consideration in an experiment is called the *universal set.* All other sets under consideration in the experiment are subsets

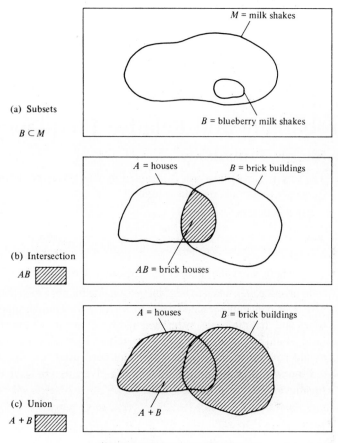

FIGURE B-1 Venn diagram.

or *events* of the universal set. This is illustrated in Fig. B-1a, where a *Venn diagram* is given. For example, *M* might denote the set containing all types of milk shakes and *B* might denote the subset of blueberry milk shakes. Thus *B* is contained in *M*, which is denoted by $B \subset M$. In parts b and c of this figure two sets, *A* and *B*, are shown. There are two basic ways of describing the combination of set *A* and set *B*. These are called *intersection* and *union*.

DEFINITION: The *intersection* of set *A* and set *B*, denoted by *AB*, is the set of elements that is common to *A* and *B*. (Mathematicians use the notation $A \cap B$.)

The intersection of *A* and *B* is analogous to the AND operation of digital logic. For example, if *A* denotes houses and *B* denotes brick buildings, then the event $C = AB$ would denote only brick houses. This is illustrated by Fig. B-1b.

DEFINITION: The *union* of set *A* and set *B*, denoted by $A + B$, is the set that contains all the elements of *A* or all the elements of *B* or both. (Mathematicians use the notation $A \cup B$.)

The union of A and B is analogous to the OR operation of digital logic. Continuing with the example just given, $D = A + B$ would be the set that contains all brick buildings, all houses, as well as all brick houses. This is illustrated in Fig. B-1c.

The events A and B are called *simple events*, and the events $C = AB$ and $D = A + B$ are called *compound events* since they are logical functions of simple events.

B-3 Probability and Relative Frequency

Simple Probability

The probability of an event A, denoted by $P(A)$, may be defined in terms of the relative frequency of A occurring in n trials.

DEFINITION[†]

$$P(A) = \lim_{n \to \infty} \left(\frac{n_A}{n} \right) \tag{B-1}$$

where n_A is the number of times that A occurs in n trials.

In practice, n is taken to be some reasonable number such that a larger value for n would give approximately the same value for $P(A)$. For example, suppose that a coin is tossed 40 times and that the heads event, denoted by A, occurs 19 times. Then the probability of a head would be evaluated as approximately $P(A) = \frac{19}{40}$, where the true value of $P(A) = 0.5$ would have been obtained if $n = \infty$ had been used.

From the definition of probability, as given by (B-1), it is seen that all probability functions have the property

$$0 \le P(A) \le 1 \tag{B-2}$$

where $P(A) = 0$ if the event A is a *null event* (does not occur) and $P(A) = 1$ if the event A is a *sure event* (always occurs).

Joint Probability

DEFINITION: The probability of a *joint event, AB,* is

$$P(AB) = \lim_{n \to \infty} \left(\frac{n_{AB}}{n} \right) \tag{B-3}$$

where n_{AB} is the number of times that the event AB occurs in n trials.

In addition, two events, A and B, are said to be *mutually exclusive* if AB is a null event, which implies that $P(AB) \equiv 0$.

[†] Here an engineering approach is used to define probability. Strictly speaking, statisticians have developed probability theory based on three axioms: (1) $P(A) > 0$, (2) $P(S) = 1$ where S is the sure event, and (3) $P(A + B) = P(A) + P(B)$ provided that AB is a null event (i.e., $AB = \emptyset$). Statisticians define $P(A)$ as being any function of A that satisfies these axioms. The engineering definition is consistent with this approach since it satisfies these axioms.

Example B-1   Evaluation of Probabilities

Let event A denote an auto accident blocking a certain street intersection during a 1-min interval. Let event B denote that it is raining at the street intersection during a 1-min period. Then event $E = AB$ would be a blocked intersection while it is raining, as evaluated in 1-min increments.

Suppose that experimental measurements are tabulated continuously for 1 week, and it is found that $n_A = 25$, $n_B = 300$, $n_{AB} = 20$, and there are $n = 10,080$ 1-min intervals in the week of measurements. ($n_A = 25$ does not mean that there were 25 accidents in a 1-week period, but that the intersection was blocked for 25 1-min periods because of car accidents; similarly for n_B and n_{AB}.) These results indicate that the probability of having a blocked intersection is $P(A) = 0.0025$, the probability of rain is $P(B) = 0.03$, and the probability of having a blocked intersection and it is raining is $P(AB) = 0.002$.

The probability of the union of two events may be evaluated by measuring the compound event directly, or it may be evaluated from the probabilities of simple events as given by the following theorem.

Theorem

Let $E = A + B$; then

$$P(E) = P(A + B) = P(A) + P(B) - P(AB) \tag{B-4}$$

PROOF. Let the event A-only occur n_1 times out of n trials, the event B-only occur n_2 times out of n trials, and the event AB occur n_{AB} times. Thus

$$P(A + B) = \lim_{n \to \infty} \left(\frac{n_1 + n_2 + n_{AB}}{n} \right)$$

$$= \lim_{n \to \infty} \left(\frac{n_1 + n_{AB}}{n} \right) + \lim_{n \to \infty} \left(\frac{n_2 + n_{AB}}{n} \right) - \lim_{n \to \infty} \left(\frac{n_{AB}}{n} \right)$$

which is identical to (B-4) since

$$P(A) = \lim_{n \to \infty} \left(\frac{n_1 + n_{AB}}{n} \right),$$

$$P(B) = \lim_{n \to \infty} \left(\frac{n_2 + n_{AB}}{n} \right), \quad \text{and} \quad P(AB) = \lim_{n \to \infty} \left(\frac{n_{AB}}{n} \right) \qquad \blacksquare$$

Example B-1 (Continued)

The probability of having a blocked intersection or rain occurring, or both, is then

$$P(A + B) = 0.0025 + 0.03 - 0.002 \approx 0.03 \tag{B-5}$$

Conditional Probabilities

DEFINITION: The probability that an event A occurs, given that an event B has also occurred, is denoted by $P(A|B)$ and is defined by

$$P(A|B) = \lim_{n_B \to \infty} \left(\frac{n_{AB}}{n_B} \right) \tag{B-6}$$

Example B-1 (Continued)

The probability of a blocked intersection when it is raining is approximately

$$P(A|B) = \tfrac{20}{300} = 0.066 \tag{B-7}$$

Theorem

Let $E = AB$; then

$$P(AB) = P(A)P(B|A) = P(B)P(A|B) \tag{B-8}$$

This is known as Bayes' theorem.

PROOF

$$P(AB) = \lim_{n \to \infty} \left(\frac{n_{AB}}{n} \right) = \lim_{\substack{n \to \infty \\ n_A \to \text{large}}} \left(\frac{n_{AB}}{n_A} \frac{n_A}{n} \right) = P(B|A)P(A) \tag{B-9}$$

It is noted that the values obtained for $P(AB)$, $P(B)$, and $P(A|B)$ in Example B-1 can be verified by the use of (B-8). ∎

DEFINITION: Two events, A and B, are said to be *independent* if either

$$P(A|B) = P(A) \tag{B-10}$$

or

$$P(B|A) = P(B) \tag{B-11}$$

Using this definition, we can easily demonstrate that events A and B of Example B-1 are not independent. On the other hand, if event A had been defined as getting a head on a coin toss, while B was the event that it was raining at the intersection, then A and B would be independent. Why?

Using (B-8) and (B-10), we can show that if a set of events $A_1, A_2, \ldots, A_n$, are independent; then a necessary condition is[†]

$$P(A_1 A_2 \cdots A_n) = P(A_1)P(A_2) \cdots P(A_n) \tag{B-12}$$

B-4 Random Variables

DEFINITION: A real *random variable* is a real-valued function defined on the events (elements) of the probability system.

[†] Equation (B-12) is not a sufficient condition for $A_1, A_2, \ldots, A_n$ to be independent [Papoulis, 1984, p. 34].

An understanding of why this definition is needed is fundamental to the topic of probability theory. So far we have defined probabilities in terms of events *A, B, C,* and so on. This method is awkward to use when the sets are objects (such as apples, oranges, etc.) instead of numbers. It is more convenient to describe sets by numerical values so that equations can be obtained as a function of numerical values instead of functions of alphanumeric parameters. This method is accomplished by using the random variable.

Example B-2   Random Variable

Referring to Fig. B-2, we can show the mutually exclusive events *A, B, C, D, E, F, G,* and *H* by a Venn diagram. These are all the possible outcomes of an experiment, so the sure event is $S = A + B + C + D + E + F + G + H$. Each

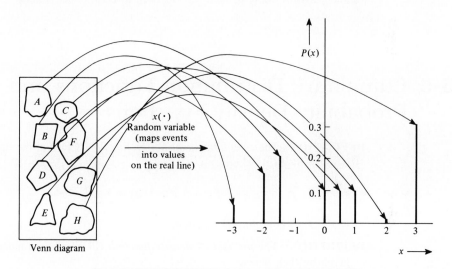

Event [·]	Value of Random Variable $x[\cdot]$	Probability of Event $P(x)$
A	0.0	0.10
B	−3.0	0.05
C	−1.5	0.20
D	−2.0	0.15
E	+0.5	0.10
F	+1.0	0.10
G	+2.0	0.00
H	+3.0	0.30
		Total = 1.00

FIGURE B-2 Random variable and probability functions for Example B-2.

of these events is denoted by some convenient value of the random variable x, as shown in the table in this figure. The assigned values for x may be positive, negative, fractions, or integers as long as they are real numbers. Since all the events are mutually exclusive, using (B-4) yields

$$P(S) = 1 = P(A) + P(B) + P(C) + P(D)$$
$$+ P(E) + P(F) + P(G) + P(H) \qquad \text{(B-13)}$$

That is, the probabilities have to sum to unity (the probability of a sure event), as shown in the table, and the individual probabilities have been given or measured as shown. For example, $P(C) = P(-1.5) = 0.2$. These values for the probabilities may be plotted as a function of the random variable x, as shown in the graph of $P(x)$. This is a *discrete* (or *point*) distribution since the random variable takes on only discrete (as opposed to continuous) values.

B-5 Cumulative Distribution Functions and Probability Density Functions

DEFINITION: The *cumulative distribution function* (CDF) of the random variable x is given by $F(a)$, where

$$F(a) \triangleq P(x \le a) \equiv \lim_{n \to \infty} \left(\frac{n_{x \le a}}{n} \right) \qquad \text{(B-14)}$$

where $F(a)$ is a unitless function.

DEFINITION: The *probability density function* (PDF) of the random variable x is given by $f(x)$, where

$$f(x) = \left. \frac{dF(a)}{da} \right|_{a=x} = \left. \frac{dP(x \le a)}{da} \right|_{a=x} = \lim_{\substack{n \to \infty \\ \Delta x \to 0}} \left[\frac{1}{\Delta x} \left(\frac{n_{\Delta x}}{n} \right) \right] \qquad \text{(B-15)}$$

where $f(x)$ has units of $1/x$.

Example B-2 (Continued)

The CDF for this example that was illustrated in Fig. B-2 is easily obtained using (B-14). The resulting CDF is shown in Fig. B-3. Note that the CDF starts at a zero value on the left ($a = -\infty$), and the probability is accumulated until the CDF is unity on the right ($a = +\infty$).

Using (B-15), we obtain the PDF by taking the derivative of the CDF. The

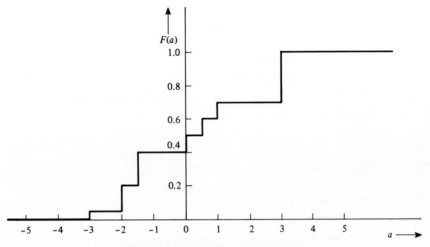

FIGURE B-3 CDF for Example B-2.

FIGURE B-4 PDF for Example B-2.

result is shown in Fig. B-4. The PDF consists of Dirac delta functions located at the assigned (discrete) values of the random variable and having weights equal to the probabilities of the associated event.[†]

[†] Left-sided delta functions are used here so that if $x = a$ happens to be a discrete point, $F(a) = P(x \leq a)$ includes all the probability from $x = -\infty$ up to and *including* the point $x = a$. See Sec. A-8 (Appendix A) for properties of Dirac delta functions.

Properties of CDFs and PDFs

Some *properties of the CDF* are as follows:

1. $F(a)$ is a nondecreasing function.
2. $F(a)$ is *right-hand* continuous. That is,

$$\lim_{\substack{\epsilon \to 0 \\ \epsilon > 0}} F(a + \epsilon) = F(a)$$

3.

$$F(a) = \lim_{\substack{\epsilon \to 0 \\ \epsilon > 0}} \int_{-\infty}^{a+\epsilon} f(x)\, dx \tag{B-16}$$

4. $0 \le F(a) \le 1$.
5. $F(-\infty) = 0$.
6. $F(+\infty) = 1$.

Note that the ϵ is needed to account for a discrete point that might occur at $x = $ a. If there is no discrete point at $x = a$, the limit is not necessary.

Some *properties of the PDF* are as follows.

1. $f(x) \ge 0$. That is, $f(x)$ is a nonnegative function.
2. $\int_{-\infty}^{\infty} f(x)\, dx = F(+\infty) = 1$. \tag{B-17}

As we will see later, $f(x)$ may have values larger than unity; however, the area under $f(x)$ is equal to unity. These properties of the CDF and PDF are very useful in checking results of problems. That is, if a CDF or a PDF violates any of these properties, you *know* that an error has been made in the calculations.

Discrete and Continuous Distributions

Example B-2 was an example of a *discrete* (or *point*) *distribution*. That is, the random variable has M discrete values $x_1, x_2, x_3, \ldots, x_M = 7$ in this example. Consequently, the CDF increased only in jumps [i.e., $F(a)$ was discontinuous] as a increased, and the PDF consisted of delta functions located at the discrete values of the random variable. In contrast to this example of a discrete distribution, there are continuous distributions, one of which is illustrated in the following example. If a random variable is allowed to take on any value in some interval, it is a *continuously distributed* random variable in that interval.

Example B-3   A Continuous Distribution

Let the random variable denote the voltages that are associated with a collection of a large number of flashlight batteries (1.5-V cells). If the number of batteries in the collection were infinite, the number of different voltage values (events) that we could obtain would be infinite, so that the distributions (PDF and CDF) would be continuous functions. Suppose that, by measurement, the CDF is

(a) Cumulative Distribution Function

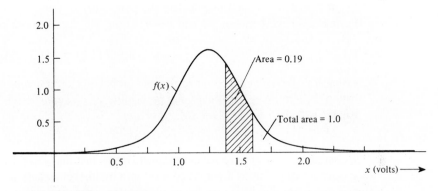

(b) Probability Density Function

FIGURE B-5 CDF and PDF for a continuous distribution (Example B-3).

evaluated first by using $F(a) = P(x \leq a) = \lim_{n \to \infty} (n_{x \leq a}/n)$, where n is the number of batteries in the whole collection and $n_{x \leq a}$ is the number of batteries in the collection with voltages less than or equal to a volts, where a is a parameter. The CDF that might be obtained is illustrated in Fig. B-5a. The associated PDF is obtained by taking the derivative of the CDF, as shown in Fig. B-5b. Note that $f(x)$ exceeds unity for some values of x, but that the area under $f(x)$ is unity (a PDF property). (You might check to see that the other CDF and PDF properties are also satisfied.)

Theorem

$$F(b) - F(a) = P(x \le b) - P(x \le a) = P(a < x \le b)$$

$$= \lim_{\substack{\epsilon \to 0 \\ \epsilon > 0}} \left[\int_{a+\epsilon}^{b+\epsilon} f(x) \, dx \right] \tag{B-18}$$

PROOF

$$F(b) - F(a) = \lim_{\substack{\epsilon \to 0 \\ \epsilon > 0}} \left[\int_{-\infty}^{b+\epsilon} f(x) \, dx - \int_{-\infty}^{a+\epsilon} f(x) \, dx \right]$$

$$= \lim_{\substack{\epsilon \to 0 \\ \epsilon > 0}} \left[\int_{-\infty}^{a+\epsilon} f(x) \, dx + \int_{a+\epsilon}^{b+\epsilon} f(x) \, dx - \int_{-\infty}^{a+\epsilon} f(x) \, dx \right]$$

$$= \lim_{\substack{\epsilon \to 0 \\ \epsilon > 0}} \left[\int_{a+\epsilon}^{b+\epsilon} f(x) \, dx \right] \qquad \blacksquare$$

Example B-3 (Continued)

Suppose that we wanted to calculate the probability of obtaining a battery having a voltage between 1.4 and 1.6 V. Using this theorem, we compute

$$P(1.4 < x \le 1.6) = \int_{1.4}^{1.6} f(x) \, dx = F(1.6) - F(1.4) = 0.19$$

(using Fig. B-5). We also realize that the probability of obtaining a 1.5-V battery is zero. Why? However, the probability of obtaining a 1.5 V $\pm$ 0.1 V battery is 0.19.

In communication systems we have digital signals that may have discrete distributions (one discrete value for each permitted level in a multilevel signal), and we have analog signals and noise that have continuous distributions. We may also have mixed distributions, which contain discrete as well as continuous values. These occur, for example, when a continuous signal and noise are clipped by an amplifier that is driven into saturation.

Theorem

If x is discretely distributed, then

$$f(x) = \sum_{i=1}^{M} P(x_i) \, \delta(x - x_i) \tag{B-19}$$

where M is the number of discrete events and $P(x_i)$ is the probability of obtaining the discrete event x_i.

This theorem was illustrated by Example B-2, where the PDF of this discrete distribution is plotted in Fig. B-4.

Theorem

If x is discretely distributed, then[†]

$$F(a) = \sum_{i=1}^{L} P(x_i) \qquad \text{(B-20)}$$

where L is the largest integer such that $x_L \le a$ and $L \le M$, where M is the number of points in the discrete distribution. Here it is assumed that the discrete points x_i are indexed so that they occur in ascending order of the index. That is, $x_1 < x_2 < x_3 < \cdots < x_M$.

This theorem was illustrated in Fig. B-3, which is a plot of (B-20) for Example B-2.

In electrical engineering problems, the CDFs or PDFs of waveforms are relatively easy to obtain by using the relative frequency approach, as described by (B-14) and (B-15). For example, the PDFs for triangular and square waves are given in Fig. B-6. These are

---

[†]Equation (B-20) is identical to $F(a) = \sum_{i=1}^{M} P(x_i)u(a - x_i)$, where $u(y)$ is a unit step function [defined in (2-49)].

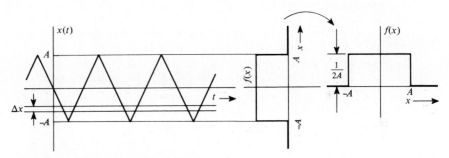

(a) Triangular Waveform and Its Associated PDF

(b) Square Waveform and Its Associated PDF

FIGURE B-6 PDFs for triangular waves and square waves.

obtained by sweeping a narrow horizontal window, Δx volts wide, vertically across the waveforms and measuring the relative frequency of occurrence of voltages in the Δx window. The time axis is divided into n intervals, and the waveform appears $n_{\Delta x}$ times in these intervals in the Δx window. A rough idea of the PDF of a waveform can also be obtained by looking at the waveform on an oscilloscope. Using *no* horizontal sweep, the intensity of the presentation as a function of the voltage (y axis) gives the PDF. (This assumes that the intensity of the image is proportional to the time that the waveform dwells in the window Δy units wide.) The PDF is proportional to the intensity as a function of y (the random variable).

B-6 Ensemble Average and Moments

Ensemble Average

One of the primary uses of probability theory is to evaluate the average value of a random variable (which represents some physical phenomenon) or to evaluate the average value of some function of the random variable. In general, let the function of the random variable be denoted by $y = h(x)$.

> **DEFINITION:** The *expected value*, which is also called the *ensemble average*, of $y = h(x)$ is given by

$$\bar{y} = \overline{[h(x)]} \triangleq \int_{-\infty}^{\infty} [h(x)]f(x)\ dx \tag{B-21}$$

This definition may be used for discrete as well as continuous random variables. Note that it is a linear operator where the operator is

$$\overline{[\cdot]} = \int_{-\infty}^{\infty} [\cdot]f(x)\ dx \tag{B-22}$$

Other authors denote the ensemble average of y by $E[y]$ or $\langle y \rangle$ as well as using this notation of $\bar{y}$. We will use the $\bar{y}$ notation since it is easier to write and more convenient to use when long equations are being evaluated with a large number of averaging operators.

Theorem

If x is a **discretely** distributed random variable, the expected value can be evaluated by using

$$\bar{y} = \overline{[h(x)]} = \sum_{i=1}^{M} h(x_i)P(x_i) \tag{B-23}$$

where M is the number of discrete points in the distribution.

PROOF. Using (B-19) in (B-21), we get

$$\overline{h(x)]} = \int_{-\infty}^{\infty} h(x) \left[\sum_{i=1}^{M} P(x_i)\, \delta(x - x_i) \right] dx$$

$$= \sum_{i=1}^{M} P(x_i) \int_{-\infty}^{\infty} h(x)\, \delta(x - x_i)\, dx$$

$$= \sum_{i=1}^{M} P(x_i)h(x_i) \qquad\blacksquare$$

Example B-4 Evaluation of an Average

We will now show that (B-23) and, consequently, the definition of expected value as given by (B-21) are consistent with the way in which we usually evaluate averages. Suppose that we have a class of $n = 40$ students who take a test. The resulting test scores are 1 paper with a grade of 100; 2 with scores of 95; 4, 90; 6, 85; 10, 80; 10, 75; 5, 70; 1, 65; and 1 paper with a score of 60. Then the class average will be

$$\bar{x} = \frac{100(1) + 95(2) + 90(4) + 85(6) + 80(10) + 75(10) + 70(5) + 65(1) + 60(1)}{40}$$

$$= 100\left(\frac{1}{40}\right) + 95\left(\frac{2}{40}\right) + 90\left(\frac{4}{40}\right) + 85\left(\frac{6}{40}\right) + 80\left(\frac{10}{40}\right) + 75\left(\frac{10}{40}\right)$$

$$+ 70\left(\frac{5}{40}\right) + 65\left(\frac{1}{40}\right) + 60\left(\frac{1}{40}\right)$$

$$= \sum_{i=1}^{9} x_i P(x_i) = 79.6 \qquad\qquad (B-24)$$

Moments

Moments are defined as ensemble averages of some specific functions used for $h(x)$. For example, for the rth moment, defined subsequently, let $y = h(x) = (x - x_0)^r$.

DEFINITION: The rth *moment* of the random variable x taken about the point $x = x_0$ is given by

$$\overline{(x - x_0)^r} = \int_{-\infty}^{\infty} (x - x_0)^r f(x)\, dx \qquad\qquad (B-25)$$

DEFINITION: The *mean m* is the first moment taken about the origin (i.e., $x_0 = 0$). Thus

$$m \triangleq \bar{x} = \int_{-\infty}^{\infty} xf(x) \, dx \tag{B-26}$$

DEFINITION: The *variance* σ^2 is the second moment taken about the mean. Thus

$$\sigma^2 = \overline{(x - \bar{x})^2} = \int_{-\infty}^{\infty} (x - \bar{x})^2 f(x) \, dx \tag{B-27}$$

DEFINITION: The *standard deviation* σ is the square root of the variance. Thus

$$\sigma = \sqrt{\sigma^2} = \sqrt{\int_{-\infty}^{\infty} (x - \bar{x})^2 f(x) \, dx} \tag{B-28}$$

As an engineer, you may recognize the integrals of (B-26) and (B-27) as related to applications in mechanical problems. The mean is equivalent to the center of gravity of a mass that is distributed along a single dimension, where $f(x)$ denotes the mass density as a function of the x axis. The variance is equivalent to the moment of inertia about the center of gravity. However, you might ask: What is the significance of the mean, variance, and other moments in electrical engineering problems? If x represents a voltage or current waveform, the mean gives the dc value of the waveform. The second moment ($r = 2$) taken about the origin ($x_0 = 0$), which is $\overline{x^2}$, gives the normalized power. σ^2 gives the normalized power in the corresponding ac coupled waveform. Consequently, $\sqrt{\overline{x^2}}$ is the rms value of the waveform and σ is the rms value of the corresponding ac coupled waveform.

In statistical terms, m gives the *center of gravity* of the PDF and σ gives us the *spread* of the PDF about this center of gravity. For example, in Fig. B-5 the voltage distribution for a collection of flashlight batteries is given. The mean is $\bar{x} = 1.25$ V and the standard deviation is $\sigma = 0.25$ V. This figure illustrates a Gaussian distribution that will be studied in detail in Sec. B-7. For this Gaussian distribution the area under $f(x)$ from $x = 1.0$ to 1.5 V, which corresponds to the interval $\bar{x} \pm \sigma$, is 0.68. Thus we conclude that 68% of the batteries have voltages within one standard deviation of the mean value (Gaussian distribution).

There are several ways to specify a number that is used to describe the typical or most common value of x. The *mean m* is one such measure that gives the center of gravity. Another measure is the *median,* which corresponds to the value $x = a$, where $F(a) = \frac{1}{2}$. A third measure is called the *mode,* which corresponds to the value of x where $f(x)$ is a maximum, assuming that the PDF has only one maximum. For the Gaussian distribution, all these measures give the same number, namely, $x = m$. For other types of distributions, the values obtained for the mean, median, and mode will usually be nearly the same number. The variance is also related to the second moment about the origin and the mean, as described by the following theorem.

Theorem

$$\sigma^2 = \overline{x^2} - (\overline{x})^2 \tag{B-29}$$

A proof of this theorem illustrates how the ensemble average operator notation is used.

PROOF

$$\sigma^2 = \overline{(x - \overline{x})^2}$$
$$= \overline{[x^2]} - \overline{[2\,x\overline{x}]} + \overline{[(\overline{x})^2]} \tag{B-30}$$

Since $\overline{[\cdot]}$ is a linear operator, $\overline{[2x\overline{x}]} = 2\overline{x}\,\overline{x} = 2(\overline{x})^2$. Moreover, $(\overline{x})^2$ is a constant and the average value of a constant is the constant itself. That is, for the constant c,

$$\overline{c} = \int_{-\infty}^{\infty} c\,f(x)\,dx = c \int_{-\infty}^{\infty} f(x)\,dx = c \tag{B-31}$$

So, using (B-31) in (B-30), we obtain

$$\sigma^2 = \overline{x^2} - 2(\overline{x})^2 + (\overline{x})^2$$

which is equivalent to (B-29). ∎

Thus there are two ways to evaluate the variance: (1) by use of the definition as given by (B-27), or (2) by use of the theorem of (B-29).

B-7 Examples of Important Distributions

There are numerous types of distributions. Some of the more important ones used in communication and statistical problems are summarized in Table B-1. Here, the equations for their PDF and CDF, a sketch of the PDF, and the formula for the mean and variance are given. These distributions will be studied in more detail in the following paragraphs.

Binomial Distribution

The binomial distribution is useful for describing digital as well as other statistical problems. Its application is best illustrated by an example.

Assume that we have a binary word that is n bits long and that the probability of sending a binary 1 is p. Consequently, the probability of sending a binary 0 is $1 - p$. We want to evaluate the probability of obtaining n-bit words that contain k binary 1's. One such word is k binary 1's followed by $n - k$ binary 0's. The probability of obtaining this word is $p^k(1 - p)^{n-k}$. There are also other n-bit words that contain k binary 1's. In fact, the number of different n-bit words containing k binary 1's is

$$\binom{n}{k} = \frac{n!}{(n - k)!k!} \tag{B-32}$$

(This can be demonstrated by taking a numerical example such as $n = 8$ and $k = 3$.) The symbol $\binom{n}{k}$ is used in algebra to denote the operation described by (B-32) and is read "the

TABLE B-1 Some Distributions and Their Properties

Name of Distribution	Type: $F(a)$ is:	Sketch of PDF	Equation for: Cumulative Distribution Function (CDF)	Probability Density Function (PDF)	Mean	Variance
Binomial	Discrete	$n=3$, $p=0.6$	$F(a) = \sum_{\substack{k=0 \\ m\le a}}^{m} P(k)$ where $P(k) = \binom{n}{k} p^k (1-p)^{n-k}$	$f(x) = \sum_{k=0}^{n} P(k)\,\delta(x-k)$ where $P(k) = \binom{n}{k} p^k (1-p)^{n-k}$	np	$np(1-p)$
Poisson	Discrete	$\lambda = 2$	$F(a) = \sum_{\substack{k=0 \\ m\le a}}^{m} P(k)$ where $P(k) = \dfrac{\lambda^k}{k!}\,e^{-\lambda}$	$f(x) = \sum_{k=0}^{\infty} P(k)\,\delta(x-k)$ where $P(k) = \dfrac{\lambda^k}{k!}\,e^{-\lambda}$	λ	λ
Uniform	Continuous		$F(a) = \begin{cases} 0, & a < \dfrac{2m-A}{2} \\[2mm] \dfrac{1}{A}\left[a - \dfrac{2m-A}{2}\right], & \left\|a-m\right\| \le \dfrac{A}{2} \\[2mm] 1, & a \ge \dfrac{2m+A}{2}\end{cases}$	$f(x) = \begin{cases} 0, & x < \dfrac{2m-A}{2} \\[2mm] \dfrac{1}{A}, & \left\|x-m\right\| \le \dfrac{A}{2} \\[2mm] 0, & x > \dfrac{2m+A}{2}\end{cases}$	m	$\dfrac{A^2}{12}$
Gaussian	Continuous		$F(a) = Q\left(\dfrac{m-a}{\sigma}\right)$ where $Q(a) \triangleq \dfrac{1}{\sqrt{2\pi}}\displaystyle\int_{\alpha}^{\infty} e^{-x^2/2}\,dx$	$f(x) = \dfrac{1}{\sqrt{2\pi}\,\sigma}\exp\!\left[-(x-m)^2/2\sigma^2\right]$	m	σ^2
Sinusoidal	Continuous		$F(a) = \begin{cases} 0, & a \le -A \\[2mm] \dfrac{1}{\pi}\left[\dfrac{\pi}{2} + \sin^{-1}\left(\dfrac{a}{A}\right)\right], & \left\|a\right\| \le A \\[2mm] 1, & a \ge A\end{cases}$	$f(x) = \begin{cases} 0, & x < -A \\[2mm] \dfrac{1}{\pi\sqrt{A^2 - x^2}}, & \left\|x\right\| \le A \\[2mm] 0, & x > A\end{cases}$	0	$\dfrac{A^2}{2}$

combination of n things taken k at a time.'' Thus the probability of obtaining an n-bit word containing k binary 1's is

$$P(k) = \binom{n}{k} p^k (1 - p)^{n-k} \qquad \text{(B-33)}$$

If we let the random variable x denote these discrete values, then $x = k$, where k can take on the values 0, 1, 2, . . ., n, and we obtain the *binomial PDF:*

$$f(x) = \sum_{k=0}^{n} P(k)\delta(x - k) \qquad \text{(B-34)}$$

where $P(k)$ is given by (B-33).

The name *binomial* comes from the fact that the $P(k)$ are the individual terms in a binomial expansion. That is, letting $q = 1 - p$,

$$(p + q)^n = \sum_{k=0}^{n} \binom{n}{k} p^k q^{n-k} = \sum_{k=0}^{n} P(k) \qquad \text{(B-35)}$$

The combinations $\binom{n}{k}$, which are also the binomial coefficients, can be evaluated by using Pascal's triangle:

$n = 0$						1					
$n = 1$					1		1				
$n = 2$				1		2		1			
$n = 3$			1		3		3		1		
$n = 4$		1		4		6		4		1	
$n = 5$	1		5		10		10		5		1

For a particular value of n, the combinations $\binom{n}{k}$, for $k = 0, 1, . . ., n$, are the elements in the nth row. For example, for $n = 3$,

$$\binom{3}{0} = 1, \quad \binom{3}{1} = 3, \quad \binom{3}{2} = 3, \quad \text{and} \quad \binom{3}{3} = 1$$

The mean value of the binomial distribution is evaluated by the use of (B-23).

$$m = \bar{x} = \sum_{k=0}^{n} x_k P(x_k) = \sum_{k=0}^{n} k P(k)$$

or

$$m = \sum_{k=1}^{n} k \binom{n}{k} p^k q^{n-k} \qquad \text{(B-36)}$$

Using the identity

$$k\binom{n}{k} = \frac{kn!}{(n-k)!k!} = \frac{n(n-1)!}{(n-k)!(k-1)!}$$

$$= n\left[\frac{(n-1)!}{((n-1)-(k-1))!(k-1)!}\right]$$

or

$$k\binom{n}{k} = n\binom{n-1}{k-1} \tag{B-37}$$

we have

$$m = \sum_{k=1}^{n} n\binom{n-1}{k-1} p^k q^{n-k} \tag{B-38}$$

Making a change in the index, let $j = k - 1$. Thus

$$m = \sum_{j=0}^{n-1} n\binom{n-1}{j} p^{j+1} q^{n-(j+1)}$$

$$= np\left[\sum_{j=0}^{n-1}\binom{n-1}{j} p^j q^{(n-1)-j}\right] = np\left[(p+q)^{n-1}\right] \tag{B-39}$$

Recalling that p and q are probabilities and $p + q = 1$, then we see that $(p+q)^{n-1} = 1$. Thus (B-39) reduces to

$$m = np \tag{B-40}$$

Similarly, it can be shown that the variance is $np(1-p)$ by using $\sigma^2 = \overline{x^2} - (\overline{x})^2$.

Poisson Distribution

The Poisson distribution (Table B-1) is obtained as a limiting approximation of a binomial distribution when n is very large and p is very small, but the product $np = \lambda$ is some reasonable size [Thomas, 1969].

Uniform Distribution

The uniform distribution is

$$f(x) = \begin{cases} 0, & x < \left(\dfrac{2m-A}{2}\right) \\[2mm] \dfrac{1}{A}, & |x-m| \le \dfrac{A}{2} \\[2mm] 0, & x > \left(\dfrac{2m+A}{2}\right) \end{cases} \tag{B-41}$$

where A is the peak-to-peak value of the random variable. This is illustrated by the sketch in Table B-1. The mean of this distribution is

$$\int_{-\infty}^{\infty} x f(x)\, dx = \int_{m-(A/2)}^{m+(A/2)} x \frac{1}{A}\, dx = m \tag{B-42}$$

and the variance is

$$\sigma^2 = \int_{m-(A/2)}^{m+(A/2)} (x - m)^2 \frac{1}{A}\, dx \tag{B-43}$$

Making a change in variable, let $y = x - m$.

$$\sigma^2 = \frac{1}{A} \int_{-A/2}^{A/2} y^2\, dy = \frac{A^2}{12} \tag{B-44}$$

The uniform distribution is useful in describing quantizing noise that is created when an analog signal is converted into a PCM signal, as discussed in Chapter 4.

Gaussian Distribution

The Gaussian distribution, which is also called the *normal distribution,* is one of the most important distributions, if not *the* most important. As discussed in Chapter 8, thermal noise has a Gaussian distribution. Numerous other phenomena can also be described by Gaussian statistics, and many theorems have been developed by statisticians that are based on Gaussian assumptions. It cannot be overemphasized that the Gaussian distribution is very important in analyzing both communication problems and problems in statistics. It can also be shown that the Gaussian distribution can be obtained as the limiting form of the binomial distribution when n becomes large, while holding the mean $m = np$ finite, and letting the variance $\sigma^2 = np(1 - p)$ be much larger than unity [Feller, 1957; Papoulis, 1984].

DEFINITION: The Gaussian distribution is

$$f(x) = \frac{1}{\sqrt{2\pi}\,\sigma} e^{-(x-m)^2/(2\sigma^2)} \tag{B-45}$$

where m is the mean and σ^2 is the variance.

A sketch of (B-45) is given in Fig. B-5, together with the CDF for the Gaussian random variable where $m = 1.25$ and $\sigma = 0.25$. The Gaussian PDF is symmetrical about $x = m$, with the area under the PDF being $\frac{1}{2}$ for $(-\infty \le x \le m)$ and $\frac{1}{2}$ for $(m \le x \le \infty)$. The peak value of the PDF is $1/(\sqrt{2\pi}\,\sigma)$ so that as $\sigma \to 0$, the Gaussian PDF goes into a δ function located at $x = m$ (since the area under the PDF is always unity).

We will now show that (B-45) is properly normalized; that is, the area under $f(x)$ is unity. This can be accomplished by letting I represent the integral of the PDF:

$$I \triangleq \int_{-\infty}^{\infty} f(x)\, dx = \int_{-\infty}^{\infty} \frac{1}{\sqrt{2\pi}\,\sigma} e^{-(x-m)^2/(2\sigma^2)}\, dx \tag{B-46}$$

Making a change in variable, let $y = (x - m)/\sigma$, then

$$I = \frac{1}{\sqrt{2\pi}\,\sigma} \int_{-\infty}^{\infty} e^{-y^2/2}\,(\sigma\,dy) = \frac{1}{\sqrt{2\pi}} \int_{-\infty}^{\infty} e^{-y^2/2}\,dy \tag{B-47}$$

The integral I can be shown to be unity by showing that I^2 is unity.

$$I^2 = \left[\frac{1}{\sqrt{2\pi}} \int_{-\infty}^{\infty} e^{-x^2/2}\,dx\right]\left[\frac{1}{\sqrt{2\pi}} \int_{-\infty}^{\infty} e^{-y^2/2}\,dy\right]$$

$$= \frac{1}{2\pi} \int_{-\infty}^{\infty} \int_{-\infty}^{\infty} e^{-(x^2+y^2)/2}\,dx\,dy \tag{B-48}$$

Make a change in the variables to polar coordinates from Cartesian coordinates. Let $r^2 = x^2 + y^2$ and $\theta = \tan^{-1}(y/x)$; then

$$I^2 = \frac{1}{2\pi} \int_0^{2\pi} \left[\int_0^{\infty} e^{-r^2/2}\,r\,dr\right] d\theta = \frac{1}{2\pi} \int_0^{2\pi} d\theta = 1 \tag{B-49}$$

Thus $I^2 = 1$ and, consequently, $I = 1$.

Up to now, we have *assumed* that the parameters m and σ^2 of (B-45) were the mean and the variance of the distribution. We need to *show* that indeed they are! This may be accomplished by writing the Gaussian form in terms of some arbitrary parameters α and β.

$$f(x) = \frac{1}{\sqrt{2\pi}\,\beta}\,e^{-(x-\alpha)^2/(2\beta^2)} \tag{B-50}$$

This function is still properly normalized, as demonstrated by (B-49). First, we need to show that the parameter α is the mean.

$$m = \int_{-\infty}^{\infty} x f(x)\,dx = \frac{1}{\sqrt{2\pi}\,\beta} \int_{-\infty}^{\infty} x e^{-(x-\alpha)^2/(2\beta^2)}\,dx \tag{B-51}$$

Making a change in variable, let $y = (x - \alpha)/\beta$; then

$$m = \frac{1}{\sqrt{2\pi}} \int_{-\infty}^{\infty} (\beta y + \alpha)e^{-y^2/2}\,dy$$

or

$$m = \frac{\beta}{\sqrt{2\pi}} \int_{-\infty}^{\infty} (ye^{-y^2/2})\,dy + \alpha\left(\int_{-\infty}^{\infty} \frac{1}{\sqrt{2\pi}}\,e^{-y^2/2}\,dy\right) \tag{B-52}$$

The first integral on the right of (B-52) is zero because the integrand is an odd function and the integral is evaluated over symmetrical limits. The second integral on the right is the integral of a properly normalized Gaussian PDF, so the integral has a value of unity. Thus (B-52) becomes

$$m = \alpha \tag{B-53}$$

and we have shown that the parameter α is the mean value.

The variance is

$$\sigma^2 = \int_{-\infty}^{\infty} (x - m)^2 f(x)\, dx$$

$$= \frac{1}{\sqrt{2\pi}\,\beta} \int_{-\infty}^{\infty} (x - m)^2 e^{-(x-m)^2/(2\beta^2)}\, dx \tag{B-54}$$

Similarly, we need to show that $\sigma^2 = \beta^2$. This will be left as a homework exercise.
The next question to answer is: What is the CDF for the Gaussian distribution?

Theorem

The cumulative distribution function (CDF) for the Gaussian distribution is

$$F(a) = Q\left(\frac{m - a}{\sigma}\right) = \tfrac{1}{2}\,\text{erfc}\left(\frac{m - a}{\sqrt{2}\,\sigma}\right) \tag{B-55}$$

where the Q function is defined by

$$Q(z) \triangleq \frac{1}{\sqrt{2\pi}} \int_{z}^{\infty} e^{-\lambda^2/2}\, d\lambda \tag{B-56}$$

and the complementary error function (erfc) is defined as

$$\text{erfc}(z) \triangleq \frac{2}{\sqrt{\pi}} \int_{z}^{\infty} e^{-\lambda^2}\, d\lambda \tag{B-57}$$

It can also be shown that

$$\text{erfc}(z) = 1 - \text{erf}(z) \tag{B-58}$$

where the error function is defined as

$$\text{erf}(z) \triangleq \frac{2}{\sqrt{\pi}} \int_{0}^{z} e^{-\lambda^2}\, d\lambda \tag{B-59}$$

The Q function and the complementary error function, as used in (B-55), give the same curve for $F(a)$. Since neither of the corresponding integrals, given by (B-56) and (B-57), can be evaluated in closed form, math tables (see Sec. A-10, Appendix A), numerical integration techniques, or closed-form approximations must be used to evaluate them. The equivalence between the two functions is

$$Q(z) = \tfrac{1}{2}\,\text{erfc}\left(\frac{z}{\sqrt{2}}\right) \tag{B-60}$$

Communication engineers often prefer to use the Q function as compared to the erfc function since solutions to problems written in terms of the Q function do not require the writing of the $\tfrac{1}{2}$ and $1/\sqrt{2}$ factors. On the other hand, the advantage of using the $\text{erf}(z)$ or $\text{erfc}(z)$ functions is that they are one of the standard functions in MathCAD and MAT-LAB, and these functions are also available on some hand calculators. However, text-books in probability and statistics usually give a tabulation of the normalized CDF. This is a tabulation of $F(a)$ for the case of $m = 0$ and $\sigma = 1$, and it is equivalent to $Q(-a)$ and

$\frac{1}{2}\operatorname{erfc}(-a/\sqrt{2})$. Since $Q(z)$ and $\frac{1}{2}\operatorname{erfc}(z/\sqrt{2})$ are equivalent, which one is used is a matter of personal preference. We use the Q-function notation in this book.

PROOF OF A THEOREM FOR THE GAUSSIAN CDF

$$F(a) = \int_{-\infty}^{a} f(x)\,dx = \frac{1}{\sqrt{2\pi}\,\sigma}\int_{-\infty}^{a} e^{-(x-m)^2/(2\sigma^2)}\,dx \qquad \text{(B-61)}$$

Making a change in variable, let $y = (m - x)/\sigma$.

$$F(a) = \frac{1}{\sqrt{2\pi}\,\sigma}\int_{\infty}^{(m-a)/\sigma} e^{-y^2/2}\,(-\sigma\,dy) \qquad \text{(B-62)}$$

or

$$F(a) = \frac{1}{\sqrt{2\pi}}\int_{(m-a)/\sigma}^{\infty} e^{-y^2/2}\,dy = Q\!\left(\frac{m-a}{\sigma}\right) \qquad \text{(B-63)}$$

Similarly, $F(a)$ may be expressed in terms of the complementary error function. ∎

As mentioned earlier, it is unfortunate that the integrals for $Q(z)$ or $\operatorname{erfc}(z)$ cannot be evaluated in closed form. However, for large values of z, very good closed-form approximations can be obtained, and for small values of z numerical integration techniques can be applied easily. A plot of $Q(z)$ is shown in Fig. B-7 for $z \geq 0$ and a tabulation of $Q(z)$ is given in Sec. A-10.

A relatively simple closed-form upper bound for $Q(z)$, $z > 0$, is

$$Q(z) < \frac{1}{\sqrt{2\pi}\,z}\,e^{-z^2/2}, \qquad z > 0 \qquad \text{(B-64)}$$

This is also shown in Fig. B-7. It is obtained by evaluating the $Q(z)$ integral by parts.

$$Q(z) = \int_{z}^{\infty} \frac{1}{\sqrt{2\pi}}\,e^{-\lambda^2/2}\,d\lambda = \int_{z}^{\infty} u\,dv = uv\Big|_{z}^{\infty} - \int_{z}^{\infty} v\,du$$

where $u = 1/(\sqrt{2\pi}\lambda)$ and $dv = \lambda e^{-\lambda^2/2}\,d\lambda$. Thus

$$Q(z) = \left(\frac{1}{\sqrt{2\pi}\,\lambda}\right)\left(-e^{-\lambda^2/2}\right)\Big|_{z}^{\infty} - \int_{z}^{\infty}\left(-e^{-\lambda^2/2}\right)\left(-\frac{1}{\sqrt{2\pi}\,\lambda^2}\,d\lambda\right)$$

Dropping the integral, which is a positive quantity, we obtain the upper bound on $Q(z)$ as given by (B-64). If needed, a lower bound may also be obtained [Wozencraft and Jacobs, 1965]. A rational function approximation for $Q(z)$ is given by (A-116) and a closed-form approximation that has an accuracy of at least 0.27% is given by (A-117).

For values of $z \geq 3$ this upper bound has an error of less than 10% when compared to the actual value for $Q(z)$. That is, $Q(3) = 1.35 \times 10^{-3}$ and the upper bound has a value of 1.48×10^{-3} for $z = 3$. This is an error of 9.4%. For $z = 4$ the error is 5.6% and for $z = 5$ the error is 3.6%. The probability of error for digital systems is often found to be a Q function. Since most useful digital systems have a probability of error of 10^{-3} or less, this upper bound becomes very useful for evaluating $Q(z)$. At any rate, if the upper bound approximation is used, we know that the value obtained indicates slightly poorer performance than is theoretically possible. In this sense, this approximation will give a worst-case result.

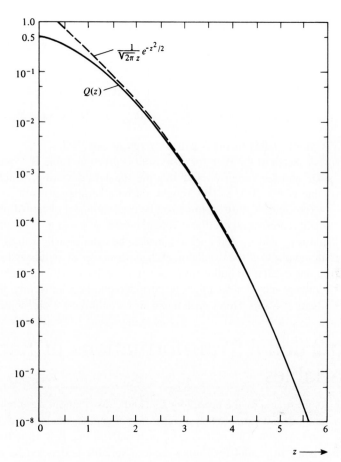

FIGURE B-7 The function $Q(z)$ and an overbound, $\dfrac{1}{\sqrt{2\pi}\,z}e^{-z^2/2}$.

For the case of z negative, $Q(z)$ can be evaluated by using the identity

$$Q(-z) = 1 - Q(z) \tag{B-65}$$

where the Q value for positive z is used (as obtained from Fig. B-7) to compute the Q of the negative value of z.

Sinusoidal Distribution

Theorem

If $x = A \sin \psi$, where ψ has the uniform distribution,

$$f_\psi(\psi) = \begin{cases} \dfrac{1}{2\pi}, & |\psi| \le \pi \\[2mm] 0, & \text{elsewhere} \end{cases} \tag{B-66}$$

then the PDF for the sinusoid is given by

$$
f_x(x) = \begin{cases} 0, & x < -A \\ \dfrac{1}{\pi\sqrt{A^2 - x^2}}, & |x| \le A \\ 0, & x > A \end{cases} \tag{B-67}
$$

A proof of this theorem will be given in Sec. B-8.

A sketch of the PDF for a sinusoid is given in Table B-1, along with equations for the CDF and the variance. Note that the standard deviation, which is equivalent to the rms value is $\sigma = A/\sqrt{2}$. This should *not* be a surprising result.

The sinusoidal distribution can be used to model observed phenomena. For example, x might represent an oscillator voltage where $\psi = \omega_0 t + \theta_0$. Here the frequency of oscillation is f_0, and ω_0 and t are assumed to be deterministic values. θ_0 represents the random startup phase of the oscillator. (When the power of an unsynchronized oscillator is turned on, the oscillation builds up from a noise voltage that is present in the circuit.) In another oscillator model, time might be considered to be a uniformly distributed random variable where $\psi = \omega_0 t$. Here, once again, we would have a sinusoidal distribution for x.

B-8 Functional Transformations of Random Variables

As illustrated by the preceding sinusoidal distribution, we often need to evaluate the PDF for a random variable that is a function of another random variable for which the distribution is known. This is illustrated pictorially in Fig. B-8. Here the input random variable is denoted by x, and the output random variable is denoted by y. Since several PDFs are involved, *subscripts* (such as x in f_x) will be used to indicate with which random variable the PDF is associated. The arguments of the PDFs may change, depending on what substitutions are made, as equations are reduced.

Theorem

If $y = h(x)$, where $h(\cdot)$ is the output-to-input (transfer) characteristic of a device **without memory,**[†] then the PDF of the output is

$$
f_y(y) = \sum_{i=1}^{M} \left. \frac{f_x(x)}{|dy/dx|} \right|_{x = x_i = h_i^{-1}(y)} \tag{B-68}
$$

where $f_x(x)$ is the PDF of the input, x. M is the number of real roots of $y = h(x)$. That is, the inverse of $y = h(x)$ gives $x_1, x_2, \ldots, x_M$ for a single value of y. $|\cdot|$ denotes the absolute value and the single vertical line denotes the evaluation of the quantity at $x = x_i = h_i^{-1}(y)$.

[†] The output-to-input characteristic $h(x)$ should not be confused with the impulse response of a linear network, which was denoted by $h(t)$.

FIGURE B-8 Functional transformation of random variables.

Two examples will now be worked out to demonstrate the application of this theorem, and then the proof will be given.

Example B-5 Sinusoidal Distribution

Let

$$y = h(x) = A \sin x \qquad \text{(B-69)}$$

where x is uniformly distributed over $-\pi$ to $+\pi$, as given by (B-66). This is illustrated in Fig. B-9. For a given value of y, say $-A < y_0 < A$, there are two possible inverse values for x, namely, x_1 and x_2, as shown in the figure. Thus $M = 2$, provided that $|y| < A$. Otherwise, $M = 0$. Evaluating the derivative of (B-69), we obtain

$$\frac{dy}{dx} = A \cos x$$

FIGURE B-9 Evaluation of the PDF of a sinusoid (Example B-5).

and for $0 \le y \le A$,

$$x_1 = \text{Sin}^{-1}\left(\frac{y}{A}\right)$$

and

$$x_2 = \pi - x_1$$

where the uppercase S in $\text{Sin}^{-1}(\cdot)$ denotes the principal angle. A similar result is obtained for $-A \le y \le 0$. Using (B-68), we find that the PDF for y is

$$f_y(y) = \begin{cases} \dfrac{f_x(x_1)}{|A \cos x_1|} + \dfrac{f_x(x_2)}{|A \cos x_2|}, & |y| \le A \\ 0, & y \quad \text{elsewhere} \end{cases} \tag{B-70}$$

The denominators of these two terms are evaluated with the aid of the triangles shown in the insert of Fig. B-9. By using this result and substituting the uniform PDF for $f_x(x)$, (B-70) becomes

$$f_y(y) = \begin{cases} \dfrac{1/2\pi}{|\sqrt{A^2 - y^2}|} + \dfrac{1/2\pi}{|-\sqrt{A^2 - y^2}|}, & |y| \le A \\ 0, & y \quad \text{elsewhere} \end{cases}$$

or

$$f_y(y) = \begin{cases} 0, & y < -A \\ \dfrac{1}{\pi \sqrt{A^2 - y^2}}, & |y| \le A \\ 0, & y > A \end{cases} \tag{B-71}$$

which is the PDF for a sinusoid as given first by (B-67). This result is intuitively obvious since we realize that a sinusoidal waveform spends most of its time near its peak values and passes through zero relatively rapidly. Thus the PDF should peak up at $+A$ and $-A$ volts.

Example B-6   PDF for the Output of a Diode Characteristic

Assume that a diode current–voltage characteristic is modeled by the ideal characteristic shown in Fig. B-10, where y is the current through the diode and x is the voltage across the diode. This type of characteristic is also called *half-wave linear rectification*.

$$y = \begin{cases} Bx, & x > 0 \\ 0, & x \le 0 \end{cases} \tag{B-72}$$

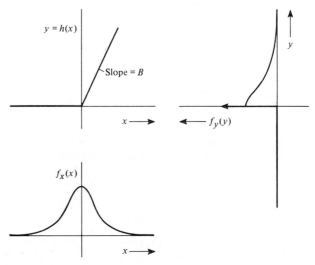

FIGURE B-10 Evaluation of the PDF out of a diode characteristic for Example B-6.

where $B > 0$. For $y > 0$, $M = 1$; and for $y < 0$, $M = 0$. However, if $y = 0$, there are an infinite number of roots for x (i.e., all $x \leq 0$). Consequently, there will be a discrete point at $y = 0$ if the area under $f_x(x)$ is nonzero for $x \leq 0$ (i.e., for the values of x that are mapped into $y = 0$). Using (B-68), we get

$$f_y(y) = \begin{cases} \dfrac{f_x(y/B)}{B}, & y > 0 \\ 0, & y < 0 \end{cases} + P(y = 0)\, \delta(y) \qquad \text{(B-73)}$$

where

$$P(y = 0) = P(x \leq 0) = \int_{-\infty}^{0} f_x(x)\, dx = F_x(0) \qquad \text{(B-74)}$$

Suppose that x has a Gaussian distribution with zero mean; then these equations reduce to

$$f_y(y) = \begin{cases} \dfrac{1}{\sqrt{2\pi}\, B\sigma}\, e^{-y^2/(2B^2\sigma^2)}, & y > 0 \\ 0, & y < 0 \end{cases} + \tfrac{1}{2}\delta(y) \qquad \text{(B-75)}$$

A sketch of this result is shown in Fig. B-10. For $B = 1$, note that the output is the same as the input for x positive (i.e., $y = x > 0$), so that the PDF of the output is the same as the PDF of the input for $y > 0$. For $x < 0$, the values of x are mapped into the point $y = 0$, so that the PDF of y contains a δ function of weight $\tfrac{1}{2}$ at the point $y = 0$.

PROOF OF THEOREM. We will demonstrate that (B-68) is valid by partitioning the x axis into intervals over which $h(x)$ is monotonically increasing, monotonically decreasing, or a constant. As we have seen in Example B-6, when $h(x)$ is a constant over some interval of x, a discrete point at y equal to that constant is possible. In addition, discrete points in the distribution of x will be mapped into discrete points in y even in regions where $h(x)$ is not a constant. ∎

Now we will demonstrate that the theorem, as described by (B-68), is correct by taking the case, for example, where $y = h(x)$ is monotonically decreasing for $x < x_0$ and monotonically increasing for $x > x_0$. This is illustrated in Fig. B-11. The CDF for y is then

$$F_y(y_0) = P(y \le y_0) = P(x_1 \le x \le x_2)$$
$$= P[(x = x_1) + (x_1 < x \le x_2)] \tag{B-76}$$

where the $+$ sign denotes the union operation. Then using (B-4), we get

$$F_y(y_0) = P(x_1) + P(x_1 < x \le x_2)$$

or

$$F_y(y_0) = P(x_1) + F_x(x_2) - F_x(x_1) \tag{B-77}$$

The PDF of y is obtained by taking the derivative of both sides of this equation.

$$\frac{dF_y(y_0)}{dy_0} = \frac{dF_x(x_2)}{dx_2} \frac{dx_2}{dy_0} - \frac{dF_x(x_1)}{dx_1} \frac{dx_1}{dy_0} \tag{B-78}$$

where $dP(x_1)/dy_0 = 0$ was used since $P(x_1)$ is a constant. Because

$$dF_x(x_2)/dx_2 = f_x(x_2) \qquad \text{and} \qquad dF_x(x_1)/dx_1 = f_x(x_1)$$

(B-78) becomes

$$f_y(y_0) = \frac{f_x(x_2)}{dy_0/dx_2} + \frac{f_x(x_1)}{-dy_0/dx_1} \tag{B-79}$$

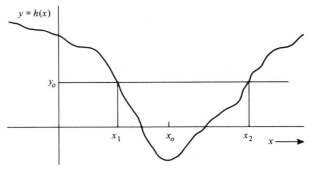

FIGURE B-11 Example of a function $h(x)$ that monotonically decreases for $x < x_0$ and monotonically increases for $x > x_0$.

At the point $x = x_1$, the slope of y is negative because the function is monotonically decreasing for $x < x_0$; thus $dy_0/dx_1 < 0$ and (B-79) becomes

$$f_y(y_0) = \sum_{i=1}^{M=2} \frac{f_x(x)}{|dy_0/dx|}\bigg|_{x=x_i=h_i^{-1}(y_0)} \tag{B-80}$$

When there are more than two intervals during which $h(x)$ is monotonically increasing or decreasing, this procedure may be extended so that (B-68) is obtained.

In concluding this discussion on the functional transformation of a random variable, it should be emphasized that the description of the mapping function $y = h(x)$ assumes that the output y, at any instant, depends on the value of the input x only at that same instant and not on previous (or future) values of x. Thus this technique is applicable to devices that contain no memory (i.e., no inductance or capacitance) elements; however, the device may be nonlinear, as we have seen in the preceding examples.

B-9 Multivariate Statistics

In Sec. B-3 the probabilities of simple events, joint probabilities, and conditional probabilities were defined. In Secs. B-4 and B-5, using the probability of simple events, we developed the concepts of PDFs and CDFs. The PDFs and CDFs involved only one random variable, so these are one-dimensional problems. Similarly, the moments involved only one-dimensional integration.

In this section multiple-dimensional problems, also called *multivariate statistics,* will be developed. These involve PDFs and CDFs that are associated with probabilities of intersecting events and with conditional probabilities. In addition, multiple-dimensional moments will be obtained as an extension of one-dimensional moments that were studied in Sec. B-6. *If the reader clearly understands the one-dimensional case* (developed in the preceding sections), *there will be little difficulty in generalizing those results to the N-dimensional case.*

Multivariate CDFs and PDFs

DEFINITION: The *N-dimensional CDF* is

$$F(a_1, a_2, \ldots, a_N) = P[(x_1 \leq a_1)(x_2 \leq a_2) \cdots (x_N \leq a_N)]$$

$$= \lim_{n \to \infty} \left[\frac{n_{(x_1 \leq a_1)(x_2 \leq a_2) \cdots (x_N \leq a_N)}}{n} \right] \tag{B-81}$$

where the notation $(x_1 \leq a_1)(x_2 \leq a_2) \cdots (x_N \leq a_N)$ is the intersection event consisting of the intersection of the events associated with $x_1 \leq a_1$, $x_2 \leq a_2$, and so on.

DEFINITION: The *N-dimensional PDF* is

$$f(x_1, x_2, \ldots, x_N) = \frac{\partial^N F(a_1, a_2, \ldots, a_N)}{\partial a_1 \partial a_2 \cdots \partial a_N}\bigg|_{\mathbf{a}=\mathbf{x}} \tag{B-82}$$

where **a** and **x** are the row vectors; $\mathbf{a} = (a_1, a_2, \ldots, a_N)$ and $\mathbf{x} = (x_1, x_2, \ldots, x_N)$.

DEFINITION: The expected value of $y = h(\mathbf{x})$ is

$$\overline{[y]} = \overline{h(x_1, x_2, \ldots, x_N)}$$

$$= \int_{-\infty}^{\infty} \int_{-\infty}^{\infty} \cdots \int_{-\infty}^{\infty} h(x_1, x_2, \ldots, x_N)$$

$$\times f(x_1, x_2, \ldots, x_N)\, dx_1\, dx_2 \cdots dx_N \tag{B-83}$$

Some *properties* of N-dimensional random variables are:

1. $f(x_1, x_2, \ldots, x_N) \geq 0$ $\tag{B-84a}$

2. $\displaystyle\int_{-\infty}^{\infty} \int_{-\infty}^{\infty} \cdots \int_{-\infty}^{\infty} f(x_1, x_2, \ldots, x_N)\, dx_1\, dx_2 \cdots dx_N = 1$ $\tag{B-84b}$

3. $F(a_1, a_2, \ldots, a_N)$

$$= \lim_{\substack{\epsilon \to 0 \\ \epsilon > 0}} \int_{-\infty}^{a_1+\epsilon} \int_{-\infty}^{a_2+\epsilon} \cdots \int_{-\infty}^{a_N+\epsilon} f(x_1, x_2, \ldots, x_N)\, dx_1\, dx_2 \cdots dx_N$$

$$\tag{B-84c}$$

4. $F(a_1, a_2, \ldots, a_N) \equiv 0$ if *any* $a_i = -\infty, \quad i = 1, 2, \ldots, N$ $\tag{B-84d}$

5. $F(a_1, a_2, \ldots, a_N) = 1$ when *all* $a_i = +\infty, \quad i = 1, 2, \ldots, N$

$$\tag{B-84e}$$

6. $P[(a_1 < x_1 \leq b_1)(a_2 < x_2 \leq b_2) \cdots (a_N < x_N \leq b_N)]$

$$= \lim_{\substack{\epsilon \to 0 \\ \epsilon > 0}} \int_{a_1+\epsilon}^{b_1+\epsilon} \int_{a_2+\epsilon}^{b_2+\epsilon} \cdots \int_{a_N+\epsilon}^{b_N+\epsilon} f(x_1, x_2, \ldots, x_N)\, dx_1\, dx_2 \cdots dx_N$$

$$\tag{B-84f}$$

The definitions and properties for multivariate PDFs and CDFs are based on the concepts of joint probabilities, as discussed in Sec. B-3. In a similar way, conditional PDFs and CDFs can be obtained [Papoulis, 1984]. Using the property $P(AB) = P(A)P(B|A)$ of (B-8), we find that the joint PDF of x_1 and x_2 is

$$f(x_1, x_2) = f(x_1)f(x_2|x_1) \tag{B-85}$$

where $f(x_2|x_1)$ is the conditional PDF of x_2 given x_1. Generalizing further, we obtain

$$f(x_1, x_2|x_3) = f(x_1|x_3)f(x_2|x_1, x_3) \tag{B-86}$$

Many other expressions for relationships between multiple-dimensional PDFs should also be apparent. When x_1 and x_2 are *independent,* $f(x_2|x_1) = f_{x_2}(x_2)$ and

$$f_{\mathbf{x}}(x_1, x_2) = f_{x_1}(x_1)f_{x_2}(x_2) \tag{B-87}$$

where the subscript x_1 denotes the PDF associated with x_1, and the subscript x_2 denotes the PDF associated with x_2. For N independent random variables this becomes

$$f_{\mathbf{x}}(x_1, x_2, \ldots, x_N) = f_{x_1}(x_1)f_{x_2}(x_2) \cdots f_{x_N}(x_N) \tag{B-88}$$

Theorem

If the Nth-dimensional PDF of x is known, then the Lth-dimensional PDF of x can be obtained when $L < N$ by

$$f(x_1, x_2, \ldots, x_L)$$

$$= \underbrace{\int_{-\infty}^{\infty} \int_{-\infty}^{\infty} \cdots \int_{-\infty}^{\infty}}_{N - L \text{ integrals}} f(x_1, x_2, \ldots, x_N) \, dx_{L+1} \, dx_{L+2} \cdots dx_N \qquad \text{(B-89)}$$

This Lth-dimensional PDF, where $L < N$, is sometimes called the **marginal PDF** since it is obtained from a higher-dimensional (Nth) PDF.

PROOF. First, show that this result is correct if $N = 2$ and $L = 1$.

$$\int_{-\infty}^{\infty} f(x_1, x_2) \, dx_2 = \int_{-\infty}^{\infty} f(x_1) f(x_2 | x_1) \, dx_2$$

$$= f(x_1) \int_{-\infty}^{\infty} f(x_2 | x_1) \, dx_2 = f(x_1) \qquad \text{(B-90)}$$

since the area under $f(x_2 | x_1)$ is unity. This procedure is readily extended to prove the Lth-dimensional case of (B-89). ∎

Bivariate Statistics

Bivariate (or joint) distributions are the $N = 2$ dimensional case. In this section the definitions from the previous section will be used to evaluate two-dimensional moments. Bivariate statistics have some very important applications to electrical engineering problems, and some additional definitions need to be studied.

DEFINITION: The *correlation* (or *joint mean*) of x_1 and x_2 is

$$m_{12} = \overline{x_1 x_2} = \int_{-\infty}^{\infty} \int_{-\infty}^{\infty} x_1 x_2 f(x_1, x_2) \, dx_1 \, dx_2 \qquad \text{(B-91)}$$

DEFINITION: Two random variables x_1 and x_2 are said to be *uncorrelated* if

$$m_{12} = \overline{x_1 x_2} = \overline{x_1} \, \overline{x_2} = m_1 m_2 \qquad \text{(B-92)}$$

If x_1 and x_2 are independent, it follows that they are also uncorrelated, but the converse is not generally true. However, as we will see, the converse is true for bivariate Gaussian random variables.

DEFINITION: Two random variables are said to be *orthogonal* if

$$m_{12} = \overline{x_1 x_2} \equiv 0 \qquad \text{(B-93)}$$

Note the similarity of the definition of orthogonal random variables to that of orthogonal functions given by (2-73).

DEFINITION: The *covariance* is

$$u_{11} = \overline{(x_1 - m_1)(x_2 - m_2)}$$

$$= \int_{-\infty}^{\infty} \int_{-\infty}^{\infty} (x_1 - m_1)(x_2 - m_2) f(x_1, x_2) \, dx_1 \, dx_2 \qquad \text{(B-94)}$$

It should be clear that if x_1 and x_2 are independent, the covariance is zero (and x_1 and x_2 are uncorrelated). The converse is not generally true, but it is true for the case of bivariate Gaussian random variables.

DEFINITION: The *correlation coefficient* is

$$\rho = \frac{u_{11}}{\sigma_1 \sigma_2} = \frac{\overline{(x_1 - m_1)(x_2 - m_2)}}{\sqrt{\overline{(x_1 - m_1)^2}} \, \sqrt{\overline{(x_2 - m_2)^2}}} \qquad \text{(B-95)}$$

This is also called the *normalized covariance.* The correlation coefficient is always within the range

$$-1 \le \rho \le +1 \qquad \text{(B-96)}$$

For example, suppose that $x_1 = x_2$; then $\rho = +1$. If $x_1 = -x_2$, then $\rho = -1$; and if x_1 and x_2 are independent, $\rho = 0$. Thus the correlation coefficient tells us, on the average, how likely a value of x_1 is to being proportional to the value for x_2.

Gaussian Bivariate Distribution

A good example of a joint ($N = 2$) distribution that is of great importance is the bivariate Gaussian distribution. The bivariate Gaussian PDF is

$$f(x_1, x_2) = \frac{1}{2\pi\sigma_1\sigma_2\sqrt{1 - \rho^2}} \, e^{-\frac{1}{2(1 - \rho^2)}\left[\frac{(x_1 - m_1)^2}{\sigma_1^2} - 2\rho\frac{(x_1 - m_1)(x_2 - m_2)}{\sigma_1\sigma_2} + \frac{(x_2 - m_2)^2}{\sigma_2^2}\right]}$$

$$\text{(B-97)}$$

where σ_1^2 is the variance of x_1, σ_2^2 is the variance of x_2, m_1 is the mean of x_1, and m_2 is the mean of x_2. Examining (B-97), we see that if $\rho = 0$, $f(x_1, x_2) = f(x_1)f(x_2)$, where $f(x_1)$ and $f(x_2)$ are the one-dimensional PDFs of x_1 and x_2. Thus if bivariate *Gaussian* random variables are uncorrelated (which implies that $\rho = 0$), they are independent.

A sketch of the bivariate (two-dimensional) Gaussian PDF is shown in Fig. B-12.

Multivariate Functional Transformation

Section B-8 will now be generalized for the multivariate case. Referring to Fig. B-13, we will obtain the PDF for **y**, denoted by $f_y(\mathbf{y})$ in terms of the PDF for **x**, denoted by $f_x(\mathbf{x})$.

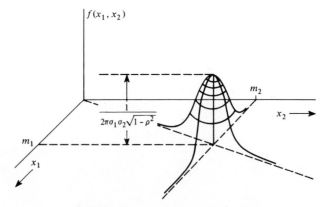

FIGURE B-12 Bivariate Gaussian PDF.

Theorem

Let $\mathbf{y} = \mathbf{h}(\mathbf{x})$ denote the transfer characteristic of a device (no memory) that has N inputs, denoted by $\mathbf{x} = (x_1, x_2, \ldots, x_N)$; N outputs, denoted by $\mathbf{y} = (y_1, y_2, \ldots, y_N)$; and $y_i = h_i(\mathbf{x})$. That is,

$$y_1 = h_1(x_1, x_2, \ldots, x_N)$$

$$y_2 = h_2(x_1, x_2, \ldots, x_N)$$
$$\vdots$$
$$\tag{B-98}$$

$$y_N = h_N(x_1, x_2, \ldots, x_N)$$

Furthermore, let $\mathbf{x}_i$, $i = 1, 2, \ldots, M$, denote the real roots (vectors) of the equation $\mathbf{y} = \mathbf{h}(\mathbf{x})$. The PDF of the output is then

$$f_{\mathbf{y}}(\mathbf{y}) = \sum_{i=1}^{M} \frac{f_{\mathbf{x}}(\mathbf{x})}{|J(\mathbf{y}/\mathbf{x})|}\Bigg|_{\mathbf{x}=\mathbf{x}_i=\mathbf{h}_i^{-1}(\mathbf{y})} \tag{B-99}$$

FIGURE B-13 Multivariate functional transformation of random variables.

where $|\cdot|$ denotes the absolute value operation and $J(\mathbf{y}/\mathbf{x})$ is the Jacobian of the coordinate transformation to $\mathbf{y}$ from $\mathbf{x}$. The Jacobian is

$$J\left(\frac{\mathbf{y}}{\mathbf{x}}\right) = \text{Det} \begin{bmatrix} \dfrac{\partial h_1(\mathbf{x})}{\partial x_1} & \dfrac{\partial h_1(\mathbf{x})}{\partial x_2} & \cdots & \dfrac{\partial h_1(\mathbf{x})}{\partial x_N} \\[2mm] \dfrac{\partial h_2(\mathbf{x})}{\partial x_1} & \dfrac{\partial h_2(\mathbf{x})}{\partial x_2} & \cdots & \dfrac{\partial h_2(\mathbf{x})}{\partial x_N} \\[2mm] \vdots & \vdots & & \vdots \\[2mm] \dfrac{\partial h_N(\mathbf{x})}{\partial x_1} & \dfrac{\partial h_N(\mathbf{x})}{\partial x_2} & \cdots & \dfrac{\partial h_N(\mathbf{x})}{\partial x_N} \end{bmatrix} \tag{B-100}$$

where $\text{Det}[\cdot]$ denotes the determinant of the matrix $[\cdot]$.

A proof of this theorem will not be given, but it should be clear that it is a generalization of the theorem for the one-dimensional case that was studied in Sec. B-8. The coordinate transformation relates differentials in one coordinate system to those in another [Thomas, 1969]:

$$dy_1 \, dy_2 \cdots dy_N = J\left(\frac{\mathbf{y}}{\mathbf{x}}\right) dx_1 \, dx_2 \cdots dx_N \tag{B-101}$$

Example B-7 PDF for the Sum of Two Random Variables

Suppose that we have a circuit configuration (such as an operational amplifier) that sums two inputs, x_1 and x_2, to produce the output

$$y = A(x_1 + x_2) \tag{B-102}$$

where A is the gain of the circuit. Assume that $f(x_1,x_2)$ is known and that we wish to obtain a formula for the PDF of the output in terms of the joint PDF for the inputs.

We can use theorem (B-99) to solve this problem. However, for two inputs we need two outputs in order to satisfy the assumptions of the theorem. This is achieved by defining an auxiliary variable for the output (say, y_2). Thus

$$y_1 = h_1(\mathbf{x}) = A(x_1 + x_2) \tag{B-103}$$

$$y_2 = h_2(\mathbf{x}) = Ax_1 \tag{B-104}$$

The choice of the equation to use for the auxiliary variable, (B-104), is immaterial, provided that it is an independent equation so that the determinant,

$J(\mathbf{y}/\mathbf{x})$, is not zero. However, the equation is usually selected so that the ensuing mathematics will be relatively simple. Using (B-103) and (B-104), we get

$$J = \text{Det} \begin{bmatrix} A & A \\ A & 0 \end{bmatrix} = -A^2 \qquad (B\text{-}105)$$

Substituting this into (B-99) yields

$$f_\mathbf{y}(y_1, y_2) = \frac{f_\mathbf{x}(x_1, x_2)}{|-A^2|} \Bigg|_{\mathbf{x} = h^{-1}(\mathbf{y})}$$

or

$$f_\mathbf{y}(y_1, y_2) = \frac{1}{A^2} f_\mathbf{x}\left(\frac{y_2}{A}, \frac{1}{A}(y_1 - y_2)\right) \qquad (B\text{-}106)$$

We want to find a formula for $f_{y_1}(y_1)$ since $y_1 = A(x_1 + x_2)$. This is obtained by evaluating the marginal PDF from (B-106).

$$f_{y_1}(y_1) = \int_{-\infty}^{\infty} f_\mathbf{y}(y_1, y_2)\, dy_2$$

or

$$f_{y_1}(y_1) = \frac{1}{A^2} \int_{-\infty}^{\infty} f_\mathbf{x}\left(\frac{y_2}{A}, \frac{1}{A}(y_1 - y_2)\right) dy_2 \qquad (B\text{-}107)$$

This general result relates the PDF of $y = y_1$ to the joint PDF of $\mathbf{x}$ where $y = A(x_1 + x_2)$. If x_1 and x_2 are *independent* and $A = 1$, (B-107) becomes

$$f(y) = \int_{-\infty}^{\infty} f_{x_1}(\lambda) f_{x_2}(y - \lambda)\, d\lambda$$

or

$$f(y) = f_{x_1}(y) * f_{x_2}(y) \qquad (B\text{-}108)$$

where $*$ denotes the convolution operation. Similarly, if we sum N independent random variables, the PDF for the sum is the $(N - 1)$-fold convolution of the one-dimensional PDFs for the N random variables.

Central Limit Theorem

If we have the sum of a number of independent random variables with arbitrary one-dimensional PDFs, the *central limit theorem* states that the PDF for the sum of these independent random variables approaches a Gaussian (normal) distribution under very general conditions. Strictly speaking, the central limit theorem does not hold for the PDF if the independent random variables are discretely distributed. In this case the PDF for the sum will consist of delta functions (not Gaussian, which is continuous); however, if the delta functions are "smeared out" (e.g., replace the delta functions with rectangles that have corresponding areas), the resulting PDF will be approximately Gaussian. Regardless, the CDF for the sum will approach that of a Gaussian CDF.

Example B-8   PDF for the Sum of Three Independent, Uniformly Distributed Random Variables

The central limit theorem will be illustrated by evaluating the exact PDF for the sum of three independent, uniformly distributed random variables. This exact result will be compared with the Gaussian PDF, as predicted by the central limit theorem.

Let each of the independent random variables x_i have a uniform distribution, as shown in Fig. B-14a. The PDF for $y_1 = x_1 + x_2$, denoted by $f(y_1)$, is obtained by the convolution operation described by (B-108) and Fig. 2-7. This result is shown in Fig. B-14b. It is seen that after only one convolution operation the PDF for the sum (which is a triangle) is going toward the Gaussian shape. The PDF for $y_2 = x_1 + x_2 + x_3$, $f(y_2)$, is obtained by convolving the triangular PDF with another uniform PDF. The result is

$$f(y_2) = \begin{cases} 0, & y_2 \leq -\frac{3}{2}A \\[2mm] \dfrac{1}{2A^3}\left(\dfrac{3}{2}A + y_2\right)^2, & -\frac{3}{2}A \leq y_2 \leq -\frac{1}{2}A \\[2mm] \dfrac{1}{2A^3}\left(\dfrac{3}{2}A^2 - 2y_2^2\right), & |y_2| \leq \frac{1}{2}A \\[2mm] \dfrac{1}{2A^3}\left(\dfrac{3}{2}A - y_2\right)^2, & \frac{1}{2}A \leq y_2 \leq \frac{3}{2}A \\[2mm] 0, & y_2 \geq \frac{3}{2}A \end{cases} \qquad \text{(B-109)}$$

This curve is plotted by the solid line in Fig. B-14c. For comparison purposes, a matching Gaussian curve, with $1/(\sqrt{2\pi}\,\sigma) = 3/(4A)$, is also shown by the dashed line. It is seen that $f(y_2)$ is very close to the Gaussian curve for $|y_2| < \frac{3}{2}A$, as predicted by the central limit theorem. Of course, $f(y_2)$ is certainly not Gaussian for $|y_2| > \frac{3}{2}A$ because $f(y_2) \equiv 0$ in this region, whereas the Gaussian curve is not zero except at $y = \pm\infty$. Thus we observe that the Gaussian approximation (as predicted by the central limit theorem) is not very good on the *tails* of the distribution. However, if the area under the distribution is needed near the mean value, the Gaussian approximation may be very good.

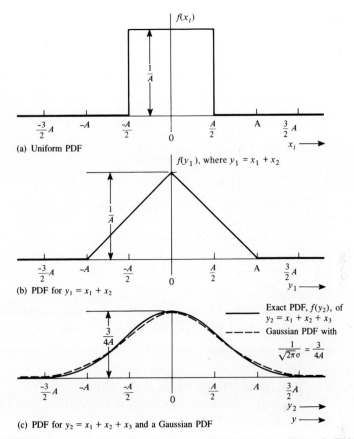

(a) Uniform PDF

(b) PDF for $y_1 = x_1 + x_2$

(c) PDF for $y_2 = x_1 + x_2 + x_3$ and a Gaussian PDF

FIGURE B-14 Demonstration of the central limit theorem (Example B-8).

PROBLEMS

B-1 A long binary message contains 1428 binary 1's and 2668 binary 0's. What is the probability of obtaining a binary 1 in any received bit?

B-2 (a) Find the probability of getting an 8 in the toss of two dice.
(b) Find the probability of getting either a 5, 7, or 8 in the toss of two dice.

B-3 Show that
$$P(A + B + C) = P(A) + P(B) + P(C)$$
$$- P(AB) - P(AC) - P(BC) + P(ABC)$$

B-4 A die is tossed. The probability of getting any face is $P(x) = \frac{1}{6}$, where $x = k = 1, 2, 3, 4, 5,$ or 6.

(a) Find the probability of getting an odd-numbered face.
(b) Find the probability of getting a 4 when an even-numbered face is obtained on a toss.

B-5 Which of the following functions satisfy the properties for a PDF. Why?

(a) $f(x) = \dfrac{1}{\pi}\left(\dfrac{1}{1 + x^2}\right)$

(b) $f(x) = \begin{cases} |x|, & |x| < 1 \\ 0, & x \text{ otherwise} \end{cases}$

(c) $f(x) = \begin{cases} \frac{1}{6}(8 - x), & 4 \le x \le 10 \\ 0, & x \text{ otherwise} \end{cases}$

(d) $f(x) = \displaystyle\sum_{k=0}^{\infty} \frac{3}{4}(\frac{1}{4})^k\, \delta(x - k)$

B-6 Show that all cumulative distribution functions must satisfy the properties given in Sec. B-5.

B-7 Let $f(x) = Ke^{-b|x|}$, where K and b are positive constants. Find the mathematical expression for the CDF and sketch the results.

B-8 Find the probability that $-\frac{1}{4}A \le y_1 \le \frac{1}{4}A$ for the triangular distribution shown in Fig. B-14b.

B-9 A triangular PDF is shown in Fig. B-14b.
(a) Find a mathematical expression that describes the CDF.
(b) Sketch the CDF.

B-10 Evaluate the PDFs for the two waveforms shown in Fig. PB-10.

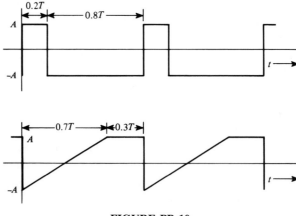

FIGURE PB-10

B-11 Let a PDF be given by $f(x) = Ke^{-bx}$ for $x \geq 0$ and zero for x negative where K and b are positive constants.

(a) Find the value required for K in terms of b.

(b) Find m in terms of b.

(c) Find σ^2 in terms of b.

B-12 A random variable x has a PDF

$$f(x) = \begin{cases} \frac{3}{32}(-x^2 + 8x - 12), & 2 < x < 6 \\ 0, & x \text{ elsewhere} \end{cases}$$

(a) Demonstrate that $f(x)$ is a valid PDF.

(b) Find the mean.

(c) Find the second moment.

(d) Find the variance.

B-13 Determine the standard deviation for the triangular distribution shown in Fig. B-14b.

B-14 (a) Find the terms in a binomial distribution for $n = 7$, where $p = 0.5$.

(b) Sketch the PDF for this binomial distribution.

(c) Find and sketch the CDF for this distribution.

(d) Find x^3 for this distribution.

B-15 For a binomial distribution, show that $\sigma^2 = np(1 - p)$.

B-16 A binomial random variable x_k has values of k where

$$k = 0, 1, \ldots, n; \qquad P(k) = \binom{n}{k}p^k q^{n-k}; \qquad q = 1 - p$$

Assume that $n = 160$ and $p = 0.1$.

(a) Plot $P(k)$.

(b) Compare the plot of part (a) with a plot $P(k)$ using the Gaussian approximation

$$\binom{n}{k}p^k q^{n-k} \approx \frac{1}{\sqrt{2\pi}\,\sigma}e^{-(k-m)^2/2\sigma^2}$$

which is valid when $npq \gg 1$ and $|k - np|$ is in the neighborhood of $\sqrt{npq}$ where $\sigma = \sqrt{npq}$ and $m = np$.

(c) Also plot the Poisson approximation

$$\binom{n}{k}p^k q^{n-k} \approx \frac{\lambda^k}{k!}e^{-\lambda}$$

where $\lambda = np$, n is large, and p is small.

B-17 An order of $n = 3000$ transistors is received. The probability that each transistor is defective is $p = 0.001$. What is the probability that the number of defective transistors in the batch is 6 or less? (*Note:* The Poisson approximation is valid when n is large and p is small.)

B-18 In a fiber optic communication system, photons are emitted with a Poisson distribution as described in Table B-1. $m = \lambda$ is the average number of photons emitted in

an arbitrary time interval, and $P(k)$ is the probability of k photons being emitted in the same interval.
(a) Plot the PDF for $\lambda = 0.5$.
(b) Plot the CDF for $\lambda = 0.5$.
(c) Show that $m = \lambda$.
(d) Show that $\sigma = \sqrt{\lambda}$.

B-19 Let x be a random variable that has a Laplacian distribution. The Laplacian PDF is $f(x) = (1/2b)e^{-|x-m|/b}$, where b and m are real constants and $b > 0$.
(a) Find the mean of x in terms of b and m.
(b) Find the variance of x in terms of b and m.

B-20 Given the Gaussian PDF

$$f(x) = \frac{1}{\sqrt{2\pi}\beta} e^{-(x-m)^2/(2\beta^2)}$$

show that the variance of this distribution is β^2.

B-21 In a manufacturing process for resistors, the values obtained for the resistors have a Gaussian distribution where the desired value is the mean value. If we want 95% of the manufactured 1-kΩ resistors to have a tolerance of $\pm 10\%$, what is the required value for σ?

B-22 Assume that x has a Gaussian distribution. Find the probability that:
(a) $|x - m| < \sigma$.
(b) $|x - m| < 2\sigma$.
(c) $|x - m| < 3\sigma$.
Obtain numerical results by using tables if necessary.

B-23 Show that:
(a) $Q(z) = \frac{1}{2} \text{erfc}\left(\frac{z}{\sqrt{2}}\right)$.
(b) $Q(-z) = 1 - Q(z)$.
(c) $Q(z) = \frac{1}{2}\left[1 - \text{erf}\left(\frac{z}{\sqrt{2}}\right)\right]$.

B-24 For a Gaussian distribution, show that:
(a) $F(a) = \frac{1}{2} \text{erfc}\left(\frac{m - a}{\sqrt{2}\sigma}\right)$.
(b) $F(a) = \frac{1}{2}\left[1 + \text{erf}\left(\frac{a - m}{\sqrt{2}\sigma}\right)\right]$.

B-25 A noise voltage has a Gaussian distribution. The rms value is 5 V and the dc value is 1.0 V. Find the probability of the voltage having values between -5 and $+5$ V.

B-26 Suppose that x is a Gaussian random variable with $m = 5$ and $\sigma = 0.6$.
(a) Find the probability that $x \leq 1$.
(b) Find the probability that $x \leq 6$.

B-27 The Gaussian random variable x has a zero mean and a variance of 2. Let A be the event such that $|x| < 3$.
(a) Find an expression for the conditional PDF $f(x|A)$.
(b) Plot $f(x|A)$ over the range $|x| < 5$.
(c) Plot $f(x)$ over the range $|x| < 5$ and compare these two plots.

B-28 Let x have a sinusoidal distribution with a PDF as given by (B-67). Show that the CDF is

$$F(a) = \begin{cases} 0, & a \le -A \\ \dfrac{1}{\pi}\left[\dfrac{\pi}{2} + \sin^{-1}\left(\dfrac{a}{A}\right)\right], & |a| \le A \\ 1, & a \ge A \end{cases}$$

B-29 (a) If x has a sinusoidal distribution with the peak value of x being A, show that the rms value is $\sigma = A/\sqrt{2}$. [*Hint:* Use (B-67).]
(b) If $x = A \cos \psi$, where ψ is uniformly distributed between $-\pi$ and $+\pi$, show that the rms value of x is $\sigma = A/\sqrt{2}$.

B-30 Given that $y = x^2$ and x is a Gaussian random variable with mean value m and variance σ^2, find a formula for the PDF of y in terms of m and σ^2.

B-31 x is a uniformly distributed random variable over the range $-1 \le x \le 1$ plus a discrete point at $x = \frac{1}{2}$ with $P(x = \frac{1}{2}) = \frac{1}{4}$.
(a) Find a mathematical expression for the PDF for x and plot your result.
(b) Find the PDF for y where

$$y = \begin{cases} x^2, & x \ge 0 \\ 0, & x < 0 \end{cases}$$

Sketch your result.

B-32 A saturating amplifier is modeled by

$$y = \begin{cases} Ax_0, & x > x_0 \\ Ax, & |x| \le x_0 \\ -Ax_0, & x < -x_0 \end{cases}$$

Assume that x is a Gaussian random variable with mean value m and variance σ^2. Find a formula for the PDF of y in terms of A, x_0, m, and σ^2.

B-33 A sinusoid with a peak value of 8 V is applied to the input of a quantizer. The quantizer characteristic is shown in Fig. 4-8a. Calculate and plot the PDF for the output.

B-34 A voltage waveform that has a Gaussian distribution is applied to the input of a full-wave rectifier circuit. The full-wave rectifier is described by $y(t) = |x(t)|$ where $x(t)$ is the input and $y(t)$ is the output. The input waveform has a dc value of 1 V and an rms value of 2 V.
(a) Plot the PDF for the input waveform.
(b) Plot the PDF for the output waveform.

B-35 Refer to Example B-6 and (B-75), which describe the PDF for the output of an ideal diode (half-wave rectifier) characteristic. Find the mean (dc) value of the output.

B-36 Given the joint density function,

$$f(x_1,x_2) = \begin{cases} e^{-(1/2)(4x_1+x_2)}, & x_1 \geq 0, x_2 \geq 0 \\ 0, & \text{otherwise} \end{cases}$$

(a) Verify that $f(x_1,x_2)$ is a density function.
(b) Show that x_1 and x_2 are either independent or dependent.
(c) Evaluate $P(1 \leq x_1 \leq 2, x_2 \leq 4)$.
(d) Find ρ.

B-37 A joint density function is

$$f(x_1,x_2) = \begin{cases} K(x_1 + x_1x_2), & 0 \leq x_1 \leq 1, \quad 0 \leq x_2 \leq 4 \\ 0, & \text{elsewhere} \end{cases}$$

(a) Find K.
(b) Determine if x_1 and x_2 are independent.
(c) Find $F_{x_1x_2}(0.5,2)$.
(d) Find $f_{x_2|x_1}(x_2|x_1)$.

B-38 Let $y = x_1 + x_2$ where x_1 and x_2 are uncorrelated random variables. Show that:
(a) $\bar{y} = m_1 + m_2$, where $m_1 = \overline{x_1}$ and $m_2 = \overline{x_2}$.
(b) $\sigma_y^2 = \sigma_1^2 + \sigma_2^2$, where $\sigma_1^2 = \overline{(x_1 - m_1)^2}$ and $\sigma_2^2 = \overline{(x_2 - m_2)^2}$.
[*Hint:* Use the ensemble operator notation similar to that used in the proof for (B-29).]

B-39 Let $x_1 = \cos\theta$ and $x_2 = \sin\theta$, where θ is uniformly distributed over $(0,2\pi)$. Show that:
(a) x_1 and x_2 are uncorrelated.
(b) x_1 and x_2 are not independent.

B-40 Two random variables x_1 and x_2 are jointly Gaussian. The joint PDF is described by (B-97) where $m_1 = m_2 = 0$, $\sigma_{x_1} = \sigma_{x_2} = 1$ and $\rho = 0.5$. Plot $f(x_1,x_2)$ for x_1 over the range $|x_1| < 5$ and $x_2 = 0$. Also give plots for $f(x_1,x_2)$ for $|x_1| < 5$ and $x_2 = 0.4$, 0.8, 1.2, and 1.6.

B-41 Show that the marginal PDF of a bivariate Gaussian PDF is a one-dimensional Gaussian PDF. That is, evaluate

$$f(x_1) = \int_{-\infty}^{\infty} f(x_1,x_2)\,dx_2$$

where $f(x_1,x_2)$ is given by (B-97). [*Hint:* Factor some terms outside the integral containing x_1 (but not x_2). Complete the square on the exponent of the remaining integrand so that a Gaussian PDF form is obtained. Use the property that the integral of a properly normalized Gaussian PDF is unity.]

B-42 (a) $y = A_1x_1 + A_2x_2$, where A_1 and A_2 are constants and the joint PDF of x_1 and x_2 is $f_x(x_1,x_2)$. Find a formula for the PDF of y in terms of the (joint) PDF of $\mathbf{x}$.
(b) If x_1 and x_2 are independent, how can this formula be simplified?

B-43 Two independent random variables x and y have the PDFs $f(x) = 5e^{-5x} u(x)$ and $f(y) = 2e^{-2y} u(y)$. Plot the PDF for w where $w = x + y$.

B-44 Two Gaussian random variables x_1 and x_2 have a mean vector $\mathbf{m}_x$ and a covariance matrix $\mathbf{C}_x$ as shown. Two new random variables y_1 and y_2 are formed by the linear transformation $\mathbf{y} = \mathbf{Tx}$.

$$\mathbf{m}_x = \begin{bmatrix} 2 \\ -1 \end{bmatrix} \qquad \mathbf{C}_x = \begin{bmatrix} 5 & -2/\sqrt{5} \\ -2/\sqrt{5} & 4 \end{bmatrix} \qquad \mathbf{T} = \begin{bmatrix} 1 & 1/2 \\ 1/2 & 1 \end{bmatrix}$$

(a) Find the mean vector for $\mathbf{y}$, which is denoted by $\mathbf{m}_y$.
(b) Find the covariance matrix for $\mathbf{y}$, which is denoted by $\mathbf{C}_y$.
(c) Find the correlation coefficient for y_1 and y_2. *Hint:* See Sec. 6-6 of [Couch, 1993].

B-45 Three Gaussian random variables x_1, x_2, and x_3 have zero mean values. Three new random variables y_1, y_2, and y_3 are formed by the linear transformation $\mathbf{y} = \mathbf{Tx}$, where

$$\mathbf{C}_x = \begin{bmatrix} 6.0 & 2.3 & 1.5 \\ 2.3 & 6.0 & 2.3 \\ 1.5 & 2.3 & 6.0 \end{bmatrix} \qquad \mathbf{T} = \begin{bmatrix} 5 & 2 & -1 \\ -1 & 3 & 1 \\ 2 & -1 & 2 \end{bmatrix}$$

(a) Find the covariance matrix for $\mathbf{y}$, which is denoted by $\mathbf{C}_y$.
(b) Write an expression for the PDF $f(y_1, y_2, y_3)$. *Hint:* See Sec. 6-6 of [Couch, 1993].

B-46 (a) Find a formula for the PDF of $y = Ax_1x_2$ where x_1 and x_2 are random variables having the joint PDF $f_\mathbf{x}(x_1, x_2)$.
(b) If x_1 and x_2 are independent, reduce the formula obtained in part (a) to a simpler result.

B-47 $y_2 = x_1 + x_2 + x_3$, where x_1, x_2, and x_3 are independent random variables. Each of the x_i has a one-dimensional PDF that is uniformly distributed over $-(A/2) \le x_i \le (A/2)$. Show that the PDF of y_2 is given by (B-109).

B-48 Use the built-in random number generator of MathCAD or MATLAB to demonstrate the central limit theorem. That is:
(a) Compute samples of the random variable y where $y = \Sigma \, x_i$ and the x_i values are obtained from the random number generator.
(b) Plot the PDF for y by using the histogram function.

Standards and Terminology for Computer Communications

C-1 Codes

Morse Code

Although the Morse code is not used in computer communications, it is listed here because a form of this code was used in the first electrical digital communication. The first electrical communication system was the telegraph, which was patented in 1840 by Samuel F. B. Morse. Table C-1 lists the International Morse Code that is used today. The timing is such that the length of the dash is three dot units. Spaces between parts of a character are equal to one dot unit, spaces between characters are three dot units, and the space between words is five dot units.

TABLE C-1 International Morse Code

A	·—	N	—·	1	·— — — —
B	—···	O	— — —	2	··— — —
C	—·—·	P	·— —·	3	···— —
D	—··	Q	— —·—	4	····—
E	·	R	·—·	5	·····
F	··—·	S	···	6	—····
G	— —·	T	—	7	— —···
H	····	U	··—	8	— — —··
I	··	V	···—	9	— — — —·
J	·— — —	W	·— —	0	— — — — —
K	—·—	X	—··—		
L	·—··	Y	—·— —		
M	— —	Z	— —··		

Period (.)	·—·—·—	Wait sign (AS)	·—···
Comma (,)	— —··— —	Double dash (break)	—···—
Interrogation (?)	··— —··	Error sign	········
Quotation mark ('')	·—··—·	Fraction bar (/)	—··—·
Colon (:)	— — —···	End of message (AR)	·—·—·
Semicolon (;)	—·—·—·	End of transmission (SK)	···—·—
Parentheses ( )	—·— —·—	International distress signal (SOS)	···— — —···

TABLE C-2 Punched Card Code

Character	Row Numbers Punched			Character	Row Numbers Punched			Character	Row Numbers Punched		
0	0			a	12	0	1	%	0	4	8
1	1			b	12	0	2	@	4	8	
2	2			c	12	0	3	#	3	8	
3	3			d	12	0	4	¢	12	2	8
4	4			e	12	0	5	<	12	4	8
5	5			f	12	0	6	(	12	5	8
6	6			g	12	0	7	†	12	6	8
7	7			h	12	0	8	|	12	7	8
8	8			i	12	0	9	!	11	2	8
9	9			j	12	11	1	)	11	5	8
A	12	1		k	12	11	2	;	11	6	8
B	12	2		l	12	11	3	¬	11	7	8
C	12	3		m	12	11	4	_	0	5	8
D	12	4		n	12	11	5	>	0	6	8
E	12	5		o	12	11	6	?	0	7	8
F	12	6		p	12	11	7	:	2	8	
G	12	7		q	12	11	8	'	5	8	
H	12	8		r	12	11	9	=	6	8	
I	12	9		s	11	0	2	¨	7	8	
J	11	1		t	11	0	3	[	12	8	2
K	11	2		u	11	0	4	\	0	8	2
L	11	3		v	11	0	5	]	11	8	2
M	11	4		w	11	0	6	\	1	8	
N	11	5		x	11	0	7	{	12	0	
O	11	6		y	11	0	8	}	11	0	
P	11	7		z	11	0	9	~	11	0	1
Q	11	8		.	12	3	8				
R	11	9		□	12	4	8				
S	0	2		&	12						
T	0	3		space	BLANK						
U	0	4		$	11	3	8				
V	0	5		*	11	4	8				
W	0	6		-	11						
X	0	7		/	0	1					
Y	0	8		,	0	3					
Z	0	9									

Punched Card

Historically, the punched card was used to enter data into mainframe computers, but today data are entered from video display terminals (VDT). The size of a standard IBM card is 3.75 in. × 7.375 in. × 0.0067 in. In the usual format it has 12 rows and 80 columns, for a total of 960 hole positions. Each column designates a single character that is defined by one, two, or three punched holes in the 12 possible positions. The punched card code is given in Table C-2.

Baudot

In 1875, Emile Baudot developed a ''multiplex telegraph'' system. The Baudot code has evolved into what is now known as the *International Telegraph Alphabet (ITA) Number 2*. This Baudot code is given in Table C-3. The Baudot code is used for teleprinter service. It is used today for wire press and radio teletype press service, although it is being replaced by the ASCII code.

The Baudot code has two serious disadvantages: (1) it has no provisions for parity bits, and (2) it is a *sequential* code. That is, the Letters (down-shift) control character is sent to place the printer in the letter printing mode, and the Figure (up-shift) control character is used to shift the printer into the figures printing mode. If an error causes a control character to be received that shifts the printer into a false mode, the printer will print a wrong string of characters until a proper control-shift character is received.

EBCDIC

The Extended Binary-Coded Decimal Interchange Code (EBCDIC) was developed in 1962 and contains 8 bits with no parity. The EBCDIC code is given in Table C-4. It is used extensively in IBM mainframe computer systems.

TABLE C-3 Baudot Code[a]

Character Case		Bit Pattern					Character Case		Bit Pattern				
Lower	Upper	5	4	3	2	1	Lower	Upper	5	4	3	2	1
A	-	0	0	0	1	1	Q	1	1	0	1	1	1
B	?	1	1	0	0	1	R	4	0	1	0	1	0
C	:	0	1	1	1	0	S	'	0	0	1	0	1
D	$	0	1	0	0	1	T	5	1	0	0	0	0
E	3	0	0	0	0	1	U	7	0	0	1	1	1
F	!	0	1	1	0	1	V	;	1	1	1	1	0
G	&	1	1	0	1	0	W	2	1	0	0	1	1
H	#	1	0	1	0	0	X	/	1	1	1	0	1
I	8	0	0	1	1	0	Y	6	1	0	1	0	1
J	Bell	0	1	0	1	1	Z	''	1	0	0	0	1
K	(	0	1	1	1	1	Letters (shift) ↓		1	1	1	1	1
L	)	1	0	0	1	0	Figures (shift) ↑		1	1	0	1	1
M	.	1	1	1	0	0	Space (SP)		0	0	1	0	0
N	,	0	1	1	0	0	Carriage return		0	1	0	0	0
O	9	1	1	0	0	0	Line feed		0	0	0	1	0
P	0	1	0	1	1	0	Blank		0	0	0	0	0

[a] 1 = mark = punch hole and 0 = space = no punch hole for paper tape.

TABLE C-4 EBCDIC Code[a]

Bit Position 8 7 6 5 \ 4 3 2 1	0000	0001	0010	0011	0100	0101	0110	0111	1000	1001	1010	1011	1100	1101	1110	1111
0000	NUL	SOH	STX	ETX	PF	HT	LC	DEL			SMM	VT	FF	CR	SO	SI
0001	DLE	DC1	DC2	DC3	RES	NL	BS	IL	CAN	EM	CC		IFS	IGS	IRS	IUS
0010	DS	SOS	FS	SYN	BYP	LF	EOB	PRE			SM			ENQ	ACK	BEL
0011					PN	RS	UC	EOT					DC4	NAK		SUB
0100	SP										¢	.	<	(	+	`|`
0101	&										!	$	*	)	;	¬
0110	-	/									`¦`	,	%	_	>	?
0111											:	#	@	'	=	"
1000		a	b	c	d	e	f	g	h	i						
1001		j	k	l	m	n	o	p	q	r						
1010			s	t	u	v	w	x	y	z						
1011																
1100		A	B	C	D	E	F	G	H	I						
1101		J	K	L	M	N	O	P	Q	R						
1110			S	T	U	V	W	X	Y	Z						
1111	0	1	2	3	4	5	6	7	8	9						□

[a]
ACK Acknowledge
BEL Bell, or alarm
BS Backspace
BYP Bypass
CAN Cancel
CC Unit backspace (word processing)
CR Carriage return
DC1 Device control 1
DC2 Device control 2
DC3 Device control 3

DC4 Device control 4
DEL Delete
DLE Data link escape
DS Digit select
EM End of medium
ENQ Enquiry
EOB End of block
EOT End of transmission
ETX End of text
FF Form feed
FS File separator

HT Horizontal tab
IFS Interchange file separator
IGS Interchange group separator
IL Idle
IRS Interchange record separator
IUS Interchange unit separator
LC Lowercase
LF Line feed (printer to next line)
NAK Negative acknowledge
NL New line (LF plus CR)

NUL Null, or all zeros
PF Punch off
PN Punch on
PRE Prefix
RES Restore
RS Record separator (or reader stop)
SI Shift in
SM Start message
SMM Repeat
SO Shift out

SOH Start of heading
SOS Start of significance
SP Space
STX Start of text
SUB Substitute
SYN Synchronous idle
UC Uppercase
VT Vertical tab

TABLE C-5 ASCII Code[a]

| Bit Position | | | | 7 0 | 0 | 0 | 0 | 1 | 1 | 1 | 1 |
| | | | | 6 0 | 0 | 1 | 1 | 0 | 0 | 1 | 1 |
4	3	2	1	5 0	1	0	1	0	1	0	1
0	0	0	0	NUL	DLE	SP	0	@	P	\	p
0	0	0	1	SOH	DC1	!	1	A	Q	a	q
0	0	1	0	STX	DC2	"	2	B	R	b	r
0	0	1	1	ETX	DC3	#	3	C	S	c	s
0	1	0	0	EOT	DC4	$	4	D	T	d	t
0	1	0	1	ENQ	NAK	%	5	E	U	e	u
0	1	1	0	ACK	SYN	&	6	F	V	f	v
0	1	1	1	BEL	ETB	'	7	G	W	g	w
1	0	0	0	BS	CAN	(	8	H	X	h	x
1	0	0	1	HT	EM	)	9	I	Y	i	y
1	0	1	0	LF	SUB	*	:	J	Z	j	z
1	0	1	1	VT	ESC	+	;	K	[	k	{
1	1	0	0	FF	FS	,	<	L	\	l	:
1	1	0	1	CR	GS	–	=	M	]	m	}
1	1	1	0	SO	RS	.	>	N	∧	n	~
1	1	1	1	SI	US	/	?	O	—	o	DEL

[a]

ACK	Acknowledge	ENQ	Enquiry	NUL	Null, or all zeros
BEL	Bell, or alarm	EOT	End of transmission	RS	Record separator
BS	Backspace	ESC	Escape	SI	Shift in
CAN	Cancel	ETB	End of transmission block	SO	Shift out
CR	Carriage return	ETX	End of text	SOH	Start of heading
DC1	Device control 1	FF	Form feed	SP	Space
DC2	Device control 2	FS	File separator	STX	Start of text
DC3	Device control 3	GS	Group separator	SUB	Substitute
DC4	Device control 4	HT	Horizontal tab	SYN	Synchronous idle
DEL	Delete	LF	Line feed	US	Unit separator
DLE	Data link escape	NAK	Negative acknowledge	VT	Vertical tab
EM	End of medium				

ASCII

The American National Standard Code for Information Interchange (ASCII) was first adopted in 1963 and updated in 1967. It was the first code specifically developed for computer communication systems. It is now the most popular code used by computer terminals. The code is shown in Table C-5. It has a total of 8 bits per character. Seven bits are completely specified as shown. The eighth bit is a parity bit that may be even or odd parity, depending on the choice selected for use in a particular installation.

C-2 DTE/DCE and Ethernet Interface Standards

A general block diagram for a computer communication system is shown in Fig. C-1. To facilitate the use of equipment supplied by different vendors, interface standards have

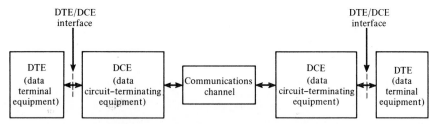

FIGURE C-1 Computer communication system.

been adopted for connection of data terminal equipment (DTE) and data communications equipment (DCE). The DTE may be a digital computer, a printer, a keyboard, and so on, and the DCE may be a modem. In addition, one type of DTE, say a printer, may be connected to another type of DTE, say a keyboard, by the same type of interface.

Numerous organizations are concerned with advancement of practical standards. Internationally, the International Telegraph and Telephone Consultative Committee (CCITT) and the International Organization for Standardization (ISO) are the best known.

In the United States, as well as internationally, four standards groups are the American National Standards Institute (ANSI), the Electronics Industries Association (EIA), the Institute of Electrical and Electronics Engineers (IEEE), and the National Communications System (NCS) of the federal government.

DTE/DCE standards are developed in terms of the following:

- The physical and electrical interface.
- The link control (software) interface that provides framing/synchronization and error detection/error correction functions.

Now several physical/electronic standards will be described.

Current Loop

Since early in the twentieth century, when mechanical teleprinter systems were developed, the current loop has been a popular interface for transmission of asynchronous serial data (see Fig. C-2). During the idle condition, the dc current in the local (interface) loop is specified to be some design value. In most teleprinters designed for computer terminal

FIGURE C-2 20-mA current (local) loop interface.

TABLE C-6 EIA RS-232C, RS-422A, RS-449, and RS-530 Interface Standards[a]

RS-449/422					RS-530			
9 Pin Aux.	37 Pin A	B	RS-449 Circuit	RS-449 Description	25 Pin A	B	RS-530 Circuit	RS-530 Description
1	1			Shield	1			Shield
5	19		SG	Signal ground	7		AB	Signal ground
9	37		SC	Send common				
6	20		RC	Receive common				
	4	22	SD	Send data	2	14	BA	Transmitted data
	6	24	RD	Receive data	3	16	BB	Receive data
	7	25	RS	Request to send	4	19	CA	Request to send
	9	27	CS	Clear to send	5		CB	Clear to send
	11	29	DM	Data mode	6	22	CC	DCE ready
	12	30	TR	Terminal ready	20	23	CD	DTE ready
	15		IC	Incoming call				
	13	31	RR	Receiver ready	8	10	CF	Receive line detector
	33		SQ	Signal quality				
	16		SR	Signaling rate selector				
	2		SI	Signaling rate indicator				
	17	35	TT	Terminal timing	24	11	DA	Transmitter timing (DTE)
	5	23	ST	Send timing	15	12	DB	Transmitter timing (DCE)
	8	26	RT	Receive timing	17	9	DD	Receiver timing (DCE)
3			SSD	Secondary send data			BA	Transmitted data
4			SRD	Secondary receive data			BB	Receive data
7			SRS	Secondary request to send				
8			SCS	Secondary clear to send		13	CB	Clear to send
2			SRR	Secondary receiver ready			DB	Transmit timing (DCE)
	10		LL	Local loopback	18		LL	Local loopback
	14		RL	Remote loopback	21		RL	Remote loopback
	18		TM	Test mode	25		TM	Test mode
	32		SS	Select standby				
	36		SB	Standby indicator				
	16		SF	Select frequency				
	28		IS	Terminal in service				
	34		NS	New signal				

SOURCE: Black Box Corporation, Pittsburgh, PA. © Black Box Corporation, 1993. All rights reserved. Reprinted by permission.

[a]DB25 references the (25-pin) connector that is commonly used for RS-232 and V.24. Pins 9 and 10 are reserved for data set testing. Pins 11, 18, and 25 are undefined. Pins 3 and 21 of RS-449 interface connector are undefined. Lead 23 of RS-232 connector may be defined as CH or CI.

use, this value is 20 mA. To send an ASCII character, the current is interrupted at the transmitting device according to the binary word for that particular ASCII character. The presence of loop current denotes a mark, and the absence of loop current denotes a space. The interruption of the current is detected at the receiving point in the loop. If needed, a number of transmitting and receiving devices may be wired in series in this local loop (where only one transmits at a time).

TABLE C-6 (*continued*)

25 Pin	EIA-RS-232C Circuit	CCITT-V.24 Circuit	Mnemonic Designation	RS-232 Description	GND	Data From DCE	Data To DCE	Control From DCE	Control To DCE	Timing From DCE	Timing To DCE
1	AA	101	FG	Protective frame ground	×						
7	AB	102	SG	Signal ground/common return	×						
		102a		DTE common	×						
		102b		DCE common	×						
2	BA	103	TD	Transmitted data			×				
3	BB	104	RD	Received data		×					
4	CA	105	RTS	Request to send					×		
5	CB	106	CTS	Clear to send				×			
6	CC	107	DSR	Data set ready				×			
20	CD	108.2	DTR	Data terminal ready					×		
22	CE	125	RI	Ring indicator				×			
8	CF	109	DCD	Received line carrier signal detector				×			
21	CG	110	SQ	Signal quality detector				×			
23	CH	111		Data signal rate selector (DTE)					×		
23	CI	112		Data signal rate selector (DCE)				×			
24	DA	113	TC	Transmitter clock signal element timing (DTE)							×
15	DB	114	TC	Transmitter clock signal element timing (DCE)						×	
17	DD	115	RC	Receiver clock signal element timing (DCE)						×	
14	SBA	118	STD	Second transmitter data			×				
16	SBB	119	SRD	Secondary received data		×					
19	SCA	120	SRTS	Secondary request to send					×		
13	SCB	121	SCTS	Secondary clear to send				×			
12	SCF	122	SDCD	Secondary received line signal detector				×			
		141		Local loopback					×		
		140		Remote loopback					×		
		142		Test indicator				×			
		116		Select standby					×		
		117		Standby indicator				×			
		126		Select transmit frequency				×			

RS-232C, RS-422A, RS-449, and RS-530 Interfaces

The RS-232C serial interface (also known as the *EIA standard interface*) was developed in 1969 by the EIA in cooperation with the Bell System and independent computer and modem manufacturers. The CCITT has adopted an interface standard, called V.24, that is very similar to the RS-232C standard. The military MIL-188c is also similar. The RS-

232C pin connections are given in Table C-6, where the EIA and CCITT circuit equivalents are listed. The standard provides for serial data transmission by using a voltage level of $-V_0$ for a binary 1 (mark) and a level of $+V_0$ for a binary 0 (space), where $3 \leq V_0 \leq 25$ V. A typical value for V_0 is 6 V. The voltage appears on the appropriate lead measured with respect to the common (signal) ground lead. This is called *unbalanced signaling* and is also known as single-ended signaling.

The RS-232C standard defines the electrical characteristics, the functional description of interchange circuits, and a list of standard applications. The type of physical connector is not specified, but a DB25 connector (25 pins) is generally used in practice.

The RS-232C interface is intended for data rates up to 20 kbits/sec and cable lengths up to 50 ft. Longer lengths are possible if twisted-pair cable is used and the loading capacitance is kept below 2500 pF. This interface is one of the most popular serial interfaces used in computer communication equipment today.

For higher data rates and longer cable lengths, the RS-422A interface was developed. This interface uses *balanced signaling* (also known as differential signaling), and, consequently, two wires are required for each circuit. This method gives greater noise and crosstalk immunity because a common signal return path is not used. The balanced-signaling technique allows the transition region between the mark and space voltage levels to be reduced so that the signal levels are $\pm V_0$, where $0.2 \leq V_0 \leq 25$ V is used for balanced signaling. The RS-422A interface uses DB37 and DB9 connectors (37- and 9-pin) as specified in the ISO 4902 standard. The pin connections are given in Fig. C-6, where the two-wire connections for each balanced circuit are specified in columns A and B. The RS-422A standard allows for data rates up to 100 kbits/sec at 4000 ft or 40 Mbits/sec at 40 ft.

The RS-449 signal interface was intended to be the successor to the RS-232C interface. The RS-449 interface connections are also given in Table C-6. A 37-pin D connector is used for the primary channel and an auxiliary 9-pin D connector is used (when needed) for a secondary channel. The 37-pin connector allows for unbalanced or (optionally) balanced signaling where the signaling levels are those for RS-232C or RS-222A, respectively. Balanced signaling allows the RS-449 interface to support data rates up to 2 Mbits/sec and cable lengths up to 667 ft.

The RS-530 interface supersedes the RS-449. It is a balanced signaling complement to the RS-232C (which uses unbalanced signaling). The RS-530 interface uses a DB-25 (25-pin) connector as described by Fig. C-3c and Table C-6. It accommodates data rates up to 2 Mbits/sec.

Centronics Parallel Interface

Printers are often connected to computing equipment by either a RS-232C serial interface or a Centronics parallel interface. Figure C-4 and Table C-7 show the 36-pin connector for the Centronics parallel interface. This interface has eight data lines that provide eight bits of data in parallel. The data are controlled by the STROB pulse. This interface uses unbalanced signaling with TTL (transistor transistor logic) levels.

(a) RS-232

(b) RS-449/422

(c) RS-530

FIGURE C-3 RS-232C, RS-449/422, and RS-530 male connectors.

IEEE-488 Interface

The IEEE-488 interface is designed to connect computer equipment with programmable instruments such as programmable voltmeters, signal sources, and power supplies. It allows programmable instruments to be easily connected together to create an *automatic test equipment* (ATE) system. This interface was first developed in 1965 by Hewlett–Packard and was known as the HP Interface Bus (HP–IB) or the General Purpose Interface Bus (GPIB). In 1975 the IEEE adopted an evolved standard, which was named the IEEE-488 interface. Table C-8 presents some details on this parallel interface. The lines are held at +5 V for a binary 0 (false) and pulled to ground for a binary 1 (true). This

SIGNAL DESIGNATION	PIN NUMBER		PIN NUMBER	SIGNAL DESIGNATION
+5V	18		36	UNDEFINED
CHASSIS GND	17		35	UNDEFINED
LOGIC GND	16		34	UNDEFINED
OSCXT	15		33	UNDEFINED
SUPPLY GND	14		32	FAULT
SELECT	13		31	INPUT PRIME
PAPER END	12		30	(R) INPUT PRIME
BUSY	11		29	(R) BUSY
ACKNOWLEDGE	10		28	(R) ACKNOWLEDGE
DATA BIT 8	9		27	(R) DATA BIT 8
DATA BIT 7	8		26	(R) DATA BIT 7
DATA BIT 6	7		25	(R) DATA BIT 6
DATA BIT 5	6		24	(R) DATA BIT 5
DATA BIT 4	5		23	(R) DATA BIT 4
DATA BIT 3	4		22	(R) DATA BIT 3
DATA BIT 2	3		21	(R) DATA BIT 2
DATA BIT 1	2		20	(R) DATA BIT 1
DATA STROBE	1		19	(R) DATA STROBE

(R) INDICATES SIGNAL GROUND RETURN

FIGURE C-4 Centronics connector.

standard allows the bus to extend over a distance of 67 ft. Every IEEE-488 device is a listener, a talker, or a controller. A *listener* is capable of receiving data from the bus, such as a printer or a programmable power supply. A *talker* is capable of transmitting data over the bus, such as a frequency counter or a voltmeter. There can be only one active talker on the bus at a time. A *controller* is a computer-type device that controls the network (including itself) and specifies which devices are active talkers or listeners. A 24-pin IEEE-488 connector is illustrated in Fig. C-5.

Ethernet (IEEE 802.3) Interface

Ethernet is a method of connecting multiple computers, servers, and peripherals together to form a *local area network* (LAN). It was first developed by the Xerox Corporation in the 1970s and supported by Digital Equipment Corporation (DEC) and Intel in 1980. In 1988 the Ethernet concept was refined by the IEEE and the IEEE 802.3 standard was published. As shown in Table C-9, this standard provides a 10-Mbit/sec serial data bus for a LAN using either coaxial cable or twisted-pair wire.

In the 10base5 (thick Ethernet) system, a 50-Ω coaxial backbone cable, up to 500 m in length, is used. The "10" in 10base5 indicates that a 10-Mbit/sec data rate is supported, "base" indicates that baseband signaling (Manchester line code) is used, and "5" indicates that the maximum backbone length is 500 m unless repeaters are used. A DTE

TABLE C-7 Centronics Parallel Interface[a]

Signal Pin No.	Return Pin No.	Signal	Direction (with Reference to Printer)	Description
1	19	STROBE	In	STROBE pulse (negative going) enables reading data.
2	20	Data 1	In	1st to 8th bits of parallel data.
3	21	Data 2	In	Each signal is at "high" level
4	22	Data 3	In	when data are logical "1" and
5	23	Data 4	In	"low" when logical "0."
6	24	Data 5	In	
7	25	Data 6	In	
8	26	Data 7	In	
9	27	Data 8	In	
10	28	ACKNLG	Out	"Low" indicates that data have been received and that the printer is ready to accept other data.
11	29	BUSY	Out	"High" indicates that the printer cannot receive data.

SOURCE: Black Box Corporation, Pittsburgh, PA. © Black Box Corporation, 1988. All rights reserved. Reprinted by permission.

[a]Pins 12, 13, 14, 15, 18, 31, 32, 34, 35, and 36 vary in function depending on application; they are commonly used for printer auxiliary controls, and error handling and indication. Pins 16 and 17 are commonly used for logic ground and chassis ground, respectively.

device with a Ethernet card is connected to the backbone cable by using a transceiver—also called a *medium attachment unit* (MAU)—in series with the backbone cable at the tap point. A cable drop then connects the transceiver to the DTE Ethernet card.

In the 10base2 (thin net or cheap net) system, a 50-Ω thin (0.25 in. diameter) coaxial cable, up to 200 m in length, is used. The DTE device is connected to this coaxial bus by inserting a BNC T-connector in series with the cable at the tap point. In this thin-net system the T-connector must be connected directly to the Ethernet card on the DTE (no drop cable allowed).

The 10base-T system uses twisted-pair wire, up to 100 m in length, to connect each DTE device with a 10base-T Ethernet card directly to a central hub. (There are no taps on the twisted-pair wire.)

Multiple 10base5, 10base2, or 10base-T systems (segments) may be connected together using a multiport repeater. A gateway may also connect the Ethernet LAN to a wide area network (WAN) which uses either coaxial cable or fiber optic cable to other networks.

TABLE C-8 IEEE-488 Interface[a]

| 24-Pin | | | | | | |
A	B	Circuit	Description	Data Line	Control Line	Handshake Line
	24	GND	Logic ground	×		
1	24	D101	Data bit 1	×		
2	24	D102	Data bit 2	×		
3	24	D103	Data bit 3	×		
4	24	D104	Data bit 4	×		
13	24	D105	Data bit 5	×		
14	24	D106	Data bit 6	×		
15	24	D107	Data bit 7	×		
16	24	D108	Data bit 8	×		
9	21	IFC	Interface Clear—used by controller to place devices into quiescent state		×	
10	22	SRQ	Service Request—used by device to request service		×	
17	24	REN	Remote Enable—used by controller to override device front panel controls		×	
5	24	EOI	End of Identity—(a) used by talker to end message, or (b) used by controller with ATN for parallel pole		×	
11	23	ATN	Attention—used by controller to end its data and listen for a command		×	
6	18	DAV	Data Valid—used by controller to indicate a control byte on data bus		×	
7	19	NRFD	Not Ready For Data—used by listener to indicate it is not ready			×
8	20	NDAC	No Data Accepted—used by listener to indicate it has not yet accepted last byte			×
	12		Shield			

[a]Column B pins are return leads to be grounded at the system ground point.

FIGURE C-5 IEEE-488 connector.

TABLE C-9 Ethernet (IEEE 802.3) Standards

Item	Thick (Standard) Ethernet	Thin Ethernet	Twisted-pair Ethernet[a]
IEEE designation	10base5	10base2	10base-T
Transmission medium	50-Ω coax	50-Ω coax	Twisted-pair wire
Cable diameter or wire size	0.4 in. diameter	0.25 in. diameter	22 to 26 AWG
Data rate	10 Mbits/sec	10 Mbits/sec	10 Mbits/sec
Maximum segment length	500 m[b]	200 m[b]	100 m
Maximum length with repeaters	4000 m	4000 m	NA
Minimum distance between taps	2.5 m	0.5 m	NA
Tab configuration	Transceiver	T-connector[c]	NA
Maximum number of taps	100	30	NA
Type of connectors used	N	BNC	NA

[a]NA, not applicable. Each device is connected to a central hub via an unshielded twisted-wire pair.
[b]Each end of the segment is terminated with a 50-Ω resistive load.
[c]T-connector must be connected directly to the Ethernet card on the DTE device.

C-3 The ISO OSI Network Model

When users are connected together, many things must be considered for orderly, efficient data transmission. This complicated problem can be understood better and the network can be maintained more easily if the different tasks are divided into layered modules. These modules are implemented in both hardware and software. Most computer network designers and manufacturers follow the layered model recommended by the ISO in its

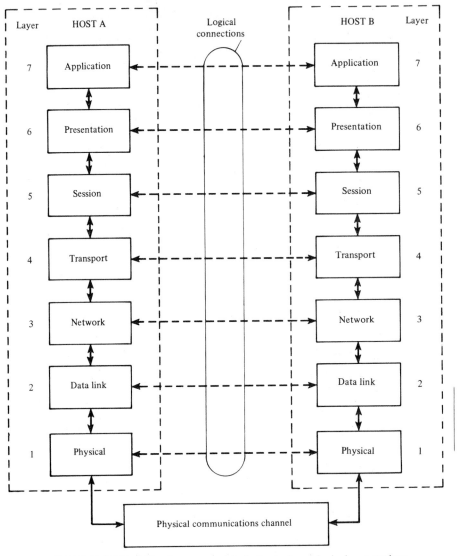

FIGURE C-6 ISO OSI reference model of physical and logical connections.

Open System Interconnection (OSI) reference model. This model is shown in Fig. C-6. This figure presents an example of two end users (host A and host B) that are connected to a data communications network via the physical channel. The physical channel may be connections via telephone company (TELCO) lines, fiber optic link, microwave radio, or satellite links.

The layered approach has many attractive features [Stallings, 1985]. By adhering to the appropriate hardware and/or software specifications that define the layer boundaries, many different vendors can supply hardware/software that will work efficiently in the overall network. Furthermore, various parts of the system can be updated and maintained by replacing or modifying the hardware/software at each layer level instead of replacing the whole system.

The functions of the various layers may be described as follows:

Layer 1—Physical. Concerned with bit transmission. Standards specify signal levels, cable connectors, and cable. For multiple-access packet transmission systems, the methods of carrier sense and collision detection are also specified.

Layer 2—Data Link. Concerned with beginning message transmission, error detection and correction, and ending message transmission.

Layer 3—Network. Concerned with choosing the route taken by the message, flow control, and message priorities.

Layer 4—Transport. Concerned with end-to-end reliability (error detection and information recovery) and maps logical addresses to end-user devices.

Layer 5—Session. Starts and stops the communication session, transfers the user from one task to another, and provides recovery from communication problems (restart) without losing data.

Layer 6—Presentation. Converts data to the appropriate syntax for the display devices (character sets and graphics) and encodes/decodes compressed data.

Layer 7—Application. Provides a log-in procedure, checks passwords, allows file upload/download and remote job entry, and tabulates system resources used for billing purposes.

C-4 Data Link Control Protocols

Data link control (DLC) protocols, also called *line protocols,* are a set of rules for operating a computer network or a public switched telephone network (PSTN). They standardize the framing, addressing, and error control techniques used in the system.

BISYNC

The Binary Synchronous Communication (BISYNC) protocol was developed in 1968 by IBM for synchronous transmission between two computers or between a computer and batch terminals. (It has been superseded by SDLC, which we will discuss subsequently.) BISYNC is a character-oriented protocol. That is, it uses characters (usually EBCDIC or

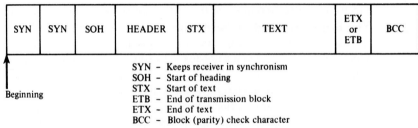

| SYN | SYN | SOH | HEADER | STX | TEXT | ETX or ETB | BCC |

Beginning

SYN – Keeps receiver in synchronism
SOH – Start of heading
STX – Start of text
ETB – End of transmission block
ETX – End of text
BCC – Block (parity) check character

FIGURE C-7 BISYNC format.

ASCII) to delineate the various fields of the message. It is also a half-duplex protocol, which means that the data flow in one direction at a time between two communication points. Periodically, an end-of-transmission-block (ETB) character is sent, which requires a response from the receiving station indicating acknowledgment of reception of error-free data (ACK) or error in the previous received block (NAK). If a NAK is received by the transmitter end, the whole block is retransmitted. This is automatic request for repeat (ARQ) error control. A typical BISYNC message is shown in Fig. C-7. The text portion is variable in length.

SDLC

Synchronous Data Link Control (SDLC) is a bit-oriented protocol. That is, instead of control characters it uses a unique flag at the beginning and end of each frame. It was developed by IBM in 1974 to provide a more versatile protocol than BISYNC. It is a full-duplex protocol, which means that data can be transmitted in both directions simultaneously. Furthermore, SDLC permits the transmission to one remote location while receiving from a different remote location on a multidrop line. SDLC also uses ARQ error control, where a station has to acknowledge correct receipt of at least the eighth preceding frame if communication is to continue. The SDLC frame is shown in Fig. C-8.

HDLC

High-Level Data Link Control (HDLC) was approved by ISO in 1975 (ISO 3309) and has been updated since then by other ISO standards. It is a packet protocol that has been adopted worldwide by many vendors. IBM's SDLC is a subset of HDLC, and ANSI's Advanced Data Communications Control Procedure (ADCCP) is equivalent to HDLC. As discussed in the next section, X.25 uses the HDLC protocol.

| BEGINNING FLAG 01111110 | ADDRESS 8 bits | CONTROL 8 bits | INFORMATION Any number of bits | FRAME CHECK 16 bits | ENDING FLAG 01111110 |

FIGURE C-8 SDLC and HDLC formats.

The general structure of the HDLC frame (packet) is shown in Fig. C-8. The address field may be extended recursively to allow more addresses. Two basic types of frames are allowed—control and information. In control frames there is no information field, and the control frame is used to set up, take down, or check a virtual link between users. In the information frame, the information field may be of any size. The information frames are numbered in sequence (by bits in the control field), so that the sending station does not have to wait for an acknowledgment of the frame just transmitted before sending another frame. The acknowledgment can be received at a later time (for error detection and recovery) since the frames are numbered. In addition, the packets may arrive out of sequence at the receiver, and the numbering allows the receiver to place the information in the correct order.

HDLC was originally developed for unbalanced operation (ISO 4335), in which one primary station controls secondary stations by sending command frames. The secondary stations respond only when polled in the normal response mode. In the asynchronous mode (not to be confused with asynchronous bit transmission), the secondary stations are allowed to send unsolicited response frames. Newer modes (ISO 6256) allow balanced operation, in which any station may initiate the setting up of a virtual call.

CCITT X.25 Protocol

The CCITT X.25 standard is entitled ''Interface Between a DTE and a DCE for Terminals Operating in the Packet Mode on Public Data Networks.'' It involves the use of data packets as the basis for creating a virtual circuit. With a virtual circuit, two users appear to have a private data connection between themselves, although they are actually sharing the same physical channel with other users. This is accomplished by breaking the serial data stream of each user into ''packets'' of data of a certain length. Each packet has a header attached, with the destination address for the packet and other control information. The packets from each user are interspersed with those of other users on the X.25 line.

The virtual circuits may be set up temporarily or permanently. A temporary virtual circuit consists of three operations: (1) setting up the call, (2) transferring the data, and (3) taking down (disconnecting) the virtual connection. In setting up the call, a logical channel number is used. With a permanent virtual connection, the logical number is assigned permanently to the customer when the X.25 line is leased and the virtual connection is always available so that data can be transferred at any instant. Thus the permanent virtual connection appears to be a private leased line to the end users.

The X.25 standard does not specify how the virtual circuits are implemented. However, X.25 is actually concerned with three layers of protocols (see the ISO OSI protocol layers as described in Sec. C-3): (1) the DCE/CTE physical layer interface, which uses the X.21 standard for synchronous data transmission; (2) the data link level, which gives the method of attaching address information to the packets according to the HDLC protocol; and (3) the network layer, which sets up the virtual circuits by the use of two different types of packets. The control packets contain control information such as CALL REQUEST (sent by the caller), CALL ACCEPT (sent by the called party), CALL CONNECT, CLEAR, and others. The data packets contain the information data that are exchanged between the users on a virtual circuit.

Asynchronous Transfer Mode (ATM)

The *asynchronous transfer mode* (ATM) is a new packet protocol that is being implemented in the public switched telephone network (PSTN). ATM allows each user to have a virtual connection with an effective data rate that matched the user's instantaneous data-rate need whether it is large or small or whether the data-rate requirement changes as time advances.

In the ATM format, as shown in Fig. C-9, data are transferred in packets or cells where a header (for data routing) is attached preceding the user's data packet [Händel and Huber, 1991; Stallings, 1992]. This is similar to the HDLC protocol, except that HDLC was designed for computer communication and ATM is designed to transport a wide variation of data rates and data types—such as digital video, digital audio, and computer data—that occur in the PSTN. Note that in ATM, the cell header has a cell loss-priority bit that distinguishes cells that might be discarded by the PSTN (without significantly disturbing that particular user) when there is some network data-overload condition. For example, a user who might tolerate data loss might be one who is sending data on a virtual channel corresponding to the reading of the water height of some river. Some of the height readings could be discarded occasionally without compromising the effectiveness of the table of readings. This data loss for some ATM users allows the ATM system to be more robust for other users that cannot tolerate data loss (and who pay premium rates for the higher-quality service).

ATM is an alternative to the *synchronous transfer mode* (STM) technology, such as T1 systems, where the user is locked in to a subscribed data rate whether or not he/she needs it. That is, with ATM the user can send packets as often as needed so that the user's effective data rate is matched to the user's needs and not to some fixed prescribed data rate as in STM technology.

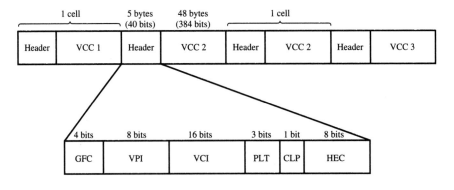

VCC Virtual channel connection   PLT Payload type
GFC Generic flow control   CLP Cell loss priority
VPI Virtual path identifier   HEC Header error control
VCI Virtual channel identifier

FIGURE C-9 ATM format.

C-5 Telephone Line Standards

Basically, a (twisted-pair) telephone line is capable of transmitting signals that have energy that is confined to the 300- to 3000-Hz frequency band.[†] (This does not mean that the signals will be undistorted when transmitted over the line.) There are two main categories of telephone service.

1. Dial-up lines, which use the normal telephone connections where calls are dialed up to almost anywhere in the world.
2. Private leased lines, which are either two-wire or four-wire lines that connect two points or multiple points on a dedicated 24-hr/day basis.

The quality of a dial-up line is difficult to predict, especially if it traverses several countries. One dial-up connection between two points may be excellent, and another, between the same two points, may be terrible.

[†] Short lines have a much wider frequency response. This is used to advantage by limited-distance modems that operate over this extended bandwidth to send data at high rates—up to 19,200 bits/sec.

TABLE C-10 C-Conditioning Specifications (Leased Lines)

Type	Frequency Range (Hz)	Frequency Response[a] (dB)	Frequency Range (Hz)	Variation in Envelope Delay (μsec)
Basic	500–2500	−2 to +8	800–2600	1750
(3002 line)	300–3000	−3 to +12		
C1	1000–2400	−1 to +3	1000–2400	1000
(Class E line)	300–2700	−2 to +6	800–2600	1750
	2700–3000	−3 to +12		
C2	500–2800	−1 to +3	1000–2600	500
(Class F line)	300–3000	−2 to +6	600–2600	1500
			500–2800	3000
C4	500–3000	−2 to +3	1000–2600	300
(Class H line)	300–3200	−2 to +6	800–2800	500
			600–3000	1500
			500–3000	3000
C5	500–2800	−0.5 to +1.5	1000–2600	100
	300–3000	−1 to +3	600–2600	300
			500–2800	600

[a] 0-dB reference is 1004 Hz.

TABLE C-11 D-Conditioning Specifications (Leased Lines)

Type	S/N (dB)	S/D (dB)	
		Second	Third
Basic (3002)	24	25	28
D	28	35	40

The characteristics of private leased lines in the United States are guaranteed to meet certain criteria. There are two different sets of specifications.

1. *C-conditioning.* This specifies the frequency response and envelope delay (which are linear distortion) characteristics of the line. These specifications are given in Table C-10.
2. *D-conditioning.* This specifies the minimum signal-to-noise ratio and the second and third harmonic (nonlinear) distortion minimum signal-to-distortion ratios. These specifications are given in Table C-11.

When a customer orders a C-conditioned line, the telephone company checks to see if a line meets the particular C-conditioning class that has been ordered. If the line does not meet the specifications, equalizers will be placed on the line so that they are met. By luck, the customer may get a much better line than he or she specifies (i.e., higher-order conditioning) when no equalization is required. The D-conditioning specifications are usually obtained by *line selection* so that the specifications are satisfied.

C-6 Modem Standards

Historically, the Bell System dominated the modem market. It calls its modems *data sets.* Since the Bell System divestiture, modems built to CCITT standards have also become popular. Table C-12 lists the modems that interface data lines from computers to analog lines. Note that voice grade lines will support bit rates up to about 19.6 kbits/sec with modems or up to 144 kbits/sec with ISDN service. DS-1 lines provide 1.544-Mb/sec service.

Table C-13 gives more details on some of the more popular modems. For personal computer data communication at 300, 1200, and 2400 bits/sec, the Bell 103, Bell 212A, and CCITT V.22bis modems, respectively, are used. Amateur radio operators use the Bell 103 standard for audio tones into and out of SSB transceivers for packet radio transmission on the HF amateur radio bands, and the Bell 202 standard is used for audio into and out of FM transceivers for packet transmission on the VHF and UHF bands.

Tables C-14 and C-15 describe the 9600 (CCITT V.32) and 14,400 (CCITT V.33) modems that use QAM signaling with trellis-coded modulation.

TABLE C-12 Modem Standards

Type	Data Rate (bits/sec)		Mode	Type of Line	Synch/ Asynch	Modulation[a]	Transmitting Frequencies (Hz)[b]	
	Normal	Fallback					Originate	Answer
Bell 103/113	0-300		FDX	2W Dial-up	Async	FSK	1070S, 1270M	2025S, 2225M
CCITT V.21	0-300		FDX	2W Dial-up	Async	FSK	980M, 1080S	1650M, 1850S
Bell 202S	1,200		HDX	2W Dial-up	Async	FSK	1200M, 2200S	
Bell 202T	1,200		FDX	4W Lease	Async	FSK	1200M, 2200S	
CCITT V.23	1,200	600	HDX	2W Dial-up	Async	FSK	1300M, 2100S, 1700S	
Bell 212A	1,200	300	FDX	2W Dial-up	Either	4DPSK	1200	2400
CCITT V.22	1,200	600	FDX	2W Dial-up	Either	FSK	Same as Bell 103 / Same as Bell 212	2400
Bell 201C	2,400		FDX	4W Lease	Either	4DPSK	1800	
CCITT V.22bis	2,400	1200	FDX	2W Dial-up	Either	16QAM	Same as CCITT V.22	2400
CCITT V.26	2,400		FDX	4W Lease	Sync	4DPSK	1800 (same as Bell 201C)	
CCITT V.26bis	2,400	1200	FDX	4W Lease	Sync	4DPSK	1800	
Bell 208A	4,800		FDX	4W Lease	Sync	8DPSK	1800	
Bell 208B	4,800		HDX	2W Dial-up	Sync	8DPSK	1800	
CCITT V.27bis	4,800	2400	FDX	4W Lease	Sync	8DPSK	1800	
Bell 209	9,600		FDX	4W Lease D	Sync	16QAM	1800	
CCITT V.29	9,600	7200/4800	FDX	4W Lease D	Sync	16QAM	1700	
CCITT V.32	9,600	4800/2400	FDX	2W Dial	Either	32QAM[c]	1700	
CCITT V.33	14,400	9600/2400	FDX	4W Lease C2	Sync	128QAM	1800	
Bell 301B	40,800		FDX	Group channel	Sync	BPSK		
Bell 303B	19,200		FDX	Half-group	Sync	VSB		
Bell 303C	50,000		FDX	Group channel	Sync	VSB		
Bell 303D	230,400		FDX	Supergroup	Sync	VSB		

[a] FSK, frequency-shift keying; BPSK, binary-phase-shift keying; MDPSK, M-ary differential phase-shift keying; VSB, vestigial sideband; MQAM, M-ary quadratic amplitude modulation.
[b] M, mark; S, space.
[c] Trellis-coded modulation is used.

557

TABLE C-13 Popular 300, 1200, and 2400 bits/sec Personal Modems[a]

	Bell System Type			CCITT
	103/113	202	212A	V.22 bis
Data	Serial binary Asynchronous Full duplex (two-wire line)	Dial-up or leased line Serial binary Asynchronous Half-duplex (two-wire line)	Serial binary Asynchronous or synchronous Full-duplex, dial-up lines (also contains a 103 type modem)	Serial binary Asynchronous or synchronous Full-duplex, dial-up (also usually contains a 212A-type modem)
Data rate	0 to 300 bits/sec	0 to 1200 bits/sec (dial-up) 0 to 1800 bits/sec (leased C2)	1200 bits/sec 600 baud (symbols/sec)	2400 bits/sec 600 baud (symbols/sec)
Modulation	FSK	FSK	QPSK ($M = 4$ phases)	QAM (16-point rectangular-type signal constellation)
Frequency/ phase assignment	Originate end / Answer end Tx: Space 1070 Hz / 2025 Hz Mark 1270 Hz / 2225 Hz Rx: Space 2025 Hz / 1070 Hz Mark 2225 Hz / 1270 Hz	Mark: 1200 Hz Space: 2200 Hz	Carrier frequencies Originate end / Answer end Tx: $f_c = 1200$ Hz / $f_c = 2400$ Hz Rx: $f_c = 2400$ / $f_c = 1200$ Hz Message (2 bits) — Phase Angle 00 — 90° 01 — 0° 10 — 180° 11 — 270°	Carrier frequencies Originate end / Answer end Tx: $f_c = 1200$ Hz / $f_c = 2400$ Hz Rx: $f_c = 2400$ Hz / $f_c = 1200$ Hz
Transmit level	0 to −12 dBm	0 to −12 dBm		
Receive level	0 to −50 dBm	0 to −50 dBm (dial-up line) 0 to −40 dBm (leased line)		

[a] Tx, Transmit; Rx, receive.

TABLE C-14 CCITT V.32 Modem Standard

Item		Signal Constellation
Data	Serial binary, Asynchronous or synchronous Full duplex over two-wire line[a]	*Option 2: 32 QAM or QPSK*
Carrier freq.	Transmit[a]: 1800 Hz Receive[a]: 1800 Hz	
Option 1 DATA rate Modulation	9600 bits/sec for high S/N 4800 bits/sec for low S/N 32 QAM, 2400 baud, for high S/N using trellis-coded modulation (see Fig. 1-9, where $n = 3$ and $m - k = 2$) with 4 data bits plus 1 coding bit per symbol QPSK, 2400 baud (states A, B, C, D) for low S/N	
Option 2 DATA rate Modulation	9600 bits/sec for high S/N 4800 bits/sec for low S/N 16 QAM, 2400 baud, for high S/N QPSK, 2400 baud (states A, B, C, D) for low S/N	*Option 2: 16 QAM or QPSK*

[a] A two-wire to four-wire hybrid is used in this modem to obtain the transmit and receive lines.

TABLE C-15 CCITT V.33 Modem Standard[a]

Item	128 QAM Signal Constellation
Data	Serial binary Synchronous Full duplex over four-wire line (two-wire for transmit and (two-wire for receive)[a]
Carrier freq.	Transmit: 1800 Hz Receive: 1800 Hz
Data rate	14,400 bits/sec
Modulation	128 QAM, 2400 baud, using trellis-coded modulation (see Fig. 1-9, where $n = 3$ and $m - k = 4$) with 6 data bits plus 1 coding bit per symbol
Fallback mode	12,000 bits/sec using 64 QAM, 2400 baud, (signal constellation not shown) and trellis-coded modulation with 5 data bits plus 1 coding bit per symbol

128 QAM Signal Constellation (axes x, y; gridlines at $\pm 2, \pm 4, \pm 6, \pm 8$)

[a]The CCITT V.33bis modem uses a two-wire line and an internal two-wire to four-wire hybrid to obtain the transmit and receive lines.

C-7 Brief Computer Communications Glossary

Acoustic Coupler. A method used to couple modem signals to the telephone line via sound transducers (microphone and headphone) that are positioned on the telephone handset.

ACU (automatic calling unit). A unit that dials up the telephone line connection on receipt of the proper data signal from a computer.

Adaptive Equalizer. An electronic circuit that automatically compensates for the changing envelope delay and frequency response of a telephone line.

ARP (Address Resolution Protocol). A TCP/IP (Transmission Control Protocol/Internet Protocol) process that maps the IP address to the Ethernet address as required by TCP/IP for use with Ethernet.

ARQ (automatic retransmission request). An error correction technique whereby the message is retransmitted when the receiver detects an error.

ASCII (American Standard Code for Information Interchange). A 7-bit plus 1-parity bit code; see Table C-5.

ASR. Automatic sending–receiving.

Asynchronous Transmission. The time intervals between transmitted characters may be of unequal length. Start and stop bits are transmitted before and after each character to synchronize the receiver clock.

ATM (asynchronous transfer mode). A new packet (or cell) protocol that is being implemented over the PSTN. See Sec. C-4.

Baud. The data transmission rate, in units of symbols per second, whereby one symbol is counted for each possible modulation level. Baud is sometimes used incorrectly by modem manufacturers to express bits per second. A baud is the same as a bit per second if each symbol represents one bit (i.e., $M = 2$ possible levels).

Baudot Code. A 5-bit code set; see Table C-3. Also known as the *International Telegraph Alphabet (ITA) Number 2*.

BISYNC (Binary-Synchronous Communications Protocol). See Sec. C-4 and Fig. C-7.

Bridge. An electronic box that connects different local area networks at the data-link layer of the OSI model; see Fig. C-6 in Sec. C-3.

Broadband Channel. A channel that has a bandwidth much greater than that required to send one VF signal.

CCITT. The Consultative Committee for International Telephone and Telegraph, an international standards group.

Circuit Switching. A physically (or electronically) switched connection that connects the line of the calling party to that of the called party.

Concentrator. A device that connects a number of low-speed, usually asynchronous, devices to a high-speed, usually synchronous, device.

Control Character. A nonprinting functional character that provides some control function (e.g., see Table C-5 for the ASCII control characters).

CRC (cyclic redundancy check). Data are checked for errors by using a polynomial algorithm. The algorithm is used to compute a check field (usually 16 bits) that is appended to the frame of data at the transmitter and used by the receiver to verify the correctness of the data.

CSMA/CD (carrier sense multiple access/collision detection). Multiple users transmit data over a common channel. If two users transmit data at the same time, the resulting collision is detected and each tries to transmit again after a predetermined time interval.

CTS. Clear-to-send line on the RS-232C interface (see Table C-6).

CXR. Carrier.

Data Set. (1) A modem or (2) a collection of data records.

DCE (data communications equipment). A modem; see Fig. C-1.

Dial-Up Line. A switched-circuit telephone line connection (as opposed to a leased line).

DTE (data terminal equipment). The equipment that provides the data source or data sink; see Fig. C-1.

EBCDIC (Extended Binary-Coded Decimal Interchange Code). An 8-bit code used primarily in IBM equipment; see Table C-4.

Echo Check. A method of checking for errors in a data system by looping the data at the receive site back to the transmitter site for comparison.

Echo Suppressor. A device that suppresses the echoes on toll lines that are caused by transmission line reflections (usually at the hybrid interface).

Envelope Delay. In the context of telephone lines, the measure of the delay through the circuit for a sinusoidal signal at a certain frequency as compared to the minimum delay, which usually occurs at a frequency of about 1800 Hz.

Ethernet. A coaxial cable local-area network that transmits data at 10 Mbits/sec with a CSMA/CD technique. It was first developed by Xerox Corporation and is now standardized by the IEEE (IEEE 802.3). See Table C-9.

FDDI (fiber distributed data interface). An ANSI standard for fiber optic computer data links with data rates up to 100 Mbits/sec.

Flow Control. Ability to stop data flow from a transmitter so that receiver buffers do not overflow.

Front-End Processor. A communications computer connected between the main computer and the remote terminals; provides line control, code conversion, data concentration, and error control.

Full Duplex. (1) A protocol that provides for simultaneous transmission of data in both directions; also, or alternatively, (2) in the context of telephone data lines, a four-wire (two-pair) circuit.

Gateway. An electronic box or logical network device that interconnects incompatible networks or devices by performing protocol conversion.

Half-Duplex. (1) A protocol that allows data to be transmitted in only one direction at a time; also, or alternatively, (2) in the context of telephone data lines, a two-wire (one-pair) circuit.

HDLC (High-Level Data Link Control Protocol). See Sec. C-4 and Fig. C-8.

Hybrid Network. A circuit that couples a two-wire telephone line to a four-wire circuit. (See Fig. 8-5.)

ISDN (integrated services digital network). A PSTN service that provides a digital data link directly to the subscriber over a twisted-pair line. See Sec. 8-3.

ISO. International Organization for Standardization.

ISO OSI Model. See Fig C-6.

LAN (local-area network).   A connection of office or campus computer facilities to each other by twisted-pair wire, coaxial cable, or fiber optic cable.

Leased Line.   A permanent line between two or more communication sites (no exchange switching) for leasing customers.

Message Switching.   *See* Store-and-Forward.

Modem.   An acronym for modulator–demodulator. A modem converts the baseband data signal to a bandpass signal for transmission over an analog telephone line, and vice versa. The Bell System calls a modem a *data set*.

Multipoint Line.   A line that connects two or more communication sites and requires the use of some type of polling and addressing mechanism for each site.

Packet.   A group of bits with appended address bits, sender identification bits, and/or other control bits.

Packet Switching.   The transfer of data by means of addressed packets. The channel is occupied only during the transmission of the packet. In this sense, there is a virtual circuit (no permanent circuit) between communication sites. See ATM, Sec. C-4.

Parity Check.   The addition of an extra noninformation bit to the data group so that the number of 1's in the group is either even or odd; permits the detection of single errors.

Polling.   In a multipoint network, the process of inquiring which sites have data to transmit.

Protocol.   The rules for control of data transmission over the communication network.

PSTN (public switched telephone network).   Common carrier facilities available for lease for transmission of audio, video, and data. See Table 8-2.

Repeater.   An electronic device that receives an attenuated electrical or optical data signal with noise and regenerates a "noise-free" high-level signal (with, possibly, some bit errors) for retransmission.

Reverse Channel.   A channel that allows the receiver in a modem to send slow-speed data to the transmitting modem for use in error control, circuit breaking, and network diagnostics.

RS-232C.   A DCE/DTE interface. See Table C-6.

RTS.   Request-to-send line on the RS-232C interface; see Table C-6.

SDLC (Synchronous Data Link Control Protocol).   See Sec. C-4 and Fig. C-8.

Server.   A computer with file storage for a LAN. The server may also link the LAN to other networks and provide protocol conversion.

Simplex Mode.   The sending of data in one direction only.

Slicing Level.   The threshold level of a comparator that determines whether the input level is converted into an output level corresponding to a binary 1 or a level corresponding to a binary 0.

Statistical Multiplexer.   A time-division multiplexer that takes advantage of the fact that there is often "dead time" on the input data channels. Thus, by dynamically adapting the time-division algorithm, a larger number of input channels can be serviced than with a fixed (nonadaptive) time-division multiplexer.

Store-and-Forward.   The process by which messages are accepted into memory and forwarded at a convenient time according to the address on the header of the message.

Switched Line.   The process by which lines from different sites are connected (switched) when a communication session is desired (e.g., the dial-up telephone network).

Synchronous Transmission.   The process by which data characters are transmitted at a fixed rate, with the transmitter and receiver being in synchronism. There are no start and stop bits, so this transmission technique is much more efficient than asynchronous transmission.

TCP/IP (Transmission Control Protocol/Internet Protocol).   A layered set of protocols to allow high-speed (e.g., Ethernet) network connection between PCs and other computers. Different types of vendor equipment can communicate with each other over the TCP/IP network. TCP/IP corresponds to Layers 3 and 4 of the OSI model as shown in Fig. C-6.

Token Bus.   A LAN that uses a unique word (a token) to be passed to a device before it can place data on the LAN for transmission.

Turnabout Time.   Time required for a modem to reverse the direction of transmission when connected to a half-duplex line.

VF (Voice Frequency) Channel.   A channel with a frequency response over the range of 300 to 3200 Hz.

X.25.   A packet protocol. See Sec. C-2.

X Terminal.   A computer terminal with a video monitor and keyboard that runs X terminal software. The X terminal is connected to a RISC (reduced instruction set computing) UNIX workstation that provides the computation power and file server functions.

Introduction to MathCAD

As described in Chapter 1, MathCAD may be run on an IBM-compatible personal computer to solve communications problems. In this appendix we describe the use of the student edition of MathCAD (Version 2.54). A template floppy disk, which contains MathCAD programs for text equations and end-of-the chapter problems that are marked with a computer symbol 🖥 , is made available to your instructor from the publisher.

D-1 General Information

1. To start MathCAD type

   drive: \path \MCAD /M filename

   \MCAD calls up MathCAD. The option /M specifies the manual calculation mode, and filename is the name of the template MathCAD program file that you want to load into MathCAD for computation. The manual calculation option requires that you press F9 for the computation; without this option, the computation will start immediately when the file is loaded (before you have a chance to set values of parameters).
2. MathCAD will use a 8087, 80287, or a 80387 math coprocessor if you have one installed. The coprocessor is not required; however, it will certainly speed up the calculations and is strongly recommended.
3. Press the function key F10 to energize the pull-down command menu. This allows you to load files, edit files, print files, and save files. The escape key allows you to enter commands by typing them instead of using the pull-down menu.
4. Regions on the MathCAD screen are created (defined) to be any one of three types:

(1) Equation—the default type; (2) Text—move cursor to a region of screen where the text is to begin, type ", followed by the text; (3) Plots—move cursor to upper-left point where a plot region is to be defined, then type @ (shift 2).

5. Other useful function keys are F1 for help, F3 for deletion or cut of a region, and F4 to paste a region.

6. MathCAD begins calculating at the upper-left corner of the screen and proceeds to the right and down. All variables used by an equation, except for a Global variable, must be defined previously. A Global variable may be defined anywhere, even on the last line. If b is a Global variable that is equal to 5, it is displayed as b $\equiv$ 5, where "$\equiv$" is entered by typing "~".

7. MathCAD is case sensitive. The variable A is not equal to the variable a. Built-in functions such as $\sin(z)$, $\log(z)$, and $fft(v)$ are specified by lowercase letters, except for some functions such as Bessel functions.

8. MathCad defines an equation such as A:=B + C to mean $A = B + C$. The ":=" is obtained by typing ":". The "=" sign is used to give a computed answer. If a variable C is to have the values 0, 5, 10, 15, 20, 25, 30, this is specified by C:=0, 5 . . . 30, where the ". . ." is obtained by typing ";". A subscript is entered by typing "[" before the subscript. Elements of vectors are indexed to begin with the subscript 0 (not 1, which will give an "undefined" vector).

9. A plot region may be defined by moving the cursor to the upper-left point where the plot region is to begin and typing @. A plot grid with undefined values for the horizontal and vertical axes will appear. Use the tab key to position cursor at points on the plot so that variables to be plotted can be typed in as well as typing in minimum and maximum values for the vertical and horizontal axes. To change the size and scale of the plot, move the cursor inside the plot region and type "f". This will bring up the plot specification menu. The default scale is logs = 0,0, which specifies a linear vertical and horizontal scale. Logs = 0,2 specifies a linear vertical scale and a logarithmic horizontal scale of two cycles, and so on. Size = 6,15 denotes a plot region of 6 (horizontal) lines and 15 columns. Type = 1 specifies that the points on the plot will be connected by a line, type = d specifies that a dot will be plotted for each point, type = v specifies that the values will be shown by diamonds, and type = V specifies that diamonds connected by lines will be plotted. (For other possibilities, see the MathCAD manual.)

10. To display a table for a set of defined or computed variable values, just place the cursor at the upper-left point where a column of tabulated values are desired and type "A=", where A is the variable to be tabulated.

11. Predefined variables are $\pi = 3.14159$ and $e = 2.71828$. π is entered by typing Alt-P (hold down the Alternate key and press p).

12. The unit step function, $u(t)$, is a built-in function denoted in MathCAD by $\Phi(t)$, where Φ is obtained by typing Alt-H.

13. Some Greek letters are available. For example, for α, type Alt-A; for β, type Alt-B; for Φ = unit step, type Alt-H; for $\pi = 3.14159$, type Alt-P; and for ω, type Alt-W. (For other possibilities, see the MathCAD manual.)

See Table D-1 for a listing of popular MathCAD operators and Table D-2 for built-in functions. (For other possibilities, see the MathCAD manual.)

TABLE D-1 Some MathCAD Operators

Operator	Type This	Operator	Type This
Help menu	F1	$\sqrt{x}$ (square root)	\x
Pull-down menu	F10	$\lvert x \rvert$ (absolute value)	|x
$x - y$ (subtraction)	x−y	$\sum_{i} x$	i$x
$x + y$ (sum)	x+y	$\prod_{i} x$	i#x
$x \cdot y$ (multiplication)	x*y	$\int f(x)\, dx$	x&f(x)
x/y (division)	x/y	$\dfrac{df(x)}{dx}$	x?f(x)
$\mathbf{x} \cdot \mathbf{y}$ (dot product)	x*y	$x > y$	x > y
$\mathbf{x} \cdot \mathbf{y}$ (matrix multiply)	x*y	$x < y$	x < y
$\mathbf{x} \times \mathbf{y}$ (cross prod)	x Alt−* y	$x \geq y$	x Alt−) y
x^{*} (conjugate)	x″	$x \leq y$	x Alt−(y
$\mathbf{x}^{T}$ (transpose)	x Alt−!	$x \neq y$	x Alt−# y
x^{y} (power)	x^y	$x \approx y$	z Alt−> y
Σx (sum of values)	Alt−$ x		

TABLE D-2 Built-in MathCAD Functions[a]

Trigonometric	Hyperbolic	Logs, exp, and complex	Bessel	Fast Fourier Transform (See Sec. 2-7)	Statistics	Miscellaneous		
						Function	Definition	
$\sin(z)$	$\sinh(z)$	$\exp(z)$	$Y0(x)$	$\mathrm{fft}(v)$	$\mathrm{mean}(v)$	$\mathrm{floor}(x)$	Greatest integer $\leq x$	
$\cos(z)$	$\cosh(z)$	$\ln(z)$	$Y1(x)$	$\mathrm{ifft}(v)$	$\mathrm{stdev}(v)$	$\mathrm{ceil}(x)$	Least integer $\geq x$	
$\tan(z)$	$\tanh(z)$	$\log(z)$[b]	$Yn(n,x)$	$\mathrm{cfft}(v)$	$\mathrm{var}(v)$	$\Phi(x)$	Unit step = $u(x)$	
$\mathrm{asin}(z)$	$\mathrm{asinh}(z)$	$\mathrm{Re}(z)$	$J0(x)$	$\mathrm{icfft}(v)$	$\Gamma(z)$	$\mathrm{mod}(x1,x2)$	Remainder of $x1/x2$	
$\mathrm{acos}(z)$	$\mathrm{acosh}(z)$	$\mathrm{Im}(z)$	$J1(x)$		$\mathrm{erf}(x)$	until $(x1,x2)$	Returns x2 until x1 < 0	
$\mathrm{atan}(z)$	$\mathrm{atanh}(z)$	$\arg(z)$	$Jn(n,x)$		$\mathrm{cnorm}(x)$[c]	$\mathrm{if}(c,x1,x2)$	Returns x1 if $c \neq 0$, x2 otherwise	
					$\mathrm{rnd}(x)$[d]			
					$\mathrm{hist}(v1,v2)$[e]			

[a]Notation used: x and y are real, z may be complex, n is an integer, v is a vector, and M is a matrix.
[b]Base 10 logarithm.
[c]This is the CDF, $F(x)$, for the Gaussian distribution with a mean of 0 and a variance of 1.
[d]Returns a random number that is uniformly distributed between 0 and x.
[e]Histogram function. v1 is a vector of allowed discrete values and v2 is the data vector (elements consist of the data values).

D-2 MathCAD Example

A MathCAD program and the corresponding computed plot for (7-23) from Sec. 7-1 is shown in Table D-3. This is file 7-23.MCD from the template floppy disk. The plot shown corresponds to Fig. 7-9 for the case when the digital modulation index is selected to be $h = 0.7$.

TABLE D-3   MathCAD Example: File 7-23.MCD

```
Ac := 1         R := 1                      1         R
** SELECT Mod. Index, h, by ***   Tb := -   DF := h· -      Tb = 1   DF = 0.35
** Global on next screen. *****        R         2


xs(f,n) := π· Tb· (f - DF· (2·n - 3))        xf(f) := 2· π· f· Tb
           sin(xs(f,n))                      xF := 2· π· DF· Tb
A(f,n)  := ─────────────                      xc(n,m) := xF· (n + m - 3)
              xs(f,n)


              cos(xf(f) - xc(n,m)) - cos(xF)· cos(xc(n,m))
B(f,n,m) := ─────────────────────────────────────────────
                              2
              1 + (cos(xF))   - 2· cos(xF)· cos(xf(f))


              2                                      2
P1(f) := A(f,1) · (1 + B(f,1,1))    P2(f) := A(f,2) · (1 + B(f,2,2))
P12(f) := 2· B(f,1,2)· A(f,1)· A(f,2)


              2
 P(f) := 0.5· Ac · Tb· (P1(f) + P2(f) + P12(f))
         See NEXT SCREEN for plot.              P(0) = 0.827
```

$$df := 1.5· \frac{R}{50} \qquad f := 0, df \ .. 1.5· R$$

** Compare with Fig. 7-9 **

h ≡ 0.7   <--SELECT

DF = 0.35
R = 1
Tb = 1

References

ABRAMOWITZ, M., and I. A. STEGUN (Editors), *Handbook of Mathematical Functions,* National Bureau of Standards, Superintendent of Documents, U.S. Government Printing Office, Washington, DC, 1964. Also available in paperback from Dover Publications, New York, 1965.

AMOROSO, F., "The Bandwidth of Digital Data Signals," *IEEE Communications Magazine,* vol. 18, no. 6, November 1980, pp. 13–24.

ANDERSON, R. R. and J. SALZ, "Spectra of Digital FM," *Bell System Technical Journal,* vol. 44, July–August 1965, pp. 1165–1189.

AOYAMA, T., W. R. DAUMER, and G. MODENA (Editors), Special Issue on Voice Coding for Communications, *IEEE Journal on Selected Areas of Communications,* vol. 6, February 1988.

ARRL, *The ARRL Handbook for the Radio Amateur,* 70th ed., L. D. Wolfgang, C. L. Hutchinson, et al. (Editors), American Radio Relay League, Newington, CT, 1993.

BASCH, E. E., and T. G. BROWN, "Introduction to Coherent Optical Fiber Transmission," *IEEE Communications Magazine,* vol. 23, May 1985, pp. 23–30.

BEDROSIAN, E. B., and S. O. RICE, "Distortion and Crosstalk of Linearly Filtered Angle-Modulated Signals," *Proceedings of the IEEE,* vol. 56, January 1968, pp. 2–13.

BELL TELEPHONE LABORATORIES, *Transmission Systems for Communications,* 4th ed., Western Electric Company, Winston-Salem, NC, 1970.

BENEDETTO, S., E. BIGLIERI, and V. CASTELLANI, *Digital Transmission Theory,* Prentice Hall, Englewood Cliffs, NJ, 1987.

BENNETT, W. R., and J. R. DAVEY, *Data Transmission,* McGraw-Hill Book Company, New York, 1965.

BENNETT, W. R., and S. O. RICE, "Spectral Density and Autocorrelation Functions Associated with Binary Frequency Shift Keying," *Bell System Technical Journal,* vol. 42, September 1963, pp. 2355–2385.

BENSON, K. B., and J. C. WHITAKER, *Television Engineering Handbook,* rev. ed., McGraw-Hill Book Company, New York, 1992.

BERGLAND, G. D., "A Guided Tour of the Fast Fourier Transform," *IEEE Spectrum,* vol. 6, July 1969, pp. 41–52.

BHARGAVA, V. K., "Forward Error Correction Schemes for Digital Communications," *IEEE Communications Magazine,* vol. 21, January 1983, pp. 11–19.

BHARGAVA, V. K., D. HACCOUN, R. MATYAS, and P. P. NUSPL, *Digital Communications by Satellite,* Wiley-Interscience, New York, 1981.

BIC, J. C., D. DUPONTEIL, and J. C. IMBEAUX, *Elements of Digital Communication,* John Wiley & Sons, New York, 1991.

BIGLIERI, E., D. DIVSALAR, P. J. MCLANE, and M. K. SIMON, *Introduction to Trellis-Coded Modulation with Applications,* Macmillan Publishing Company, New York, 1991.

BLAHUT, R. E., *Theory and Practice of Error Control Codes,* Addison-Wesley Publishing Company, Reading, MA, 1983.

BLANCHARD, A., *Phase-Locked Loops,* Wiley-Interscience, New York, 1976.

BÖRJESSON P. O., and C.-E. W. SUNDBERG, Simple Approximations for the Error Function $Q(x)$ for Communication Applications," *IEEE Transactions on Communications,* vol. COM-27, March 1979, pp. 639–643.

BOWRON, P., and F. W. STEPHENSON, *Active Filters for Communications and Instrumentation,* McGraw-Hill Book Company, New York, 1979.

BREMERMANN, H., *Distributions, Complex Variables and Fourier Transforms,* Addison-Wesley Publishing Company, Reading, MA, 1965.

BRILEY, B. E., *Introduction to Telephone Switching,* Addison-Wesley Publishing Company, Reading, MA, 1983.

BROADCASTING, *Broadcasting Yearbook,* Broadcasting Publications, Inc., Washington, DC, 1991.

BYLANSKI, P., and D. G. W. INGRAM, *Digital Transmission Systems,* Peter Peregrinus Ltd., Stevenage, Herts, England, 1976.

CAMPANELLA, M., U. LoFASO, and G. MAMOLA, "Optimum Pulse Shape for Minimum Spectral Occupancy in FSK Signals," *IEEE Transactions on Vehicular Technology,* vol. VT-33, May 1984, pp. 67–75.

CARLSON, A. B., *Communication Systems,* 3rd ed., McGraw-Hill Book Company, New York, 1986.

CATTERMOLE, K. W., *Principles of Pulse-Code Modulation,* American Elsevier, New York, 1969.

CCITT STUDY GROUP XVII, "Recommendation V.32 for a Family of 2-Wire, Duplex Modems Operating on the General Switched Telephone Network and on Leased Telephone-Type Circuits," *Document AP VIII–43–E,* May 1984.

CHAKRABORTY, D., "VSAT Communication Networks: An Overview," *IEEE Communications Magazine,* vol. 26, no. 5, May 1988, pp. 10–24.

CHAPMAN, R. C. (Editor), "The SLC96 Subscriber Loop Carrier System," *AT&T Bell Laboratories Technical Journal,* vol. 63, no. 10, Part 2, December 1984, pp. 2273–2437.

CHILDERS, D., and A. DURLING, *Digital Filtering and Signal Processing,* West Publishing Company, New York, 1975.

CHORAFAS, D. N., *Telephony, Today and Tomorrow,* Prentice Hall, Englewood Cliffs, NJ, 1984.

CLARK, G. C., and J. B. CAIN, *Error–Correction Coding for Digital Communications,* Plenum Publishing Corporation, New York, 1981.

COOPER, G. R., and C. D. McGILLEM, *Modern Communications and Spread Spectrum,* McGraw-Hill Book Company, New York, 1986.

COUCH, L. W., "A Study of a Driven Oscillator with FM Feedback by Use of a Phase-Lock-Loop Model," *IEEE Transactions on Microwave Theory and Techniques,* vol. MTT-19, no. 4, April 1971, pp. 357–366.

COUCH, L. W., *Digital and Analog Communication Systems,* 4th ed., Macmillan Publishing Company, New York, 1993.

COURANT, R., and D. HILBERT, *Methods of Mathematical Physics,* Vol. 1, Wiley-Interscience, New York, 1953.

DAMMANN, C. L., L. D. McDANIEL, and C. L. MADDOX, "D2 Channel Bank: Multiplexing and Coding," *Bell System Technical Journal,* vol. 51, October 1972, pp. 1675–1700.

DAVENPORT, W. B., JR., and W. L. ROOT, *An Introduction to the Theory of Random Signals and Noise,* McGraw-Hill Book Company, New York, 1958.

DAVIDOFF, M. R., *The Satellite Experimenter's Handbook,* American Radio Relay League, Newington, CT, 1984.

DAVIS, D. W., and D. L. A. BARBER, *Communication Networks for Computers,* John Wiley & Sons, New York, 1973.

DEANGELO, J., "New Transmitter Design for the 80's," *BM/E (Broadcast Management/Engineering),* vol. 18, March 1982, pp. 215–226.

DECINA, M., and G. MODENA, "CCITT Standards on Digital Speech Processing," *IEEE Journal on Selected Areas of Communications,* vol. 6, February 1988, pp. 227–234.

DEFFEBACH, H. L., and W. O. FROST, "A Survey of Digital Baseband Signaling Techniques," *NASA Technical Memorandum NASATM X-64615,* June 30, 1971.

DEJAGER, F., "Delta Modulation: A Method of PCM Transmission Using a 1-Unit Code," *Phillips Research Report,* no. 7, December 1952, pp. 442–466.

DEJAGER, F., and C. B. DEKKER, "Tamed Frequency Modulation: A Novel Method to Achieve Spectrum Economy in Digital Transmission," *IEEE Transactions on Communications,* vol. COM–26, May 1978, pp. 534–542.

DHAKE, A. M., *Television Engineering,* McGraw-Hill Book Company, New Delhi, India, 1980.

DIXON, R. C., *Spread Spectrum Systems,* 2nd ed., John Wiley & Sons, New York, 1984.

DORF, R. C. (Editor-in-Chief), *The Electrical Engineering Handbook,* CRC Press, Boca Raton, FL, 1993.

EDELSON, B. I., and A. M. WERTH, "SPADE System Progress and Application," *COM–SAT Technical Review,* Spring 1972, pp. 221–242.

EILERS, C. G., "TV Multichannel Sound—The BTSC System," *IEEE Transactions on Consumer Electronics,* vol. CE–31, February 1985, pp. 1–7.

FEHER, K., *Digital Communications: Satellite/Earth Station Engineering,* Prentice Hall, Englewood Cliffs, NJ, 1981.

FELLER, W., *An Introduction to Probability Theory and Its Applications,* John Wiley & Sons, New York, 1957, p. 168.

FIKE, J. L., and G. E. FRIEND, *Understanding Telephone Electronics,* 2nd ed., Texas Instruments, Dallas, 1984.

FINK, D. G., and H. W. BEATY (Editors), *Standard Handbook for Electrical Engineers,* McGraw-Hill Book Company, New York, 1978.

FLANAGAN, J. L., M. R. SCHROEDER, B. S. ATAL, R. E. CROCHIERE, N. S. JAYANT, and J. M. TRIBOLET, "Speech Coding," *IEEE Transactions on Communications,* vol. COM–27, April 1979, pp. 710–737.

FOLEY, J., "Iridium: Key to World Wide Cellular Communications," *Telecommunications,* vol. 25, October 1991, pp. 23–28.

FORNEY, G. D., "The Viterbi Algorithm," *Proceedings of the IEEE,* vol. 61, March 1973, pp. 268–273.

GALLAGHER, R. G., *Information Theory and Reliable Communications,* John Wiley & Sons, New York, 1968.

GARDNER, F. M., *Phaselock Techniques,* 2nd ed., John Wiley & Sons, New York, 1979.

GARDNER, F. M., and W. C. LINDSEY (Guest Editors), Special Issue on Synchronization, *IEEE Transactions on Communications,* vol. COM–28, no. 8, August 1980.

GERSHO, A., "Charge-Coupled Devices: The Analog Shift Register Comes of Age," *IEEE Communications Society Magazine,* vol. 13, November 1975, pp. 27–32.

GERSON, I. A., and M. A. JASIUK, "Vector Sum Excited Linear Prediction (VSELP) Speech Coding at 8kb/s," *International Conf. on Acoustics, Speech, and Signal Processing,* Albuquerque, NM, April 1990, pp. 461–464.

GLISSON, T. L., *Introduction to System Analysis,* McGraw-Hill Book Company, New York, 1986.

GOLDBERG, R. R., *Fourier Transforms,* Cambridge University Press, New York, 1961.

GOODMAN, D. J., "Trends in Cellular and Cordless Communication," *IEEE Communications Magazine,* vol. 29, June 1991, pp. 31–40.

GRIFFITHS, J., *Radio Wave Propagation and Antennas,* Prentice Hall, Englewood Cliffs, NJ, 1987.

GROB, B., *Basic Television,* 4th ed., McGraw-Hill Book Company, New York, 1975.

GRUBB, J. L., "The Traveller's Dream Come True," *IEEE Communications Magazine,* vol. 29, November 1991, pp. 48–51.

GUPTA, S. C., "Phase Locked Loops," *Proceedings of the IEEE,* vol. 63, February 1975, pp. 291–306.

HA, T. T., *Digital Satellite Communications,* Macmillan Publishing Company, New York, 1986.

HA, T. T., *Digital Satellite Communications,* 2nd ed., John Wiley & Sons, New York, 1989.

HAMMING, R. W., "Error Detecting and Error Correcting Codes," *Bell System Technical Journal,* vol. 29, April 1950, pp. 147–160.

HÄNDEL, R., and M. N. HUBER, *Integrated Broadband Networks,* Addison-Wesley Publishing Company, Reading, MA, 1991.

HARRIS, A., "The New World of HDTV," *Electronics Now,* vol. 64, May 1993, pp. 33–40 and p. 72.

HARRIS, F. J., "On the Use of Windows for Harmonic Analysis with the Discrete Fourier Transform," *Proceedings of the IEEE,* vol. 66, January 1978, pp. 51–83.

HARRIS, F. J., "The Discrete Fourier Transform Applied to Time Domain Signal Processing," *IEEE Communications Magazine,* vol. 20, May 1982, pp. 13–22.

HARTLEY, R. V., "Transmission of Information," *Bell System Technical Journal,* vol. 27, July 1948, pp. 535–563.

HAUS, H. A., Chairman IRE Subcommittee 7.9 on Noise, "Description of Noise Performance of Amplifiers and Receiving Systems," *Proceedings of the IEEE,* vol. 51, no. 3, March 1963, pp. 436–442.

HAYKIN, S., *Communication Systems,* 2nd ed., John Wiley & Sons, New York, 1983.

HOLMES, J. K., *Coherent Spread Spectrum Systems,* Wiley-Interscience, New York, 1982.

HSING, T. R., C. CHEN, and J. A. BELLISIO, "Video Communications and Services in the Copper Loop," *IEEE Communications Magazine,* vol. 31, January 1993, pp. 62–68.

HUANG, D. T., and C. F. VALENTI, "Digital Subscriber Lines: Network Considerations for ISDN Basic Access Standard," *Proceedings of the IEEE,* vol. 79, February 1991, pp. 125–144.

IRMER, T., "An Overview of Digital Hierarchies in the World Today," *IEEE International Conference on Communications,* San Francisco, June 1975, pp. 16–1 to 16–4.

IRWIN, J. D., *Basic Engineering Circuit Analysis,* 3rd ed., Macmillan Publishing Company, New York, 1993.

JACOBS, I., "Design Considerations for Long-Haul Lightwave Systems," *IEEE Journal on Selected Areas of Communications,* vol. 4, December 1986, pp. 1389–1395.

JAMES, R. T., and P. E. MUENCH, "AT&T Facilities and Services," *Proceedings of the IEEE,* vol. 60, November 1972, pp. 1342–1349.

JAYANT, N. S., "Digital Encoding of Speech Waveforms," *Proceedings of the IEEE,* May 1974, pp. 611–632.

JAYANT, N. S., "Coding Speech at Low Bit Rates," *IEEE Spectrum,* vol. 23, August 1986, pp. 58–63.

JAYANT, N. S., and P. NOLL, *Digital Coding of Waveforms,* Prentice Hall, Englewood Cliffs, NJ, 1984.

JERRI, A. J., "The Shannon Sampling Theorem: Its Various Extensions and Applications: A Tutorial Review," *Proceedings of the IEEE,* vol. 65, no. 11, November 1977, pp. 1565–1596.

JORDAN, E. C. (Editor), *Reference Data for Engineers: Radio, Electronics, Computer, and Communications,* 7th ed., Howard W. Sams & Company, Indianapolis, IN, 1985.

JORDAN, E. C., and K. G. BALMAIN, *Electromagnetic Waves and Radiating Systems,* 2nd ed., Prentice Hall, Englewood Cliffs, NJ, 1968.

JURGEN, R. K., "High-Definition Television Update," *IEEE Spectrum,* vol. 25, April 1988, pp. 56–62.

JURGEN, R. K., "The Challenges of Digital HDTV," *IEEE Spectrum,* vol. 28, April 1991, pp. 28–30 and 71–73.

KAUFMAN, M., and A. H. SEIDMAN, *Handbook of Electronics Calculations,* McGraw-Hill Book Company, New York, 1979.

KRAUS, J. D., *Radio Astronomy,* 2nd ed., Cygnus-Quasar Books, Powell, OH, 1986.

KRAUSS, H. L., C. W. BOSTIAN, and F. H. RAAB, *Solid State Radio Engineering,* John Wiley & Sons, New York, 1980.

LAM, S. S., "Satellite Packet Communications, Multiple Access Protocols and Performance," *IEEE Transactions on Communications,* vol. COM–27, October 1979, pp. 1456–1466.

LANCASTER, D., "Hardware Hacker: Caller Number Delivery," *Radio-Electronics,* vol. 62, August 1991, pp. 69–72.

LEE, W. C. Y., "Elements of Cellular Mobile Radio Systems," *IEEE Transactions on Vehicular Technology,* vol. VT–35, May 1986, pp. 48–56.

LEE, W. C. Y., *Mobile Cellular Telecommunications Systems,* McGraw-Hill Book Company, New York, 1989.

LEIB, H., and S. PASUPATHY, "Error-Control Properties of Minimum Shift Keying," *IEEE Communications Magazine,* vol. 31, January 1993, pp. 52–61.

LIN, S., and D. J. COSTELLO, JR., *Error Control Coding,* Prentice Hall Englewood Cliffs, NJ, 1983.

LINDSEY, W. C., and C. M. CHIE, "A Survey of Digital Phase-Locked Loops," *Proceedings of the IEEE,* vol. 69, April 1981, pp. 410–431.

LUCKY, R. W., and H. R. RUDIN, "Generalized Automatic Equalization for Communication Channels," *IEEE International Communication Conference,* vol. 22, 1966.

LUCKY, R. W., J. SALZ, and E. J. WELDON, *Principles of Data Communication,* McGraw-Hill Book Company, New York, 1968.

MANASSEWITSCH, V., *Frequency Synthesizers,* 3rd ed., Wiley-Interscience, New York, 1987.

MARKLE, R. E., "Single Sideband Triples Microwave Radio Route Capacity," *Bell Systems Laboratories Record,* vol. 56, no. 4, April 1978, pp. 105–110.

MARKLE, R. E., "Prologue, The AR6A Single-Sideband Microwave Radio System," *Bell System Technical Journal,* vol. 62, December 1983, pp. 3249–3253. (The entire December 1983 issue deals with the AR6A system.)

MCELIECE, R. J., *The Theory of Information and Coding (Encyclopedia of Mathematics and Its Applications,* vol. 3), Addison-Wesley Publishing Company, Reading, MA, 1977.

MENNIE, D., "AM Stereo: Five Competing Options," *IEEE Spectrum,* vol. 15, June 1978, pp. 24–31.

MIYAOKA, S., "Digital Audio Is Compact and Rugged," *IEEE Spectrum,* vol. 21, March 1984, pp. 35–39.

MOTOROLA, *Telecommunications Device Data,* Motorola Semiconductor Products, Austin, TX, 1985.

MUMFORD, W. W., and E. H. SCHEIBE, *Noise Performance Factors in Communication Systems,* Horizon House–Microwave, Dedham, MA, 1968.

MURPHY, E., "Whatever Happened to AM Stereo?" *IEEE Spectrum,* vol. 25, March 1988, p. 17.

NILSSON, J. W., *Electric Circuits,* 3rd ed., Addison-Wesley Publishing Company, Reading, MA, 1990.

NORTH, D. O., "An Analysis of the Factors Which Determine Signal/Noise Discrimination in Pulsed-Carrier Systems," *RCA Technical Report,* PTR–6–C, June 1943; reprinted in *Proceedings of the IEEE,* vol. 51, July 1963, pp. 1016–1027.

NYQUIST, H., "Certain Topics in Telegraph Transmission Theory," *Transactions of the AIEE,* vol. 47, February 1928, pp. 617–644.

OKUMURA, Y., and M. SHINJI (Guest Editors) Special Issue on Mobile Radio Communications, *IEEE Communications Magazine,* vol. 24, February 1986.

OLMSTED, J. M. H., *Advanced Calculus,* Appleton-Century-Crofts, New York, 1961.

O'NEAL, J. B., "Delta Modulation and Quantizing Noise, Analytical and Computer Simulation Results for Gaussian and Television Input Signals," *Bell System Technical Journal,* vol. 45, January 1966(a), pp. 117–141.

O'NEAL, J. B., "Predictive Quantization (DPCM) for the Transmission of Television Signals," *Bell System Technical Journal,* vol. 45, May–June 1966(b), pp. 689–721.

OPPENHEIM, A. V., and R. W. SCHAFER, *Digital Signal Processing,* Prentice Hall, Englewood Cliffs, NJ, 1975.

OPPENHEIM, A. V., and R. W. SCHAFER, *Discrete-Time Signal Processing,* Prentice Hall, Englewood Cliffs, NJ, 1989.

PANDHI, S. N., "The Universal Data Connection," *IEEE Spectrum,* vol. 24, July 1987, pp. 31–37.

PANTER, P. F, *Modulation, Noise and Spectral Analysis,* McGraw-Hill Book Company, New York, 1965.

PAPOULIS, A., *Probability, Random Variables and Stochastic Processes,* 3rd ed., McGraw-Hill Book Company, New York, 1991.

PEEBLES, P. Z., *Communication System Principles,* Addison-Wesley Publishing Company, Reading, MA, 1976.

PEEBLES, P. Z., *Digital Communication Systems,* Prentice Hall, Englewood Cliffs, NJ, 1987.

PEEBLES, P. Z., *Probability, Random Variables, and Random Signal Principles,* 3rd ed., McGraw-Hill Book Company, New York, 1993.

PEEK, J. B. H., "Communications Aspects of the Compact Disk Digital Audio System," *IEEE Communications Magazine,* vol. 23, February 1985, pp. 7–15.

PETERSON, W. W., and E. J. WELDON, *Error-Correcting Codes,* MIT Press, Cambridge, MA, 1972.

PETTIT, R. H., *ECM and ECCM Techniques for Digital Communication Systems,* Lifetime Learning Publications (a division of Wadsworth, Inc.), Belmont, CA, 1982.

PRATT, T., and C. W. BOSTIAN, *Satellite Communications,* John Wiley & Sons, New York, 1986.

PROAKIS, J. G., *Digital Communications,* 2nd ed., McGraw-Hill Book Company, New York, 1989.

QURESHI, S., "Adaptive Equalization," *IEEE Communications Magazine,* vol. 20, March 1982, pp. 9–16.

RAMO, S., J. R. WHINNERY, and T. VANDUZER, *Fields and Waves in Communication Electronics,* 2nd ed., John Wiley & Sons, Inc., New York, 1984.

RANA, A. H., J. MCCOSKEY, and W. CHECK, "VSAT Technology, Trends and Applications," *Proceedings of the IEEE,* vol. 78, July 1990, pp. 1087–1095.

RAPPAPORT, T. S., "Characteristics of UHF Multipath Radio Channels in Factory Buildings," *IEEE Transactions on Antennas and Propagation,* vol. 37, August 1989, pp. 1058–1069.

RHEE, S. B., and W. C. Y. LEE (Editors), Special Issue on Digital Cellular Technologies, *IEEE Transactions on Vehicular Technology,* vol. VT-40, May 1991.

RICE, S. O., "Mathematical Analysis of Random Noise," *Bell System Technical Journal,* vol. 23, July 1944, pp. 282–333, and vol. 24, January 1945, pp. 46–156; reprinted in *Selected Papers on Noise and Stochastic Processes,* N. Wax (Editor), Dover Publications, New York, 1954.

ROSE, R. B., "MIMIMUF: A Simplified MUF–Prediction Program for Microcomputers," *QST,* vol. 66, December 1982, pp. 36–38.

ROSE, R. B., "Technical Correspondence: MIMIMUF Revisited," *QST,* vol. 68, March 1984, p. 46.

ROWE, H. E., *Signals and Noise in Communication Systems,* D. Van Nostrand Company, Princeton, NJ, 1965.

RYAN, J. S. (Editor), Special Issue on Telecommunications Standards, *IEEE Communications Magazine,* vol. 23, January 1985.

RYDER, J. D., and D. G. FINK, *Engineers and Electrons,* IEEE Press, New York, 1984.

SABIN, W. E., and E. O. SCHOENIKE, *Single-Sideband Systems and Circuits,* McGraw-Hill Book Company, New York, 1987.

SALTZBERG, B. R., T. R. HSING, J. M. CIOFFI, and D. W. LIN (Editors), Special Issue on High-Speed Digital Subscriber Lines, *IEEE Journal on Selected Areas in Communications,* vol. 9, August 1991.

SCHILLING, D. L., R. L. PICKHOLTZ, and L. B. MILSTEIN, "Spread Spectrum Goes Commercial," *IEEE Spectrum,* vol. 27, August 1990, pp. 40–45.

SCHILLING, D. L., L. B. MILSTEIN, R. L. PICKHOLTZ, M. KULLBACK, and F. MILLER, "Spread Spectrum for Commercial Communications," *IEEE Communications Magazine,* vol. 29, April 1991, pp. 66–67.

SCHWARTZ, B. K., "The Analog Display Services Interface," *IEEE Communications Magazine,* vol. 31, April 1993, pp.70–75.

SHANMUGAN, K. S., *Digital and Analog Communication Systems,* John Wiley & Sons, New York, 1979.

SHANMUGAN, K. S., and A. M. BREIPOHL, *Random Signals: Detection, Estimation and Data Analysis,* John Wiley & Sons, New York, 1988.

SHANNON, C. E., "A Mathematical Theory and Communication," *Bell System Technical Journal,* vol. 27, July 1948, pp. 379–423, and October 1948, pp. 623–656.

SHANNON, C. E., "Communication in the Presence of Noise," *Proceedings of the IRE,* vol. 37, January 1949, pp. 10–21.

SINNEMA, W., and R. MCPHERSON, *Electronic Communications,* Prentice Hall Canada, Inc., Scarborough, Ontario, Canada, 1991.

SIPERKO, C. M., "LaserNet: A Fiber Optic Intrastate Network (Planning and Engineering Considerations)," *IEEE Communications Magazine,* vol. 23, May 1985, pp. 31–45.

SKLAR, B., *Digital Communications,* Prentice Hall, Englewood Cliffs, NJ, 1988.

SLEPIAN, D., "On Bandwidth," *Proceedings of the IEEE,* vol. 64, no. 3, March 1976, pp. 292–300.

SMITH, B., "Instantaneous Companding of Quantized Signals," *Bell System Technical Journal,* vol. 36, May 1957, pp. 653–709.

SMITH, J. R., *Modern Communication Circuits,* McGraw-Hill Book Company, New York, 1986.

SOLOMON, L., "The Upcoming New World of TV Reception," *Popular Electronics,* vol. 15, no. 5, May 1979, pp. 49–62.

SPILKER, J. J., *Digital Communications by Satellite,* Prentice Hall, Englewood Cliffs, NJ, 1977.

STALLINGS, W., *Data and Computer Communications,* 3rd ed., Macmillan Publishing Company, New York, 1992.

STALLINGS, W., *ISDN and Broadband ISDN,* Macmillan Publishing Company, New York, 1992.

STARK, H., F. B. TUTEUR, and J. B. ANDERSON, *Modern Electrical Communications,* Prentice Hall, Englewood Cliffs, NJ, 1988.

STIFFLER, J. J., *Theory of Synchronous Communication,* Prentice Hall, Englewood Cliffs, NJ, 1971.

SUNDE, E. D., *Communications Engineering Technology,* John Wiley & Sons, New York, 1969.

SWEENEY, P., *Error Control Coding,* Prentice Hall, Englewood Cliffs, NJ, 1991.

TAUB, H., and D. L. SCHILLING, *Principles of Communication Systems,* 2nd ed., McGraw-Hill Book Company, New York, 1986.

THOMAS, J. B., *An Introduction to Statistical Communication Theory,* John Wiley & Sons, New York, 1969.

UNGERBOECK, G., "Channel Coding with Multilevel/Phase Signals," *IEEE Transactions on Information Theory,* vol. IT–28, January 1982, pp. 55–67.

UNGERBOECK, G., "Trellis-Coded Modulation with Redundant Signal Sets," Parts 1 and 2, *IEEE Communications Magazine,* vol. 25, no. 2, February 1987, pp. 5–21.

VAN DER ZIEL, A., *Noise in Solid State Devices and Circuits,* Wiley-Interscience, New York, 1986.

VITERBI, A. J., "When Not to Spread Spectrum: A Sequel," *IEEE Communications Magazine,* vol. 23, April 1985, pp. 12–17.

VITERBI, A. J., and J. K. OMURA, *Principles of Digital Communication and Coding,* McGraw-Hill Book Company, New York, 1979.

WEI, L., "Rotationally Invariant Convolutional Channel Coding with Expanded Signal Space. Part II. Nonlinear Codes," *IEEE Journal on Selected Areas in Communications,* vol. SAC–2, no. 2, September 1984, pp. 672–686.

WHITTAKER, E. T., "On Functions Which Are Represented by the Expansions of the Interpolation Theory," *Proceedings of the Royal Society* (Edinburgh), vol. 35, 1915, pp. 181–194.

WIENER, N., *Extrapolation, Interpolation, and Smoothing of Stationary Time Series with Engineering Applications,* MIT Press, Cambridge, MA, 1949.

WOZENCRAFT, J. M., and I. M. JACOBS, *Principles of Communication Engineering,* John Wiley & Sons, New York, 1965.

WYLIE, C. R., JR., *Advanced Engineering Analysis,* John Wiley & Sons, New York, 1960.

YOUNG, P. H., *Electronic Communication Techniques,* Merrill Publishing Co., Columbus, OH, 1990.

ZIEMER, R. E., and R. L. PETERSON, *Digital Communications and Spread Spectrum Systems,* Macmillan Publishing Company, New York, 1985.

ZIEMER, R. E., and W. H. TRANTER, *Principles of Communications,* 3rd ed., Houghton Mifflin Company, Boston, 1990.

ZIEMER, R. E., W. H. TRANTER, and D. R. FANNIN, *Signals and Systems,* 2nd ed., Macmillan Publishing Company, New York, 1989.

ZOU, W. Y., "Comparison of Proposed HDTV Terrestrial Broadcasting Systems," *IEEE Transactions on Broadcasting,* vol. 37, December 1991, pp. 145–147.

Answers to Selected Problems

Chapter 1

1-4   1.97 bits

1-8 $H = 3.084$ bits

1-10 $H = 3.32$ bits, $T = 1.66$ sec

Chapter 2

2-9   36 dB

2-10   (a) 4.08×10^{-14} W   (b) -103.9 dBm   (c) 1.75 μV

2-16 $S(f) = -\dfrac{A}{\omega^2} + Ae^{-j\omega T_0}\left(\dfrac{1}{\omega^2} + j\dfrac{T_0}{\omega}\right)$,   where $\omega = 2\pi f$.

Note that $S(0) = AT_0^2/2$.

2-40   (a) $(\sin 4t)/(4t)$ (b) 7

2-45   (a) $-0.4545A$ (b) $0.9129A$

2-46   (a) The expression for $v(t)$ over one period is

$$v(t) = \begin{cases} \dfrac{3A}{T}t, & 0 < t < \tfrac{1}{3}T \\[2mm] \dfrac{-3A}{T}\left(t - \dfrac{2}{3}T\right), & \tfrac{1}{3}T < t < \tfrac{5}{6}T \\[2mm] \dfrac{3A}{T}(t - T), & \tfrac{5}{6}T < t < T \end{cases}$$

(b) $c_n = \begin{cases} \tfrac{1}{4}A, & n = 0 \\[2mm] \dfrac{3Ae^{-j2\pi n/3}}{(\pi n)^2}, & n = \text{odd} \\[2mm] 0, & \text{other } n \end{cases}$

(c) $V_{\text{rms}} = A/2$ (d) BW $= (1/T)$ Hz

2-48   (a) $(A_1 + A_2)/\sqrt{2}$ (b) $\left(\sqrt{A_1^2 + A_2^2}\right)/\sqrt{2}$ (c) $|A_2 - A_1|/\sqrt{2}$

(d) $\left(\sqrt{A_1^2 + A_2^2}\right)/\sqrt{2}$ (e) $\left(\sqrt{A_1^2 + A_2^2}\right)/\sqrt{2}$

2-56 $c_n = \begin{cases} \dfrac{AT^2}{2T_0}, & n = 0 \\[4mm] \dfrac{A\{e^{-j2\pi nT/T_0}[1 + j2\pi n(T/T_0)] - 1\}}{(2\pi n)^2/T_0}, & n \neq 0 \end{cases}$

2-63 (a) $c_n = \begin{cases} 0, & n = \text{even} \\[3mm] \dfrac{4}{n^2\pi^2}, & n = \text{odd} \end{cases}$ \qquad (b) $\frac{1}{3}$ W

Chapter 3

3-5 (a) $\mathcal{P}_x(f) = \dfrac{32\pi^2}{1 + (6\pi f)^2}$ \qquad (b) $\mathcal{P}_{ave} = 52.6$ W

3-9 (a) $\mathcal{P}_x(f) = \frac{5}{8}\delta(f + \frac{2}{3}f_0) + \frac{1}{4}\delta(f) + \frac{5}{8}\delta(f - \frac{2}{3}f_0)$

(b) $\mathcal{P}_y(f) = \frac{45}{104}\delta(f + \frac{2}{3}f_0) + \frac{1}{4}\delta(f) + \frac{45}{104}\delta(f - \frac{2}{3}f_0)$

(c) $P = 1.12$ W out

3-16 (a) 6.28 msec \qquad (b) 160

3-18 (a) 4 bits/word \qquad (b) 5 kbits/sec

3-27 $B_{eq} = \dfrac{B_{null}}{2}$

Chapter 4

4-3 (a)

$$W_s(f) = d \sum_{n=-\infty}^{\infty} \frac{\sin \pi nd}{\pi nd} \begin{cases} 1, & |f - nf_s| \leq 2500 \\[3mm] \dfrac{-1}{1500}(|f - nf_s| - 4000), & 2500 \leq |f - nf_s| \leq 4000 \\[3mm] 0, & f \text{ elsewhere} \end{cases}$$

where $d = 0.5$ and $f_s = 10,000$

(b)

$$W_s(f) = 0.5\left(\frac{\sin \pi\tau f}{\pi\tau f}\right) \sum_{k=-\infty}^{\infty} \begin{cases} 1, & |f - kf_s| \leq 2500 \\[3mm] \dfrac{-1}{1500}(|f - kf_s| - 4000), & 2500 \leq |f - kf_s| \leq 4000 \\[3mm] 0, & f \text{ elsewhere} \end{cases}$$

where $\tau = 50 \times 10^{-6}$ and $f_s = 10,000$

4-8 $W_s(f) = -j\left(\dfrac{1 - \cos(\pi f/f_s)}{\pi f/f_s}\right)$

$$\times \sum_{k=-\infty}^{\infty} \begin{cases} 1, & |f - kf_s| \le 2500 \\ \dfrac{-1}{1500}(|f - kf_s| - 4000), & 2500 \le |f - kf_s| \le 4000 \\ 0, & f \text{ elsewhere} \end{cases}$$

4-10 **(a)** 200 samples/sec **(b)** 9 bits/word **(c)** 1.8 kbits/sec **(d)** 900 Hz

4-16 **(a)** 5 bits **(b)** 27 kHz

4-26 **(a)** $\mathcal{P}(f) = \dfrac{A^2 T_b}{4}\left[\dfrac{\sin(\frac{1}{2}\pi f T_b)}{\frac{1}{2}\pi f T_b}\right]^2$

(b) $\mathcal{P}(f) = \dfrac{A^2 T_b}{4}\left[\dfrac{\sin(\frac{1}{4}\pi f T_b)}{\frac{1}{4}\pi f T_b}\right]^2 [\sin(\frac{1}{4}\pi f T_b)]^2$

4-38 **(a)** 32.4 kbits/sec **(b)** 10.8 ksymbols/sec **(c)** 5.4 kHz

4-39 **(a)** 3.2 ksymbols/sec **(b)** 0.5

4-46 **(a)** 5.33 kbits/sec **(b)** 667 Hz

4-47 **(a)** 10.7 kbits/sec **(b)** 1.33 kHz

4-58 **(a)** 0.00534 **(b)** 0.427

4-67 **(a)** 11 bits/character **(b)** 20 terminals

4-70 **(a)** 13,896 **(b)** 5095 **(c)** 1273 **(d)** 159 **(e)** 23

4-77 **(a)** 40 Hz **(b)** 1280 Hz

Chapter 5

5-8 **(a)** $g(t) = 500 + 200 \sin \omega_a t$, AM, $m(t) = 0.4 \sin \omega_a t$

(b) $x(t) = 500 + 200 \sin \omega_a t$, $y(t) = 0$

(c) $R(t) = 500 + 200 \sin \omega_a t$, $\theta(t) = 0$

(d) 2.7 kW

5-19 48.3%

5-22 $K\sqrt{m^2(t) + [\hat{m}(t)]^2}$, yes

5-27 **(a)** $(j2\pi f)/[j2\pi f + K_d K_v F_1(f)]$

(b) $(j2\pi f)(f_1 + jf)/[j2\pi f(f_1 + jf) + K_d K_v f_1]$

5-34 **(a)** 107.6 MHz **(b)** RF: At least 96.81–96.99 MHz; IF: 10.61–10.79 MHz

(c) 118.3 MHz

Chapter 6

6-1   **(a)** 6.99 dBk   **(b)** 707 V   **(d)** 7025 W   **(e)** 18,050 W

6-6 $S(f) = \dfrac{1}{2}\left[\displaystyle\sum_{n=-\infty}^{\infty} c_n \delta(f - f_c - nf_m) + \sum_{n=-\infty}^{\infty} c_n^* \delta(f + f_c + nf_m)\right]$

where $c_n = \dfrac{A_c}{2\pi}\left[2\theta_1\left(\dfrac{\sin n\theta_1}{n\theta_1}\right) + 2A_m \dfrac{\cos n\theta_1 \sin\theta_1 - n\sin n\theta_1 \cos\theta_1}{1 - n^2}\right]$,

$A_m = 1.2$, and $\theta_1 = 146.4°$

6-7   **(a)** $s(t) = (\cos\omega_1 t + 2\cos 2\omega_1 t)\cos\omega_c t$,   where $\omega_1 = 1000\pi$

(b) $S(f) = \frac{1}{4}[\delta(f - f_c + f_1) + \delta(f + f_c - f_1) + \delta(f - f_c - f_1)$
$\qquad\qquad + \delta(f + f_c + f_1)] + \frac{1}{2}[\delta(f - f_c + 2f_1) + \delta(f + f_c - 2f_1)$
$\qquad\qquad + \delta(f - f_c - 2f_1) + \delta(f + f_c + 2f_1)]$

(c) 1.25 W   **(d)** 4.5 W

6-14   **(b)** $s(t) = \Pi(t)\cos\omega_c t - \dfrac{1}{\pi}\ln\left(\dfrac{|t + \frac{1}{2}|}{|t - \frac{1}{2}|}\right)\sin\omega_c t$

(c) $\max[s(t)] = \infty$

6-24   **(a)** $f_{BPF} = 12.96$ MHz, $B_{BPF} = 48.75$ kHz   **(b)** 7.96 or 17.96 MHz

(c) 9.38 kHz

6-26   **(a)** $m(t) = 0.2\cos(2000\pi t)$, $M_p = 0.2$ V, $f_m = 1$ kHz

(b) $m(t) = -0.13\sin(2000\pi t)$, $M_p = 0.13$ V, $f_m = 1$ kHz

(c) $P_{AV} = 2500$ W, $P_{PEP} = 2500$ W

6-31 $S(f) = \frac{1}{2}[G(f - f_c) + G^*(-f - f_c)]$, where
$G(f) = \sum_{n=-\infty}^{\infty} J_n(0.7854)\,\delta(f - nf_m)$, $f_c = 146.52$ MHz,
and $f_m = 1$ kHz. $B = 3.57$ kHz

6-35 $S(f) = \frac{1}{2}[\sum_{n=-\infty}^{\infty} c_n\,\delta(f - f_c - nf_m) + \sum_{n=-\infty}^{\infty} c_n^*\,\delta(f + f_c + nf_m)]$, where
$c_n = 5(e^{j\beta} - 1)\left(\dfrac{\sin(n\pi/2)}{n\pi/2}\right)$, $f_m = 1$ kHz, $\beta = 0.7854$, and $f_c = 60$ MHz

6-39   **(a)** 5.5 Hz

(b) $S(f) = \dfrac{A_c}{2}\left\{\delta(f - f_c) + \delta(f + f_c) + \dfrac{D_f}{2\pi}\displaystyle\sum_{\substack{n=-\infty \\ n\neq 0}}^{\infty}\left(\dfrac{c_n}{nf_m}\right)\right.$

$\left. \times\, [\delta(f - f_c - nf_m) - \delta(f + f_c - nf_m)]\right\}$,

where $c_n = 5e^{-jn\pi/2}\left(\dfrac{\sin(n\pi/2)}{n\pi/2}\right)$ $(n \neq 0)$,

$D_f = 6.98$ rads/V-sec, $f_m = 100$ Hz, and $f_c = 30$ MHz

6-42 $\mathscr{P}(f) \approx 0.893[2\delta(f - f_c + 5f_0) + \delta(f - f_c + 3f_0)$
$+ \delta(f - f_c - f_0) + 2\delta(f - f_c - 3f_0) + \delta(f - f_c - 5f_0)$
$+ 2\delta(f + f_c - 5f_0) + \delta(f + f_c - 3f_0) + \delta(f + f_c + f_0)$
$+ 2\delta(f + f_c + 3f_0) + \delta(f + f_c + 5f_0)]$

where $f_0 \triangleq \dfrac{D_f}{2\pi} = 15.9$ kHz and $f_c = 2$ GHz

6-45   **(a)** 20 kHz

(b) $S(f) = \frac{1}{2}[M_1(f - f_c) + M_1(f + f_c)] + \dfrac{j}{2}[M_2(f + f_c) - M_2(f - f_c)]$

Chapter 7

7-1   **(a)** $S(f) = \frac{1}{2}[X(f - f_c) + X^*(-f - f_c)]$,

where $X(f) = \dfrac{A_c}{2} \displaystyle\sum_{n=-\infty}^{\infty} \left(\dfrac{\sin(n\pi/2)}{n\pi/2}\right) \delta(f - \tfrac{1}{2}nR)$, $R = 2400$

(b) 4.8 kHz

7-8   **(a)** 3.6 kHz   **(b)** 8.6 kHz

7-22
$$\mathscr{P}_s(f) = \dfrac{K}{4}\left\{\left(\dfrac{\sin\left[\pi(f - f_c)\dfrac{\ell}{R}\right]}{\left[\pi(f - f_c)\dfrac{\ell}{R}\right]}\right)^2 + \left(\dfrac{\sin\left[\pi(f + f_c)\dfrac{\ell}{R}\right]}{\left[\pi(f + f_c)\dfrac{\ell}{R}\right]}\right)^2\right\}$$

where $f_c = 1.2$ kHz

7-32   **(a)** 2400 bits/sec   **(b)** $(P_e)_{\text{overall}} = 1.11 \times 10^{-14}$

Chapter 8

8-9   **(a)** 25.6 dB   **(b)** 36.3 W   **(c)** −54.9 dBm

8-13 $G_a = \dfrac{h_{fe}^2 R_s}{h_{oe}(R_s + h_{ie})^2}$

8-17   **(a)** 129 K   **(b)** −76.6 dBm

8-19 3.2×10^{-7}

8-22   **(a)** 19.8 dB   **(b)** 7.52 dB   **(c)** 4.67 dB

8-34   12.84-m diameter

8-40   20.6 kW

Appendix B

B-1   0.3486

B-2   **(a)** 5/36   **(b)** 15/36

B-4   **(a)** 1/2   **(b)** 1/3

B-8   0.4375

B-11   **(a)** b **(b)** $1/b$ **(c)** $1/b^2$

B-17 $P = 0.966$

B-21   51.0

B-26   **(a)** 1.337×10^{-11} **(b)** 0.9520

B-30 $f(y) = \begin{cases} \dfrac{1}{2\sigma\sqrt{2\pi y}}\, [e^{-(\sqrt{y}+m)^2/(2\sigma^2)} + e^{-(\sqrt{y}-m)^2/(2\sigma^2)}], & y \geq 0, \\ 0, & y < 0 \end{cases}$

B-35 $B\sigma/\sqrt{2\pi}$

B-37   **(a)** 1/6   **(b)** Yes   **(c)** 1/12

   (d) $f(x_2|x_1) = \begin{cases} \frac{1}{12}(1 + x_2), & 0 \leq x_1 \leq 1, \quad 0 \leq x_2 \leq 4 \\ 0, & \text{otherwise} \end{cases}$

B-46   **(a)** $f_y(y) = \displaystyle\int_{-\infty}^{\infty} \dfrac{1}{|Ax|}\, f_x\!\left(\dfrac{y}{Ax}, x\right) dx$ **(b)** $f_y(y) = \displaystyle\int_{-\infty}^{\infty} \dfrac{1}{|Ax|}\, f_{x_1}\!\left(\dfrac{y}{Ax}\right) f_{x_2}(x)\, dx$

Index

Absolute bandwidth, 122
Acoustic coupler, 561
Active filter, 247–250
ACU, 561
Adaptive delta modulator, 195–197
Adaptive equalizer, 561
Adaptive equalizing filter, 179, 185, 561
Address resolution protocol (TCP/IP), 561
Advanced mobile phone system (AMPS), 447–451
Aliasing, 104
 discrete Fourier transform, 117
 PAM, 138
Allocations, frequency, 11–12
ALOHA packet data transmission, 421–422
AM to PM conversion, 241
Amplifier, 250–256
 bandpass, 253–256
 classes A,B,C,D,E,G,T, and S, 255–256
 IF, 283–284, 286
 nonlinear, 251–256
 output, 280
Amplitude companded single sideband (ACSSB), 308–309
Amplitude modulation (AM), 295–302
 broadcast standards, 300–302
 complex envelope, 234–235, 295
 detector, see Envelope detector
 detector, see Product detector
 generation of, 298–300
 modulation efficiency, 297
 power, 239

signal-to-noise ratio, 335–337
 spectrum, 238, 298
 stereo transmission, 301–302
Amplitude response, linear system, 92
Amplitude shift keying (ASK)
 See On-off keying
Amplitude spectrum, 44
 See also Spectrum
Analog
 cellular telephone, 447–452
 S/N for modulated systems, 337
 signal, 8
 source, 8
 switching (telephone), 404
 system, 8
 waveform, 8
Analog subscriber loop, 400, 405
Analog-to-digital converter (ADC)
 counting or ramp, 146–147
 parallel or flash, 147
 serial, 147
 types, 146–148
 See also Pulse code modulation
Analytic function, 98
Angle modulation, 311–330
 See also Frequency modulation
 See also Phase modulation
ANSI, 541
Answers to selected problems, 578–583
Antennas, 423–425
 effective area, 425
 gain, 423–425
Antipodal signaling, 368
Aperture (PAM), 142
Aperiodic waveform, 35

Armstrong FM method, 325
ARQ (automatic retransmission request), 19, 552, 561
ASCII code, 540, 561
Aspect ratio, 455, 468, 470
ASR, definition, 561
Asymmetric sideband signals, 304–311
Asynchronous digital line, 202
Asynchronous transmission, 561
AT&T TDM hierarchy, 206
ATM (asynchronous transfer mode), 554, 561
Attenuator
 effective input-noise temperature, 432
 noise figure, 432
Audio mixer, 260
Autocorrelation function
 definition, 63
 m-sequence, 383–384
 time average, 63
 Wiener-Khintchine theorem, 63
Automatic repeat request (ARQ), 19, 552, 561
Automatic test equipment (ATE), 545
Available noise power, 427
Available power gain, 428, 433
Avalanche photodiode (APD), 443
Average
 dc value, 36
 effective input-noise temperature, 430
 information, 17
 noise figure, 429
 power, 37, 63, 237
 time, 35

Average effective input-noise temperature, 430
Average noise figure, 429
Average power, 37, 63
    AM signal, 297
    bandpass signal, 237
    SSB signal, 307

Balanced FM detector, 268–273
    discriminator, 270–273, 442
Balanced modulator, 262
Balanced signaling, 544
Bandlimited waveforms, 98
Bandpass
    amplifier, 253–256
    channel, 6, 230, 239–243
    definition, 6, 231
    dimensionality theorem, 245
    distortionless transmission, 242–243
    filter, 239–241
    limiter, 256–258
    representation, 230–233
    sampling theorem, 243–245
    signal power, 237–238
    spectrum, 236–237
    waveform, 230–246
Bands, frequency, 11–12
Bandwidth, 120–128
    absolute, 122
    AM signal, 298
    bounded spectrum, 124
    BPSK signal, 126
    coding, 28
    equivalent, 122–123
    estimation, 108
    FCC, 123
    FM, 322–323, 361
    modulated systems, 337
    multilevel signal, 176
    noise, 122–123
    null-to-null, 123
    PCM, 148–149
    PM, 322–323
    power, 123
    SSB signal, 305–306
    3-dB, 122
Baseband
    definition, 6, 230
    waveform, 230
BASIC program, FSK spectrum, 360
Basic rate ISDN, 405
Basis functions, 66
Basis set, 65–67
    complete, 66
    orthonormal, 66
    vector, 106
Baud, 106, 112, 173, 561
Baudot code, 538, 561

Bayes theorem, 496
BCH codes, 21–22
Bell 103 modem, 357–361, 557, 558
Bell 212A modem, 558, 557
Bent-pipe transponder, 413
BER (Bit Error Rate)
    See Probability of bit error
Bessel filter, 249–250
Bessel function, of first kind, 317–323
Binary phase-shift keying (BPSK),
        124–128, 350, 353–355
    bandwidth, 126
    detector, 355
    probability of bit error, 378, 379
    spectrum, 354
    with coding, 25–27
    See also Differential phase-shift keying
Binary signaling, 109–111, 155–158,
        349–363
    line coding formats, 155–158
    See also Digital signaling
Binit, 16
Binomial distribution, 507–510
Bipolar high-density line codes, 163
Bipolar signaling, 157, 162–164
    probability of bit error, 378, 379
    spectrum, 162–164
BISYNC protocol, 551–552, 561
Bit error rate (BER), 168–169
    See also probability of bit error
Bit interleaved TDM, 202
Bit rate, 106, 112
Bit synchronizer, 170–173, 378–379
    early-late gate, 171–173
    square-law, 172
Bits
    data, 107, 109–111
    information, 16–18
    parity, 20–21
Bivariate statistics, 523–524
Black and white television, 452–471
Block codes, 21–22, 27
Boltzmann's constant, 426
Bound, $Q(z)$ function, 514
Bounded spectrum bandwidth, 124
Bridge, 561
Broadband ISDN, 405
Butterworth filter, 249–250

C-conditioning, data line, 555–556
Calculus, 480–485
Caller ID, 401
Capacity, channel, 18, 26, 335–336
Cardinal series, 99
Carrier
    circuits, 231, 281–287
    delay, 243

frequency, 231–236
    synchronization, 267, 378–379
Carrier-to-noise ratio (C/N), 435–437
Carson's rule, 322–323, 361
Cascaded devices
    noise figure, 433
    noise temperature, 435
Case studies of communication
        systems, 395–478
CATV channels, 469
Causal response, 91
Cavity filter, 248–250
CCIR, 10
    TV standard, 465, 468
CCITT, 10
    TDM hierarchy, 209
    V.22 bis modem, 557, 558
    V.24 interface, 543–544
    V.32 modem, 557, 559
    V.33 modem, 557, 560
    X.25 interface, 553
Cellular telephone systems, 445–452
    AMPS, 448–449
    ETACS, 448
    GSM, 450
    JDC, 450
    JTACS, 448
    NADC, 450
    NAMPS, 449
    NTACS, 449
    standards, 448–450
Center of gravity, 506
Central (telephone) office, 399–405
Central limit theorem, 527–528
Centronics parallel interface, 544–545
Ceramic filter, 247–250
Channel, 5–7
    capacity, 18, 26, 335–336
    CATV, 469
    coding, 19
    common signaling, SPADE, 418–420
    distortionless, 95
    fading, 7
    FM broadcast, 333
    hardwire, 7
    I, 233, 234, 282, 286
    multipath, 7
    noise, 287
    Q, 233, 234, 282, 286
    reverse, 563
    softwire, 7
    television, 465, 469
    two-way radio, 333
Character interleaved TDM, 202
Chebychev filter, 249–250
Chip, 381
Chrominance signal, television, 461
Circuit
    frequency modulator, 313

phase modulator, 313
telephone, 399–405
Circuit switching, 561
Class
  A,B,C,D FM stations, 334
  A,B,C,D,E,G amplifier, 255–256
  I,II,III,IV AM stations, 300–301
Code, Gray, 146
Code rate, 20–21
Code-division multiple access
  (CDMA), 386–387, 416
Codes
  ASCII, 540
  Baudot, 538
  EBCDIC, 538–539
  Morse, 536
  pseudonoise, 381
  punched IBM card, 537
  sequential, 538
Coding, 19–29
  ARQ, 19, 552, 561
  bandwidth, 28
  BCH, 21
  block, 21–22, 27
  channel, 19
  concatenated, 27
  convolutional, 22–25, 27
  cyclic, 21
  decoding, 22–25
  differential, 164–166
  encoding, 21, 22–23
  error correction, 21
  error detection, 21
  FEC, 19
  gain, 25–28
  hard decisions, 25, 27
  interleaving, 25
  Maximal-length, 22, 381–384
  optimum performance, 26, 30
  performance, 25–28
  rate, 20–21
  Reed-Solomon, 22, 27
  sequential decoding, 22
  soft decisions, 24–25, 27
  speech, 197
  systematic, 21
  TCM, 28
  threshold, 26
  tree, 24
  Viterbi decoding, 24, 27
Coefficients
  cardinal series, 99
  Fourier series, 68–72
  orthogonal series, 64
  Taylor series, 64
Coherent detector, 268
Color television, 459–464
Common carrier systems, 395,
  410–411

Common signaling channel, SPADE,
  418–420
Communication
  analog, 8
  computer, 536–564
  digital, 8
  history, 2–5
  ideal, 18–19, 26, 30
  system, 5–7
Communication system computer
  simulation, 9–10, 565–569
Commutator, 199
Companding, 153–155
  A-law, 153
  Dolby and DBX, 336–339
  T1 system, 210
  u-law, 153
Comparator level, 215
Complex envelope, 231–233
  AM, 234–235, 295
  device output, 280
  down-converter output, 259, 280
  DSB-SC, 234–235, 302
  FM, 234–235, 311–312
  limiter output, 280
  modulation, 233–236
  PM, 234–235, 311–312
  power, evaluation of, 237–238
  QM, 234–235
  SSB-AM-SC, 234–235, 305
  SSB-EV, 234–235
  SSB-PM, 234–235
  SSB-SQ, 234–235
  up-converter output, 259, 280
  vectorscope presentation, 462
Complex Fourier series, 68–70
Compound event, 494
Compressor, 153
  See also Companding
Computer communications, 536–564
  ATM protocol, 554
  balanced signaling, 544
  BISYNC, 551–552
  CCITT X.25 interface, 553
  Centronics interface, 544–545
  codes used, 536–540
  data link control protocols, 551–554
  DS lines, 207
  DTE/DCE interface, 540–549
  ethernet interface, 546–549
  glossary, 561–564
  HDLC, 552–553
  IEEE-488 interface, 545–549
  ISDN, 405–409
  modems, 556–560
  modem, Bell 103, 357–361, 557,
  558
  modem, Bell 212A, 557, 558
  modem, CCITT V.22 bis, 557, 558

  modem, CCITT V.32, 557, 560
  modem, CCITT V.33, 557, 560
  OSI network model, 550–551
  RS-232C interface, 542–544
  RS-422A interface, 542–544
  RS-449 interface, 542–544
  RS-530 interface, 542–544
  SDLC, 552
  SONET, 210
  telephone line standards, 555–556
  T1 line, 207–212
  unbalanced signaling, 544
Computer modems, 556–560
  See also Modem
Computer network, ISO OSI model,
  550–551
Computer protocols
  See Data link control
Computer simulation, 9–10, 565–569
Computer solutions, 9, 565–569
Concatenated codes, 27
Concentrator, 561
Conditional probability, 496
Constraint length, convolutional code,
  22
Continuous distribution, 500
Continuous-phase FSK, 356
Continuously variable slope DM
  (CVSD), 195–197
Control character, 561
Conversion, AM to PM, 241
Converter, up and down, 258–264
Convolution
  definition, 58, 49
  linear system, 91
Convolutional codes, 22–25, 27
Correlation, 523
Correlation coefficient, 524
Correlation functions, autocorrelation,
  63
Costas phase-locked loop, 302–304
  demodulation of DSB-SC and BPSK,
  302–304
  for carrier synchronization, 354
Counting ADC, 146–147
Covariance, 524
CRC (cyclic redundancy check), 561
Cross modulation distortion, 255
Crosstalk, 199
Crystal filter, 247–250
CSMA/CD, 562
CTS, 562
Cumulative distribution function
  (CDF), 498, 521
  continuous distribution, 500
  discrete distribution, 500
  N-dimensional, 521
  properties, 500, 522
  table of, 508

Current loop interface, 541
Current spectrum, 43
CXR, 562
Cyclic coding, 21

D-conditioning, data line, 556
Data circuit-terminal equipment (DCE), 541
Data communication
  See Computer communications
  See Digital signaling
  See Probability of bit error
Data link control (DLC) protocols, 551–554
  BISYNC, 551–552
  HDLC, 552–553
  SDLC, 552
Data set, 562
Data terminal equipment (DTE), 541
Data transmission
  See Computer communication
  See Digital signaling and Modem
DBX noise reduction, 336–339
Dc value, 36
DCE (data communications equipment), 541, 562
Decibel, 40–42
  dBk, 42
  dBm, 42
  dBmV, 42
  dBrn, 42
  dBw, 42
  gain, 40
  power level, 42
  signal-to-noise, 41
Decision
  hard, 25, 27
  soft, 24–25, 27
Deemphasis and preemphasis in FM, 328–330
Definite integrals, 484–485
Definition
  bandpass, 231
  baseband, 230
  complex envelope, 232
  derivative, 480
  Dirac delta function, 50
  frequency, 43, 313
  integral, 481
  modulation, 231, 233–236
  random variable, 496
  real envelope, 232
  rectangular pulse, 53
  Se(x) function, 54
  set, 492
  triangular pulse, 54
  trigonometric, 479
  unit step function, 51

Delay
  carrier, 243
  group, 243
  time, 95, 242–243
Delta function
  Dirac, 50, 487–489
  Kronecker, 65
  spectra, 72–77
Delta modulation, 190–197
  adaptive, 195–197
  See also continuously variable slope (CVSD)
Demand-assigned multiple access (DAMA), 416, 417–418
Derivative, 480
  rules, 480
  table of, 480–481
Detector
  avalanche photodiode, 443
  balanced discriminator, 270–273
  coherent, 268
  Costas PLL, 302–304
  envelope, 265–266
  FM, 268–273, 277–278
  FM stereo, switching, 347
  FM, threshold extension, 442
  IQ, 286
  noncoherent, 268
  optimum digital, 352–353
  output, 280
  phase, 267, 274
  phase-locked loop, 273–279
  PIN diode (optical), 443
  PLL, coherent AM, 279
  PLL, FM or PM, 277–278
  product, 266–268, 286
  quadrature FM, 271
  See also Digital receivers
  See also Feedback demodulators
  slope, 268
  zero-crossing, 271–272
Deterministic waveform, 9
Dial-up line, 562
Dialing, pulse and touch-tone, 399, 401
Differential calculus, 480–481
Differential coding, 164–166
Differential phase-shift keying (DPSK), 355
  probability of bit error, 378, 379
Differential pulse-code modulation (DPCM), 186–190
Digital
  advantages of, 8
  repeater, 167–168
  signal, 8, 105–114
  signal formats, 155–177
  source, 7
  system, 8
  system link budget, 437

  waveform, 8
  See also Computer communications
  See also Digital receivers
  See also Digital signaling
Digital computer simulation, 9–10, 565–569
Digital modulation
  See Digital signaling
Digital modulation index, 354
Digital receivers
  See Probability of bit error
Digital signaling
  antipodal, 368
  bipolar, 157, 162–164
  BPSK, 350, 353–355
  cellular telephone, 450
  DPCM, 186–190
  DPSK, 355
  DS-1, DS-2, etc. data lines, 207
  FSK, 350–351, 356–363
  ISDN, 405–409
  Manchester, 157, 164
  MPSK, 364–366, 368–369
  MSK, 371–374
  multilevel, bandpass, 363–391
  multilevel, baseband, 111–114, 173–176
  NRZ, 155
  OOK, 349–350, 351–353
  OQPSK, 368
  Polar, 156, 160–162
  QAM, 366–370
  QPSK, 364–366, 368–369, 27
  RZ, 155
  SONET, 210
  spectral efficiency, 375, 377
  synchronization, 378–379
  telephone standards, 204–212, 403–411
  unipolar, 156, 162
  2B1Q, 407–408
  See also Pulse code modulation
Digital subscriber line, 405–409
Digital switching (telephone), 404
Digital-to-analog converter (DAC), 146–147
  multilevel signaling, 112, 363–371
Dimensionality theorem, 104
  bandpass, 245
  bandwidth estimation, 108
Dirac delta function, 50, 487–489
  even-sided, 488–489
  impulse response, 91
  left-sided, 488
  properties of, 488–489
  spectrum, 61
Direct method for FM, 325
Direct sequence spread spectrum, 381–387

See also Spread spectrum
Dirichlet conditions, 44
Discontinuous phase FSK, 356
Discrete Fourier transform (DFT),
 114–120
 MathCAD, 115
 examples, 118–121
Discrete random variables, 500
 CDF of, 503
 ensemble average of, 504
 PDF of, 502
Discriminator, frequency, 270, 442
Distortion
 cross modulation, 255
 harmonic, 252
 intermodulation, 253–256
 linear, 95
 nonlinear, 251–256
 third-order, 253–256
Distortionless transmission, 95–96,
 242–243
 bandpass, 242–243
 channel, 95
Distribution
 binomial, 507–510
 continuous, 500
 discrete, 500
 Gaussian, bivariate, 524
 Gaussian, one-dimensional, 511–515
 mixed, 502
 N-dimensional, 521
 Poisson, 510
 sinusoidal, 515–516
 uniform, 510
Dolby noise reduction, 336–339
Double balanced mixer, 262–264
Double-sideband suppressed carrier
 (DSB-SC), 302
 complex envelope, 234–235, 302
 demodulation of, 302–304
 signal-to-noise ratio, 335–337
Doubler stage, 265
Down converter, 258–264, 280
DS-1, DS-2, DS-3, etc. lines, 207
DTE (data terminal equipment), 562
DTE/DCE interface, 541, 562
Dual tone multiple frequency (DTMF),
 401
Duplex, half and full, 562

Early-late bit synchronizer, 171–173
E_b/N_0, 437
 link budget evaluation, 437
EBCDIC code, 538–539, 562
Echo check, 562
Echo suppressor (hybrid), 562
Effective input-noise temperature, 430
 attenuator, 432
 average, 430

cascaded linear devices, 435
 spot, 430
 transmission line, 432
Effective isotropic radiated power
 (EIRP), 423–424
Effective radiated power (ERP), 456
Efficiency
 conversion efficiency, 298–300
 modulation, 297
 spectral, 176–177, 369–370
EIA, 541, 543
Electromagnetic spectrum, 11–12
Electromagnetic wave propagation,
 10–16
Electronic service number (ESN), 449
Electronic switching system (ESS), 404
Encoder
 ADC, 146–148
 DAC, 147–148
Energy calculation, from waveform, 40
Energy signal, 40, 35
Energy spectral density (ESD), 48
Ensemble average
 mean, 506
 N-dimensional, 522
 rth moment, 505
 standard deviation, 506
 variance, 506
Ensemble of events
 See also Random processes
Entropy, 17
Envelope
 complex, 232, 235–236
 real, 232, 265
 See also Complex envelope
Envelope delay, 243, 562
Envelope detector, 265–266, 280
Equalizing filter, 178, 185
 adaptive, 179, 185, 561
 PAM, 142
 zero-forcing, 183–186
Equivalent bandwidth, 122–123
erf(x) function
 See $Q(z)$ function
erfc(x) function
 See $Q(z)$ function
Error, quantizing, 145
Error correction codes
 See Coding
Error function
 See $Q(z)$ function
Error probability
 See also Probability of bit error
 See also Probability of error
Error rate
 See Probability of bit error
 See Probability of error
Ethernet (IEEE 802.3) interface,
 546–549, 562

Euler's theorem, 479
Even-sided delta function, 488–489
Event
 compound, 494
 independent, 496
 null, 494
 simple, 494
 sure, 494
Expandor, 153
 See also Companding
Expected value
 N-dimensional, 522
 one-dimensional, 504
 See also Ensemble average
Extremely high frequency (EHF), 12
Eye pattern, 166–167

Fading channels, 7
False frame sync, 201
Fast frequency-shift keying (FFSK),
 372
FCC bandwidth, 123
FDDI (fiber distributed data interface),
 562
Federal Communication Commission
 (FCC), 10
 See also Standards
Feedback communications, 19, 552,
 561
Feedback demodulators
 Costas PLL, 302–304
 PLL, 273–279
Fiber optic systems, 443–445
 SONET, 210
Field intensity, 424
Field rate, television, 453, 455
Filter
 active, 247–250
 bandpass, 239–241
 Bessel, 249–250
 Butterworth, 249–250
 cavity, 248–250
 ceramic, 247–250
 Chebyshev, 249–250
 crystal, 247–250
 distortion, 96, 242–243
 equalizing, 142, 179
 equivalent lowpass, 239–241
 intersymbol interference, 177–186
 LC, 246–250
 linear, 90
 linear prediction, 186
 mechanical, 247–250
 nonlinear, 251–256
 passive, 246–250
 PLL tracking, 273
 prediction for DPCM, 186
 raised cosine-rolloff, 180–183
 RC low pass, 93–95

Filter *(Continued)*
  surface acoustic wave, 248–250
  time constant, 94
  transmission line, 248–250
  transversal, 183–186, 187
  zero-forcing equalizer, 183–186
  See also Linear filter
Fixed assigned multiple access
  (FAMA), 416–418
Flash ADC, 147
Flat-top PAM, 139–143
Flow control, 562
See CA of RS-232C circuit, 543, 562
FM detector
  See Detector
Formats, digital signal, 155–177
Forward error correction (FEC), 19
  See Coding
Four-quadrant multiplier, 260
Four-wire circuit, 399, 402
Fourier series, 68–72
  complex, 68–70
  fundamental frequency, 68
  polar, 70–72
  quadrature, 69–70
  truncated, 77–79
Fourier transform
  definition, 43
  discrete, 114
  examples DFT, 118–121
  properties, 46–47
  table, 61
  theorems, 49
Frame rate, television, 453, 455
Frame synchronization, 199–201, 378–
  379
Free space intrinsic impedance, 424
Free space loss, 425, 437
Frequency
  allocations, 10–12
  allocations, *also see* Standards
  carrier, 231–233
  definition, 43
  fundamental, 68
  IF, 283–284, 286
  instantaneous, 268, 313
  Nyquist, 100
  spectrum, 43
Frequency demodulation: *See* Detector
Frequency deviation, 315
Frequency division multiplexing
  (FDM), 330–331
Frequency hopped spread spectrum,
  381
  See Spread spectrum
Frequency modulation (FM), 311–330
  bandwidth of, 322–323, 361
  Bessel functions, 317–323
  Carson's rule, 322–323, 361
  circuit, 313

complex envelope, 234–235,
  311–312
detector, 268–273, 277–278, 442
direct generation, 325
FCC channels, 333
frequency multiplier, 264–265
index, 315, 333
indirect generation, 325
narrowband, 323–325
preemphasis and deemphasis, 328–
  330
quadrature detector, 271
representation of, 234–235, 311–334
signal-to-noise ratio, 335–337
standards, 331–334
stereo, 330–332, 459
threshold extension, 442
transmitter, 344
TV audio, 456, 459
wideband, 325–328
  See also Detector
  See also Digital signaling
Frequency multiplier, 264–265, 280
Frequency response, linear system, 92
Frequency synthesizer, 279
Frequency translation, 49, 258–264
Frequency, definition, 43, 313
Frequency-division multiple access
  (FDMA), 416, 417
Frequency-division multiplexing, 396
Frequency-shift keying (FSK),
  350–351, 356–363
  Bell 103 modem, 357–361, 557, 558
  probability of bit error, 378, 379
  spectrum, 358–363
Friis' theorem
  noise, 433
  signal, 425
Front-end processor, 562
Full duplex, 562
Function
  analytic, 98
  autocorrelation, 63
  bandlimited, 98
  Bessel, 317–323
  CDF, 498, 521
  Dirac delta, 50, 487–489
  frequency response, 92
  impulse response, 91
  Kronecker delta, 65
  linear system output, 91
  orthogonal, 65
  orthonormal, 65
  PDF, 498, 522
  power transfer, 93
  $Q(z)$, 490–491, 513–515
  rectangular pulse, 53
  $Sa(x)$, 54, 489
  sinc, 54, 56
  transfer, 92

triangular pulse, 54, 56
unit step, 51
Functional transformation
  N-dimensional PDF, 525
  one-dimensional, 516
Fundamental frequency, 68

Gain
  antenna, 423–425
  coding, 25–28
  dB, 40
  power, 93
  processing, 386
Galaxy satellite, 413–414, 438–439
Gateway, 562
Gating, 135–139
Gaussian
  area under PDF, 490–491, 513–515
  bivariate PDF, 524
  CDF, 513
  mean, 511
  one-dimensional PDF, 511
  random variable, 511–515
  variance, 511
General purpose interface bus (GPIB),
  545–549
Geosynchronous orbit, 412
Glossary, computer communications,
  551–564
Granular noise
  DM, 191–194
  PCM, 151
Graph
  Bessel function, 322
  $Q(z)$ function, 515
Gray code, 146
Ground wave propagation, 12–14
Group delay, 243
Group FDM signal, 396–397
GSM cellular telephone, 450

Half duplex, 562
Half-power bandwidth, 122
Half-wave linear rectifier, 518
Hamming distance, 21
Hard decision, 25, 27
Hard limiter, 256–258, 280
Hardwire channel, 7
Harmonic distortion, 252
Hartley, 16
HDLC (high-level data link protocol),
  552–553, 562
High-definition television (HDTV),
  468–471
High-level modulation, 300
High-side injection, 260
Hilbert transform, 305
  table of, 487
  used in SSB, 234–235, 305
History of communication, 2–5

Hold-in range, PLL, 273, 276
Horizontal resolution, television, 456
HP interface bus, 545–549
Hunting noise in PCM, 151
Hybrid (telephone) network, 402, 403, 562

I channel, 233, 234, 282, 286
IBM punched card code, 537
Ideal communication system, 26–27, 30–33, 336
Ideal envelope detector, 265
Ideal system S/N, 335–336
Identities, trigonometric, 479–480
Idle channel noise in PCM, 151
IEEE, 541, 545
IEEE 802.3 (ethernet) interface, 546–549
IEEE-488 interface, 545–549
Image response, 284–285
Impulse
    function, 50, 487–489
    response, 91
    sampling, 101–104
In-phase component, 233, 234, 282, 286
    television, 460
Incoherent detector, 268
Indefinite integrals, 482–484
Independent
    events, 496
    random variables, 522
Independent sideband (ISB), 301
    See also Single sideband
Indeterminate forms, 481
Index
    digital modulation, 354
    frequency modulation, 315, 333
    percent AM, 296
    phase modulation, 315
Indirect method for FM, 325
Information, 16–18
    analog, 8
    average, 17
    bits, 16
    capacity, 18, 26, 335
    digital, 7, 16
    entropy, 17
    rate, 18
    S/N of ideal system, 335–336
    sink, 2, 8
    source, 2, 6, 16
Injection locking, 277
Input-noise temperature, cascaded devices, 435
Instantaneous frequency, 313
Instantaneous power, 37
Instantaneous sample PAM, 139–143
Integral, 481–485
    calculus, 481–485

definition, 481
evaluation by parts, 482
evaluation techniques, 482
table of, 482–485
Integrate-and-dump filter, 352
Integrated service digital network (ISDN), 405–409
Intelligent time-division multiplexer, 202
Intercarrier signal, 457
Intercept point, 253–254
Interface
    Centronics, 544–545
    ethernet, 546–549
    IEEE-488, 545–549
    RS-232C, 542–544
    RS-422A, 542–543
    RS-449, 542–544
    RS-530, 542–544
    X.25, 553
    See also Data link control
    See also ISDN
    See also Standards
Interference, 287
Interlacing, television, 453
Intermediate frequency (IF), 283–284, 286
Intermodulation
    distortion, 253–256
    interference, 287
International Telecommunications Union (ITU), 10
Intersection of sets, 493
Intersymbol interference (ISI), 177–186
Intrinsic impedance, 424
Ionospheric scatter propagation, 15
IQ detector, 286
ISDN (integrated services digital network), 405–409, 562
    broadband, 405
    narrowband, 405–409
    NT1, NT2, 406–407
    S interface, 406–407
    T interface, 406–407
    U interface, 406–407
    2B1Q line code, 407–408
ISO OSI computer network model, 550–551
ISO standard organization, 541, 550
Isotropic radiation, 424

Jacobian, 526
$J_n(\beta)$ Bessel functions, 318–323
Joint
    CDF and PDF, 521, 522
    mean, 523
    probability, 494

Kronecker delta function, 65

L'Hospital's rule, 481
LAN, 563
Laser diode, fiber optic, 443
LC filter, 246–250
Leakage, discrete Fourier transform, 117
Learning sequence, 179
Leased line, 563
Leibniz's rule, 481
Light-emitting diode (LED), fiber optics, 443
Limiter, 256–258, 280
Line coding, 155–158, 407–408
    advantages and disadvantages, 157–158
    bipolar high-density, 163
    power spectral density, 158–164
    spectral efficiency, 177
    T1-carrier, 210
    T1G-carrier, 211–212
    2B1Q, 407–408
Line resolution, television, 454–456, 468
Line spectra (delta functions), 72–77
Line-of-sight propagation, 14–15
Linear
    amplifier, 250–251
    distortion, 95
    modulation, 234–235
    operator, 35, 90
    system, 90
Linear filter, 90–98
    See Filter
Linear prediction speech coding, 197
Linear systems
    AM to PM conversion, 241
    amplitude response, 92
    convolution integral, 91
    distortionless transmission, 95–96, 242–243
    impulse response, 91
    output, 91
    phase response, 92
    PM to AM conversion, 241
    power transfer function, 93
    spectrum of output, 92
    time-invariant, 90
    transfer function, 92
    with sinusoidal inputs, 93
Link budget, 435–442, 444
    Carrier-to-noise (C/N), 435–437
    fiber optic, 444
    satellite, 438–443
Link budget analysis, 423–443
List of symbols, xix
Loading coils, 211
Loading factor, companding, 155
Local loop (telephone), 399–400, 405
Look angles to satellite, 440
Loop: See Phase-locked loop

Loss, free space, 425, 437
Low frequency (LF), 11
Low probability of intercept (LPI), 380
Low-side injection, 259
Lower single-sideband (LSSB), 304
Luminance signal, television, 461

M-ary phase-shift keying (MPSK), 364–366, 368–369
M-sequence waveform, 381–384
Magnitude response, linear system, 92
Magnitude spectrum, 44
    See also Spectrum
Manchester signaling, 157, 164
Marginal PDF, 523
Mark (binary signaling), 155–156, 356, 358
Mastergroup FDM signal, 396–397
Matched filter, 168
Math tables, 479–491
MathCAD, 9, 565–569
    DFT, 115
    example, 569
    FFT examples, 118–121
    functions, 568
    operators, 567
    quick start, 565–569
MATLAB, 9
Maximal-length codes, 22, 381–384
MC145472 ISDN U transceiver, 407
MC145474 ISDN S/T interface, 407
MC14554 telephone codec, 407
Mean value, 506
    See also Dc value
Measure, information, 16
Mechanical filter, 247–250
Median (statistics), 506
Medium frequency (MF), 11
Message switching, 563
Microwave bands, 11–12
Millimeter band, 12
Minimum-shift keying (MSK), 371–374
    FFSK, 372
    probability of bit error, 378, 379
    Type I, 372
    Type II, 372
Mixed distributions, 502
Mixer, 258–264
    audio, 260
    double balanced, 262–264
    output, 280
    single balanced, 262
    unbalanced, 262
Mobile radio
    cellular telephone, 445–452
    FM, 333
Mobile telephone switching office (MTSO), 446

Mode (statistics), 506
Model
    communication system, 6
    OSI computer network, 550–551
Modem, 556–560, 563
    Bell 103, 357–361, 557, 558
    Bell 212A, 557, 558
    definition, 563
    standards, 556–560
    V.22bis, 367, 557, 558
    V.32, 557, 559
    V.32bis, 560
    V.33, 557, 560
Modulation
    AM, 234–235, 295–304
    complex envelope, 233–236
    definition, 6, 231, 233–236
    DM, 190–197
    DPCM, 186–190
    DSB-SC, 302
    efficiency, 297
    FM, 311–330
    independent sideband (ISB), 301
    negative AM, 296
    PAM, 135–143
    PCM, 143–155
    percent AM, 296
    PM, 311–330
    positive AM, 296
    PWM and PPM, 212–216
    spectrum, 236–237
    SSB-SC, 304–308
    VSB, 309–311
    See also Digital signaling
Moments
    mean, 506
    one-dimensional, 505
    r-th moment, 505
    standard deviation, 506
    two-dimensional, 523
    variance, 506
Morse code, 536
MTS stereo sound, 459
Multichannel television sound (MTS), 459
Multilevel signaling
    bandpass, 363–371
    baseband, 111–114, 173–176
    T1G-carrier, 211–212
Multimodal fiber optics, 443
Multipath propagation, 7
Multiple access, 419–426
    code-division, 386–387, 416
    demand assigned, 416, 417–418
    fixed assigned, 416
    frequency division, 416
    time-division, 416, 420–422
Multiplexing
    code-divison, 386–387, 416

frequency division, 330, 331
time-division, 197–212, 396, 410–411
Multiplier
    four-quadrant, 260
    frequency, 264–265
    mixer, 258–264
    produce detector, 266–268
    single-quadrant, 260
    two-quadrant, 260
Multipoint line, 563
Multivariate
    functional transformation, 525
    statistics, 521–523
Mutually exclusive, 494

N-dimensional, statistics, 521–523
Narrowband angle modulation, 323–324
Narrowband ISDN, 405
National Television System Committee (NTSC), 460
Nats, 16
Natural sample PAM, 135–139
Negative amplitude modulation, 296
Network, linear, 90
Noise
    available power, 427
    bandpass digital systems, 376–379
    bandwidth, 122–123
    definition, 33
    effective input-noise temperature, 430
    envelope-phase representation, 233, 245–246
    equivalent bandwidth, 122–123
    eye pattern, 166–167
    granular, 191–194
    in AM, DSB, FM, and PCM systems, 334–337
    interference, 287
    PCM, 149–153
    power available, 427
    quadrature-component representation, 233
    quantizing, 145–146
    slope overload, 191–194
    source temperature, 427
    sources, 425–428
    thermal, 425–426
    See also Distributions
    See also Probability of bit error
    See also Signal-to-noise
Noise figure
    attenuator, 433
    average, 429
    cascaded devices, 433
    spot, 429
    transmission line, 433

Noise reduction, Dolby and DBX, 336–339
Noise temperature, 427, 430–431
  system, 436
Noncoherent detector, 268
Nonlinear
  amplifier, 251–256
  channel, 287
  distortion, 251–256
Nonreturn-to-zero signal, 155
Nonuniform quantizing, 153–155
Normalized covariance, 524
Normalized orthogonal functions, 65
Normalized power, 39
  bandpass signal, 237
North American TDM hierarchy, 206
NRZ signal, 155
NT1/2 ISDN network termination, 407
Null event, 494
Null-to-null bandwidth, 123
Numeric assignment module (NAM), 449
Nyquist frequency, 100
Nyquist's
  first method (zero ISI), 179–186
  second method, 186
  third method, 186

Offset quadrature phase-shift keying (OQPSK), 368
On-off keying (OOK), 349–350, 351–353
  detector, 353
  fiber optics, 443
  probability of bit error, 378, 379
One-sided delta function, 488
One-sided spectrum, 72
Open system interconnection (OSI) model, 550–551
Operator
  absolute value, 44
  angle, 42, 71
  conjugate, 46
  convolution, 58
  ensemble average, 504
  Fourier transform, 43
  Hilbert transform, 305, 486–487
  imaginary part, 69
  linear, 35, 90
  real part, 69
  time average, 35
Optimum code performance, 26, 30
Optimum digital receivers
  See Digital receivers
Orthogonal
  functions, 65
  random variables, 523
  series, 66
Orthonormal functions, 65, 107

Oscillator
  synchronization, 277
  voltage-controlled, 273
Overload, receiver, 287
Overload noise in PCM, 150

Packet data transmission, 421, 563
Packet switching, 563
Paley-Wiener criterion, 91
Parallel ADC, 147
Parity bits, 20
Parity check, 563
Parseval's theorem, 47
Pascal's triangle, 509
Peak envelope power (PEP), 238
  AM signal, 298
  SSB signal, 307
Peak frequency deviation, 315
Percent amplitude modulation, 296
Performance
  analog systems, 334–337
  coding, 25–28
  digital systems, 169, 378–379
  ideal system, 26, 30, 336
Periodic signal
  spectra, 72, 76
  waveform, 35
Personal computer solutions, 9
Phase
  peak deviation, 315
  response, 92
  spectrum, 44
Phase delay, 243
Phase detector
  sawtooth characteristic, 274
  sinusoidal characteristic, 267, 274
  triangle characteristic, 274
Phase error, PLL, 275
Phase modulation (PM), 311–330
  circuit, 313
  complex envelope, 234–235, 311–312
  index, 315
  signal-to-noise ratio, 337
  See also Phase-shift keying
Phase reversal keying (PRK)
  See Binary phase-shift keying
Phase shift keying
  See Binary phase shift keying
  See Differential phase-shift keying
  See M-ary phase shift keying
  See Quadrature phase-shift keying
Phase spectrum, 44
Phase-locked loop (PLL), 273–279
  analog, 274
  as a tracking filter, 273
  Costas, 302–304
  digital, 274

for carrier synchronization, 354
for coherent AM detection, 279
for FM or PM demodulation, 277–278
for frequency synthesis, 279
Phasor, 42
Physically realizable waveform, 33–35
Picket-fence effect, DFT, 117
Pilot signal, 330–332, 459
PIN diode, 443
Plank's constant, 426
PM to AM conversion, 241
Point distributions, 500
Poisson distribution, 510
Poisson sum formula, 73
Polar Fourier series, 70–72
Polar signaling, 156, 160–162
  probability of bit error, 378, 379
  spectrum, 160–162
Polling, 563
Positive amplitude modulation, 296
Power
  Am signal, 239
  average, 37, 63
  bandpass signal, 237
  decibel value, 42
  instantaneous, 37
  normalized, 39
  peak envelope, 238–256
  thermal noise, 425–426
Power bandwidth, 123
Power density, 424
Power efficiency, 298–300
Power gain, available, 428, 433
Power signal, 40, 35
Power spectral density (PSD), 62
  ASK, 352
  bandpass signal, 236
  bipolar RZ signal, 162–164
  BPSK, 354
  deterministic, 62
  FSK, 358–363
  line codes, 158–164
  Manchester NRZ signal, 164
  MPSK, 368–392
  MSK, 372–374
  multilevel signal, 175, 369
  periodic waveforms, 76
  polar NRZ signal, 160–162
  QAM, 368–370
  spread spectrum, 384–385
  square wave, 77
  thermal noise, 426
  unipolar NRZ signal, 159–160
  unipolar RZ signal, 162
  WBFM, 326
  See also Spectrum
Power transfer function, 93
Prediction filter, DPCM, 186

Preemphasis and deemphasis in FM, 328–330
Primary rate ISDN, 405
Probability, 494–498
  conditional, 496
  joint, 494
  relative frequency, 494
  simple, 494
  See also Distributions
Probability and random variables, 492–535
Probability density function (PDF), 498, 522
  central limit theorem, 527–528
  conditional, 522
  for sum of two random variables, 527
  joint, 522
  marginal, 523
  measurement of, 503–504
  N-dimensional, 522
  properties of, 500, 522
  table of, 508
  See also Distributions
Probability distribution function
  See Cumulative distribution function
Probability of bit error, 7, 25, 169, 378–379
  baseband signaling, 169
  Bipolar NRZ or RZ, 169
  BPSK with coding, 26–27
  Manchester NRZ or RZ, 169
  OOK, BPSK, FSK, DPSK, QPSK, MSK, 378–379
  optimum coding, 26, 30
  Polar NRZ or RZ, 169
  repeaters, 169
  Shannon's limit, 26, 30
  Unipolar NRZ or RZ, 169
  unipolar, polar, bipolar, 378–379
  with coding, 25–27
Probability of error
  Shannon's limit, 26, 30
  See also Probability of bit error
Probability of false frame sync, 201
Processing gain, spread spectrum, 386
Product detector, 266–268, 280
Professional carrier, television, 459
Propagation
  ground wave, 12–14
  line-of-sight (LOS), 14–15
  radio frequency, 10–16
  sky-wave, 14
Properties
  block codes, 22
  CDF, 500, 522
  Dirac delta function, 488–489
  Fourier series, 69
  Fourier transform, 46–47
  PDF, 500, 522

$Q(z)$ function, 490
  waveforms, 33–35
Protocol
  definition, 563
  See also Computer communications
  See also Data link control
Pseudonoise (PN) code, 381
Pseudoternary signal, 157, 162–164
PSTN (public switched telephone network), 395, 409–411, 563
Pull-in range, PLL, 273, 276
Pulse amplitude modulation (PAM), 135–143
  flat-top, 139–143
  instantaneous sampling, 139–143
  natural sampling, 135–139
  spectrum, 135, 140
Pulse aperture, 142
Pulse code modulation (PCM), 143–155
  bandwidth, 148–149
  differential, 186–190
  eye pattern of, 166–167
  PSD of, 158–164
  S/N, 149–153
  S/N for BPSK signaling, 336
  T1 PCM system, 207–212
  See also Time-division multiplexing
Pulse dialing, 399–400, 404
Pulse duration modulation (PDM)
  See Pulse width modulation (PWM)
Pulse position modulation (PPM), 212–216
Pulse resolution for no ISI, 179–186
Pulse time modulation, 212–216
Pulse width modulation (PWM), 212–216
  for high power AM, 299–300
Punched IBM card, 537
Punched tape, 155–156

Q channel, 233, 234, 282, 286
$Q(z)$ function
  approximation for, 490, 514–515
  definition, 513
  Gaussian CDF, 513
  graph of, 515
  properties of, 490
  table, 491
  upper bound, 514
Q, quality factor, 246–247
Quadrature amplitude modulation (QAM), 366–370
  spectrum, 368–370
Quadrature amplitude-shift keying: See Quadrature amplitude modulation (QAM)
Quadrature FM detector, 271
Quadrature Fourier series, 69–70

Quadrature modulation
  color television, 460–461
  complex envelope, 234–235
  QAM, 366–370
Quadrature phase-shift keying (QPSK), 364–366, 368–369
  probability of bit error, 378, 379
  spectrum, 368–369
  with coding, 27
Quadrature-phase component, 233, 234, 282, 286
Quantizing
  A-law, 153
  noise, 145–146
  nonuniform, 153–155
  μ-law, 153
  uniform, 145

Radar, bands, 11–12
Radiation resistance, 431
Radio frequency
  filters, 246–250
  propagation, 10–16
Raised cosine-rolloff filter, 180–183
Ramp analog-to-digital converter (ADC), 146–147
Random variables
  average value of, 504, 522
  CDF of, 498, 521
  central limit theorem, 527–528
  continuous, 500
  definition, 496
  functional transformation, 516, 525
  independent, 522
  N-dimensional, 521–522
  orthogonal, 523
  PDF of, 498, 522
  sum of, 526
  See also Distributions
Random waveform, 9
Raster scanning, 452–456
Rate
  baud, 106
  bit, 106
  code, 20–21
  information, 18
  source, 18
Rayleigh's energy theorem, 47
RC low-pass filter, 93–95
  distortion, 97
Received power, 425
Receiver, 283–287
  black-and-white television, 458
  color television, 463
  fiber optic, 443
  general, 283–287
  overload, 287
  satellite, 438–443
  spread spectrum, 382, 388
  SSB, phasing method, 343

SSB, product detection, 308
superheterodyne, 283–287
TRF, 283
See also Digital receivers
See also Probability of bit error
See also Probability of error
See also Signal-to-noise ratio
Rectangular pulse
definition, 53
spectrum, 54, 56
Reed-Solomon codes, 22, 27
References, 570–577
Regenerative repeater: *See* Repeater
Relative frequency (probability), 494
Remote (telephone) terminal (RT), 402–404
Repeater, 167–168, 563
BER, 169
Response
amplitude, 92
frequency, 92
image, 284–285
impulse, 91
phase, 92
Return-to-zero (RZ) signal, 155
Reverse channel, 563
Right-hand continuous, 500
Ring (telephone) lead, 399–400
Ringer equivalence number (REN), 401
Rms value, 39
RS-232C interface, 542–544
RS-422A interface, 542–544
RS-449 interface, 542–544
RS-530 interface, 542–544
Rth moment, 505
RTS (request to send), 563
RZ signal, 155

S interface, ISDN, 406–407
$Sa(x)$ function, 54, 56
sampling theorem, 99
spectrum of, 54, 56
table of, 489
Sample space, 493
Sampling frequency, 100, 244
Sampling theorem, 99
bandpass, 243–245
flat-top, 139–143
Satellite
communications, 409–411, 438–443
data transmission, 419–426
Galaxy, 413–414, 438–439
link budget, 438–443
look angles, 440
packet transmission, 421–422
satellite-switched TDMA (SS-TDMA), 416
telephone transmission, 417–423
television transmission, 414–415, 438–443

VSAT, 422
Scatter propagation, 15–16
Scrambling, 25
SDLC (synchronous data link protocol), 552, 563
Second audio program (SAP), television, 459
Sequential code, 538
Serial ADC, 147
Series
cardinal, 99
Fourier, 68–72
orthogonal, 66
table of, 485–486
Taylor, 64
Server, 563
Set, 492
Shannon channel capacity, 18, 26, 335–336
Shift-register sequences, 381–384
Sifting property, 51
Signal
analog, 8
asynchronous, 202
balanced, 544
bandpass, 6, 230–246
baseband, 6, 134–218
chrominance, television, 461
definition, 33
deterministic, 9
digital, 8, 105–114
digital formats, 155–177
energy, 40, 35
fiber optic, 443–445
image, 284–285
luminance, television, 461
multilevel, 173–176
periodic, 35
phasor, 42
pilot, 330, 332, 459
power, 39, 35
power received, free space, 425
processing, 6
random, 9
satellite, 409–411, 438–443
space, 106
spread spectrum, 380–388
start-stop, 202
synchronous, 201
telephone, 398–409
television, 452–459
unbalanced, 544
vector representation, 106–108
VF, 205, 402–404, 564
See also Digital signaling
See also Modulation
See also Signal constellation
See also Standards
Signal constellation, 365, 367, 558–560
CCITT V.22 bis, 558, 559

CCITT V.32, 559
CCITT V.33, 560
television, 462
Signal-to-noise (S/N)
Carrier-to-noise (C/N), 435–437
decibels, 41
DM, 194
DPCM, 187
ideal system, 335–336
link budget, 435–437
modulated systems, 337
PCM, 149–153
received via free space, 436
Simple event, 494
Simple probability, 494
Simplex, 563
Simulation of communication systems, 9–10, 565–569
Sin $(x)/x$ function, 54
Sinc function, 54
See also $Sa(x)$ function
Single channel per carrier (SCPC), 417
Single sideband (SSB), 304–309
amplitude companded, 308–309
average power, 307
complex envelope, 234–235, 305
filter receiver, 308
filter transmitter, 308
peak envelope power, 307
phasing receiver, 343
phasing transmitter, 307
spectrum of, 307
SSB-AM-SC, 234–235, 304–308
SSB-EV, 234–235
SSB-FM, 234–235
SSB-PM, 234–235
SSB-SQ, 234–235
Weaver's method, 341
Single-balanced mixer, 262
Single-mode fiber optics, 443
Single-quadrant multiplier, 260
Sinusoidal, phasor notation, 42
Sinusoidal distribution, 515–516
Sky noise temperature, 441
Sky-wave propagation, 14
Slant range, satellite, 440
SLC-96 remote terminal, 404
Slicing level, 215, 563
Slope detector, 268
Slope overload noise, DM, 191–194
Soft decision, 24–25, 27
Softwire channel, 7
SONET, 210
Source, 7–8
Source coding, 19
Source rate, 18
Space (binary signaling), 155–156, 356, 358
SPADE system, 417–420

Spectral efficiency, 375, 377
    bandpass digital signals, 370, 375, 377
    multilevel signal, 176–177, 369–370
    TCM, 28
Spectrum
    AM signal, 238–239, 298
    amplitude, 44
    analyzers, 44
    bandpass signal, 236–237
    current, 43
    damped sinusoid, 50
    definition, 43
    digital signals, *see* Power spectral density
    dirac delta function, 61
    DSB-SC signal, 302
    energy, 48
    exponential pulse, 45
    FM signal, 316–328
    folded, 104
    frequency variable, 43
    line, 72–77
    magnitude, 44
    NBFM, 335
    one-sided, 72
    PAM, 135, 140
    periodic square wave, 74–75
    periodic waveform, 72, 76
    phase, 44
    PM signal, 316–328
    power spectral density, 62
    rectangular pulse, 54, 56
    $Sa(x)$ pulse, 54
    SSB signal, 307
    switched, sinusoid, 60
    television, 457, 465, 468, 469
    triangular pulse, 56, 57
    two-sided, 43
    unit step, 61
    voltage, 43
    VSB signal, 310–311
    See also Power spectral density
Speech coding, 197
    cellular telephone, 451–452
    linear prediction, 197
    subband coding, 197
    vector quantization, 197
    VSELF, 197
Split-phase coding, 157, 164
Spot effective input-noise temperature, 430
Spot noise figure, 429
Spread spectrum (SS), 380–388
    code-division multiple access, 386–387, 416
    direct sequence, 381–387
    effect of interference, 386–387
    frequency hopping, 387–388

hybrid, 381
    overlay, 387
    PN sequence, 381–384
    response to noise, 386–387
    spreading signal, 381
Square-law bit synchronizer, 172
Squaring loop, 302–304
Standard deviation, 506
Standards
    AM broadcast, 300–302
    ATM protocol, 554
    CATV, 469
    CCITT V.24 interface, 543
    cellular telephone, 448–450
    Centronics interface, 544–545
    computer communications, 536–564
    computer modems, 556–560
    ethernet, 546–549
    FM broadcast, 331–334
    frequency allocations, 10–12
    IEEE-488 interface, 545–549
    intermediate frequencies, 286
    ISDN, 405–409
    ISO OSI model, 550–551
    RS-232C interface, 542–544
    RS-422A interface, 542–544
    RS-449 interface, 542–544
    SONET, 210
    telephone, 204–212, 397–411
    telephone, data line, 555–556
    television, 455, 465–470
Start-stop signaling, 202
Statistical averages
    See Ensemble average
Statistical independence, 496, 522
Statistical time-division multiplexer, 202, 563
Statistics
    bivariate, 523–524
    N-dimensional, 521–523
    one-dimensional, 498–507
Step size, delta modulation, 191–194
Stereo sound
    AM broadcasting, 301–302
    Dolby & DBX noise reduction, 336–339
    FM broadcast, 330–334
    television, MTS, 459
Store and forward, 563
Stored program control, 404
Stuff bits, 202
Subband speech coding, 197
Subscriber (telephone) loop
    analog, 398–400
    digital, 405–409
Successive approximation ADC, 147
Super high frequency (SHF), 11
Supergroup FDM signal, 396–397
Superheterodyne receiver, 283–287

Superposition, 90
Suppressed carrier, 302
Sure event, 494
Surface acoustic wave (SAW) filter, 248–250
Switched line, 564
Switching detector, FM stereo, 347
Switching modulator, 261–262
Synchronization
    bit, 170–173
    digital signaling, 378–380
    frame or word, 199–201
    oscillator, 277
    television, 454, 463–464
Synchronous detector, 266–268
Synchronous digital line, 201
Synchronous orbit, 412
Synchronous transmission, 564
Systematic block code, 21
Systems
    analog, 8
    cellular telephone, 445–452
    communication, 2, 6–8, 231
    computer, 536–564
    digital, 8
    Dolby and DX, 336–339
    fiber optic, 443–445
    ideal, 18–19, 26, 30
    linear, 90
    link budget, 435–437
    noise temperature, 435
    performance, *see* Power spectral density
    performance, *see* Probability of bit error
    performance, *see* Signal-to-noise (S/N)
    performance, *See* Spectrum
    satellite, 409–411, 438–443
    spread spectrum, 380–388
    telephone, 398–411, 445–450
    time invariant, 90
    transfer functions, 92
    See also Linear systems

T interface, ISDN, 406–407
Table
    ASCII code, 540
    Baudot code, 538
    Bessel functions, 318–321
    block codes, 22
    capacities of PSTN, 409–411
    CDF, 508
    Centronics interface, 547
    communication system components, 280
    derivatives, 480–481

DS-0, DS-1, .. DS-5 signaling, 207
EBCDIC code, 539
ethernet standards, 549
Fourier theorems, 49
Fourier transforms, 61
HDTV standards, 470
Hilbert transforms, 487
IBM card code, 537
IEEE-488 interface, 548
integrals, 482–485
MathCAD functions, 568
MathCAD operators, 567
Morse code, 536
PDFs, 508
probability of bit error, 169, 378
$Q(z)$ tabulation, 491
RS-232C interface, 542–543
RS-422A interface, 542–543
RS-449 interface, 542–543
S/N for modulation systems, 337
$Sa(x)$, 489
series expansions, 485–486
SONET, 210
spectral efficiency of digital signals, 377
T-carrier, 208
trigonometry, 479–480
See also Standards
Tamed frequency modulation (TFM), 374
Taylor series, 64
TCP/IP, 564
TDM hierarchy
  CCITT, 209
  North American, 206
  SONET, 210
Telecommunication systems, 395–397
Telephone, 398–409
  analog subscriber line, 405
  analog switching, 404
  ATM protocol, 554
  C-type conditioned line, 555–556
  caller ID, 401
  capacities of PSTN, 409–411
  cellular radio, 445–452
  central office, 399–405
  D-type conditioned line, 556
  data-line standards, 555–556
  digital switching, 404
  DS type line standards, 207
  FDM hierarchy, 397
  hybrid, 402, 403, 562
  ISDN, 405–409
  remote terminal, 402–404
  ringer equivalence number (REN), 401
  SLC-96, 404
  SONET, 210

  subscriber line, analog, 399–400, 405
  subscriber line, digital, 405–409
  systems, 398–409
  TDM hierarchy, 204–212
  tip and ring, 399
  TSI switching, 404
  T1 PCM system, 207–212
  via fiber optic cable, 443–445
  via satellite, 417–423
Television, 452–471
  black and white, 452–459
  channels, 465, 469
  chrominance signal, 461
  color, 459–464
  high-definition (HDTV), 468–471
  line resolution, 454–456, 468
  luminance signal, 461
  MTS stereo sound, 459
  standards, 455, 465–470
  TVRO satellite terminal, 438–443
  vectorscope, 462
  via satellite, 414–415, 438–443
  waveform, sync pulses, 466
Temperature
  noise, 430
  sky noise, 441
10base5, 10base2, and 10base-T ethernet, 546–549
Theorem
  bandpass dimensionality, 245
  bandpass sampling, 243–245
  Bayes, 496
  central limit, 527–528
  dimensionality, 104
  Euler's, 479
  Fourier transforms, 49
  Parseval's, 47
  sampling, 99
  Shannon channel capacity, 18
  Wiener-Khintchine, 63
Theory of distributions, 51
Thermal noise, 426
Third-order distortion, 253–256
Three-decibel bandwidth, 122
Threshold extension for FM, 442
Time average operator, 35
Time constant, 94
Time-division multiple access (TDMA), 416, 420–422
Time-division multiplexing (TDM), 197–212, 396, 410–411
  bandpass systems, 396, 410–411
  bit interleaved, 202
  CCITT hierarchy, 209
  character interleaved, 202
  North American hierarchy, 206
  SONET, 210
  stuff bits, 202

Time-invariant system, 90
Time-slot-interchange switching, 404
Timing, eye pattern, 166–167
Tip (telephone) lead, 399–400
Token bus, 564
Total harmonic distortion, 252
Touch-tone (telephone), 401
Tracking filter, PLL, 273
Transfer function
  linear system, 92
  power, 93
  RC filter, 93
  voltage, 92
Transform
  Fourier, 43
  Hilbert, 305, 486–487
Transformation
  N-dimensional PDF, 525
  one-dimensional PDF, 515
Transmission line
  effective input-noise temperature, 432
  filter, 248–250
  noise figure, 436
Transmission, free space, 425
Transmitters, 5–6, 281–282
  AM, 298–300
  FM, 344
  SSB, 307–308
  SSB, Weaver's method, 341
  VSB, 310, 456–457
  See also Digital signaling
Transponder, 413
Transversal filter
  for DPCM, 187
  zero-forcing ISI, 183–186
Tree codes, 20, 22–25
Trellis-coded modulation (TCM), 28
TRF receiver, 283
Triangular pulse
  definition, 54
  spectrum, 56, 57
Trigonometry
  definitions, 479
  identities, 479–480
Tripler stage, 265
Tropospheric scatter propagation, 16
Truncated Fourier series, 77–79
Trunked mobile radio, 446
Turnabout time (modem), 564
TVRO terminal, 438–443
Two-quadrant multiplier, 260
Two-sided spectrum, 43
Two-tone test, 253–255
Two-way FM radio, 333
  See cellular telephone, 445–452
Two-wire circuit, 399, 402
2B1Q line code, 407–408

T1 PCM system, 207–212
T1G PCM system, 211–212

U interface, ISDN, 406–407
UART, 147
Ultra high frequency (UHF), 11
Unbalanced mixer, 262
Unbalanced QPSK, 368
Unbalanced signaling, 544
Uncorrelated random variables, 523
Uniform
    distribution, 510–511
    PDF, 510
    quantizer, 145
Union of sets, 493
Unipolar signal, 156, 159–160
    probability of bit error, 378, 379
    spectrum, 159–160
Unit step function
    definition, 51
    spectrum, 61
Up converter, 258–264, 280
Upper single sideband (USSB), 304
USART, 147

V.22bis modem, 558, 557
V.32 modem, 559, 557
V.32bis modem, 560
V.33 modem, 560, 557
Value
    dc, 36
    rms, 39

Variable, random, 496
Variance, 506
Vector
    phasors, 42
    representation of waveforms,
        106–107
Vector quantization speech coding, 197
Vector signal, 106–108
Vectorscope, 462
Venn diagram, 493
Vertical resolution, television, 454
Very high frequency (VHF), 11
Very low frequency (VLF), 11
Very small scale aperture terminals
    (VSAT), 422
Vestigial sideband (VSB), 309–311,
    456–457
VF (voice frequency), 205, 402–404,
    564
Viterbi decoding, 24
Vocoders, 197
    cellular telephone, 451
Voltage spectrum, 43
Voltage-controlled oscillator (VCO),
    273
VSELF speech coding, 197

Waveform
    analog, 8
    bandlimited, 98
    bandpass, 231
    baseband, 230

deterministic, 9
device output, 280
digital, 8
dimensions, 105, 106
energy, 40
m-sequence, 381–384
monitor, television, 452
noise, 33
periodic, 35
physically realizable, 33–35
power, 39
random, 9
signal, 33
Waveform coders, 197
Waveform monitor, 452
Wavelength, 13
Weaver's method of SSB, 341
Wideband frequency modulation
    (WBFM), 325–328
Wiener-Khintchine theorem, 63
Windowed waveform, 115
Word synchronization, 199–201,
    378–379

X terminal, 564
X.25 protocol, 553, 564

Zero-crossing bandwidth, 123
Zero-crossing detector, 271–272
Zero-forcing transversal filter, 183–186
Zero-padding, 117

TABLE 2-1 Some Fourier Transform Theorems[a]

Operation	Function	Fourier Transform
Linearity	$a_1 w_1(t) + a_2 w_2(t)$	$a_1 W_1(f) + a_2 W_2(f)$
Time delay	$w(t - T_d)$	$W(f)e^{-j\omega T_d}$
Scale change	$w(at)$	$\dfrac{1}{|a|} W\left(\dfrac{f}{a}\right)$
Conjugation	$w*(t)$	$W*(-f)$
Duality	$W(t)$	$w(-f)$
Real signal frequency translation [$w(t)$ is real]	$w(t)\cos(\omega_c t + \theta)$	$\frac{1}{2}[e^{j\theta} W(f - f_c) + e^{-j\theta} W(f + f_c)]$
Complex signal frequency translation	$w(t)e^{j\omega_c t}$	$W(f - f_c)$
Bandpass signal	$\mathrm{Re}\{g(t)e^{j\omega_c t}\}$	$\frac{1}{2}[G(f - f_c) + G*(-f - f_c)]$
Differentiation	$\dfrac{d^n w(t)}{dt^n}$	$(j2\pi f)^n W(f)$
Integration	$\displaystyle\int_{-\infty}^{t} w(\lambda)\, d\lambda$	$(j2\pi f)^{-1} W(f) + \frac{1}{2} W(0)\, \delta(f)$
Convolution	$w_1(t) * w_2(t)$ $= \displaystyle\int_{-\infty}^{\infty} w_1(\lambda) \cdot w_2(t - \lambda)\, d\lambda$	$W_1(f) W_2(f)$
Multiplication[b]	$w_1(t) w_2(t)$	$W_1(f) * W_2(f) = \displaystyle\int_{-\infty}^{\infty} W_1(\lambda)\, W_2(f - \lambda)\, d\lambda$
Multiplication by t^n	$t^n w(t)$	$(-j2\pi)^{-1} \dfrac{d^n W(f)}{df^n}$

[a] $\omega_c = 2\pi f_c$.

[b] *denotes convolution as described in detail by (2-62).